M. J. Engle

Mathematical Methods

for Engineering and Science Students

BAcHU ntsumi

Edward Arnold

First published 1987 by
Edward Arnold (Publishers) Ltd
41 Bedford Square, London WC1B 3DQ

Edward Arnold
3 East Read Street
Baltimore, MD 21202, USA

Edward Arnold (Australia) Ltd
80 Waverley Road, Caulfield East
Victoria 3145
Australia

To the memory of my father

British Library Cataloguing in Publication Data
Englefield, M. J.
   Mathematical methods
   1. Engineering mathematics   2. Mathematical physics
   I. Title
   510'.2462   TA330

   ISBN 0 7131 3525 5

Text set in 10/12 pt Times Digiset
Printed and bound in Great Britain by J. W. Arrowsmith, Bristol

Preface

For users of mathematics who are not mathematical specialists, an understanding of concepts and theorems usually comes through examples and exercises, instead of through a study of definitions and proofs designed to be rigorous rather than enlightening. To provide a course suitable for engineering or physical science students, this book presents theoretical work informally, with very few proofs. The topics appearing have all been included at the suggestion of teachers in university engineering or physical science departments. Although the emphasis is on calculational and manipulative techniques, some space is devoted to discussing the limit concept, which is fundamental to all calculus, and to explaining the definition of integral as the limit of a sequence of sums. However, the formal definitions of limits are placed in an Appendix.

The distinctive features of this text are the following. Summaries of important procedures are collected in Appendix B, in the form of flow charts where appropriate; commonly used derivatives, integrals, limits and series are tabulated. In writing a book for **users** of mathematics it seems desirable to stress methods of checking answers. This is unpopular with students (even in examinations), but calculations are only useful when the mistakes have been removed. The formulation of a check also improves understanding of the technique, and sometimes illustrates relations between concepts. For example, differentiation examples are constructed to check integration examples appearing later. This book regards numerical methods as an important complement to analytic work. Some rudimentary programs in BASIC and FORTRAN appear in Appendix C. Numerical examples illustrate the concept of convergence and the definitions of integral as a limit. The traditional treatment of systematic integration is fortified by a flow chart for selecting the technique required, and completed by the advocacy of numerical methods in suitable cases. Differentials are defined geometrically and regarded as desirable tools for differentiation.

Readers are assumed to have studied previously an informal treatment of differentiation, with the rules for composite and inverse functions; exponential and logarithmic functions; Cartesian coordinates in space; integration (at least as the reverse of differentiation); and matrix multiplication and addition. A knowledge of complex numbers is assumed in the main text, but an introductory treatment is given in Appendix A.

The first two chapters treat vector algebra and its application to curves and planes in three-dimensional space. The possible results of intersection problems are used later in Chapter 17 in the algebraic solution of linear equations by reduction to triangular or diagonal form. Geometrical interpretations are given for the case of three unknowns, using the equations of planes and lines from Chapter 2. The section on computation of an inverse matrix by reduction to diagonal form assumes a knowledge of matrix multiplication. The self-contained sections on determinants obtain their definition through conditions for consistency of homogeneous equations, and give various applications, including Cramer's rule.

Chapters 3, 4 and 5 discuss functions, limits and continuity, respectively. The treatment of limits is informal, with the actual definitions given in Appendix D. L'Hopital's rule is given in the form of an exercise, but discussed further after the treatment of Taylor series in Chapter 16. Techniques for differentiating real, complex and vector functions of a real variable are given in Chapter 6, which also includes sections on partial derivatives, curve sketching, and the mean value theorem.

Chapter 7 deals with the numerical solution of an equation for one unknown. Newton (-Raphson), bisection, and iteration methods are used and truncation and rounding errors considered.

The basic facts about convergence and absolute convergence of series are introduced in Chapter 8. Tests for convergence are restricted to the comparison test, but the ratio test appears in an exercise, and the integral (Maclaurin–Cauchy) test is included in the exercises on Chapter 10. Chapter 16 builds on this basis, proceeding from the familiar example of the geometric series to the Maclaurin and Taylor series for the expansion of a given (analytic) function. Computations using these series stress the bounds that can be obtained on the errors. Fourier series are described, including the complex form.

The work in Chapter 12 on complex equations and functions makes considerable use of geometric interpretations in the Argand diagram. This is also used to show the convergence of the complex geometric series in Chapter 16.

Chapter 9 is devoted to the definition of an integral as the limit of a sum, and its connection with antiderivatives via the fundamental theorem of the calculus. A systematic discussion of methods of obtaining antiderivatives (indefinite integrals) follows in Chapter 10. The objective is not just to describe the techniques, but to show when each should be used, and indeed to point out that an elementary function may not have an antiderivative that can be expressed in terms of elementary functions. A flow chart facilitates the selection of a suitable technique for a given integrand. This topic is completed by Chapter 15 on numerical integration, where the computations again stress bounds on the errors.

Integrals along a curve, and double integrals, are treated in Chapter 11. The former are set in terms of work done by a force in motion along the curve; the latter are only considered in Cartesian coordinates, showing the alternative orders of integration, and giving the volume interpretation.

The introduction to analytic methods of solving differential equations in Chapter 13 concentrates mainly on the second-order linear example with constant coefficients. The possibility of complex solutions is mentioned, using the complex exponential function, which has been defined in the previous chapter. These equations are solved by the alternative Laplace transform method in Chapter 20. Numerical solutions of first- and second-order differential equations are given in Chapter 19, deriving the computer programs (improved Euler and fourth-order Runge–Kutta formulas) in Appendix C.

Chapter 14 gives the geometric interpretation of partial derivatives in terms of tangents to a surface, and introduces differentials geometrically as components of displacements in the tangent plane. The conditions for maxima and minima of a function of two variables are deduced. Chapter 18 gives the alternative interpretation in terms of level curves in the domain of the function. This is then extended to level surfaces of functions of three variables, and the results applied to approximations, implicit differentiation, and line integrals of conservative vector fields.

The programs in Appendix C are presented to illustrate and utilize the mathematical techniques, and are not claimed to be examples of excellent programming.

In general the above description indicates possible alternative chapters for teaching purposes; for example, Chapter 17 could be read immediately after Chapter 3.

The following flow chart illustrates the interdependence of the chapters.

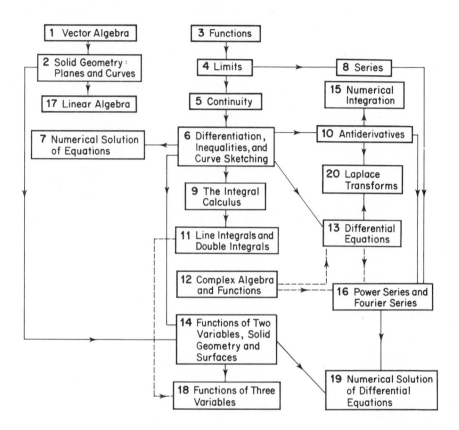

Some topics and techniques are included as exercises rather than in the main text. In such cases the index will indicate the relevant exercise.

The trend towards introducing mathematical concepts via applications is not followed here. In order for such motivation to be successful it must be finely tuned to the interests of the reader, suggesting that discussion of applications is best left as class-work, so that teachers can provide whatever is desirable for their particular group of students. Also the modelling of an applied problem may well be more difficult to understand than the associated mathematics, in which case the introduction of the application distracts attention from the essential mathematical subject matter.

Each subsection concludes with a few exercises intended to test understanding of its material. Answers to these are given at the end of the same chapter. Then further exercises conclude the chapter. Answers to many of these are in Appendix F at the end of the book, although sometimes checks are suggested instead. Worked examples are numbered so that the first two digits show the section in which they appear: Example 2.38 is the eighth in Section 2.3.

Mr Neil Cameron gave valuable advice on the presentation of limits in Appendix D.

I am also indebted to Miss Denise Christie for most of the typing, to Mrs Jean Sheldon and Mrs Drew Troon for their fine artwork, and to many Engineering students of Monash University who eliminated mistakes and errors in preliminary versions of the text.

M. J. Englefield
1986

Contents

Preface   iii

1 Vector Algebra   **1**
   1.1   Vector Quantities   1
   1.2   Components   5
   1.3   The Scalar Product   9
   1.4   The Vector Product   12
   1.5   Triple Products   15
   1.6   Vector Equations   18
   1.7   Matrix Representation of Vector Algebra   19
   Answers to Exercises   20
   Further Exercises on Chapter 1   21

2 Solid Geometry: Planes and Curves   **23**
   2.1   Surfaces   23
   2.2   The Equation of a Plane   24
   2.3   The Equations of a Line   26
   2.4   Intersection of a Line and a Plane   30
   2.5   Intersection of Two Lines   31
   2.6   The Equations of a Curve   34
   2.7   Intersections with Curves   36
   Answers to Exercises   39
   Further Exercises on Chapter 2   40

3 Functions   **45**
   3.1   Basic Concepts   45
   3.2   The Power Function   49
   3.3   Hyperbolic Functions   50
   3.4   Functions Relating Several Variables   55
   3.5   Sequences   61
   3.6   Bounded Functions   63
   Answers to Exercises   69
   Further Exercises on Chapter 3   69

4 Limits   **73**
   4.1   The Concept of Limit as $x \to a$ 73
   4.2   The Concept of Limit as $x \to \infty$ 80
   4.3   Theorems on Limits   82
   4.4   Techniques for Evaluating Limits   85
   Table of Limits   91

Answers to Exercises 91
Further Exercises on Chapter 4 92

5   Continuity **95**
5.1   Continuous Functions 95
5.2   Properties of Continuous Functions 98
Answers to Exercises 101
Further Exercises on Chapter 5 102

6   Differentiation, Inequalities, and Curve Sketching ... **105**
6.1   Definitions, Notation, and Rules 105
6.2   Logarithmic Differentiation 112
6.3   Higher Derivatives 114
6.4   Vector Functions 118
6.5   Functions Defined Parametrically 120
6.6   Functions Defined Implicitly 124
6.7   The Mean Value Theorem 127
6.8   Curve Sketching 131
6.9   Inequalities 139
6.10 Partial Derivatives 145
6.11 Complex Functions 148
Answers to Exercises 152
Table of Derivatives 154
Further Exercises on Chapter 6 155

7   Numerical Solution of Equations **161**
7.1   Newton's Method 161
7.2   Errors 168
7.3   The Bisection Method 171
7.4   Direct Iteration 173
7.5   Summaries of Methods for Finding a Root r of $f(x) = 0$ ... 176
Answers to Exercises 177
Further Exercises on Chapter 7 178

8   Series **179**
8.1   Convergence of Series 179
8.2   Notation 185
8.3   The Comparison Tests 187
8.4   Absolute Convergence 189
Answers to Exercises 191
Further Exercises on Chapter 8 192
Table of Series 195

9   The Integral Calculus **197**
9.1   Definition of the Riemann Integral 197
9.2   Applications 199
9.3   Properties of the Riemann Integral 205
9.4   The Fundamental Theorem 209

9.5 Evaluation of Riemann Integrals   213
9.6 Vector Functions and Complex Functions   216
Answers to Exercises   218
Further Exercises on Chapter 9   219

10 Antiderivatives   **225**
10.1 Standard Results   225
10.2 Substitution, or Change of Variable   226
10.3 Integration by Parts   230
10.4 Rational Functions   235
10.5 Reduction Formulas   240
10.6 Systematic Integration   244
10.7 Improper Integrals   247
Answers to Exercises   252
Table of Antiderivatives   253
Table of Reduction Formulas   254
Further Exercises on Chapter 10   254

11 Line Integrals and Double Integrals   **259**
11.1 Length of a Space Curve given Parametrically   259
11.2 Work done during Motion along a Curve   263
11.3 Further Techniques for Line Integrals   266
11.4 Alternative Derivation of the Work Formula   270
11.5 Integrals of Functions of Two Variables   271
11.6 Specification of Regions   277
11.7 Evaluation of Double Integrals   280
Answers to Exercises   287
Further Exercises on Chapter 11   289

12 Complex Algebra and Functions   **293**
12.1 De Moivre's Theorem   293
12.2 Powers of Complex Numbers   296
12.3 Solution of Polynomial Equations   299
12.4 Complex Functions as Mappings between Complex Planes   301
12.5 The Complex Exponential Function   306
Answers to Exercises   308
Further Exercises on Chapter 12   311

13 Differential Equations   **315**
13.1 Separable First-Order Equations   315
13.2 First-Order Linear Equations   320
13.3 Second-Order Linear Equations   323
13.4 Linear Equations with Constant Coefficients   325
13.5 Reduction of Order   331
13.6 Change of Variable   333
13.7 The Use of Complex Functions   334
13.8 Some Applications of Differential Equations   338
Hints and/or Answers to Exercises   347
Further Exercises on Chapter 13   348

14 Functions of Two Variables, Solid Geometry and Surfaces   **355**
  14.1   Geometric Interpretation of Partial Derivatives   355
  14.2   Tangent Planes   358
  14.3   Differentials   361
  14.4   Tangent Lines   365
  14.5   Composite Functions   367
  14.6   Maxima and Minima   368
  Answers to Exercises   374
  Further Exercises on Chapter 14   374

15 Numerical Integration   **377**
  15.1   The Trapezoidal Rule   377
  15.2   Simpson's Rule   381
  15.3   Derivation of Bounds on the Trapezoidal Rule Error   384
  15.4   General Integration Procedures   387
  Answers to Exercises   391
  Further Exercises on Chapter 15   392

16 Power Series and Fourier Series   **395**
  16.1   Series of Functions   395
  16.2   Properties of Power Series   396
  16.3   Expansion of a Given Function   400
  16.4   Taylor's Series   404
  16.5   Errors   406
  16.6   Evaluation of Limits   411
  16.7   Fourier Series   414
  16.8   Properties of Fourier Series   419
  16.9   Fourier Series with only Sine or only Cosine Terms   424
  16.10 Complex Series   429
  Answers to Exercises   433
  Further Exercises on Chapter 16   435
  Table of Power Series   438

17 Linear Algebra   **441**
  17.1   Geometrical Classification of Linear Equations   441
  17.2   Solution by Gaussian Elimination   444
  17.3   The Inverse of a Matrix   450
  17.4   Determinants and Homogeneous Equations   454
  17.5   Properties of Determinants   458
  17.6   Applications of Determinants   461
  Answers (or checks) for Exercises   467
  Further Exercises on Chapter 17   468

18 Functions of Three Variables   **473**
  18.1   Level Curves   473
  18.2   Differentials and Directional Derivatives   476
  18.3   Gradient Vector (Two-dimensional)   477
  18.4   Functions of Three Variables   479

18.5   Implicit Differentiation   481
18.6   Composite Functions   484
18.7   Conservative Functions   486
Answers to Exercises   490
Further Exercises on Chapter 18   491

19 Numerical Solution of Differential Equations   493
19.1   Introduction   493
19.2   Euler Formulas   494
19.3   Comparison of Formulas   496
19.4   Fourth-Order Runge Formula   499
19.5   Computer Implementation   500
19.6   Second-Order Equations   501
Answers to Exercises   504
Further Exercises on Chapter 19   505

20 Laplace Transforms   507
20.1   Definition of the Laplace Transform   507
20.2   Inversion of Transforms   509
20.3   Solution of Differential Equations using Laplace Transforms   511
Answers to Exercises   514
Table of Laplace Transforms and Inversions   515
Further Exercises on Chapter 20   515

Appendix A   Complex Numbers   517
A.1   Introduction   517
A.2   Complex Algebra   518
A.3   Complex Conjugates   522
A.4   The Interpretation of Complex Numbers   523
A.5   Polar Form of Complex Numbers   526
A.6   Geometric Interpretation of Multiplication and Division   531
A.7   Sets of Points in the Complex Plane   534
Answers to Exercises   538

Appendix B   Flow Diagrams or Summaries of Mathematical Procedures   543

Appendix C   Computer Programs   549

Appendix D   Formal Definitions of Limiting Processes   561

Appendix E   Change of Variable in an Integral   569

Appendix F   Answers (or checks) to Selected Exercises   571

Appendix G   Table of Antiderivatives   595

Appendix H   Formulas from Elementary Mathematics   597

Index   601

1
Vector Algebra

1.1 Vector Quantities

If an object is set in motion by pushing it, the movement produced depends on the direction of the push. In mechanics, a push, or anything else causing motion, is called a force. To describe a force it is evidently essential to state the direction in which the force acts. Similarly if a jet leaves an airport, to describe its change of position after an hour's flying needs a statement of both its distance from the airport and the direction in which it lies. A change of position is called a **displacement**, or a translation. Force and displacement, which involve **direction** as well as **magnitude**, are examples of **vector** quantities. Another example is angular velocity of motion in three dimensions: the magnitude is the speed of rotation, and the direction is the axis of rotation. Other quantities, such as temperature, which do not involve a direction, are called **scalar** quantities.

Any vector quantities may be represented on a diagram by displacements with the same (relative) directions, and with lengths proportional to the magnitudes of the quantities. Each displacement requires an arrow to indicate the sense. For example, suppose the displacements in Fig. 1.1 represent wind velocities: *a* represents a wind blowing to the north at 10 km/hour, *d* represents a wind to the south of the same speed, *b* represents a 15 km/hour wind to the east, and *c* represents a wind to the south-east of magnitude 22 km/hour.

The **magnitude** of the vector *a* is denoted by $|a|$ or *a*. In Fig. 1.1, $|b| = b = 15$ km/hr. The magnitude is positive, and is also called the **modulus** of the vector. Vectors must have the same magnitude and direction to be **equal**. In Fig. 1.1, $a \neq d$ although $a = d$. However,

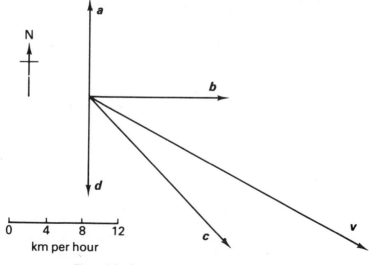

Figure 1.1   Representation of wind velocities

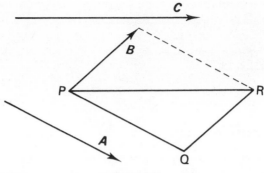

Figure 1.2

the starting point of the displacement does not matter, so that $\overrightarrow{PQ} = A$ in Fig. 1.2. The magnitude of a displacement $\overrightarrow{PQ}$ is written PQ.

Vector algebra defines the sum of two vectors, the difference of two vectors and several kinds of product. The definitions used are determined partly by the physical applications, and partly to obtain satisfactory mathematical properties. Suppose two forces F and G are applied to an object. The resulting motion could be obtained by applying a single force H, which is equivalent to F and G together. Obviously it is convenient to define the sum of two vectors so that $H = F + G$, if this is possible without introducing inconsistencies. Similarly if a power boat is driven south-east at 22 km/hour (c in Fig. 1.1), and there is a tide flowing east at 15 km/hour (b in Fig. 1.1), the actual velocity v relative to the shore is produced by the combined effect of c and b. This can be written $v = c + b$ with a suitable definition of sum. Now for displacements, there is an obvious geometric **definition of sum**: $\overrightarrow{PQ} + \overrightarrow{QR} = \overrightarrow{PR}$ (Fig. 1.2). This is therefore adopted as the definition of the sum of any two vector quantities, modified so that the initial points of the displacements are superfluous. For example, in Fig. 1.2, $\overrightarrow{PQ} = A$, $\overrightarrow{QR} = B$, and $\overrightarrow{PR} = C$, so $A + B = C$. This figure also illustrates why the definition is often called the **parallelogram law of addition**: if the vectors to be added are represented by displacements (B and $\overrightarrow{PQ}$) from the same point, a parallelogram can be constructed having these displacements as adjacent sides, and the sum is represented by the displacement along the diagonal. Since velocities are displacements per unit time, the same addition law will apply, for example $v = c + b$ in Fig. 1.1. The validity of the law for forces is a postulate of mechanics, which can be tested by experiment.

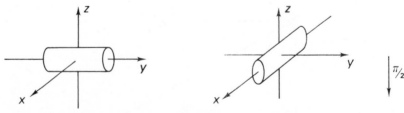

Figure 1.3

Three-dimensional rotations are examples of quantities which have an associated direction, that of the axis of rotation, but are not vector quantities because they do not combine like displacements. Figure 1.3 shows a cylinder rotated through an angle $\frac{1}{2}\pi$ about the negative z-axis. This rotation could be represented by a displacement of length

$\frac{1}{2}\pi$ in the negative z-direction, as shown. Two successive rotations about different axes are equivalent to a single rotation about another axis (cf. the above discussion for forces). However the displacement corresponding to this single rotation is not the vector sum by the parallelogram law of the displacements corresponding to the two successive rotations.

The above discussion shows how the definition of sum is formulated to describe certain physical applications. On the other hand multiplication of a vector by a number is defined so as to retain familiar mathematical results. Applying the addition law to vectors with the same direction shows that $A + A$ is a vector in the same direction but with twice the magnitude, and $A + A + A$ has the same direction and three times the magnitude. It is natural to write $2A$ for $A + A$ and $3A$ for $A + A + A$, etc., giving $2A + A = 3A$. Similarly if B has the same length as A but the opposite direction, then $2A + B = A$, suggesting that B should be called $-A$ or $(-1)A$. These considerations suggest the following *definition*:

> *if A is a vector, and λ a positive number, λA is a vector with the same direction as A, but with magnitude multiplied by λ; if μ is a negative number, then μA has the opposite sense to A, and magnitude multiplied by $|\mu| = -\mu$.*

The distributive and associative laws

$$\lambda A + \mu A = (\lambda + \mu)A, \ \lambda(\mu A) = (\lambda\mu)A \tag{1.1}$$

then hold for all numbers λ and μ, provided the definition is completed by introducing a **zero vector 0** with zero magnitude: $0A = 0$ for any vector A.

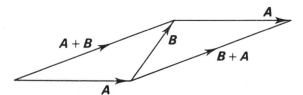

Figure 1.4   Commutative law for vector addition

When these geometrical definitions are used, other algebraic laws are consequences of simple geometrical properties. The **commutative law of addition** $A + B = B + A$ corresponds to the equality of opposite sides of a parallelogram (Fig. 1.4), and the **distributive law** $\lambda(A + B) = \lambda A + \lambda B$ corresponds to the constant ratio of corresponding sides of similar triangles (Fig. 1.5). One of the advantages of using vector algebra in physical problems is that such theorems, embedded in the formalism, are automatically applied in the analysis.

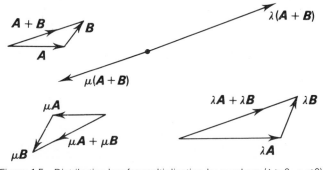

Figure 1.5   Distributive law for multiplication by numbers ($\lambda > 0$, $\mu < 0$)

Example 1.10

If A, B, and C are collinear points, O any other point, and CB = λAB, express $\overrightarrow{OC}$ in terms of $\overrightarrow{OA}$, $\overrightarrow{OB}$ and λ (see Fig. 1.6 which illustrates the case $0 < \lambda < 1$).

Since

$$AC = AB - CB = AB(1 - \lambda), \qquad \overrightarrow{CA} = (1 - \lambda)\overrightarrow{BA}$$

and

$$\lambda\overrightarrow{CA} = \lambda(1 - \lambda)\overrightarrow{BA} = (1 - \lambda)(\lambda\overrightarrow{BA}) = (1 - \lambda)\overrightarrow{BC} = -(1 - \lambda)\overrightarrow{CB}.$$

Thus

$$\lambda\overrightarrow{CA} + (1 - \lambda)\overrightarrow{CB} = \mathbf{0} \quad (*)$$

If O is any other point,

$$\overrightarrow{OC} = \lambda\overrightarrow{OC} + \lambda\overrightarrow{CA} + (1 - \lambda)\overrightarrow{OC} + (1 - \lambda)\overrightarrow{CB}$$
$$= \lambda(\overrightarrow{OC} + \overrightarrow{CA}) + (1 - \lambda)(\overrightarrow{OC} + \overrightarrow{CB})$$
$$= \lambda\overrightarrow{OA} + (1 - \lambda)\overrightarrow{OB}. \qquad\qquad (1.2)$$

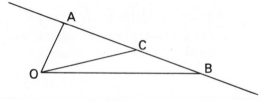

Figure 1.6   CB = λAB

The above example uses the distributive law (1.1). Reversing the steps proves the converse, i.e. if $\overrightarrow{OC} = \lambda\overrightarrow{OA} + (1 - \lambda)\overrightarrow{OB}$, then C is a point of the line AB. All points of the line are covered by allowing $\lambda > 1$ and $\lambda < 0$ for the parts outside the segment AB.   □

Note that for any λ and μ, the equation $\overrightarrow{OC} = \lambda\overrightarrow{OA} + \mu\overrightarrow{OB}$ implies that the point C is in the plane OAB. (Figure 1.7 illustrates the case where λ and μ are both positive.)

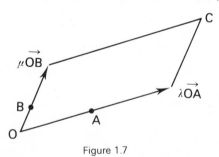

Figure 1.7

Subtraction of $\mathbf{A}$ means the addition of $-\mathbf{A}$: $\mathbf{B} - \mathbf{A} = \mathbf{B} + (-1)\mathbf{A}$. Then $\mathbf{A} + (\mathbf{B} - \mathbf{A}) = \mathbf{B}$, and

$$\boxed{\overrightarrow{OQ} - \overrightarrow{OP} \text{ is } \overrightarrow{PQ}\text{, the vector from P to Q.}}$$

(Figure 1.8).

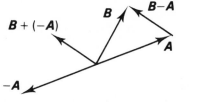
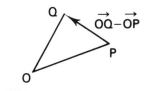

Figure 1.8

Exercise (answer on p. 20)

1.1.1 Suppose A, B, C are points on a line such that B is the midpoint of AC. Express the vector $\overrightarrow{OC}$ in terms of $\overrightarrow{OA}$ and $\overrightarrow{OB}$.

1.2 Components

The effectiveness of vector methods in physical applications depends largely on the fact that the definitions and theorems are independent of any system of coordinates used, but calculations usually require choosing a coordinate system relative to some convenient set of mutually perpendicular axes Ox, Oy, Oz. The **components** of a displacement $\overrightarrow{OP} = A$ are the Cartesian coordinates of P relative to the axes, the lengths of the sides of the rectangular box shown in Fig. 1.9, with signs according to the octant in which P lies.

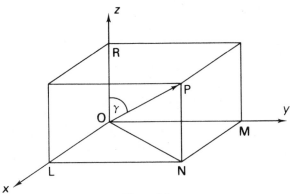

Figure 1.9

Thus the components of A are

$$A_x = OL = MN, \qquad A_y = OM = LN, \qquad A_z = OR = NP \qquad (1.3)$$

and

$$A^2 = |A|^2 = (OP)^2 = ON^2 + NP^2 = OL^2 + LN^2 + NP^2$$

$$\boxed{A^2 = A_x^2 + A_y^2 + A_z^2} \qquad (1.4)$$

expresses the magnitude of A in terms of the components. A **unit vector** has magnitude 1. If i, j and k are unit vectors in the directions of the axes, then in Fig. 1.9 $\overrightarrow{OL} = (OL)i$, $\overrightarrow{LN} = (LN)j$, $\overrightarrow{NP} = (NP)k$, so

$$\overrightarrow{OP} = \overrightarrow{OL} + \overrightarrow{LN} + \overrightarrow{NP} = (OL)i + (LN)j + (NP)k$$

and

$$A = A_x i + A_y j + A_z k. \tag{1.5}$$

Using a diagram like Fig. 1.9, it can be seen that the components of a sum $A + B$ (or a difference $A - B$) are obtained by adding (or subtracting) the components of A and B.

Example 1.20

Given the points $A(-1, 1, -2)$, $B(0, 2, -1)$ and $C(1, -2, -3)$, find D so that ABDC is a parallelogram, and verify that the diagonals of this parallelogram bisect each other.

If O is the origin of coordinates, the given information may be written $\overrightarrow{OA} = -i + j - 2k$, $\overrightarrow{OB} = 2j - k$, $\overrightarrow{OC} = i - 2j - 3k$. The coordinates of D will be the components of $\overrightarrow{OD} = \overrightarrow{OB} + \overrightarrow{BD} = \overrightarrow{OB} + \overrightarrow{AC}$. (Putting $\overrightarrow{BD} = \overrightarrow{AC}$ makes ABDC a parallelogram, as in Fig. 1.10.) Since

$$\overrightarrow{AC} = \overrightarrow{AO} + \overrightarrow{OC} = \overrightarrow{OC} - \overrightarrow{OA} = 2i - 3j - k,$$

$$\overrightarrow{OD} = 2i - j - 2k, \quad \text{and D is } (2, -1, -2).$$

If M is the midpoint of BC, then from Example 1.10 $\overrightarrow{AM} = \frac{1}{2}\overrightarrow{AB} + \frac{1}{2}\overrightarrow{AC}$. Since $\overrightarrow{AB} = \overrightarrow{OB} - \overrightarrow{OA} = i + j + k$, $\overrightarrow{AM} = \frac{1}{2}(3i - 2j)$.

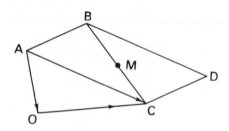

Figure 1.10

But $\overrightarrow{AD} = \overrightarrow{OD} - \overrightarrow{OA} = 3i - 2j$.

(i) Since $\overrightarrow{AD} = 2\overrightarrow{AM}$, $\overrightarrow{AD}$ and $\overrightarrow{AM}$ have the same direction, so the diagonal AD passes through M, i.e. AD bisects BC.

(ii) Since $\overrightarrow{AD} = 2\overrightarrow{AM}$, $AM = MD = \frac{1}{2}AD$, i.e. BC bisects AD.   □

Using the distributive laws, the algebraic operations already defined appear in terms of components as

$$\lambda A = \lambda(A_x i + A_y j + A_z k) = (\lambda A_x)i + (\lambda A_y)j + (\lambda A_z)k \tag{1.6}$$

$$(A_x i + A_y j + A_z k) + (B_x i + B_y j + B_z k)$$

$$= (A_x + B_x)i + (A_y + B_y)j + (A_z + B_z)k. \tag{1.7}$$

These equations mean that any vector A can be described by the triple of real numbers (A_x, A_y, A_z), with the laws

$$\lambda(A_x, A_y, A_z) = (\lambda A_x, \lambda A_y, \lambda A_z)$$

$$(A_x, A_y, A_z) + (B_x, B_y, B_z) = (A_x + B_x, A_y + B_y, A_z + B_z)$$

(1.8)

corresponding to equations (1.6) and (1.7).

If $\overline{OP}$ in Fig. 1.9 represents a vector quantity A such as force or velocity, then the components of A are the quantities represented by OL, OM and OR. Equations (1.4)–(1.7) remain true. Since it may be necessary to refer different quantities to the same axes, the unit vectors i, j and k are always taken to be dimensionless.

Example 1.21

The following table shows the components of the velocities in Fig. 1.1, on p. 1, relative to axes Ox pointing east, Oy pointing north, and Oz vertical. All z components are zero (see Fig. 1.11).

Vector	a	d	b	c	v
x-component	0	0	15	$11\sqrt{2}$	$15 + 11\sqrt{2}$
y-component	10	−10	0	$-11\sqrt{2}$	$-11\sqrt{2}$

We can write, for example, $v = (15 + 11\sqrt{2})i - 11\sqrt{2}j$.

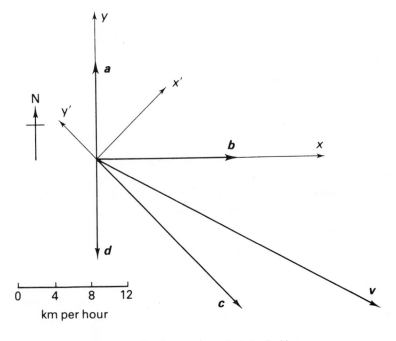

Figure 1.11 Components of wind velocities

The table illustrates the results $d = -a$ and $b + c = v$ in accordance with equations (1.8). Alternatively, using $\mathrm{O}x'$ pointing north-east, and $\mathrm{O}y'$ pointing north-west gives

Vector	a	d	b	c	v
x'-component	$5\sqrt{2}$	$-5\sqrt{2}$	$15/\sqrt{2}$	0	$15\sqrt{2}$
y'-component	$5\sqrt{2}$	$-5\sqrt{2}$	$-15/\sqrt{2}$	-22	$-22-(15/\sqrt{2})$

We can write, for example, $b = (15/\sqrt{2})i' - (15/\sqrt{2})j'$. These components have the dimension km/hour. □

For a mathematically rigorous theory of vectors, one approach is to define the vectors as triples of real numbers, and use equations (1.8) as definitions. However this obscures the most important advantage of using vector algebra, namely that the operations are independent of any choice of coordinate axes. Similarly, although there may be some mathematical advantage to defining vectors as displacements all emanating from the same origin, this restriction must be removed to take full advantage of vector algebra in physical applications.

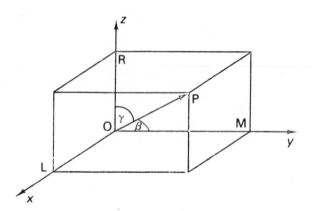

Figure 1.12   Direction of vector

In equation (1.4) the magnitude of A is expressed in terms of components. The direction of A relative to the coordinate axes $\mathrm{O}xyz$ in Fig. 1.12 is described by the angles $\alpha = <\mathrm{POL}$, $\beta = <\mathrm{POM}$, $\gamma = <\mathrm{POR}$ which $\overrightarrow{\mathrm{OP}}$ makes with the directions of the axes. To give the direction it is sufficient to consider the unit vector along $\overrightarrow{\mathrm{OP}}$, which is

$$\left(\frac{1}{\mathrm{OP}}\right)\overrightarrow{\mathrm{OP}} = \frac{1}{\mathrm{OP}}(\mathrm{OL}i + \mathrm{OM}j + \mathrm{OR}k). \tag{1.9}$$

The three numbers $\cos\alpha = \mathrm{OL}/\mathrm{OP}$, $\cos\beta = \mathrm{OM}/\mathrm{OP}$, $\cos\gamma = \mathrm{OR}/\mathrm{OP}$ are called the **direction-cosines** of the direction $\overrightarrow{\mathrm{OP}}$, and are usually given to specify this direction relative to the axes. Since they are the components of the unit vector (1.9), they satisfy

$$\cos^2\alpha + \cos^2\beta + \cos^2\gamma = 1. \tag{1.10}$$

The components of A, which are $A \cos \alpha$, $A \cos \beta$, and $A \cos \gamma$, each have the form $A \cos \theta$ where θ is the angle between A and the corresponding axis. The axes can be chosen in any convenient way.

So we define the *component of A in any direction* as $A \cos \theta$, where θ is the angle between A and the direction $(0 \leqslant \theta \leqslant \pi)$.

Exercises (answers on p. 20)

1.2.1   For each of the following pairs of points, write down the vector $\overrightarrow{AB}$ in terms of components, and calculate its length AB.

(i) $A(1, 0, 2)$, $B(3, 1, 4)$;

(ii) $A(-1, 1, -2)$, $B(1, 7, 1)$;

(iii) $A(2, -2, 1)$, $B(4, 4, -2)$.

1.2.2   Let $A = 4i + j - k$, $B = -2i + 3j$.

(i) Express $3A + 2B$ and $2A - 3B$ in component form.

(ii) If P is the point $(1, 2, 3)$, find points Q and R such that $\overrightarrow{PQ} = A$, $\overrightarrow{PR} = B$, and obtain the vector $\overrightarrow{QR}$.

1.2.3   For each of the following vectors, find the magnitude and direction-cosines, and illustrate the results with a sketch:

(i) $2i - j - k$.

(ii) $3i - 4k$.

(iii) $-2i + 3j + 6k$.

1.3   The Scalar Product

The angle between two non-zero vectors is always defined, since the two vectors can be taken from the same point. If θ is the angle between A and B, the **scalar product** (or **dot** product) of A and B is defined by

$$A \cdot B = AB \cos \theta. \qquad (1.11)$$

This number is positive if θ is acute, negative if θ obtuse, and zero if A and B are perpendicular. Since $\cos(-\theta) = \cos \theta$, the sense of the angle is irrelevant, and $B \cdot A = A \cdot B$. Applying the cosine formula to the triangle shown in Fig. 1.13 gives

$$|A + B|^2 = A^2 + B^2 - 2AB \cos(\pi - \theta)$$

so that, as $\cos \theta = -\cos(\pi - \theta)$,

$$A \cdot B = (|A + B|^2 - A^2 - B^2)/2. \qquad (1.12)$$

The right side of equation (1.12) can be evaluated in terms of components using equations (1.8) and (1.4), to obtain

$$\boxed{A \cdot B = A_x B_x + A_y B_y + A_z B_z.} \qquad (1.13)$$

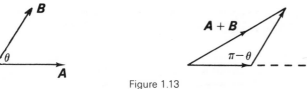

Figure 1.13

From equations (1.13) and (1.8) it is easy to verify the laws

$$\boldsymbol{A} \cdot (\boldsymbol{B} + \boldsymbol{C}) = \boldsymbol{A} \cdot \boldsymbol{B} + \boldsymbol{A} \cdot \boldsymbol{C} \tag{1.14}$$

$$(\lambda \boldsymbol{A}) \cdot \boldsymbol{B} = \boldsymbol{A} \cdot (\lambda \boldsymbol{B}) = \lambda (\boldsymbol{A} \cdot \boldsymbol{B}). \tag{1.15}$$

Defining $\boldsymbol{A}\lambda = \lambda\boldsymbol{A}$, this can be extended to

$$\lambda (\boldsymbol{A} \cdot \boldsymbol{B}) = \boldsymbol{A}\lambda \cdot \boldsymbol{B} = \boldsymbol{A} \cdot \boldsymbol{B}\lambda \tag{1.16}$$

i.e. the number λ can be written anywhere in the product. Conversely, it is often convenient to remove numerical factors before using equation (1.13) to evaluate a scalar product.

To make equations (1.14)–(1.16) always correct, it is necessary to define $\boldsymbol{A} \cdot \boldsymbol{B} = 0$ if either $\boldsymbol{A} = \boldsymbol{0}$ or $\boldsymbol{B} = \boldsymbol{0}$. Then equation (1.13) also applies in this case.

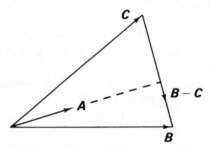

Figure 1.14 $\boldsymbol{B}$ and $\boldsymbol{C}$ have same component along $\boldsymbol{A}$

Thus the scalar product satisfies familiar rules of algebra. However cancellation is invalid: $\boldsymbol{A} \cdot \boldsymbol{B} = \boldsymbol{A} \cdot \boldsymbol{C}$ does not imply $\boldsymbol{B} = \boldsymbol{C}$ or $\boldsymbol{A} = \boldsymbol{0}$. The reason is that a scalar product can be zero without either factor vanishing, when they are perpendicular. Figure 1.14 shows vectors $\boldsymbol{A}$, $\boldsymbol{B}$ and $\boldsymbol{C}$ for which $\boldsymbol{A} \cdot \boldsymbol{B} = \boldsymbol{A} \cdot \boldsymbol{C}$, because $\boldsymbol{A}$ is perpendicular to $\boldsymbol{B} - \boldsymbol{C}$. Breakdown of the cancellation law may also be expected from the fact that $\boldsymbol{B} = \boldsymbol{C}$ or $\boldsymbol{A} = \boldsymbol{0}$ each express three equations between numbers (one for each component), whereas $\boldsymbol{A} \cdot \boldsymbol{B} = \boldsymbol{A} \cdot \boldsymbol{C}$ is only one equation, of first degree in the components, and cannot be expected to imply three equations.

Example 1.30
Find the angle between the vectors

$$\boldsymbol{A} = 2\boldsymbol{i} - \boldsymbol{j} + 2\boldsymbol{k} \quad \text{and} \quad \boldsymbol{B} = 3\boldsymbol{i} + 12\boldsymbol{j} - 4\boldsymbol{k}.$$

Method: find the cosine of the angle from the scalar product (1.11).
From equation (1.4), $A^2 = 9$, $B^2 = 169$, so $A = 3$, $B = 13$.
From equation (1.13), $\boldsymbol{A} \cdot \boldsymbol{B} = 6 - 12 - 8 = -14$. (As a check, this may also be calculated from equation (1.12), with $\boldsymbol{A} + \boldsymbol{B} = 5\boldsymbol{i} + 11\boldsymbol{j} - 2\boldsymbol{k}$, $|\boldsymbol{A} + \boldsymbol{B}|^2 = 25 + 121 + 4 = 150$, $\boldsymbol{A} \cdot \boldsymbol{B} = (150 - 9 - 169)/2 = -14$. This also checks the previous evaluation of A^2 and B^2.)
Finally, from equation (1.11), $\cos \theta = -14/39$, $\theta = \pi - 1.204 = 1.938$ or $111°$. $\square$

The scalar product also supplies a compact formula for the component of a vector in any given direction. The component of $\boldsymbol{A}$ in the direction of $\boldsymbol{B}$ is

$$\boxed{A \cos \theta = (\boldsymbol{A} \cdot \boldsymbol{B})/B \quad (\boldsymbol{B} \neq \boldsymbol{0}).}$$

The component in the direction of a unit vector e is just $A \cdot e$. In particular, equation (1.5) on p. 6 can be written

$$A = (A \cdot i)i + (A \cdot j)j + (A \cdot k)k. \qquad (1.17)$$

Example 1.31
Express $A = 2i - j + 2k$ as a sum of two vectors, one parallel to $B = 3i + 12j - 4k$, and the other perpendicular to B.

Method: the magnitude of the vector parallel to B is $(A \cdot B)/B$, the component of A in the direction of B.

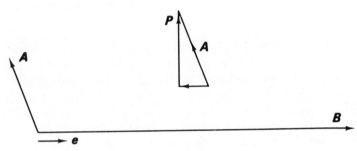

Figure 1.15

From Example 1.30, the component of A in the direction of B is $-14/13$, and $e = (3i + 12j - 4k)/13$ is a unit vector in the direction of B. So the required vector parallel to B is $(-14/13)e$ or $(-42i - 168j + 56k)/169$, as shown in Fig. 1.15. If $A = (-14/13)e + P$, then

$$P = A + (14e/13) = (338i - 169j + 338k)/169 + (42i + 168j - 56k)/169$$

$$= (380i - j + 282k)/169.$$

Check: is P perpendicular to B? Its scalar product with B is (the factor $1/169$ can be omitted, since only the direction of the vector is in question)

$$(380 \times 3) - (1 \times 12) - (282 \times 4) = 1140 - 12 - 1128 = 0.$$

Hence

$$A = 2i - j + 2k = \frac{-42i - 168j + 56k}{169} + \frac{380i - j + 282k}{169}.$$

The two parts may be called the **vector resolutes** (or **projections**) of A in the directions parallel and perpendicular to B. □

In drawing Figs 1.10 and 1.15 to illustrate the examples, it is unnecessary to show the coordinate axes, and doing so would confuse the picture. The methods used do not depend on the coordinate systems chosen.

In the working of Example 1.31 it was also convenient to divide a vector by a number (169). In general, division by λ means multiplication by the reciprocal $1/\lambda$. However division by a vector is never used, since a reciprocal of a vector is never defined.

The scalar product $A \cdot A$ is often written A^2, so that $A^2 = A^2$.

Exercises (answers on p. 20)

1.3.1 Express the vector $2i - 5j + 4k$ as a sum of two vectors, one parallel to $a = i - 2j + 4k$, and the other perpendicular to a.

1.3.2 Find the angles of the triangle formed by the points $P(1, -2, 5)$, $Q(2, 1, 7)$, $R(7, 6, -10)$.

1.3.3 Find the angles of the triangle formed by the points $A(2, 1, 0)$, $B(1, 0, 2)$, $C(0, 2, 1)$.

1.3.4 What is the vector projection of $(i + 4j + k)$ in the direction of $(2i - j - k)$?

1.4 The Vector Product

The product of a number and a vector is a vector, and the scalar product of two vectors is a number.

> The **vector product** $A \times B$ (or **cross** product) is a vector with (i) magnitude $AB \sin \theta$ where θ is the (positive) angle between A and B (ii) direction perpendicular to both A and B, and (iii) sense given by the right-hand rule: if the right hand is placed so that A lies along the first finger and B lies across the hand to the little finger, then the thumb can point along the direction $A \times B$ (which is perpendicular to the palm, from (ii)). The sense rule may also be stated by saying that the rotation from A to B would move a screw with right-hand thread in the direction $A \times B$.

The product is shown in Fig. 1.16. As with the scalar product, this definition assumes A and B nonzero, and the definition is completed by $A \times B = 0$ if either $A = 0$ or $B = 0$. From part (i) of the definition

$$A \times A = 0 \tag{1.18}$$

(since $\theta = 0$). To apply the right-hand rule (iii) to $B \times A$, the hand must be placed so that the left factor B is along the first finger, i.e. turned over compared to the $A \times B$ position. Hence (see Fig. 1.16)

$$\boxed{(A \times B) = -(B \times A).} \tag{1.19}$$

Also, as with the scalar product, a numerical factor can be placed anywhere in the product, i.e.

$$(\lambda A) \times B = A \times (\lambda B) = \lambda (A \times B). \tag{1.20}$$

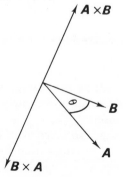

Figure 1.16   Vector product

From the sine formula of trigonometry, $|A \times B|$ is twice the area of the triangle having A and B as adjacent sides; alternatively $|A \times B|$ is the area of the parallelogram having A and B as adjacent sides.

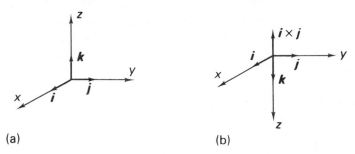

(a)   (b)

Figure 1.17   (a) Right-handed axes. (b) Left-handed axes

Next consider the vector products of the perpendicular unit vectors i, j and k. For any perpendicular vectors, $|A \times B| = AB$, so $i \times j$ is a unit vector, and it is perpendicular to both i and j. Choosing the positive z-direction along $i \times j$ therefore gives (Fig. 1.17(a))

$$i \times j = k, \qquad j \times k = i, \qquad k \times i = j \tag{1.21}$$

$$j \times i = -k, \qquad k \times j = -i, \qquad i \times k = -j \tag{1.22}$$

$$i \times i = j \times j = k \times k = 0. \tag{1.23}$$

These results are easily written down without reference, since equations (1.21) contain cyclic permutations of $i \times j = k$, and then equations (1.22) follow from equation (1.19). The axes are called *right-handed*; left-handed axes (Fig. 1.17(b)) giving $i \times j = -k$, etc., are not usually used.

For the vector product, equation (1.19) shows that the commutative law of multiplication does not hold, and it is easy to construct examples violating the associative law. Thus $(i \times i) \times j = 0 \times j = 0$, but $i \times (i \times j) = i \times k = -j \neq 0$. The cancellation law again fails, owing to equation (1.18). Figure 1.18 shows vectors A, B and C for which $A \times B = A \times C$ and $A \neq 0$, $B \neq C$ (A is parallel to $B - C$). However the distributive law

$$A \times (B + C) = (A \times B) + (A \times C) \tag{1.24}$$

does hold, although it is convenient to defer proving this result until the next section.

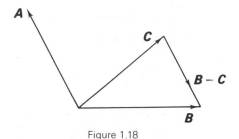

Figure 1.18

Assuming this result for the present, a formula for $A \times B$ in terms of components may be derived. By repeated application of equation (1.24)

$$(A_x i + A_y j + A_z k) \times (B_x i + B_y j + B_z k) \tag{1.25}$$

becomes a sum of nine terms like $(A_x i) \times (B_z k)$, and then using equation (1.20) gives $(A_x B_z)(i \times k)$ for example, so that the nine terms may be evaluated using equations (1.21)-(1.23). This procedure may be explicitly followed for vectors given in terms of components.

Example 1.40

For the vectors $A = 2i - j + 2k$, $B = 3i + 12j - 4k$,

$$\begin{aligned}
A \times B &= (2i - j + 2k) \times (3i + 12j - 4k) \\
&= 6(i \times i) + 24(i \times j) - 8(i \times k) - 3(j \times i) - 12(j \times j) \\
&\quad + 4(j \times k) + 6(k \times i) + 24(k \times j) - 8(k \times k) \\
&= 24k + 8j + 3k + 4i + 6j - 24i, \quad \text{using equations (1.21)-(1.23)} \\
&= -20i + 14j + 27k.
\end{aligned}$$

Check: is this perpendicular to both A and B?

$A \cdot (-20i + 14j + 27k) = -40 - 14 + 54$, using equation (1.13), is zero. Similarly $B \cdot (-20i + 14j + 27k) = -60 + 168 - 108$ is also zero. Thus $A \times B = -20i + 14j + 27k$. □

Treating (1.25) as in this example yields a general formula which is conveniently written in terms of a determinant:

$$A \times B = \begin{vmatrix} i & j & k \\ A_x & A_y & A_z \\ B_x & B_y & B_z \end{vmatrix}. \tag{1.26}$$

Students familiar with determinants may therefore do Example 1.40 as follows:

$$\begin{vmatrix} i & j & k \\ 2 & -1 & 2 \\ 3 & 12 & -4 \end{vmatrix} = i(4 - 24) - j(-8 - 6) + k(24 + 3) = -20i + 14j + 27k.$$

Direct use of equations (1.21)-(1.23) is probably easier if one or more components of the factors are zero. Determinants will be defined and discussed in Section 17.4.

Example 1.41

Find a unit vector perpendicular to both $i + 3k$ and $2j - k$.

Method: take a cross product to give a perpendicular vector, and then convert this to a unit vector.

$$(i + 3k) \times (2j - k) = 2k - 6i + j, \quad \text{using equations (1.21)-(1.23)}$$

$$= -6i + j + 2k = p \quad \text{say.}$$

Then, using equation (1.4) on p. 5, $p^2 = 36 + 1 + 4 = 41$, so multiplying p by $(1/\sqrt{41})$ will give a unit vector. This process is called **normalizing** the vector p, and gives

$$(-6/\sqrt{41})i + (1/\sqrt{41})j + (2/\sqrt{41})k.$$

Check: is this a unit vector, and is it perpendicular to both given vectors?

Using equation (1.4), $(36/41) + (1/41) + (4/41) = 1 \ (= 1^2)$, so it is a unit vector.

To determine whether p is perpendicular, the normalization factor $(1/\sqrt{41})$ can be omitted. Using equation (1.13) on p. 9,

$$(-6i + j + 2k) \cdot (i + 3k) = -6 + 6 \quad \text{and} \quad (-6i + j + 2k) \cdot (2j - k) = 2 - 2,$$

so the required conditions are satisfied. (The check on the direction of p is better done before normalizing.)   □

Exercises (answers on p. 20)

1.4.1   Show that the equation $(4i - 5j - 6k) \times (i + 2j - 3k) = 27i + 12j + 8k$ is incorrect.

1.4.2   Evaluate $(i + j - k) \times (2i - j + k)$ and $(i + j - k) \times (i - 2j + 2k)$. Comment on the results.

1.4.3   Let $A = i - 4j - 2k$, $B = 5i - 3j + 9k$.
  (i) Find a vector perpendicular to both A and B.
  (ii) Find the two unit vectors that are perpendicular to both A and B.

1.4.4   If $r \times s = 2i + j + k$, what is $2s \times 3r$?

1.4.5   Show that, for any vector r,

$$i \times (i \times r) + j \times (j \times r) + k \times (k \times r) = -2r.$$

1.4.6   Show that the area of the triangle PQR with corners P(6, 1, 3), Q(2, −3, 1) and R(−5, 1, 7) is $\sqrt{909} = 30.15$.

1.5   Triple Products

Three types of triple product may be formed from three vectors:
  (i) $(A \cdot B)C$ is a vector parallel to C, since $(A \cdot B)$ is a number;
  (ii) $(A \times B) \cdot C$ is a number, called a **scalar triple product**;
  (iii) $(A \times B) \times C$ is a vector, called a **vector triple product**.

The scalar triple product has a simple geometrical meaning. Suppose the three vectors are drawn from the same point O, and that C does not lie in the plane of A and B. Then there is a parallelepiped (a box whose opposite faces are parallel parallelograms) determined by the three vectors along adjacent edges, meeting at O (Fig. 1.19). The volume of this parallelepiped is (area of base) × (perpendicular height). Taking the face containing A and B as the base, the area of the base is $|A \times B|$. The volume is $|A \times B|C \cos \theta$, where θ is the acute angle between C and the perpendicular to the base. But this is just $(A \times B) \cdot C$, since θ is also the angle between $(A \times B)$ and C.

However Fig. 1.20 shows that there is another case. When C and $A \times B$ are on opposite sides of the base, the angle between C and' $A \times B$ is the obtuse angle $\pi - \theta$. Then $\cos \theta = -\cos(\pi - \theta)$, and the volume is $-(A \times B) \cdot C$. Since $(A \times B) \cdot C = |A \times B|C \cos(\pi - \theta) < 0$ in this case, the statement that the volume of the parallelepiped is $|(A \times B) \cdot C|$ covers both cases.

Alternatively, the face containing B and C may be regarded as the base, so that the volume is also $|(B \times C) \cdot A| = \pm(B \times C) \cdot A$, with the ± signs according to whether $B \times C$

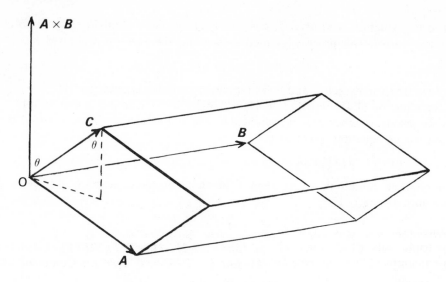

Figure 1.19   Parallelepiped

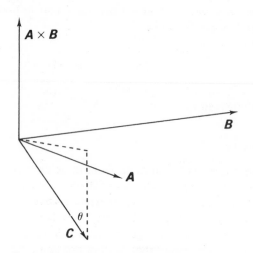

Figure 1.20   Vectors along edges of parallelepiped

and A are on the same or opposite sides of the new base. From Fig. 1.19, $B \times C$ and A are on the same side of the new base in that case, so

$$(A \times B) \cdot C = (B \times C) \cdot A \qquad (1.27)$$

In Fig. 1.20, $B \times C$ and A are on opposite sides of the plane containing B and C so equating the two expressions for the volume gives

$$-(B \times C) \cdot A = -(A \times B) \cdot C.$$

This is just equation (1.27) again, and this equation also obviously holds when A, B, C are coplanar, because the vector product of any pair is perpendicular to the third, so both sides of equation (1.27) are zero.

Since the scalar product is commutative, equation (1.27) can be written

$$(A \times B) \cdot C = A \cdot (B \times C), \tag{1.28}$$

that is, the cross and dot may be interchanged. Using also the sign change when the factors in a vector product are reversed, one can obtain

$$(A \times B) \cdot C = (B \times C) \cdot A = (C \times A) \cdot B \tag{1.29}$$

$$= -(B \times A) \cdot C = -(A \times C) \cdot B = -(C \times B) \cdot A \tag{1.30}$$

(In these equations, the brackets could be omitted, since for example $A \times (B \cdot C)$ is meaningless).

The triple scalar product is unchanged if a cyclic permutation is applied to the factors, as in equations (1.29), and changes sign if any of the other three possible permutations are made, as in equations (1.30). The product may be evaluated using whichever of the formulas in (1.29) has the easiest cross product and checked using one of the others.

The distributive law (1.24) for the vector product can now be proved. Let $w = A \times (B + C) - (A \times B) - (A \times C)$, so that it is necessary to show that $w = 0$, which can be done by showing that $w = 0$. Now

$$w^2 = w \cdot w = w \cdot \{A \times (B + C)\} - w \cdot (A \times B)$$

$$- w \cdot (A \times C), \quad \text{using equation (1.14) on p. 10}$$

$$= (w \times A) \cdot (B + C) - (w \times A) \cdot B$$

$$- (w \times A) \cdot C, \quad \text{using equation (1.28)}$$

$$= (w \times A) \cdot (B + C - B - C), \quad \text{using equation (1.14)}$$

$$= (w \times A) \cdot 0 = 0.$$

Using equation (1.26) for $B \times C$ in terms of components, one gets

$$A \cdot (B \times C) = \begin{vmatrix} A_x & A_y & A_z \\ B_x & B_y & B_z \\ C_x & C_y & C_z \end{vmatrix}. \tag{1.31}$$

Students familiar with the properties of determinants (see Section 17.5) will recognize that equations (1.29) and (1.30) correspond to the invariance or change of sign of a determinant when its rows are rearranged.

Consider the x-component of the vector triple product $(A \times B) \times C$. This is

$$(A \times B)_y C_z - (A \times B)_z C_y = (A_z B_x - A_x B_z) C_z - (A_x B_y - A_y B_x) C_y,$$

using equation (1.26), or (1.25) and equations (1.21)–(1.23)

$$= (A_z C_z + A_y C_y) B_x - (B_z C_z + B_y C_y) A_x$$

$$= (A \cdot C) B_x - (B \cdot C) A_x,$$

since two terms $A_x B_x C_x$ cancel in the last expression. Treating the y- and z-components of $(A \times B) \times C$ in the same way shows that

$$\boxed{(A \times B) \times C = (A \cdot C)B - (B \cdot C)A} \tag{1.32}$$

Since $A \cdot C$ and $B \cdot C$ are numbers, the right side of equation (1.32) is evidently a vector coplanar with A and B. The consistency of this can be seen in Figs 1.19 and 1.20: $(A \times B) \times C$ is perpendicular to $(A \times B)$, and so is in the plane of A and B.

Exercise (answers on p. 20)

1.5.1   If $a = 2i + j + 3k$, $b = 3i + 2j + 2k$, $c = i + 4j + 4k$, evaluate

    (i) $(a \times b) \cdot c$,

    (ii) $(a \times b) \times c$,

    (iii) $a \times (b \times c)$.

1.6   Vector Equations

This section will discuss examples of finding the vectors r satisfying some given algebraic equation. Since the unknown vector r has three components, say $r = xi + yj + zk$, there are three unknowns (x, y, z). If the given equation is a scalar equation, with r only appearing in scalar products, then one cannot expect a unique solution, or even a finite number of solutions.

Example 1.60

Solve $r \cdot r = 4$.

This is equivalent to $r = 2$; all vectors of magnitude 2 are solutions.   □

On the other hand, a vector equation is equivalent to three scalar equations, and a unique solution of 3 equations in 3 unknowns is more likely.

Example 1.61

Solve

$$3r + \{r \times (j + k)\} = 6i + 2j - k. \tag{1}$$

Method 1: take scalar and vector products with $j + k$. This gives

$$3r \cdot (j + k) + 0 = (6i + 2j - k) \cdot (j + k) = 1 \tag{2}$$

and

$$3r \times (j + k) + \{r \times (j + k)\} \times (j + k) = (6i + 2j - k) \times (j + k).$$

The vector triple product on the left side can be simplified using equation (1.32) and the right side evaluated. This gives

$$3r \times (j + k) + \{r \cdot (j + k)\}(j + k) - (j + k)^2 r = 6k - 6j + 2i + i.$$

The first term on the left can be written in terms of r using (1); r can be eliminated from the second term using (2), and since $(j+k)^2 = 2$,

$$3(6i+2j-k-3r)+\tfrac{1}{3}(j+k)-2r = 3i-6j+6k$$

$$15i+(37j/3)-(26k/3) = 11r.$$

$$r = (45i+37j-26k)/33. \tag{3}$$

Method 2: suppose $r = xi+yj+zk$. Then

$$r \times (j+k) = xk - xj + yi - zi$$

and (1) becomes

$$3(xi+yj+zk)+(y-z)i-xj+xk = 6i+2j-k.$$

Equating components

$$3x+y-z = 6$$

$$-x+3y = 2$$

$$x+3z = -1.$$

Solving by elimination: $y = 37/33$, $z = -26/33$, $x = 45/33$ as in (3).

Check: substitute (3) into the given equation (1). Take the numerical factor $\tfrac{1}{33}$ outside the cross-product, leaving

$$(45i+37j-26k) \times (j+k) = 45k-45j+37i+26i = 3(21i-15j+15k)$$

$$3r+\{r \times (j+k)\} = \tfrac{1}{11}(45i+37j-26k+21i-15j+15k)$$

$$= \tfrac{1}{11}(66i+22j-11k) \quad \text{as required.} \quad \square$$

Exercise (answer on p. 20)
1.6.1   Solve $2r + r \times (i-k) = 2i - j - k.$

1.7   Matrix Representation of Vector Algebra

Readers who are familiar with matrix algebra can see that equations (1.8) on p. 7 are exactly the definitions of multiplication of a matrix by a number λ and addition of two matrices, applied to a row matrix with 3 columns. For the operations in equations (1.8) a vector is naturally represented by a row matrix, or equally well by a column matrix with three rows, the matrix elements being the components.

It is also possible to represent the scalar and vector products by matrix operations. For example

$$A \cdot B = [A_x A_y A_z] \begin{bmatrix} B_x \\ B_y \\ B_z \end{bmatrix}.$$

A representation of $A \times B$ is given in Exercise 1.8 at the end of this chapter.

Answers to Exercises 1.1.1–1.6.1

1.1.1 $2\overrightarrow{OB} - \overrightarrow{OA}$.

1.2.1   (i) $2i + j + 2k, 3$
(ii) $2i + 6j + 3k, 7$
(iii) $2i + 6j - 3k, 7$.

1.2.2   (i) $8i + 9j - 3k, 14i - 7j - 2k$
(ii) $Q(5, 3, 2), R(-1, 5, 3), \overrightarrow{QR} = -6i + 2j + k$.

1.2.3   (i) $\sqrt{6}$; $\cos \alpha = 0.816, \cos \beta = \cos \gamma = -0.408$
(ii) 5; $\cos \alpha = 0.6, \cos \beta = 0, \cos \gamma = -0.8$
(iii) 7; $\cos \alpha = -\frac{2}{7}, \cos \beta = \frac{3}{7}, \cos \gamma = \frac{6}{7}$.

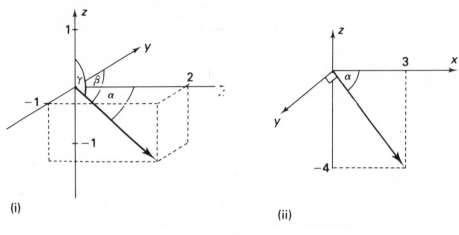

(i)   (ii)

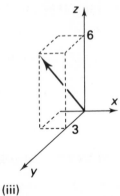

(iii)

1.3.1 $\frac{4}{3}(i - 2j + 4k) + \frac{1}{3}(2i - 7j - 4k)$
Check: vectors in brackets have zero dot product.

1.3.2 $90°, 79°, 11°$.   **1.3.3** $60°, 60°, 60°$.   **1.3.4** $-i + \frac{1}{2}j + \frac{1}{2}k$.

1.4.1 $(i + 2j - 3k) \cdot (27i + 12j + 8k) = 27 \neq 0$.

1.4.2 $-3j - 3k$ for both products; see Fig. 1.18 on p. 13.

1.4.3 (i) $42i + 19j - 17k$ (or any scalar multiple). (ii) $\pm 0.02(42i + 19j - 17k)$.

1.4.4 $-6(r \times s) = -12i - 6j - 6k$.

1.5.1 (i) 20. (ii) $16i + 17j - 21k$. (iii) $40i - 20j - 20k$.

1.6.1 $r = \frac{3}{4}i - \frac{1}{2}j - \frac{3}{4}k$.

Further Exercises on Chapter 1

1.1 The sum of the lengths of two adjacent sides of a triangle is greater than the third side. What inequalities does this give for $|a+b|$ and for $|a-b|$?

1.2 Derive equations (1.13), (1.14) and (1.15) by using equations (1.8) and (1.4).

1.3 Consider the triangle with vertices A(1, 2, −1), B(3, 4, 0) and C(9, −2, 7).
 (i) Find the vectors along the sides (in terms of i, j and k).
 (ii) By taking scalar products, find the interior angles.
 (iii) By taking a vector product, find the area of the triangle.

1.4 Find the angle between the diagonal of a cube and the diagonal of one of its faces.

1.5 State which of the following are meaningless: (i) $(a+b)/6$ (ii) $a+b/6$ (iii) a/b (iv) $a\cdot b+c$ (v) ab (vi) $a\cdot bc$ (vii) $a\cdot b\cdot c$ (viii) $a\cdot b/a\times c$ (ix) $a\times b/a\cdot c$ (x) $a\cdot b/b\cdot c$ (xi) a/a (xii) $1/a$ (xiii) $a\times b\times c$.
 In which of these expressions would it be better to use brackets?

1.6 Simplify $\{(A\times B)\times C\}+\{(B\times C)\times A\}+\{(C\times A)\times B\}$ by using equation (1.32) on p. 18.

1.7 Express $(A\times B)\times(C\times D)$ in the form $\lambda A+\mu B$.

1.8 Show that, if $A=A_x i+A_y j+A_z k$ is represented by the matrix

$$A_M = \begin{bmatrix} 0 & -A_z & A_y \\ A_z & 0 & -A_x \\ -A_y & A_x & 0 \end{bmatrix},$$

 then $A_M B_M - B_M A_M$ represents $A\times B$. Use this representation to do Example 1.40 and Exercise 1.6.

1.9 (i) If A and B are nonzero vectors of equal length, show that $A+B$ bisects the angle between A and B.
 (ii) Find a vector that bisects the angle between $3i+4j+6k$ and $7i+6j+2k$.

1.10 (i) Assuming that the volume of a tetrahedron is $\frac{1}{3}$ (base area) × (height), use an argument like that for the parallelepiped (Section 1.5) to show that the volume is $\frac{1}{6}|A\times B\cdot C|$ where A, B, C, are vectors along intersecting edges.
 (ii) Show that A(1, 6, 2), B(1, 3, −1), C(4, 3, 2) and D(4, 6, −1) are the corners of a regular tetrahedron, and calculate its volume.

1.11 Suppose A, B, P and Q are the points with coordinates A(−1, 1, 2), B(1, 0, 3), P(5, −2, 5) and Q(−5, 3, 0).
 (i) Show that the vectors $\overrightarrow{AB}$ and $\overrightarrow{AP}$ have the same direction.
 (ii) Show that Q lies on the straight line through A and B.

1.12 Show that, for any vectors a, b, r
 (i) $(a+b)\times(a-b)=-2(a\times b)$
 (ii) $(i\times r)\times i+(j\times r)\times j+(k\times r)\times k=2r$.

1.13 In a model of the methane molecule CH_4, the H atoms are at the corners of a regular tetrahedron at a distance d from the C atom at the centre. Axes are chosen so that the C atom is at the origin, one H atom is on the positive z-axis, and one H atom is in the Oyz plane.
 (i) Find the angle between two C—H bonds (the lines joining C and H atoms).
 (ii) Find the position vectors of the H atoms (relative to O).

1.14 Let $A = 2i + 2j + k$ and $B = 2i + 10j - 11k$
    (i) Find the (scalar) component of A in the direction of B.
    (ii) Find the vector projection of B onto A.
    (iii) Evaluate $A \times B$.
    (iv) Evaluate $(A + B) \times (A - B)$.
    (v) Find the volume of the parallelepiped with vertices at $(0, 0, 0)$, $(2, 2, 1)$, $(2, 10, -11)$, $(4, 12, -10)$, $(3, 1, 3)$, $(5, 3, 4)$, $(5, 11, -8)$ and $(7, 13, -7)$.

1.15 Suppose A, B, C, D are the points with coordinates $A(-1, 1, 2)$, $B(1, 0, 3)$, $C(0, 1, 5)$ and $D(3, -2, -1)$
    (i) Find a vector N which is perpendicular to the plane through A, B and C.
    (ii) Show that $\overline{AD}$ is perpendicular to N. What can therefore be said about the four points?
    (iii) Show that $E(4, 5, 2)$ is not in the plane through A, B and C.

1.16 (i) Consider the points $P_1(1, 3, 1)$, $P_2(0, -1, 4)$, $P_3(2, 2, 1)$ and $P_4(10, 29, -20)$. Show that $\overrightarrow{P_3P_4}$ is perpendicular to $\overrightarrow{P_1P_2} \times \overrightarrow{P_2P_3}$. Interpret geometrically.
    (ii) Given a set of points $P_1, P_2, P_3, \ldots, P_n$ $(n > 3)$, how would you test whether they are coplanar?

1.17 Consider the points $O(0, 0, 0)$, $P_1(2, 2, 2)$, $P_2(2, 10, -11)$ and $P_3(3, 1, 3)$.
    (i) Find P_4 (give the coordinates) so that $OP_1P_4P_2$ is a parallelogram.
    (ii) Find P_5 so that $OP_1P_5P_3$ is a parallelogram.
    (iii) Find P_6 so that $OP_2P_6P_3$ is a parallelogram.
    (iv) Find P_7 so that $OP_1P_5P_3P_2P_4P_7P_6$ is a parallelepiped, and determine its volume.

1.18 Show that, for any vectors A, B and C,

$$A \times (B \times C) + B \times (C \times A) + C \times (A \times B) = 0.$$

1.19 Let $a = i - j + 2k$, $b = 2i + j + k$, and $c = i + 2j - k$.
    (i) Evaluate $(a \times b) \cdot c$ and comment on the geometrical significance of the result.
    (ii) Also evaluate $a \cdot (b \times c)$, $b \cdot (c \times a)$, and $c \cdot (a \times b)$.

1.20 Given the points $P(1, 3, 1)$, $Q(2, 2, 5)$, $R(6, 1, 7)$ and $S(9, 8, 8)$, find the volume of the parallelepiped with one corner at P and edges PQ, PR, PS. Give the coordinates of the other four corners of the parallelepiped.

1.21 Solve the equation $3r + \{r \times (i + j)\} = 7i - 4j$.

2

Solid Geometry: Planes and Curves

2.1 Surfaces

In elementary two-dimensional geometry using Cartesian coordinates, the points (x, y) satisfying a given relation, such as $x^2 = y + 1$, may lie on a curve. This can be plotted by substituting specific values of x in the relation and solving for the corresponding values of y. Above each point on the x-axis, one (or more) points are plotted, giving the curve. To extend this procedure to three-dimensional (or solid) geometry, with a relation between three coordinates (x, y, z), one can substitute specific values of x and y in the relation and solve for the corresponding value(s) of z. This determines one (or more) points above each point in the $x - y$ plane, giving a **surface**.

Example 2.10
The relation $x^2 + y^2 + z^2 = 1$ is satisfied by all points at unit distance from the origin, so that the corresponding surface is the sphere of radius one centred on the origin. Note that the upper and lower hemispheres can be described separately by the equations $z = \pm(1 - x^2 - y^2)^{1/2}$. □

Example 2.11
What does the relation $x^2 + y^2 = 1$ represent in solid geometry?

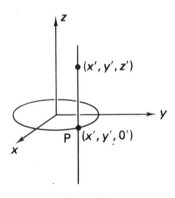

Figure 2.1

In two-dimensional geometry, this relation represents the circle of radius 1 centred on the origin. Obviously in three dimensions the equation is still satisfied by all points on this circle in the $x - y$ plane (Fig. 2.1). If P is any point of this circle, consider the line through P parallel to Oz. All points on this line have the same x- and y-coordinates, and so they all satisfy the relation $x^2 + y^2 = 1$. Taking such lines through all points of the circle gives a cylinder with axis Oz. This cylindrical surface is represented by the relation $x^2 + y^2 = 1$. □

Example 2.12

What does the relation $y = mx + c$ represent in solid geometry?

From the two-dimensional case, the relation is satisfied by all points on a line in the $x - y$ plane (or $z = 0$ plane). Again all points on vertical lines through this line also satisfy the relation, which therefore represents a vertical plane.   □

These examples illustrate the fact that not only does a single equation correspond to a surface, but a single equation cannot specify a curve.

Example 2.13

Adding the extra condition $z = 0$ will specify a curve in the $x - y$ plane. Thus the circle of radius 1 centred on the origin is most simply given as

$$x^2 + y^2 = 1, \qquad z = 0. \tag{2.1}$$

The points satisfying both equations are the intersection of the cylindrical surface $x^2 + y^2 = 1$ and the plane $z = 0$. The same circle can also be described by

$$x^2 + y^2 + z^2 = 1, \qquad z = 0, \tag{2.2}$$

as it is the intersection of the sphere and the plane, or

$$x^2 + y^2 + z^2 = 1, \qquad x^2 + y^2 = 1 \tag{2.3}$$

corresponding to it being the intersection of the sphere and the cylinder.   □

Exercises (answers on p. 39)

2.1.1   What do the following relations represent in solid geometry?
(i) $y = x^2$,
(ii) $y^2 + z^2 = 1$,
(iii) $x^2 + y^2 = 0$.

2.1.2   What do the following pairs of equations represent in solid geometry?
(i) $y = x$, $z = 0$,
(ii) $x^2 + y^2 = 1$, $z = 1$,
(iii) $y^2 + z^2 = 1$, $x = 0$.

2.1.3   Give the equations representing the following surfaces:
(i) a sphere of radius 2, centre $(0, 0, 0)$,
(ii) a sphere of radius 1, centre $(1, -1, 2)$,
(iii) a cylinder with axis the y-axis, and circular cross-section of radius 1.

2.2   The Equation of a Plane

There is a unique direction perpendicular to any given plane, and the plane is completely determined given this normal direction and one point on the plane. Suppose $N = Ai + Bj + Ck$ is a vector in the normal direction and $Q(a, b, c)$ is a point of the plane (Fig. 2.2). Then $P(x, y, z)$ is a point of the plane if and only if $\overrightarrow{QP}$ is perpendicular to N. But

$$\overrightarrow{QP} = \overrightarrow{OP} - \overrightarrow{OQ} = (x - a)i + (y - b)j + (z - c)k$$

so $\overrightarrow{QP} \cdot N = (x-a)A + (y-b)B + (z-c)C = 0$. If $D = aA + bB + cC$, then

the equation of the plane is

$$Ax + By + Cz = D \qquad\qquad\qquad \textbf{(2.4)}$$

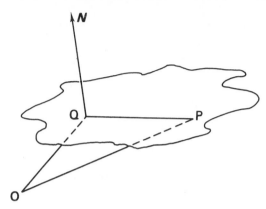

Figure 2.2   Normal **N** to plane

Example 2.20
Find the equation of the plane which is perpendicular to $2i - j + k$ and passes through $Q(-1, 2, 1)$.

Taking $N = 2i - j + k$ gives $A = 2$, $B = -1$, $C = 1$ in equation (2.4). Then

$$2x - y + z = D$$

passes through Q if $-2 - 2 + 1 = D$, so the required equation is

$$2x - y + z = -3. \quad \square$$

Conversely,

any equation of the form (2.4) represents a plane, and from the equation one can immediately write down $Ai + Bj + Ck$ as a vector along the normal,

i.e. perpendicular to the plane.

Example 2.21
Find the distance of the point $P(2, -3, 4)$ from the plane $x + 2y + 2z = 13$.

Suppose Q is the foot of the perpendicular from P to the plane. Then $d = PQ$ is the required distance, and $\overrightarrow{PQ}$ has the opposite direction to $N = i + 2j + 2k$, which is normal to the plane (Fig. 2.3). Since $N^2 = 1^2 + 2^2 + 2^2 = 9$, $N = 3$, and $(i + 2j + 2k)/3$ is the unit vector in the direction of N. Hence $\overrightarrow{PQ} = -d(i + 2j + 2k)/3$ and

$$\overrightarrow{OQ} = \overrightarrow{OP} + \overrightarrow{PQ} = (2i - 3j + 4k) + \overrightarrow{PQ}$$

$$= (2 - d/3)i + (-3 - 2d/3)j + (4 - 2d/3)k.$$

Hence Q has coordinates $(2-d/3, -3-2d/3, 4-2d/3)$; and these satisfy the plane equation, since Q is on the plane:

$$(2-d/3)+2(-3-2d/3)+2(4-2d/3)=13.$$

This gives $d=-3$.

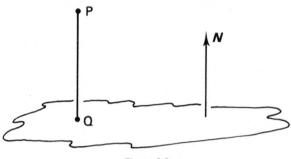

Figure 2.3

However the distance PQ should be positive. The reason for the negative value is that the expression for $\overrightarrow{PQ}$ was obtained assuming that N points out of the plane on the same side as P, as in Fig. 2.3. However the sense of N was not known when this figure was drawn; the negative value obtained for d indicates that N actually has the opposite sense to that shown in the figure and points out of the plane on the opposite side to P. In either case the computation can be performed as above, and the modulus of the result taken. Thus $PQ=3$.

Checks: $d=-3$ gives $(3, -1, 6)$ for Q, and so $(3, -1, 6)$ should satisfy the plane equation. It does, because $3+(2\times-1)+(2\times6)=13$. Also $Q(3, -1, 6)$

$$\Rightarrow \overrightarrow{PQ}=\overrightarrow{OP}-\overrightarrow{OQ}=(2i-3j+4k)-(3i-j+6k)=-i-2j-2k,$$

$$PQ^2=(-1)^2+(-2)^2+(-2)^2=9, \ PQ=3. \quad \square$$

Equations of surfaces and curves can be given in a vector form involving $r=xi+yj+zk$. Thus equation (2.4) can be written $N\cdot r=D$, and the sphere in Example 2.10 can be represented by $r\cdot r=1$.

Exercises (answers on p. 39)

2.2.1   Which of the points $A(1, 1, 0)$, $B(0, 1, 1)$ and $C(1, 0, 1)$ lie on the plane $2x-y+z=3$?

2.2.2   For each of the following planes, write down a vector normal to the plane: (i) $3x+4y-z=1$, (ii) $3x+4y-z=0$, (iii) $y=1$, (iv) $x=y$

2.2.3   Which of the planes (i) $x+y+2z=3$, (ii) $2x+2y-2z=1$, (iii) $2x+2y-2z=2$, and (iv) $x+y-z=2$ are parallel to the plane $x+y-z=1$?

2.2.4   Which of the vectors $a=i-j+k$, $b=-2i-j+k$, $c=4i+2j-2k$ and $d=2i+j+4k$ are perpendicular to the plane $2x+y-z=4$?

2.3   The Equations of a Line

Since a line may be specified as the intersection of two planes through it, a line may evidently be represented by two equations of the form (2.4). This representation is not

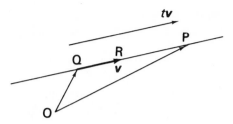

Figure 2.4

unique, since there are an infinity of planes through any line. More importantly, such a representation would not display any obvious features of the line, such as its direction.

Any line has a unique direction v, and is completely specified given also one point $Q(a, b, c)$ on it (Fig. 2.4). Then $P(x, y, z)$ is on the line if and only if $\overrightarrow{QP}$ is parallel to v, i.e. $\overrightarrow{QP} = tv$ for some number t. Hence

$$\overrightarrow{OP} = \overrightarrow{OQ} + tv. \tag{2.5}$$

This is called the **vector parametric equation** of the line:

any value of t gives the position vector of a point on the line, and any point on the line corresponds to a unique value of the parameter t. For a given line the equation is not unique, since any point on the line can be chosen for Q, and any vector along the line (in either direction) can be chosen for v. With any such different choice, a different symbol should be used for the parameter, since its values will not be the same.

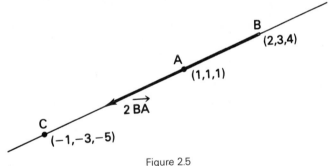

Figure 2.5

Example 2.30
Consider the line joining the points A$(1, 1, 1)$ and B$(2, 3, 4)$ (Fig. 2.5). Then either $\overrightarrow{OA} = i + j + k$ or $\overrightarrow{OB} = 2i + 3j + 4k$ could be used for $\overrightarrow{OQ}$ in equation (2.5), and the vectors $\overrightarrow{AB} = i + 2j + 3k$, $\overrightarrow{BA} = -i - 2j - 3k$ or $2\overrightarrow{BA} = -2i - 4j - 6k$, for example, could be used for v. Thus the three equations (writing r for $\overrightarrow{OP}$)

$$r = (i + j + k) + t(i + 2j + 3k)$$
$$r = (i + j + k) + u(-2i - 4j - 6k)$$
$$r = (2i + 3j + 4k) + s(-i - 2j - 3k)$$

each describe the line. The parameter value associated with any point depends on which equation is used. For example, the points A, B, and C are obtained with $t = 0$, 1, and -2 respectively; or with $u = 0$, $-\frac{1}{2}$, and 1; or with $s = 1$, 0, and 3. □

Equation (2.5) could also be put in the form (1.2). If R is the point with $t = 1$ (Fig. 2.4), then $v = \overrightarrow{OR} - \overrightarrow{OQ}$, so $\overrightarrow{OP} = t\overrightarrow{OR} + (1 - t)\overrightarrow{OQ}$.

The vector equation (2.5) contains three scalar equations between components. If $v = li + mj + nk$, then since $\overrightarrow{OP} = xi + yj + zk$ and $\overrightarrow{OQ} = ai + bj + ck$, the three equations are

$$x = a + tl, \; y = b + tm, \; z = c + tn. \tag{2.6}$$

These are the **Cartesian parametric equations** of the line. They are equivalent to

$$\frac{x - a}{l} = \frac{y - b}{m} = \frac{z - c}{n} \tag{2.7}$$

since each quotient is equal to t. Equations (2.7) are called the **standard** (or symmetric) **Cartesian equations** of the line. The representations (2.5), (2.6) and (2.7) all display the direction $(li + mj + nk)$ of the line, and the coordinates (a, b, c) of one point of the line.

It is possible for one or two of the numbers l, m and n to be zero. The standard Cartesian equations may still be used provided a zero denominator is taken to mean that the numerator is also zero. For example $(y - 2)/0$ indicates $y = 2$, as given by equations (2.6) if $m = 0$.

The standard form (2.7) contains only two independent equations. For example $(x - a)/l = (y - b)/m$ and $(x - a)/l = (z - c)/n$ are independent, and imply the third equation $(y - b)/m = (z - c)/n$. Each equation has the form (2.4) and is therefore a plane, and taking two of them describes the line as the intersection of these two planes.

Example 2.31
The equations

$$\frac{x + 1}{1} = \frac{y + 3}{2} = \frac{z + 5}{3} \tag{2.8}$$

describe the line in Fig. 2.5. So do the equations

$$\frac{x - 1}{-2} = \frac{y - 1}{-4} = \frac{z - 1}{-6}. \tag{2.9}$$

From equations (2.8) or (2.9), the equations of three different planes intersecting in the line can be written down, e.g. $2x - y = 1$ from the first pair of equations in (2.8). □

Example 2.32
Find standard Cartesian equations of the line of intersection of the planes $x + y + z = 5$, $4x + y + 2z = 15$.

Method: if M and N are normal to the planes, then $(M \times N)$ is perpendicular to each normal, and so is in each plane, and therefore along the line of intersection

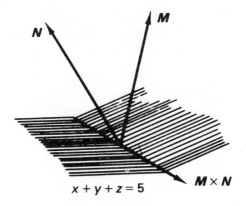

Figure 2.6

(see Fig. 2.6). Its components give the denominators in (2.7). The numerators require one point of the line—any point satisfying both given plane equations.

Take $M = i + j + k$, $N = 4i + j + 2k$. Then

$$M \times N = \begin{vmatrix} i & j & k \\ 1 & 1 & 1 \\ 4 & 1 & 2 \end{vmatrix} = i(2-1) - j(2-4) + k(1-4) = i + 2j - 3k.$$

(This could also be obtained as in Example 1.40 on p. 14.)

Check: $(i + 2j - 3k) \cdot M = 0 = (i + 2j - 3k) \cdot N$.

Subtracting the two plane equations to eliminate y gives $3x + z = 10(*)$, which is satisfied by $x = 3$, $z = 1$. Substituting into $x + y + z = 5$ gives $y = 1$. Thus $(3, 1, 1)$ is on both planes.

Check: $4 \times 3 + 1 + 2 \times 1 = 15$.

Standard equations of the line of intersection are therefore

$$(x-3)/1 = (y-1)/2 = (z-1)/(-3).$$

Check: Find another point on both planes by taking a different solution of $(*)$, say $x = 1$, $z = 7$. Then $y = -3$ gives $(1, -3, 7)$ which satisfies both plane equations, and so is on the line of intersection, and must satisfy the line equations found:

$$(1-3)/1, \ (-3-1)/2, \ 6/(-3) \text{ are all equal (to } -2).$$

The check contains an alternative method: once two points $(3, 1, 1)$ and $(1, -3, 7)$ on the line have been found, the vector joining them can be taken as the vector along the line. Thus

$$li + mj + nk = (3-1)i + (1-(-3))j + (1-7)k$$

and the line is represented by $(x-3)/2 = (y-1)/4 = (z-1)/(-6)$.   □

Two given planes intersect in a line unless they are parallel or identical. The exceptional cases are obvious from the plane equations, since the normals are parallel. For example, $3x - y = 2$ and $-6x + 2y = -4$ represent the same plane; $3x - y = 2$ and $9x - 3y = 4$ represent parallel planes.

Exercises (answers on p. 39)

2.3.1 For each of the following lines, write down the coordinates of a point on the line, and a vector having the direction of the line:
  (i) $r = 3i + j + t(2j - k)$,
  (ii) $x = 2 - 3s, \; y = s, \; z = -1 + s$,
  (iii) $x - 1 = (y + 2)/-2 = z/2$.

2.3.2 Determine whether any of the points A($-1, -1, 0$), B($0, 1, 2$), C($1, 2, 3$) or D($4, -1, 2$) lie on any of the following lines:
  (i) $r = j + 2k + s(i + j + k)$,
  (ii) $(x + 2)/2 = (y + 3)/4 = (z + 1)/2$,
  (iii) $r = 2i + 2k + u(4i - 2j)$,
  (iv) $x - 5 = y = (z - 2)/0$.

2.3.3 Find the equation of the line joining $(2, 1, -1)$ and $(3, 0, 0)$,
  (i) in vector parametric form,
  (ii) in Cartesian symmetric form.

2.4 Intersection of a Line and a Plane

The intersection of a given line and plane may be found by substituting the parametric equations of the line into the plane equation and solving for the parameter value of the point of intersection.

Example 2.40

Find the intersection of the plane $x + y + 7z = 6$ and the line $(x - 10)/(-26) = y/4 = (2z + 1)/6$.

(The given line equations are not quite in standard form, in which the last term would be $(z + \frac{1}{2})/3$.) Putting each quotient equal to a parameter t gives the parametric equations

$$x = 10 - 26t, \qquad y = 4t, \qquad 2z = -1 + 6t. \qquad (*)$$

Substitute into the plane equation, and solve for t:

$$(10 - 26t) + 4t + 7(-\tfrac{1}{2} + 3t) = 6, \; t = \tfrac{1}{2}.$$

Substituting in ($*$), the point on the line with parameter $t = \frac{1}{2}$ is $(-3, 2, 1)$.

Check: This satisfies the given line equations: $(-13)/(-26) = \frac{2}{4} = \frac{3}{6}$; and the given plane equation: $-3 + 2 + 7 = 6$.
  Thus the line meets the plane in the point $(-3, 2, 1)$. $\square$

This method always results in an equation of the form $at = b$, which has three cases. If $a \neq 0$, $t = b/a$ gives a unique solution and the line intersects the plane in a single point. If $a = 0$ and $b \neq 0$, there is no t giving a point on the line and the plane, which must therefore be parallel. If $a = b = 0$, *any* value of t gives a point on both the plane and the line, which therefore lies in the plane. These arguments can be confirmed by explicitly finding a and b in terms of vector equations. If the plane equation is $N \cdot r = D$ (vector form of equation (2.4)), and the line equation is $r = s + tv$ (cf. equation (2.5)), substituting as in Example 2.40 gives

$$N \cdot (s + tv) = D, \qquad (N \cdot v)t = -(N \cdot s) + D.$$

The cases $a = N \cdot v = 0$ occur when the plane normal N is perpendicular to the line direction v, so that the line is parallel to or in the plane. From equation (2.5), s is a point of the line, and the case $b = 0$ requires $N \cdot s = D$, showing that s is also a point of the plane. If one point of the line is in the plane, and the line is perpendicular to the normal, the whole line must lie in the plane (Fig. 2.7).

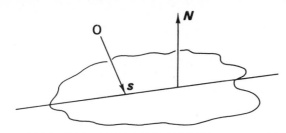

Figure 2.7

Exercise (answers on p. 39)

2.4.1 For each of the following lines, state whether the line intersects the plane $2x - y + 3z = 6$ in a unique point:

(i) $r = t(i + j + k)$,

(ii) $r = i - j - k + s(4i - j - 3k)$,

(iii) $(x+1)/2 = (y-1)/3 = z/5$,

(iv) $-x + 1 = y - 1 = z + 6$.

2.5 Intersection of Two Lines

In three dimensions there are four geometric possibilities for the intersection when two sets of line equations are given:

(i) the equations may represent the same line, as discussed in Examples 2.30 and 2.31;

(ii) the lines may have no common point because they are parallel;

(iii) the lines may have no common point, but not be parallel (Fig. 2.8);

(iv) the lines may intersect in a single point.

The lines in Fig. 2.8 are called **skew**. Assuming that the line equations are given in one of the forms (2.5), (2.6), or (2.7), the directions v_1 and v_2 can be read off, and also the coordinates of one point on each line, say Q_1 and Q_2. In cases (i) and (ii), v_2 must be a scalar multiple of v_1. These cases can therefore be separated from cases (iii) and (iv) by

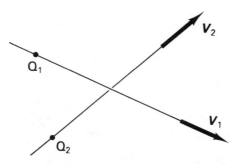

Figure 2.8   Skew lines

inspection, and distinguished from each other by ascertaining whether the point Q_1 on the first line is also on the second line. If so, the lines coincide; if not they are parallel. If v_2 is not a multiple of v_1, assuming a point of intersection gives simultaneous equations for its parameter. These equations have no solution in cases (ii) and (iii), a unique solution in case (iv), and are identically satisfied in case (i). If necessary, the first step is to put one line equation in the parametric form (2.6), and the other in the standard Cartesian form (2.7).

Example 2.50

Investigate the intersection, if any, of the line represented by

$$r = i - 2j + t(2i + j + 3k) \tag{1}$$

with the lines represented by

$$r = 9i + 2j + 12k + s(4i + 2j + 6k) \tag{2}$$

$$x = -4 + u, \qquad y = (9 + u)/2, \qquad z = (-1 + 3u)/2 \tag{3}$$

$$r = 2i + 2j + 4k + w(3i - 2j + 2k) \tag{4}$$

$$(x - 2)/3 = (y - 2)/2 = (z - 4)/2. \tag{5}$$

The given equations display the directions of the five lines: $v_1 = 2i + j + 3k$, $v_2 = 4i + 2j + 6k$, $v_3 = i + \frac{1}{2}j + \frac{3}{2}k$ (from the coefficients of the parameter u), $v_4 = 3i - 2j + 2k$, and $v_5 = 3i + 2j + 2k$ (from the denominators). One point on each line can also be read off: $Q_1(1, -2, 0)$, $Q_2(9, 2, 12)$, $Q_3(-4, \frac{9}{2}, -\frac{1}{2})$, $Q_4(2, 2, 4)$ and $Q_5(2, 2, 4)$.

Taking (1) in components gives the Cartesian parametric form

$$x = 1 + 2t, \qquad y = -2 + t, \qquad z = 3t \tag{*}$$

and then eliminating t gives the standard form

$$(x - 1)/2 = y + 2 = z/3. \tag{†}$$

The Cartesian form of (2) is $x = 9 + 4s$, $y = 2 + 2s$, $z = 12 + 6s$. Substituting into (†) gives simultaneous equations

$$(9 + 4s - 1)/2 = 2s + 2 + 2 = (12 + 6s)/3$$

for the parameter s of any point of (2) which is on (1). Since these equations are identically satisfied (true for all s), all points of (2) lie on (1). Thus (1) and (2) represent the same line.

Checks: Do they have the same direction? Yes, because $v_2 = 2v_1$. Is Q_1 a point of (2)? This requires a value of the parameter s such that

$$\overrightarrow{OQ_1} = i - 2j = 9i + 2j + 12k + s(4i + 2j + 6k)$$

and $s = -2$ gives this.

Substituting (3) into (†) gives $(-5 + u)/2 = (13 + u)/2 = (-1 + 3u)/6$ which have no solution (since the first reduces to $-5 = 13$). Thus (1) and (3) represent lines with no common point. Since $v_3 = v_1/2$, the lines are parallel.

Check: Is Q_1 on (3)? This requires $1 = -4 + u$, $-2 = (9 + u)/2$ and $0 = (-1 + 3u)/2$ which are impossible to satisfy, so the lines are different.

Substituting the Cartesian form of (4) into (†) gives

$$(2+3w-1)/2 = 2-2w+2 = (4+2w)/3$$

with the unique solution $w = 1$. Hence (1) and (4) represent lines which intersect in a single point. Substituting $w = 1$ into (4) gives $r = 5i + 6k$, so the point of intersection is $(5, 0, 6)$.

Checks: Is $(5, 0, 6)$ on (1)? Yes, because $5i + 6k = i - 2j + t(2i + j + 3k)$ is satisfied by $t = 2$. Since v_4 is not a scalar multiple of v_1, the equations cannot represent the same line.

Since (5) is already in standard form, it is easiest to substitute (*) into (5), giving $(2t-1)/3 = (t-4)/2 = (3t-4)/2$. There is no solution, since the first equality gives $t = -10$ and the second requires $t = 0$. No point of (1) is on (5). Since v_5 is not a multiple of v_1, equations (1) and (5) represent skew lines.

Check: Substitute the parametric form of (5) into (†), giving

$$(3p+2-1)/2 = 2p+2+2 = (2p+4)/3$$

for the parameter p of any point of (5) which is on (1). Again the equations are inconsistent, i.e. have no solution.   □

The above working suggests that parallel and skew lines can be distinguished without explicitly examining their directions, because in the parallel case the coefficient of the parameter has the same value on each side of each equality, and each equation reduces to $0u = k \neq 0$. In general, substituting

$$x = \alpha + t\lambda, \qquad y = \beta + t\mu, \qquad z = \gamma + t\nu \tag{2.10}$$

into

$$(x-a)/l = (y-b)/m = (z-c)/n \tag{2.7}$$

gives

$$\frac{\alpha - a + t\lambda}{l} = \frac{\beta - b + t\mu}{m} = \frac{\gamma - c + t\nu}{n}$$

and the parameter term cancels if $\lambda/l = \mu/m = \nu/n$, which is just the condition for equations (2.10) and (2.7) to represent lines with the same direction.

If lines intersect, but a mistake is made in the calculation, the false result deduced will (almost certainly) be that the lines are skew. Unfortunately any check for skew lines is somewhat negative, since it cannot consist of substituting a solution back into given equations. If skew lines are deduced, therefore, considerable care should be taken over the check. An independent test can be formulated as follows: in the other cases (i), (ii) and (iv), the lines lie in a plane, so v_1, v_2, and $\overline{Q_1 Q_2}$ are coplanar, and the scalar triple product (see p. 16) of these vectors is zero. Again the check is unsatisfactory in the sense that a mistake will change a zero scalar product into a non-zero one indicating skew lines, but the alternative formulas (1.27)–(1.30) should allow satisfactory checking of a scalar triple product.

Exercises (answers on p. 39)

2.5.1   Show that the equations

$$r = 3i + j + k + t(i - j)$$

and

$$r = 3i + j + k + s(i + j)$$

represent different lines.

2.5.2   Show that the equations

$$r = 3i + j + k + t(i - j + 2k)$$

and

$$r = i + 3j - 3k - s(-i + j - 2k)$$

represent the same line.

2.6   The Equations of a Curve

The examples in Section 2.1 indicated that two equations between the coordinates x, y and z are required to represent a curve. One example of such equations is the standard equations of a straight line (see p. 28). A line may also be given by three parametric equations as in (2.6) on p. 28.

> More generally, for any continuous functions f, g and h, the parametric equations
>
> $$x = f(t), \qquad y = g(t), \qquad z = h(t) \tag{2.11}$$
>
> will represent a curve.

(Continuous functions will be discussed and formally defined in Section 5.1.) These equations may be written in the vector form

$$r(t) = f(t)i + g(t)j + h(t)k. \tag{2.12}$$

Eliminating t from equations (2.11) provides two Cartesian equations.

Example 2.60

$$r(t) = (\cos t)i + (\sin t)j + 0k$$

(in which the last term would normally be omitted). Since $z = 0$ this can only represent points in the $x - y$ plane, and since $|r| = (\cos^2 t + \sin^2 t)^{1/2} = 1$, points satisfying the equation all lie at unit distance from the origin. In fact the equation represents the unit circle in the Oxy plane, already considered in Example 2.13. Taking components gives $x = \cos t$, $y = \sin t$, $z = 0$ corresponding to equations (2.11) and eliminating t gives equations (2.1). To get the whole circle it is sufficient to consider $0 \le t < 2\pi$ as the domain of the parameter t (Fig. 2.9).   □

Example 2.61

$$x = \cos t, \qquad y = \sin t, \qquad z = t.$$

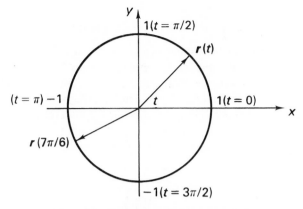

Figure 2.9   Parameters of points on a circle

The equations for x and y are the same as in the previous example, so the points of the curve only differ from those of Fig. 2.9 through their z-coordinate. Thus the points lie on the cylinder $x^2 + y^2 = 1$ (cf. p. 23, Example 2.11 and Fig. 2.1). As t increases from 0 to 2π, the points go round the cylinder, and their height z steadily increases from 0 to 2π, giving one complete turn of a helix (Fig. 2.10).   □

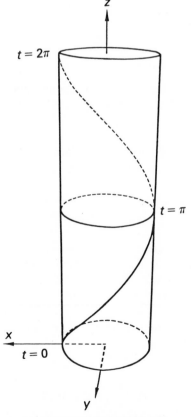

Figure 2.10   Helix (on cylinder)

Example 2.62

$$r(t) = (\cos t)i + (\cos t)j + (\sin t)k.$$

The parameter may be eliminated from $x = \cos t = y$, $z = \sin t$ by writing $x = y$, $x^2 + z^2 = 1$. Now $x = y$ represents a vertical plane (cf. Example 2.12 on p. 24), and $x^2 + z^2 = 1$ represents a cylinder with the y-axis as axis (cf. Example 2.11). The curve is the ellipse forming the intersection of these two surfaces (Fig. 2.11). The equations of this ellipse could also be written $x^2 + z^2 = 1$, $y^2 + z^2 = 1$, exhibiting the curve as the intersection of two cylinders. □

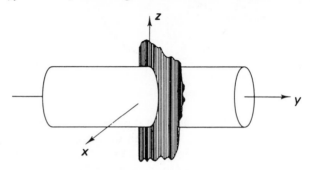

Figure 2.11   Plane section of cylinder

Exercise (answer on p. 39)

2.6.1   Write the equations given in Exercises 2.1.2 (p. 24) and 2.3.2 (ii) and (iv) (p. 30) in vector parametric form.

2.7   Intersections with Curves

The method used to find the intersection of a line and plane in Section 2.4 will give the intersections of any curve with any surface. Similarly the procedure (p. 32) of Example 2.50 may be used to find the intersection, if any, of two space curves. The resulting method will now be summarized.

(i) If necessary, put equations of curve in parametric form.

(ii) Substitute parametric equations of curve into Cartesian equation of surface (or equations of second curve).

(iii) Solve the resulting equations for the parameter values of intersections.

(iv) Substitute values found in (iii) into equations of curve to get the coordinates of the points of intersection.

(v) Check that these points are on the surface (or second curve).

(vi) If (iii) gives no solutions this indicates no intersection: for two curves this can be checked by repeating the work with the curves interchanged; for a curve and a surface the geometry of the situation may be considered. It is also possible for the equations considered in (iii) to be identities, since a curve may lie wholly on a surface, or two sets of curve equations may be different representations of the same curve.

Example 2.70

Investigate the intersections of the curve

$$r(t) = t^2(i + j) + 2tk$$

with the plane $Ax + By + Cz + D = 0$ as the plane varies.

In the following the steps are numbered as in the above summary.

   (i) The curve equations are $x = t^2 = y$, $z = 2t$.

   (ii) Substituting into plane equation: $At^2 + Bt^2 + 2Ct + D = 0$.

   (iii) If $A + B \neq 0$, this is a quadratic equation, with solutions

$$t = \{-C \pm \sqrt{(C^2 - AD - BD)}\}/(A + B) \qquad (*)$$

provided $C^2 \geqslant (A + B)D$.

   If $A + B = 0$ and $C \neq 0$, the solution is $t = -D/2C$.

   If $A + B = C = 0$, the equation is inconsistent unless $D = 0$, in which case all values of t satisfy the equation.

These different cases are now considered separately. $A = B = C = 0$ need not be considered, as $D = 0$ would not represent a plane.

Case 1: $A + B \neq 0$, $C^2 > AD + BD$

   (iv) The intersections are $(t_1^2, t_1^2, 2t_1)$ and $(t_2^2, t_2^2, 2t_2)$ where t_1 and t_2 are the two values of t given by $(*)$.

   (v) Unless numerical values of A, B, C, D are given, the check merely verifies that $(*)$ does give solutions of a quadratic equation.

Case 2: $A + B \neq 0$, $C^2 = AD + BD$. Same as Case 1 but $t_1 = t_2$ so there is only one intersection.

Case 3: $A + B = 0$, $C \neq 0$.

   (iv) There is one intersection $(D^2/4C^2, D^2/4C^2, -D/C)$.

   (v) $(AD^2/4C^2) + (BD^2/4C^2) - D + D = 0$ because $B = -A$.

Case 4: $A + B = C = D = 0$.

   (vi) The curve lies in the plane $(x = y)$.

Case 5: $A + B = C = 0$, $D \neq 0$.

   (vi) There are no intersections. This is consistent geometrically with Case 4, because the planes $x - y = (D/B) \neq 0$ are parallel to $x - y = 0$, the plane containing the curve.

   Using a different coordinate system defined by $i' = (i + j)/\sqrt{2}$, $j' = (i - j)/\sqrt{2}$ gives $r = t^2/\sqrt{2}\,i' + 2t k$ for the curve, showing that it is in the plane $y' = 0$, and is the parabola $x' = t^2\sqrt{2}$, $z = 2t$ or $z^2 = x'2\sqrt{2}$ (Fig. 2.12).

Case 6: $A + B \neq 0$, $C^2 < AD + BD$.

   (iii) $(*)$ has no solution.

   (iv) It is clear from Fig. 2.12 that there will be planes that do not intersect the parabola, and also that there are planes which touch the parabola in one point, so that Case 2 is expected.

   The line of intersection of the plane $Ax + By + Cz + D = 0$ and the plane $x = y$ containing the parabola is represented by the equations

$$x/(-C) = y/(-C) = (z + D/C)/(A + B),$$

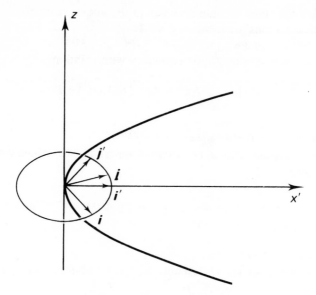

Figure 2.12　Parabola in $x'-z$ plane

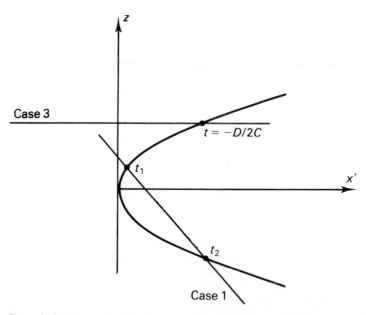

Figure 2.13　Lines show intersection of $x'-z$ plane and $Ax + By + Cz + D = 0$

with the usual convention that a zero denominator implies the numerator is zero. Thus in Case 3, $A + B = 0 \Rightarrow z = -D/C$, and the line is horizontal. As in Fig. 2.13 the line meets the parabola in a single point, and the parabola passes through the plane. If $(A + B) \neq 0$, the line is not horizontal, so in Case 2 the line must touch the parabola without crossing it, and the parabola touches the plane without passing through it, as in Fig. 2.14. Examples of Cases 1 and 6 are also shown.　□

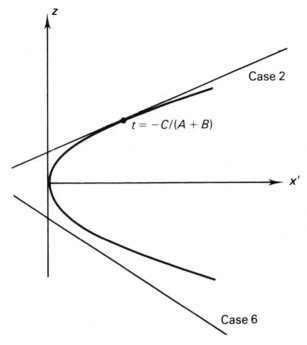

Figure 2.14   Lines show intersection of $x'-z$ plane and $Ax+By+Cz+D=0$

Answers to Exercises 2.1.1–2.6.1

2.1.1   (i) A parabolic cylinder (formed by lines parallel to the z-axis).
(ii) A circular cylinder with the x-axis as axis, and cross-section of radius 1.
(iii) The z-axis.

2.1.2   (i) The line in the Oxy plane through O and bisecting the angle xOy.
(ii) A circle in the plane $z=1$, radius 1, centre $(0,0,1)$.
(iii) A circle in the Oyz plane, radius 1, centre $(0,0,0)$.

2.1.3   (i) $x^2+y^2+z^2=4$ (ii) $(x-1)^2+(y+1)^2+(z-2)^2=1$
(iii) $x^2+z^2=1$.

2.2.1   C

2.2.2   (i), (ii) $\lambda(3i+4j-k)$, for any $\lambda\neq0$. (iii) λj. (iv) $\lambda(i-j)$.

2.2.3   (ii) and (iv)   **2.2.4** b and c

2.3.1   Answers not unique.

2.3.2   A on (ii); B on (i) and (iii); C on (i); D on (iii) and (iv).

2.3.3 $r=2i+j-k+t(i-j+k)$; $x-2=1-y=z+1$.

2.4.1   (i) Yes. (ii) No. (iii) Yes. (iv) No.

2.6.1   Answers not unique, but simplest are
(i) $r=t(i+j)$ (ii) $r=(\cos t)i+(\sin t)j+k$.
(iii) $r=(\cos t)j+(\sin t)k$ (iv) $r=-2i-3j-k+t(i+2j+k)$
(v) $r=5i+2k+t(i+j)$.

To check these, or any other answers to **2.6.1** (and **2.3.3**), write the answer in Cartesian, parametric form, and substitute into the non-parametric equations, which should be satisfied for any value of the parameter.

Further Exercises on Chapter 2

2.1   Find equations representing the planes specified by the following conditions.
   (i) Parallel to the plane $4x - y - z = 3$, and passing through $(-1, 2, 3)$.
   (ii) Passing through $(1, 2, 2)$, $(3, -1, 1)$ and $(2, 2, 1)$.
   (iii) Passing through $(1, 2, 1)$ and $(2, 4, -1)$, and perpendicular to the plane $2x - 3y + 2z = 4$.

2.2   Find a unit vector n normal to the plane $3x - 6y + 2z = 2$. Write down the coordinates of (i) a point P of this plane (ii) the point Q determined by $\overrightarrow{PQ} = \lambda n$. Hence calculate the perpendicular distance between the parallel planes $3x - 6y + 2z = 2$, $3x - 6y + 2z = 4$.

2.3   If the coordinates of P and Q each satisfy

$$Ax + By + Cz = D \tag{2.4}$$

show that $\overrightarrow{PQ}$ is perpendicular to $N = Ai + Bj + Ck$.
[This shows that equation (2.4) represents a plane.]

2.4   What are the equations of the line through the point $(2, 8, -3)$ and parallel to $i + j + 2k$
   (i) in vector parametric form (2.5)
   (ii) in Cartesian parametric form (2.6)
   (iii) in symmetric Cartesian form (2.7)?
   State whether the following points are on this line: $(2, 8, -3)$, $(1, 1, 2)$, $(1, 7, -5)$, $(0, 6, -7)$, $(2, 8, 0)$, $(0, 8, -3)$, $(42, 48, 37)$. For those that are on the line, give their parameter values determined by your answer (i) or (ii).

2.5   Express the equations

$$(x - 1)/3 = -y/5 = (3z - 2)/6$$

in the vector parametric form (2.5). Show that this line is parallel to the plane $x + y + z = 6$.

2.6   Find the direction-cosines of the line

$$2x + y - z = 3, \qquad x - y + 4z = 6.$$

2.7   Find the equation of the plane through the point $(2, -1, 3)$ and containing the line $r = i + j + t(-i + k)$.

2.8   Find the intersection (if any) of the line

$$x - 1 = (y + 2)/3 = z/2$$

with each of the planes (i) $x + y = 3$. (ii) $2x - z = 1$. (iii) $2x - z = 2$.

2.9   Investigate the intersection of the plane $x - 2y + 3z = 1$ with (i) $4y = 2x + 6z - 2$ (ii) $x + y = 3$ (iii) $x - 2y + 3z = 0$. In each case give either the direction of the line of intersection or a geometric explanation of why there is no such line.

2.10   Determine whether the line

$$r = 2i + j + s(i - j + k)$$

meets the lines
   (i) $r = 3i - k + u(-i + j + k)$
   (ii) $1 - x = y - 2 = z$
   (iii) $r = 2i + 3j + 2k + t(i + j + k)$,
   giving the point of intersection where one exists, or explaining the situation geometrically.

2.11 What does the result of Exercise 1.5.1(i) imply regarding the intersection of lines (1) and (5) in Example 2.50 (on p. 32)?

2.12 Verify that the lines

$$x-2=(y-2)/3=z-3 \quad \text{and} \quad x-2=y-3=(z-4)/2$$

are skew.

2.13 Describe geometrically the curves represented by the following equations:

(i) $r = i \sin t + j \cos t + k$

(ii) $r = i \cos t + k \sin t$

(iii) $r = ja \cos t + kb \sin t$

(iv) $r = 2i \cos t + tj + 2k \sin t$

(in each of which t is the parameter).

State whether the following points are on (iv), giving the parameter value for those which are: $(0,0,0)$, $(2,0,0)$, $(0,2,0)$, $(2,0,2)$, $(1,0,\sqrt{3})$, $(1,\pi/3,\sqrt{3})$, $(-\sqrt{3}, -7\pi/6, 1)$, $(0, 25\pi/2, -2)$.

2.14 Find the points of intersection (if any) of the circle $r = i \cos t + j \sin t$ and the plane $(-1+\sqrt{3})x + (1+\sqrt{3})y + 2z = 2$.

2.15 Find the points of intersection (if any) of the parabola

$$y^2 = 4x, \qquad z + 1 = 0$$

and the plane $2x - y - 7z + 5 = 0$. What are the conditions (on a, b, c, and d) for the plane $ax + by + cz + d = 0$ not to intersect this parabola?

2.16 Show that the curve

$$r = (t^3 - t^2 + 3t)i + (1 + t - t^2)j + (t^3 + 2t + 3)k$$

lies in a plane. Give the equation of the plane.

2.17 Obtain the equation of the ellipse in Example 2.62 and Fig. 2.11 relative to the axes $Ox'y'z$ used in Example 2.70 and Fig. 2.12 (see pp. 36 and 37).

2.18 Use the method of Exercise 2.2 to obtain a formula for the perpendicular distance between the parallel planes

$$Ax + By + Cz = D, \qquad Ax + By + Cz = E.$$

2.19 Use the method of Example 2.21 to obtain a formula for the distance of the point $P(X, Y, Z)$ from the plane $Ax + By + Cz = D$.

2.20 Express the line equations

$$x - 1 = (y+2)/3 = z/2$$

in parametric form

(a) using x as the parameter;

(b) using y as the parameter;

(c) using z as the parameter.

For what lines (if any) is it not possible to choose any one of the coordinates as parameter?

2.21 (i) Find an equation for the plane through $A(1, -2, 1)$ and perpendicular to the vector from the origin to A.

(ii) Find an equation for the plane through $B(a, b, c)$ and perpendicular to the vector from the origin to B.

2.22 Show that the lines

$$r = 2i + 2j + 3k + t(i + 3j + k)$$

and

$$x - 2 = \tfrac{1}{4}(y - 3) = \tfrac{1}{2}(z - 4)$$

intersect, and find the equation of the plane that contains them.

2.23 Show that the line of intersection of the planes

$$x + 2y - 2z = 5, \; 5x - 2y - z = 0$$

is parallel to the line

$$r = -3i + k + t(2i + 3j + 4k).$$

Find the equation of the plane containing the two lines.

2.24 Find the length of the perpendicular from the origin onto the line

$$(x - 2)/3 = (y - 1)/4 = (2 - z)/5.$$

2.25 Find the coordinates of the point P at which the lines

$$r = i + j + k + t(i - j), \qquad r = -4i + j + s(4i + j + k)$$

intersect. Find the vector parametric equations of a line through P which is coplanar with the two given lines and bisects the angle between them.

2.26 Find equations representing the following surfaces:
(i) the plane which is parallel to the vector $R = 2i + j - k$ and contains the points P(1, 1, 0) and Q(0, 2, 3);
(ii) the sphere with centre C(-1, 0, 1) and passing through P(1, -3, 7).

2.27 Show that the lines

$$3x - 6 = \tfrac{3}{2}y - 3 = z - 5$$

and

$$x - \tfrac{5}{2} = \tfrac{1}{2}y = \tfrac{1}{3}z - \tfrac{1}{2}$$

are distinct and parallel, and find an equation for the plane containing them.

2.28 Consider the lines

$$r = i + 2j - k + t(2i + 3j - k) \tag{L1}$$

$$r = -i + j + 2k + s(3i + 2j + k) \tag{L2}$$

(i) Find the vector which joins the point with parameter t on (L1) to the point with parameter s on (L2).
(ii) Obtain the equations (use dot products) which hold when the vector in (i) is perpendicular to both (L1) and (L2).
(iii) By solving the equations found in (ii) for s and t, obtain the coordinates of the ends of the common perpendicular to (L1) and (L2), and its length. (The shortest distance between the lines.)

2.29 Find the shortest distance between the lines

$$\frac{x + 2}{2} = \frac{y}{3} = \frac{z + 4}{4} \quad \text{and} \quad -\frac{1}{2}x = \frac{y + 2}{3} = \frac{1}{2}z.$$

2.30 Find the equation of the line joining A$(-2, -1, 4)$ and B$(1, 5, -2)$.
Find the following points on the line:
  (i) P where AP$=3$ and BP$=6$;
  (ii) Q where AQ$=3$ and BQ$=12$;
  (iii) R where AR$=6$ and BR$=3$.

2.31 Find the equation of the plane that contains the point $(1, 3, 2)$ and the line

$$\tfrac{1}{2}(x-3) = \tfrac{1}{8}(y-3) = z+1.$$

2.32 Find standard Cartesian equations for the line of intersection of the planes

$$x+3y-5z = 10, \qquad 6x-y+z = 0.$$

2.33 Find the intersections of the curve

$$r = i + (2t+1)j + (1+t^2)k$$

with the plane

$$21x = y + 9z.$$

2.34 Find the intersection (if any) of the lines

$$r = 2i + 5k + s(i+2j+k),$$

$$r = 3i - 3j + k + t(2i-j-3k).$$

2.35 Find the equation of the plane which passes through P$(1, 1, 0)$ and contains the line

$$x-2 = 3-y = \tfrac{1}{2}(z-5).$$

2.36 (i) Find the equation of the plane which passes through A$(1, -1, 1)$ and B$(2, 1, 2)$, and is perpendicular to the plane $2x+5y+4z = 9$.
  (ii) With A and B as in (i), find equations for the line which passes through the midpoint of AB, is perpendicular to AB, and lies in the plane $x = z$.

2.37 Find the equation of the plane which is parallel to the planes

$$x+2y-2z = 6, \qquad x+2y-2z = -3$$

and is midway between them.

2.38 Show that the lines

$$r = 2i + 2j + 3k + t(i+3j+k)$$

and

$$x-3 = -2y-4 = 2z-6$$

intersect, and find the angle between them.

2.39 Find the points of intersection of the curve

$$r = \sqrt{2}j \cos t + \sqrt{2}k \sin t$$

and the plane

$$3x + y + z = 0.$$

Give the equation of a plane which does not intersect this curve, explaining why there is no intersection.

2.40 Show that one pair of the three lines

$$\frac{x-1}{2}=\frac{y-1}{-4}=\frac{z-5}{-1} \tag{1}$$

$$r = 4i - j + 4k + t(-i + 6j + k) \tag{2}$$

$$x = 2 - 4s, \qquad y = 4 + 8s, \qquad z = 4 + 2s \tag{3}$$

are parallel, another pair intersect in a point P, and the third pair are skew. Give the coordinates of P.

3
Functions

3.1 Basic Concepts

A (binary) **relation** between sets A and B establishes a pairing (x, y) associating elements x of A with elements y of B. When A and B are sets of real numbers, the relation may be illustrated by a graph.

Example 3.10

$$A = \{1, 2, 3\}, \qquad B = \{4, 5, 6, 7\}$$

with pairing

1	2	3
4, 5	4	4, 7

This relation can be written as the set of ordered pairs $(1, 4)$, $(1, 5)$, $(2, 4)$, $(3, 4)$, $(3, 7)$, which may be depicted in a graph as in Fig. 3.1(a). □

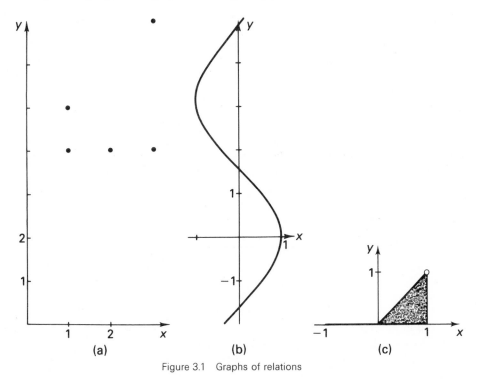

Figure 3.1   Graphs of relations

Example 3.11

$$\{(x, y): -1 \leqslant x \leqslant 1, \cos y = x\}.$$

Here A is the closed interval $[-1, 1]$, and B is the set R of all real numbers, which is alternatively denoted by $(-\infty, \infty)$. Figure 3.1(b) shows part of the graph of this relation. □

Example 3.12

$$\{(x, y): -1 \leqslant x \leqslant 1, 0 \leqslant y \leqslant \max(x, 0)\}.$$

If $x \leqslant 0$, $\max(x, 0) = 0$ and $y = 0$ is the only element of $B = R$ corresponding to x. The graph of this relation includes all of the shaded region in Fig. 3.1(c). □

A function is a relation in which a unique element of B is associated with each element of A. The **domain** of the function is the set A, and the **range** of the function is the set of elements of B used in the correspondence. If a function is denoted by f, the usual notation denotes by $f(x)$ the element of B corresponding to x in A. For the commonly used functions with standard names the brackets in $f(x)$ are omitted. Thus for $f = \sin$, $\sin x$ is written for the value, rather than $\sin(x)$.

Example 3.13

Tables of elementary functions often give $\sin \theta$ to four decimal places for values of θ from $0°$ to $90°$ in steps of $1'$. The information contained in such a table is compactly described as

$$\sin \theta, \ \theta = 0°(1')90°, \ 4\text{D}. \tag{3.1}$$

In the present context, the table may be regarded as the definition of a function, the domain D being the 5400 values of θ considered, and the range R the numbers appearing in the table. The graph is a set of 5400 isolated points. □

Example 3.14

The logarithmic function $\ln x$ (or $\log x$) has domain $R^+ = (0, \infty)$, and may be defined as the function which is an antiderivative (or indefinite integral) of $g(x) = 1/x$, satisfying $\ln 1 = 0$. The last condition fixes the arbitrary constant featuring in the antiderivative. Using a prime to denote derivative, the defining properties of ln are

$$\ln' x = 1/x \ (x > 0), \qquad \ln 1 = 0. \tag{3.2}$$

If $f(x) = \ln ax$, then

$$f'(x) = \frac{a}{ax} \quad \text{(composite function)}$$

$$= \frac{1}{x} = \ln' x,$$

so $f(x)$ and $\ln x$ differ by a constant: $\ln ax = C + \ln x$. Since C is independent of x, it can be found by putting $x = 1$: $\ln a = C + \ln 1 = C$. Thus

$$\ln ax = \ln a + \ln x. \tag{3.3}$$

Similarly if q is a rational number (a quotient m/n where m and $n \neq 0$ are integers), then

$$\ln x^q = q \ln x. \tag{3.4}$$

The graph of ln is shown in Fig. 3.2. ☐

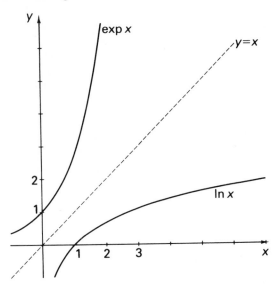

Figure 3.2   Logarithmic and exponential functions

Example 3.15
The exponential function exp x is the inverse of the logarithmic function. Its domain is therefore $R = (-\infty, \infty)$, the range of ln x, and its range is R^+, the domain of ln x. The graphs of $y = \ln x$ and $y = \exp x$ (which means $x = \ln y$) are reflections of each other in the line $x = y$, as in Fig. 3.2. Properties (3.2) and (3.3) of the logarithmic function imply the following properties of the exponential function:

$$\exp' = \exp, \quad \exp(0) = 1, \quad \exp(a+b) = (\exp a)(\exp b). \tag{3.5}$$

If x is real, and q is rational, then equation (3.4) implies $\exp(xq) = (\exp x)^q$. ☐

In physical applications, the elements of the domain and range of a function are usually values of physical quantities occurring in the application. These quantities are called **variables**: the **independent variable** is the one associated with the domain, and the **dependent variable** the one associated with the range.

If the domain of a function is the largest set D of real numbers for which the rule is meaningful, then D will be called the **natural domain**, or **maximal domain** and the specification of D may be omitted.

Example 3.16
What is the maximal domain of the function $\ln(\sin x)$? The function ln is only defined for positive values of the independent variable, so the maximal domain contains those values of x for which $\sin x$ is positive, i.e. $(0, \pi)$, $(2\pi, 3\pi)$, etc., thus the natural domain is

$$\cdots \cup (-2\pi, -\pi) \cup (0, \pi) \cup (2\pi, 3\pi) \cup (4\pi, 5\pi) \cup \cdots$$

or $\{x: 2n\pi < x < 2n\pi + \pi, n \text{ integer}\}$. This **composite** function of ln and sin is sometimes denoted by ln ∘ sin. □

A function can be regarded as a mapping of the elements x in its domain onto the elements $f(x)$ in its range. The notation $x \to f(x)$ emphasizes this viewpoint. When x and $f(x)$ are real numbers, the mapping (or function) can be described as type $R \to R$, or as an $(R \to R)$ mapping.

For any relation between sets A and B there is an **inverse relation** between B and A obtained by reversing the order of all pairs. The inverse of a function f may not be a function, since $f(x_1) = f(x_2)$ is possible (with $x_1 \neq x_2$), and the inverse relation would associate $f(x_1)$ with both x_1 and x_2.

A function has an inverse function only if it is one-to-one, for example ln. The functions sin, cos and tan are periodic, and so not one-to-one. This means, for example, that the ordered pairs defined in Example 3.11 give a relation and not a function. In order to define the inverse circular functions, it is necessary to define **restrictions** of the original functions by restricting the domains to give one-to-one functions. The standard restrictions Sin, Cos and Tan (note the capital letters) are shown in Fig. 3.3(a). The resulting inverse functions, shown in Fig. 3.3(b), have domains and ranges as follows:

Function	Sin^{-1}	Cos^{-1}	Tan^{-1}	
Domain	$[-1, 1]$	$[-1, 1]$	$(-\infty, \infty)$	(3.6)
Range	$[-\pi/2, \pi/2]$	$[0, \pi]$	$(-\pi/2, \pi/2)$.	

However there is no universal convention for notation (e.g. arcsin is also used for Sin^{-1}, etc.), and $\sin^{-1}$ must usually be interpreted as the function. The context should make it clear when the relation is being discussed; the value assigned to the function, indicated in the last row of (3.6), is then called the **principal value** of the relation.

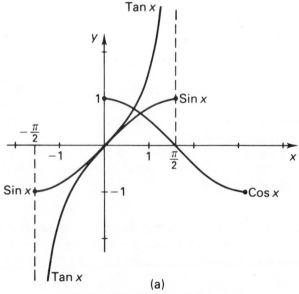

(a)

Figure 3.3(a)   Trigonometric functions

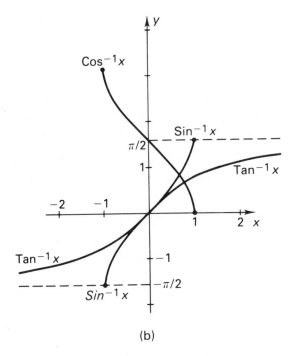

(b)

Figure 3.3(b)   Inverse functions

Exercises (answers on p. 69)

3.1.1 Which of the following relations are functions?

(i) $\{(x, y): 0 \leqslant x \leqslant 1, y = x^2\}$ (ii) $\{(x, y): 0 \leqslant x \leqslant 1, x = y^2\}$

(iii) $\{(x, y): 0 \leqslant x \leqslant 1, x = y^3\}$ (iv) $\{(x, y): a < x < b, x = \tan y\}$.

Give the domain and range of the functions.

3.1.2 Evaluate (i) $e^{\ln 3}$. (ii) $\ln(e^3)$. (iii) $e^{-\ln 2}$. (iv) $\ln(e^{-2})$.

3.1.3 What are the maximal domain and the range of the function

$$f(x) = (x^2 - 5x + 6)^{-1}.$$

Does f^{-1} exist?

3.1.4 Derive equation (3.4) from the definition of ln x, using the method in the text for equation (3.3).

3.2   The Power Function

The power function a^x has an elementary definition when a is real and positive and x is rational, say $x = m/n$ where m and $n > 0$ are integers. This is $a^x = \sqrt[n]{a^m}$, with

$$a^m = \begin{cases} a \times a \times \cdots \times a \ (m \text{ factors}) & \text{if } m > 0 \\ 1 & \text{if } m = 0 \\ 1/a^{-m} & \text{if } m < 0 \end{cases} \tag{3.7}$$

and the resulting function satisfies the laws

$$a^x a^y = a^{x+y}, \qquad (a^x)^y = a^{xy}. \tag{3.8}$$

From equation (3.4) on p. 47

$$a^x = \exp(x \ln a) \qquad (3.9)$$

and the natural domain of the mapping $x \mapsto \exp(x \ln a)$ is all real numbers. So equation (3.9) can be used to *define* a^x for all real x, and when x is rational this will give the same value as equations (3.7). The resulting power function is called an **extension** of the original function, whose domain consisted of the rational numbers only.

In order for such an extension to be useful, it should retain some of the properties of the original function. In this case equations (3.8) still hold, as a consequence of the exponential theorem (3.5), on p. 47, e.g.

$$\exp(x \ln a) \exp(y \ln a) = \exp\{(x+y) \ln a\}.$$

Defining $e = \exp 1$, so that $\ln e = 1$, and putting $a = e$ in equation (3.9) shows that $\exp x = e^x$. This power notation is usually used for the exponential function, except when the index is a complicated expression.

Exercise (answers on p. 69)
3.2.1   Evaluate: (i) 2^3. (ii) 2^{-4}. (iii) $8^{2/3}$. (iv) $16^{-3/4}$. (v) $2^{\sqrt 2}$. (vi) $2^{-\sqrt 3}$.

3.3 Hyperbolic Functions

The hyperbolic functions sinh and cosh are defined by

$$\sinh x = (e^x - e^{-x})/2, \qquad \cosh x = (e^x + e^{-x})/2. \qquad (3.10)$$

Their graphs are easily deduced from that of e^x, since e^{-x} is just the reciprocal of e^x (Fig. 3.2); alternatively, the graph of e^{-x} is just that of e^x with the direction of the x-axis reversed. Since $\cosh x$ is an even function, and $\sinh x$ is an odd function, that is

$$\cosh(-x) = \cosh x, \qquad \sinh(-x) = -\sinh x \qquad (3.11)$$

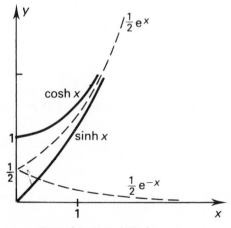

Figure 3.4   Hyperbolic functions

it is easiest to consider first the graphs for positive x (Fig. 3.4), and then use the symmetry (3.11) to complete the curves (Fig. 3.5).

Algebraic properties of hyperbolic functions are a consequence of the result $e^{a+b} = e^a e^b$.

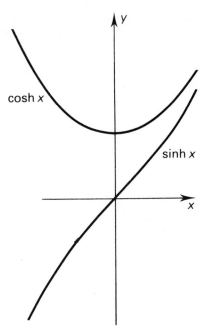

Figure 3.5   Hyperbolic functions

Example 3.30

Simplify (i) $\cosh^2 x - \sinh^2 x$, (ii) $\sinh x \cosh x$.

(i)
$$\cosh^2 x - \sinh^2 x = \{(e^x + e^{-x})^2 - (e^x - e^{-x})^2\}/4$$
$$= \{(e^x + e^{-x}) + (e^x - e^{-x})\}\{(e^x + e^{-x}) - (e^x - e^{-x})\}/4$$
$$= e^x e^{-x} = e^0 = 1.$$

$$\boxed{\cosh^2 x - \sinh^2 x = 1.} \qquad (3.12)$$

(ii)
$$\sinh x \cosh x = (e^x - e^{-x})(e^x + e^{-x})/4$$
$$= \{(e^x)^2 - (e^{-x})^2\}/4$$
$$= (e^{2x} - e^{-2x})/4 = \tfrac{1}{2}\sinh 2x. \quad \square$$

Similarly the derivatives of these functions may be obtained directly from the definitions. Again using a prime to denote derivative,

$$\boxed{\begin{aligned} \sinh' x &= \tfrac{1}{2}(e^x - e^{-x})' = \tfrac{1}{2}(e^x + e^{-x}) = \cosh x \\ \cosh' x &= \tfrac{1}{2}(e^x + e^{-x})' = \tfrac{1}{2}(e^x - e^{-x}) = \sinh x. \end{aligned}}$$

$$(3.13)$$
$$(3.14)$$

Comparing these results with $\cos^2 x + \sin^2 x = 1$, $2 \sin x \cos x = \sin 2x$, $\sin' = \cos$, and $\cos' = -\sin$, shows a remarkable similarity between the properties of the hyperbolic functions and those of the circular functions. The nomenclature for the hyperbolic functions was suggested by this analogy: cosh is cos (hyperbolic), or the hyperbolic cosine. The origin of the term hyperbolic was the fact that whereas $x = \cos t$, $y = \sin t$ are parametric equations for the circle $x^2 + y^2 = 1$, $x = \cosh t$, $y = \sinh t$ are parametric equations for the hyperbola $x^2 - y^2 = 1$ (Fig. 3.6).

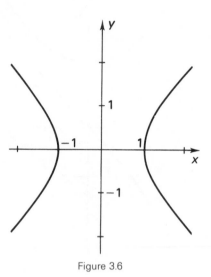

Figure 3.6

The results proved in Example 3.30 are merely the simplest of the large number of algebraic identities which may be written down from a knowledge of trigonometric formulas connecting circular functions.

In any such algebraic relation, sinh and cosh can replace sin and cos provided the sign is changed before any product of two sines.

Example 3.31
In $\sin 3x = 3 \sin x - 4 \sin^3 x$ write $4 \sin^3 x = 4 \sin x(\sin x \sin x)$. Then the product of sines in the brackets means a sign change, giving

$$\sinh 3x = 3 \sinh x + 4 \sinh^3 x.$$

Check:

$$4 \sinh^2 x = (e^x - e^{-x})^2 = e^{2x} + e^{-2x} - 2.$$
$$\sinh x(3 + 4 \sinh^2 x) = \tfrac{1}{2}(e^x - e^{-x})(e^{2x} + e^{-2x} + 1)$$
$$= \tfrac{1}{2}(e^{3x} + e^{-x} + e^x - e^x - e^{-3x} - e^{-x})$$
$$= \sinh 3x. \quad \square$$

The above rule can be extended to include expressions containing $\tan x$ by defining

$$\tanh x = \sinh x / \cosh x. \qquad (3.15)$$

Note that the rule applies only to algebraic results, and not to equations (3.13) and (3.14) giving derivatives, although even there only suitable sign changes are required. Similarly, differentiating the quotient in equation (3.15) gives

$$\tanh' = \{(\cosh)(\sinh') - (\cosh')(\sinh)\}/\cosh^2$$
$$= 1/\cosh^2 \text{ using equations (3.12)-(3.14)}$$

$$\tanh' = \operatorname{sech}^2 \text{ on defining } \operatorname{sech} x = 1/\cosh x.$$

An explanation of this analogy between circular and hyperbolic functions will appear in Chapter 6. The correspondence between properties is not evident from the graphs of the functions (Figs 3.3 and 3.5). However an analogy might be anticipated if the functions were obtained by solving differential equations. The circular functions are solutions of the harmonic motion equation $y'' = -y$, whereas the hyperbolic functions are solutions of $y'' = +y$, with only a sign difference between the two differential equations. Thus $\sin x$ ($\sinh x$) could be defined as the odd solution of $y'' = -y$ ($+y$) having slope 1 at $x = 0$; and $\cos x$ ($\cosh x$) could be defined as the even solution of $y'' = -y$ ($+y$) having the value 1 at $x = 0$.

Since $\sinh$ is a one-to-one function, the inverse function $\sinh^{-1}$ can be immediately defined by

$$y = \sinh^{-1} x \text{ if and only if } x = \sinh y. \qquad (3.16)$$

Since $\cosh$ is not a one-to-one function, to consider an inverse it is first necessary to define a restriction $\cosh$ which is one-to-one. This is conventionally done by restricting the domain to $x \geqslant 0$, and then the inverse is defined by

$$y = \cosh^{-1} x \text{ if and only if } x = \cosh y \qquad (y \geqslant 0, x \geqslant 1). \qquad (3.17)$$

The graphs of these inverse functions, obtained by reflecting in the line $y = x$ the graphs of $\sinh$ and $\cosh$, are shown in Fig. 3.7.

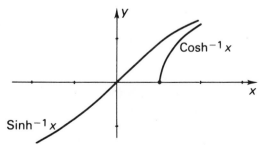

Figure 3.7   Inverse hyperbolic functions

As the hyperbolic functions are simple combinations of the exponential function, which has the logarithmic function as its inverse, relations may be expected between the inverse hyperbolic functions and the function ln. To derive these relations, the defining equations (3.16) and (3.17) are solved for e^y.

Example 3.32

Express $\sinh^{-1} x$ in terms of the function ln.

From equation (3.16)

$$x = \sinh y = (e^y - e^{-y})/2.$$

Multiply by $2e^y$ and rearrange:

$$(e^y)^2 - 2xe^y - 1 = 0.$$

The solutions of this quadratic equation in e^y are $x \pm \sqrt{(x^2 + 1)}$, but since $\sqrt{(x^2 + 1)} > \sqrt{x^2} = |x|$, $x < \sqrt{(x^2 + 1)}$, and the lower sign is impossible because $e^y > 0$. Hence

$$\boxed{\sinh^{-1} x = \ln\{x + \sqrt{(x^2 + 1)}\}.}\qquad(3.18)$$

Check: If $y = \ln\{x + \sqrt{(x^2 + 1)}\}$, show that $y = \sinh^{-1} x$, which requires showing that $\sinh y = x$. Since $e^y = x + \sqrt{(x^2 + 1)}$,

$$e^{-y} = \frac{1}{x + \sqrt{(x^2 + 1)}} = \frac{x - \sqrt{(x^2 + 1)}}{x^2 - (x^2 + 1)} = -x + \sqrt{(x^2 + 1)}$$

and $\sinh y = \frac{1}{2}(e^y - e^{-y}) = x.$ $\square$

Example 3.33

Express $\mathrm{Cosh}^{-1} x$ in terms of the function ln. Starting from equation (3.17), and proceeding as in Example 3.32, yields $e^y = x \pm \sqrt{(x^2 - 1)}$. With $x = \mathrm{Cosh}\, y$, the extra condition $y \geq 0$ appears, so that $e^y \geq 1$. Since

$$\{x + \sqrt{(x^2 - 1)}\}\{x - \sqrt{(x^2 - 1)}\} = x^2 - (x^2 - 1) = 1,$$

the two values obtained are reciprocals, and the smaller is less than one. The lower sign obviously gives the smaller, so this is eliminated.

$$x + \sqrt{(x^2 - 1)} \geq 1,$$

and

$$\boxed{y = \mathrm{Cosh}^{-1} x = \ln\{x + \sqrt{(x^2 - 1)}\}. \quad \square}\qquad(3.19)$$

Note that equations (3.18) and (3.19) imply that the composite functions $\exp(\sinh^{-1} x)$ and $\exp(\mathrm{Cosh}^{-1} x)$ can immediately be simplified to algebraic expressions. A similar remark applies to $\sinh(\ln x)$ or $\cosh(\ln x)$.

Finally, consider the behaviour of these functions as $x \to \infty$, that is, as x becomes larger and larger without any limit. From the graphs it is clear that, as $x \to \infty$, $\sinh x \to \infty$ and

$\cosh x \to \infty$, but it is easy to say a little more than this. Since $e^{-x} = 1/e^x \to 0$ as $x \to \infty$, which means that e^{-x} can be made as small as required by taking x large enough, the values of both $\sinh x$ and $\cosh x$ get closer and closer to the values of $\frac{1}{2}e^x$ (Fig. 3.4 on p. 50). Moreover the differences between the functions can be made arbitrarily small by taking x large enough. These results may be expressed by writing

$$\sinh x \to \tfrac{1}{2}e^x, \qquad \cosh \to \tfrac{1}{2}e^x, \quad \text{as } x \to \infty \tag{3.20}$$

and are referred to as the **asymptotic behaviour** of the function.

Equations (3.20) imply corresponding results for the inverse functions. Since $x = \frac{1}{2}e^y \Leftrightarrow y = \ln 2x$, the function inverse to $\frac{1}{2}e^x$ is $\ln 2x$, giving

$$\sinh^{-1} x \to \ln(2x), \qquad \text{Cosh}^{-1} x \to \ln(2x), \quad \text{as } x \to \infty. \tag{3.21}$$

This is consistent with equations (3.18) and (3.19): for very large values of x, 1 is negligible compared to x^2, and replacing $x^2 \pm 1$ by x^2 gives (3.21).

Exercises (answers on p. 69)

3.3.1 Which of the following functions are even or odd? (i) $y = x^2 + x$. (ii) $y = x^2 - x^4$. (iii) $y = x^3 + x$. (iv) $y = \exp(-x^3)$.

3.3.2 Assuming that $e^{1.1} = 3.00$, find the values of (i) $\ln 3$. (ii) $\cosh 1.1$. (iii) $\sinh 1.1$. (iv) $\sinh 2.2$.

3.3.3 How do the functions $f(x) = \exp(\text{Cosh}^{-1} x)$ and $g(x) = x + \sqrt{(x^2 - 1)}$ differ?

3.4 Functions Relating Several Variables

So far in this Chapter, all the functions considered have had domain and range either R or some subset of R, and have described therefore a relationship between two variables only. A graphical illustration of such a function is obtained using the natural correspondence between the real numbers and the points of the axis used for the domain variable. The application of mathematics to physical problems, which are set in three-dimensional space, requires quantities having a value at each point of space. Such quantities are described by functions with domain some region of space, each point of which is specified by the values of three coordinates, for example Cartesian coordinates (x, y, z). Thus the domain of the function is described by three independent real variables.

Example 3.40

A liquid is in a cubical box of side 10 cm. Its temperature T can have a different value at each point. A function F may therefore be defined, with domain the set of points of the liquid, by associating with each point P the value of the temperature at P: $T = F(P)$. The range of F is the set of values of T existing in the liquid.

To get a mathematical description of F allowing the calculation of T for any P, it is necessary to introduce coordinates for P. Here it is natural to take Cartesian coordinates relative to an origin O at one corner of the box and axes along the sides through O. There are then three independent variables x, y, and z and the function $T = F(x, y, z)$ is called a function of three variables. Its domain is the set of triples

$$\{(x, y, z): 0 \leqslant x \leqslant 10, 0 \leqslant y \leqslant 10, 0 \leqslant z \leqslant 10\}.$$

If a formula or algorithm for calculating T from (x, y, z) is known, then the range of F can be explicitly determined. For example, if $T = (3x + 2y + z)°C$, then $F(x, y, z) = 3x + 2y + z$; O is the coldest point, the hottest point is the other end of the diagonal through O, and the range of F is $[0, 60]$. □

When many variables appear in a problem, the number of different symbols required is often reduced by using the same symbol for both the function and the dependent variable. The above temperature function would then be denoted by $T(P)$ or $T(x, y, z)$.

In any such example the variation with time t is usually also of interest, leading to functions of four (independent) variables, such as $T(x, y, z, t)$. On the other hand many physical situations have some symmetry which allows the number of independent spatial coordinates to be reduced.

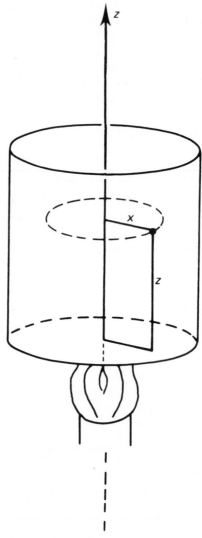

Figure 3.8   Cylinder of liquid: symmetry about z-axis

Example 3.41

At time $t = 0$ a cylinder of height 10 cm and radius 5 cm contains a liquid at its freezing point temperature $f°C$. The liquid is boiled using a Bunsen flame placed below the axis of the cylinder (Fig. 3.8). From the physical symmetry, the properties of the liquid depend only on the height above the base of the cylinder and the radial distance from the axis, and not on the angular position around the axis. So it is sufficient to consider points in a plane through the axis (in fact in a half-plane) and only two coordinates (x, z) are needed. Then the value at time t of the temperature T defines a function G of three independent variables with domain $\{(x, z, t): 0 \leqslant x \leqslant 5, 0 \leqslant z \leqslant 10, t \geqslant 0\}$: $T = G(x, z, t)$. The stated initial condition will be $G(x, z, 0) = f$; and the range of the function G will be $[f, b]$, where $b°C$ is the boiling point of the liquid. A formula allowing T to be calculated from (x, z, t) is not obvious, but might be determined either from experiment or the theory of the heating process.   □

When a quantity takes different values at different spatial points, so that two or three of the independent variables are spatial coordinates, it is possible and often convenient to specify the points by their position vectors relative to some origin. The domain is then a set of vectors. For example, the domain of the function F in Example 3.40 could be written

$$\{r: r = xi + yj + zk, 0 \leqslant x \leqslant 10, 0 \leqslant y \leqslant 10, 0 \leqslant z \leqslant 10\}.$$

Similarly the domain of G in Example 3.41 is

$$\{(r, t): r = xi + zk, 0 \leqslant x \leqslant 5, 0 \leqslant z \leqslant 10, t \geqslant 0\}.$$

Example 3.42

The domain corresponding to the surface of a sphere of radius 2 centred at $(0, 1, 0)$ is

$$\{r: |r - j| = 2\} = \{(x, y, z): x^2 + (y - 1)^2 + z^2 = 4\}.$$

The equation specifying which vectors r or triples (x, y, z) are in the set is just the equation of the sphere. In mathematics the word **sphere** is taken to mean the surface; the domain including all the interior points as well is called a (spherical) **ball**. In this example this would be the set

$$\{r: |r - j| \leqslant 2\} = \{(x, y, z): x^2 + (y - 1)^2 + z^2 \leqslant 4\}.   □$$

Similarly a **circular disc** means the plane region bounded by a circle.

The set of all ordered pairs (x, y) of real numbers is denoted by R^2, and the set of all ordered triples (x, y, z) is R^3. The functions in Examples 3.40 and 3.41 are mappings of the type $R^3 \rightarrow R$. In these examples, the use of vectors to describe the domain is merely a notational convenience which may be employed for a mapping of R^2 or R^3 into R. The function is the same whether the domain is described by using two or three scalar position variables or one vector variable, and the symbol R^3 is used to denote either the set of all triples, or the set of all vectors, or the set of all spatial points.

Vector quantities, that is quantities involving a direction (cf. Section 1.1), often vary with time or position, requiring the use of vector functions whose values are vectors. For example, at any time t the fluid at any point (x, y, z) in a heated liquid will have some velocity q. The resulting velocity function $F: q = F(x, y, z, t)$ is a function with four independent variables x, y, z and t, and therefore a mapping of type $R^4 \to R^3$. The values of the function can always be written in terms of components, say $q = ui + vj + wk$, and the range can be regarded as either a set of vectors q or a set of triples (u, v, w). This function will often be written $q(x, y, z, t)$, indicating the dependent variable q and the independent variables, with no separate symbol for the function. Any vector function can also be regarded, through the components, as three functions of type $R^4 \to R$. Thus, putting

$$q(x, y, z, t) = u(x, y, z, t)i + v(x, y, z, t)j + w(x, y, z, t)k$$

stresses the fact that each component is a function ($R^4 \to R$) of the four independent variables.

Example 3.43

A bubble expands with a radial velocity of 2 cm/s. When the radius is 3 cm, the function giving the velocity at any point of the bubble (a spherical surface) is given by the rule $q = (2/3)r$ with domain $\{r: |r| = 3\}$, taking the origin at the centre of the bubble. The range of the function $q(r)$ is $\{q: q = 2\}$.

Alternatively, putting $q = ui + vj + wk$, $r = xi + yj + zk$, the three component functions are

$$u(x, y, z) = 2x/3, \qquad v(x, y, z) = 2y/3, \qquad w(x, y, z) = 2z/3.$$

Each component function has the range $[-2, 2]$. $\square$

Any vector function of position ($R^3 \to R^3$) is called a **vector field**; functions of type $R^3 \to R$ are **scalar fields** if their values are the same in any coordinate system. Important examples occur in electromagnetic theory: the electric and magnetic fields are vector fields, while the charge density is an example of a scalar field. In fluids, pressure and temperature are scalar fields.

As already seen, a function of type $R \to R$ is often illustrated by a graph. Analogous geometric illustrations for functions of several variables are not usually so useful, but Chapter 2 has indicated the possibilities. Any function of type $R^2 \to R$ has a rule of the form $z = f(x, y)$, which represents a surface in a three-dimensional space in which x, y and z are coordinates.

Example 3.44

Consider the function w of type $R^2 \to R$ representing the lower half of the sphere in Example 2.10. Its rule is $z = w(x, y) = -\sqrt{(1 - x^2 - y^2)}$ and its domain is the circular disc $\{(x, y): (x^2 + y^2) \leq 1\}$. It could also be described as

$$w(r) = -\sqrt{(1 - r^2)} \quad \text{where } |r| \leq 1.   \square$$

Spheres and cylinders are examples of surfaces which cannot be represented by **functions** in which the independent variables are Cartesian coordinates, although they can be represented by **relations**.

Any function of type $R \to R^3$ has a rule which can be written in the vector form $r = f(t)i + g(t)j + h(t)k$, which represents a space curve. If a function is of type $R \to R^2$, the rule has the same form with $h(t) = 0$, and so represents a plane curve. An important application is when $r(t)$ is the position at time t of a moving particle. Its velocity $v(t)$ and acceleration $a(t)$ are functions of the same type, which can also be represented as curves in three dimensions.

Example 3.45

A function $(R \rightarrow R^3)$ representing one complete turn of a helix on a cylinder of radius 1 is, according to Example 2.61 on p. 35,

$$r(t) = i \cos t + j \sin t + kt \qquad (0 \leqslant t \leqslant 2\pi).$$

The domain is $[0, 2\pi]$; the range is the set of all vectors from the origin to points of the curve. The rule

$$(x, y, z) = (\cos t, \sin t, t) \qquad (0 \leqslant t \leqslant 2\pi)$$

gives the same function $r(t)$ in a different notation, mapping the interval $[0, 2\pi]$ onto the points (x, y, z) of the helix. $\square$

Example 3.46

A function $(R \rightarrow R^2)$ representing a circle of radius 1 is $r(t) = i \cos t + j \sin t$, used in Example 2.60; the domain can be any interval of length not less than 2π, for example $[0, 2\pi)$ which results in a one-to-one function. $\square$

In the previous two examples, the symbol r has been used to denote both the function and the value of the independent variable.

Because of the correspondence, discussed in Section A.4, between vectors in a plane and complex numbers,* a function of type $R^2 \rightarrow R$ can also be regarded as a mapping from complex numbers into real numbers $(C \rightarrow R)$. This would be called a real function of a complex (independent) variable; the dependent variable is real. The domain would be a set of complex numbers, often specified as a region of the complex plane, and the range a set of real numbers. Similarly a function of type $R \rightarrow R^2$ can be regarded as a mapping $(R \rightarrow C)$ from real to complex numbers. The domain is a set of real numbers, and the range a set of complex numbers which can be illustrated as a curve in the complex plane. For such functions the rule is stated with the convention that z denotes a complex variable. The equivalence of complex numbers and vectors may be useful in visualizing the function.

Example 3.47

(i) $f(z) = -\sqrt{(1 - |z|^2)}$. The natural domain is $|z| \leqslant 1$; replacing z by r shows that the equivalent $(R^2 \rightarrow R)$ mapping is w in Example 3.44. Thus the range of f is $[-1, 0]$.

(ii) The function g of type $R \rightarrow C$ with rule $z = g(t) = \cos t + i \sin t$ and domain $(0 \leqslant t < 2\pi)$ is the analogue of the function $(R \rightarrow R^2)$ in Example 3.46. The range of g is the set of complex numbers of unit modulus, i.e. $\{z : |z| = 1\}$, and g can be represented by the unit circle in the Argand diagram.

(iii) The function $z = a + tb$, where t is a real independent variable, and a and b are complex constants, represents a line in the complex plane. This follows by considering equation (2.5) with the third components of $\overline{OQ}$ and v set equal to zero (see p. 27). $\square$

For any type of function, the basic concepts of domain, range, and composite function, and the existence of an inverse if and only if the function is one-to-one, all remain valid.

---

* Readers who have not previously met complex numbers should defer this paragraph and Example 3.47 until after reading the introduction to complex numbers in Appendix A.

Example 3.48

Consider the vector function q of type $R^3 \to R^3$ with the rule

$$q(r) = ui + vj + wk, \qquad u = x + 2y - 3z$$

$$v = 2x + 5y - 6z \qquad (3.22)$$

$$w = 3x + 10y - 8z$$

and domain all vectors $r = xi + yj + zk$. Because the function q is one-to-one, equations (3.22) can be solved for x, y, and z, giving

$$x = 20u - 14v + 3w$$

$$y = -2u + v \qquad (3.23)$$

$$z = 5u - 4v + w,$$

the rule of the inverse function $r(q)$. The matrix of coefficients in equations (3.23) is the inverse of the matrix of coefficients in equations (3.22). (Inverse matrices are treated in Section 17.3).   □

Example 3.49

Consider the functions f and u defined by

$$f(x, y) = \sqrt{(y^2 - x^2)} \quad \text{with domain } \{(x, y): y \geqslant x \geqslant 1\};$$

$$u(x) = 0 \quad \text{if } x \leqslant 0, \qquad u(x) = 2 \quad \text{if } x > 0, \quad \text{with domain R}.$$

What are the maximal domains of the functions
   (i) $\text{Cosh}^{-1} \circ f(x, y) = \text{Cosh}^{-1}(\sqrt{(y^2 - x^2)})$
   (ii) $f\{\ln|x|; u(x)\}$?

   (i) The range of f is $[0, \infty)$ but the domain of Cosh^{-1} is $[1, \infty)$, so values of f in $[0, 1)$ cannot be transmitted through the composite function, and the domain must be restricted to exclude such values of f. Thus the required domain is the subset of the domain of f determined by $\sqrt{(y^2 - x^2)} \geqslant 1$. This implies $y^2 - x^2 \geqslant 1$, since $(y^2 - x^2)$ is not negative in the domain of f. Hence only points on or above the rectangular hyperbola $y^2 - x^2 = 1$ can be taken (Fig. 3.9).

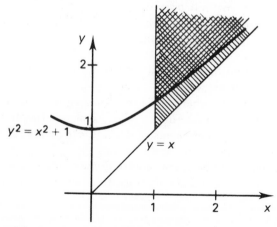

Figure 3.9   Domain of f shaded; domain of $\text{Cosh}^{-1} \circ f$ cross-hatched

(ii) This function has one independent variable x, and its domain is a subset of R. From the domain of f, which requires

$$(\text{second variable}) \geq (\text{first variable}) \geq 1$$

only values of u and $\ln$ satisfying $u(x) \geq \ln|x| \geq 1$ can be transmitted into f. This immediately excludes $x \leq 0$, for which $u(x) = 0$, and also $0 < x < e$, for which $\ln|x| = \ln x < 1$. Also $u(x) = 2$ for all $x \geq 0$, so there is the further restriction $2 \geq \ln x$ or $x \leq e^2$. The reasons for the exclusion of various regions of the x-axis are indicated by the diagram.

The domain is therefore $[e, e^2]$. The range is $[0, \sqrt{3}]$, the function decreasing from $f(1, 2) = \sqrt{3}$ to $f(2, 2) = 0$ as x increases from e to e^2.

Checks: Is the domain found a subset of the domains of the functions u and $\ln$? Yes, $[e, e^2]$ is a subset of R, and of $R \setminus \{0\}$. Does the rule give a value for all values of x in the domain found? On $[e, e^2]$, $u(x) = 2$, and $f(v, 2) = \sqrt{(4 - v^2)}$ makes sense for $-2 \leq v \leq 2$; in $[e, e^2]$, $\ln|x|$ transmits values v in $[1, 2]$, to which the rule can be applied. However these checks are negative in the sense that the answer obtained could still be incorrect. □

Example 3.410
In Example 2.30 three different equations are given, all representing the same line AB. Each gives the rule of a function $(R \to R^3)$:

$$r(t) = i + j + k + t(i + 2j + 3k)$$

$$R(u) = i + j + k + u(-2i - 4j - 6k)$$

$$\rho(s) = 2i + 3j + 4k + s(-i - 2j - 3k),$$

and these may be obtained from each other by simple compositions of the type $R \to R \to R^3$. Thus $R = r \circ f$ where $f(u) = -2u$, and $\rho = r \circ g$ where $g(s) = 1 - s$; in alternative notation $R(u) = r(-2u)$, $\rho(s) = r(1 - s)$. □

Exercises (answers on p. 69)
3.4.1 Consider the function $A = f(l, w, h)$ where A is the total surface area of a rectangular solid with length l, width w and height h. State the domain, range and rule of this function.
3.4.2 If q is the vector field of Example 3.48, what are the values of $q(i)$, $q(j)$ and $q(i - j + k)$?

3.5 Sequences

A **sequence** is a function with domain the set of natural numbers (positive integers). The value $s(n)$ corresponding to the integer n is usually written s_n and called the nth term of the sequence; and $\{s_n\}$ denotes the sequence.

Example 3.50

The sequence $\{s_n = a + (n-1)d\}$ where a, d are some fixed numbers, is called an **arithmetic progression**; the sequence $\{g_n = ar^{n-1}\}$, where a, r are some fixed numbers, is called a **geometric progression**. The terms of the arithmetic progression are

$$a, a+d, a+2d, a+3d, \ldots$$

and the **terms** of the geometric progression are

$$a, ar, ar^2, ar^3, \ldots.$$

It is often convenient to include 0 in the domain of the sequence. Thus the arithmetic and geometric progressions could be specified by

$$s_n = a + nd, \qquad g_n = ar^n, \qquad (n = 0, 1, 2, \ldots). \quad \square$$

More generally, the domain may be any subset of integers. For example the geometric progression $1, 4, 16, 64, \ldots$ may be specified as $g_n = 4^{n-1}$, $g_n = 4^n$ $(n = 0, 1, 2, \ldots)$, or as $g_n = 2^n$ $(n = 0, 2, 4, \ldots)$. In this book the domain will be all positive integers unless otherwise indicated.

Frequently equations are solved by using a repetitive approximation procedure in which each repetition of the process improves the approximation. A sequence may then be defined with its nth term s_n the approximate result obtained by the nth application of the process.

Example 3.51

Consider the process of division to evaluate decimal approximations to $7/3$. Then s_n can be defined as the result appearing after the evaluation of the nth decimal place. Thus

$$s_1 = 2.3 = 2 + (3/10)$$

$$s_2 = 2.33 = 2 + (3/10) + (3/100)$$

$$s_3 = 2.333 = 2 + (3/10) + (3/100) + (3/1000)$$

$$s_n = 2 + (3/10) + (3/10^2) + (3/10^3) + \cdots + (3/10^n).$$

The purpose of writing each approximation as a sum is to show that s_n can be obtained by adding n terms of a geometric progression:

$$s_n = 2 + \sum_{k=1}^{n} 3(1/10)^k.$$

The kth term of the geometric progression, $g_k = 3(1/10)^k$, is just the amount added by the kth repetition of the approximation procedure, in this case the evaluation of the kth decimal place. $\square$

In general, if the nth application of an approximation procedure adds an amount v_n to the approximation, then the successive approximations are

$$\left. \begin{array}{l} s_1 = v_1, \qquad s_2 = v_1 + v_2, \qquad s_3 = v_1 + v_2 + v_3, \ldots \\ \cdots s_n = s_{n-1} + v_n = v_1 + v_2 + \cdots + v_{n-1} + v_n, \ldots \end{array} \right\} \qquad (3.24)$$

The numbers v_n also form a sequence. Because of equations (3.24), the following general problem is of interest: given a sequence $\{v_n\}$, what can be said about the sequence $\{s_n\}$ with terms defined by (3.24)? The numbers v_n are then called the **terms of a series**. Chapters 8 and 16 will be devoted to the study of series.

Example 3.52
Consider decimal approximations to

$$3/7 = 0.428571\ 428571\ 428571\ 42\ldots.$$

(i) Defining v_n as the amount added by the evaluation of the nth decimal place, and s_n as the approximation rounded down to n decimal places, gives the sequences $\{v_n\}$ and $\{s_n\}$ with terms

$$v_1 = 0.4, \qquad v_2 = 0.02, \qquad v_3 = 0.008, \qquad v_4 = 0.0005, \qquad v_5 = 0.00007, \ldots$$

$$s_1 = 0.4, \qquad s_2 = 0.42, \qquad s_3 = 0.428, \qquad s_4 = 0.4285, \qquad s_5 = 0.42857, \ldots.$$

(ii) In view of the recurring nature of the decimal, it is better to define s_n as the approximation to $6n$ decimal places, and v_n as the amount added in the evaluation of the last six places. The sequence $\{v_n\}$ is then a geometric progression:

$$v_1 = 0.428571 = s_1$$

$$v_2 = (0.428571)/10^6, \qquad s_2 = v_1 + v_2 = 0.428571\ 428571$$

$$v_3 = (0.428571)/10^{12}, \qquad s_3 = v_1 + v_2 + v_3$$

$$v_n = (0.428571)(1/10^6)^{n-1}. \quad \square$$

The range of a sequence may also be a set of complex numbers, a set of vectors, or a set of functions. Important examples of sequences of functions are
   (i) the nth term of the sequence $\{v_n\}$ is the function with rule $x \to x^n$ and domain R. It is sufficient to write $v_n(x) = x^n$;
   (ii) $v_n(x) = x^n$ $(-1 < x < 1)$, i.e. the functions have domain $(-1, 1)$, and are restrictions of the functions in (i);
   (iii) $v_n(x) = \sin nx$ $(0 \leqslant x \leqslant \pi)$.

Exercises (answers on p. 69)
3.5.1 Evaluate, to 2 decimal places, the first five terms of the sequence

$$s_n = (1 + 1/n)^n.$$

3.5.2 Give a geometric description of a sequence of points P_n with position vectors $\overrightarrow{OP}_n$ forming an arithmetic progression.

3.6 Bounded Functions

Suppose B is any set of real numbers. If a and b are any two numbers in the set, and $a \neq b$, then either $a < b$ or $b < a$, and an **order** can be assigned to the elements of the set. If the number of elements is finite, there must be a greatest element and a least element. This may not be true when the number of elements is not finite.

Example 3.60

(i) The closed interval $[0, 2]$ has a greatest element 2 and a least element 0; (ii) the half-open interval $(0, 2] = [0, 2] \backslash \{0\}$ has a greatest element 2, but no least element; (iii) the interval $[0, 2)$ has a least element 0, but no greatest element; (iv) the open interval $(0, 2)$ has neither a greatest nor a least element. (Readers who do not regard these statements as obvious should consider arguments such as:

suppose $(0, 2)$ does have a least number $x > 0$; then $(x/2) > 0$ is in $(0, 2)$ and $(x/2) < x$, contradicting the assumption that x is the least number.)   □

Although $(0, 2]$ has no least element, there is a number, namely 0, with the following properties:

(i) all elements of the set are greater than 0;

(ii) 0 is the largest number with this property.

The fact that 2 is the largest number in $(0, 2]$ can be stated in a similar way:

(i) all elements of the set are less or equal to 2;

(ii) 2 is the smallest number with this property.

These considerations suggest the following definitions:

> (a) The number M is the **supremum** (or **sup**) of the set B of real numbers if
> (i) every element of B is less or equal to M, (ii) M is the smallest number with this property.

Example 3.61

(i) the intervals $(a, b), [a, b], (a, b]$ and $[a, b)$ all have sup b; (ii) the set $\{n^2: n = 1, 2, 3, \ldots\}$ has no sup; (iii) the set $\{1, -2, 5, -4, 2, 3\}$ has sup 5.   □

If the sup M is in the set B, it must be the greatest element, and is called the **maximum** or **max** of the set.

> (b) The number m is the **infimum** or **inf** of the set B of real numbers if
> (i) every element of B is greater or equal to m, (ii) m is the largest number with this property.

If m is in the set, it must be the least element, and is called the **minimum** or **min** of the set.

Example 3.62

(i) $[a, b]$ has inf a and min a;

(ii) $(a, b]$ has inf a and no min;

(iii) 0 is not the inf of $(1, 2)$, since it is not the *largest* number which is less or equal to all numbers in $(1, 2)$;

(iv) $\{n^2: n = 1, 2, 3, \ldots\}$ has inf 1, which is also the min;

(v) $\{1/x: 0 < x < 1\}$ has inf 1 but no min.   □

If the number of elements in B is not finite, then (i) either B has a sup, or arbitrarily large numbers can be found in B, and (ii) either B has an inf, or arbitrarily large negative numbers can be found in B. If the number of elements in B is finite, the largest is the sup and max, while the smallest is the inf and min.

Example 3.63
The set $\{1/x: 0 < x < 1\}$ has no sup. Given any number L, however large, the set contains numbers greater than L (take $x < 1/L$).   □

These definitions may be applied to any function mapping into the real numbers, so that the range B is a set of real numbers. The sup, inf, max and min of the function, if they exist, are the sup, inf, max, and min of its range, i.e. of its set of values. For a given function their values are usually obvious from a rough sketch of the graph. For the functions considered in Sections 3.2 and 3.3, illustrated in Fig. 3.10, one has

Function	ln	exp	Sin^{-1}	Cos^{-1}	Tan^{-1}	sinh	cosh	$\sinh^{-1}$	Cosh^{-1}
Sup	none	none	$\pi/2$	π	$\pi/2$	none	none	none	none
Max	none	none	$\pi/2$	π	none	none	none	none	none
Inf	none	0	$-\pi/2$	0	$-\pi/2$	none	1	none	0
Min	none	none	$-\pi/2$	0	none	none	1	none	0

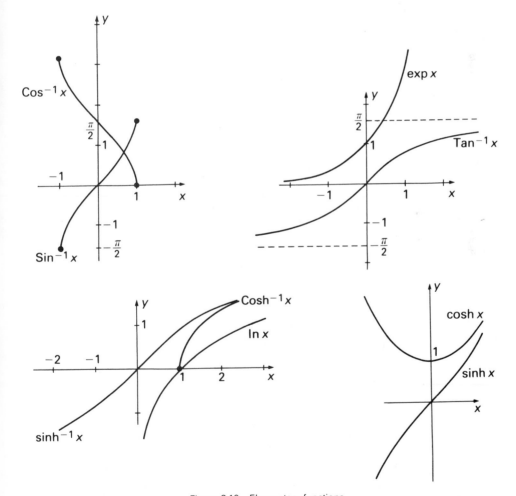

Figure 3.10   Elementary functions

Example 3.64

Consider the sequences $\{s_n\}$ and $\{g_k\}$ defined in Example 3.51 on p. 62. The terms of $\{g_k\}$, namely $0.3, 0.03, 0.003, \ldots$ obviously have 0.3 as sup and max. They get smaller and smaller, but are always positive. Thus this sequence has inf 0, but no minimum.

The terms of $\{s_n\}$, namely $2.3, 2.33, 2.333, \ldots$ get larger and larger, so the sequence has inf and min 2.3. At any stage of the division, the approximation gets closer to $\frac{7}{3}$ by adding a positive number g_n. Thus all terms of s_n are less than $\frac{7}{3}$, but any number less than $\frac{7}{3}$ is eventually exceeded on calculating a sufficiently large number of decimal places. Thus the sequence has sup $\frac{7}{3}$, but no max.   □

Example 3.65

Consider the function f with domain $[-2, 2]$ and rule

$$f(x) = -1 \quad \text{if } -2 \leqslant x \leqslant -1, \qquad f(x) = x^2 \quad \text{if } -1 < x < 2, \qquad f(2) = 2.$$

The graph is shown in Fig. 3.11. f has inf and min -1, sup 4, and no max.   □

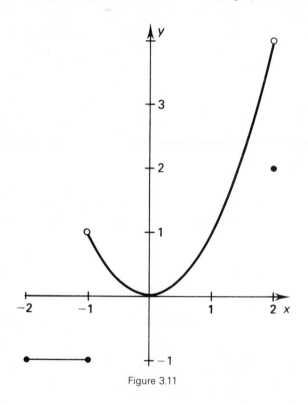

Figure 3.11

Example 3.66

(i) Consider the function f defined on R with rule

$$f(x) = 1/|x-2| \ (x \neq 2); \qquad f(2) = 0.$$

The graph of $|x-2|$ is easily obtained from that of $(x-2)$ by reflecting the negative portion in the x-axis (Fig. 3.12); taking reciprocals of the values in this graph leads to the graph of f shown in Fig. 3.13.

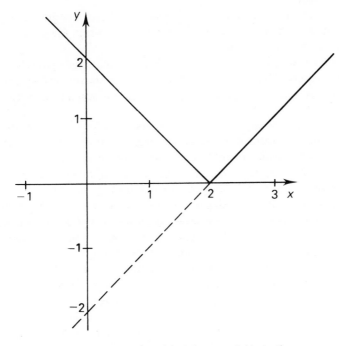

Figure 3.12 $y=|x-2|$ (solid); $y=x-2$ (dashed)

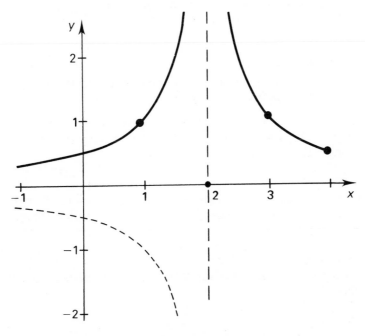

Figure 3.13 $y=1/|x-2|$ (solid); $y=1/(x-2)$ (dashed)

Alternatively, since $1/|x-2|=|1/(x-2)|$, one can obtain the graph of f from that of $1/(x-2)$, by reflecting the negative values in the x-axis. From the graph, f evidently has no sup or max, but has inf 0, which is the min.

(ii) Consider the restriction of f which is a sequence obtained by restricting the domain to the positive integers. The range of this sequence is shown by the dots in Fig. 3.13. Evidently inf and min are again 0, but the sequence has sup and max 1.   ☐

A function with a sup is said to be **bounded above**; a function with an inf is **bounded below**; and a function is **bounded** if it has a sup and an inf. A function is either bounded, or takes values which are arbitrarily large (positive or negative).

The above concepts apply to functions into the real numbers, which can be ordered. If the domain is also a set of real numbers, then increasing and decreasing functions may be defined: a function f is **increasing** on an interval if, for any numbers $x<x'$ in the interval, $f(x)<f(x')$; a function f is **decreasing** on an interval if, for any numbers $x<x'$ in the interval, $f(x)>f(x')$. The statement that f is increasing (or decreasing) with no interval specified, means that f is increasing (or decreasing) on its whole domain.

For the functions considered in Sections 3.1 and 3.2, the following results may be written down, especially with reference to Figs 3.2–3.7 (see pp 47–53).

(i) The function considered in Example 3.13 is increasing (see p. 46);

(ii) the function sin is increasing on $[0, \pi/2]$ and decreasing on $[\pi/2, \pi]$;

(iii) the functions ln, exp, Sin, tan, Sin^{-1}, Tan^{-1}, sinh, sinh^{-1}, and Cosh^{-1} are all increasing;

(iv) the functions Cos and Cos^{-1} are decreasing;

(v) and the function cosh is decreasing on $(-\infty, 0]$ and increasing on $[0, \infty)$.

If a function has a derivative, the sign of the derivative indicates whether the function is increasing or decreasing. Also the behaviour of a composite function may be deduced from that of its components. For example since ln is increasing, $\ln\{g(x)\}$ is increasing or decreasing with $g(x)$ on any interval.

Example 3.67

Let $f(x)=\ln(x^2+2bx+c)$, where $b^2\geq c$. If $r_1=-b-\sqrt{(b^2-c)}$ and $r_2=-b+\sqrt{(b^2-c)}$, then $x^2+2bx+c=0$ at r_1 or r_2, and so the natural domain of f is $(-\infty, r_1)\cup(r_2, \infty)$. Since $g(x)=x^2+2bx+c$ is decreasing on $(-\infty, r_1)$, so is f; and similarly f is increasing on (r_2, ∞).

Check: $f'(x)=2(x+b)/(x^2+2bx+c)$, and the denominator is positive throughout the domain of f. In $(-\infty, r_1)$, $x+b<r_1+b<0$, so f is decreasing; in (r_2, ∞), $x+b>r_2+b>0$, so f is increasing.   ☐

Example 3.68

An arithmetic progression $\{a+nd\}$ is an increasing sequence if $d>0$, and is a decreasing sequence if $d<0$. A geometric progression $\{ar^n\}$ is an increasing sequence if $a>0$ and $r>1$, or if $a<0$ and $0<r<1$.   ☐

Exercises (answers on p. 69)

3.6.1   The functions $f_i(x)$ each have rule $f_i(x)=\ln x$, but different domains D_i:

    (i) $D_1=(0, 1)$,

    (ii) $D_2=(0, 1]$,

    (iii) $D_3=[1, e]$,

    (iv) $D_4=(1, \infty)$.

For each function, state whether there is a sup, inf, max or min, and give the values of those which exist.

3.6.2 State whether the function

$$f(x) = \frac{1}{|x - \frac{1}{2}|} \qquad (x \neq \tfrac{1}{2}); \qquad f(\tfrac{1}{2}) = -1$$

has a sup, inf, max, or min, and give the values of those which exist. Consider the function (a sequence) having the same rule as f but with domain restricted to the positive integers.

State whether this function has a sup, inf, max or min, and give the values of those which exist.

Answers to Exercises 3.1.1–3.6.2

3.1.1 (i) and (iii), with domain and range both $[0, 1]$ for both functions.

3.1.2 (i) 3, (ii) 3, (iii) $\frac{1}{2}$, (iv) -2.

3.1.3 Maximal domain $R\backslash\{2, 3\}$, range $R\backslash(-4, 0]$, no inverse.

3.2.1 (i) 8, (ii) $\frac{1}{16}$, (iii) 4, (iv) $\frac{1}{8}$, (v) 2.67, (vi) 0.298.

3.3.1 (ii) even, (iii) odd.

3.3.2 (i) 1.1, (ii) $\frac{5}{3}$, (iii) $\frac{4}{3}$, (iv) $\frac{40}{9}$.

3.3.3 f has domain $[1, \infty)$; g has domain $(-\infty, -1] \cup [1, \infty)$ (or $|x| \geqslant 1$).

3.4.1 Domain $\{(l, w, h): l > 0, w > 0, h > 0\}$
Range $(0, \infty)$
Rule $f(l, w, h) = 2lw + 2lh + 2hw$

3.4.2 $q(i) = i + 2j + 3k$
$q(j) = 2i + 5j + 10k$
$q(i - j + k) = -4i - 9j - 15k.$

3.5.1 2.00, 2.25, 2.36, 2.44, 2.48.

3.5.2 If $\overrightarrow{OP}_n = a + nd$, the points P_n lie on the straight line through the point a with direction d, and are equally spaced at a distance d apart.

3.6.1 (i) $\sup = 0$, no inf, min or max
(ii) $\sup = \max = 0$, no inf or min
(iii) $\sup = \max = 1$, $\inf = \min = 0$
(iv) $\inf = 0$, no sup, min or max.

3.6.2 f has $\inf = \min = -1$, no max or sup. Restriction of f to a sequence has $\max = \sup = 2$, $\inf = 0$, no min.

Further Exercises on Chapter 3

3.1 The signum function is defined by

$$\operatorname{sgn} x = -1 \quad \text{if } x < 0, \qquad \operatorname{sgn} 0 = 0, \qquad \operatorname{sgn} x = 1 \quad \text{if } x > 0.$$

Sketch the graph of the function

$$f(x) = \{2 + \operatorname{sgn}(x^2 - 1)\}/3, \qquad (-2 < x < 2)$$

and state the range of f. Is the identity $\operatorname{sgn} x = x/|x|$ correct?

3.2 Simplify the following expressions: (i) $e^{-\ln x}$, (ii) $e^{2\ln(x^2)}$, (iii) $\exp(\ln x + 3 \ln y)$, (iv) $e^{x + 2\ln x}$, (v) $\ln(e^{-x})$, (vi) $\ln(e^{3x}/x)$.

3.3 What are the maximal (or natural) domains of the following functions? (i) $\operatorname{Tan}^{-1}(e^x)$, (ii) $\operatorname{Cos}^{-1}(e^x)$,   (iii) $\operatorname{Sin}^{-1}(e^{-x})$,   (iv) $\ln(x^2 - 6x + 8)$,   (v) $\ln(6 \sin x - \sin^2 x - 8)$, (vi) $\ln|x^2 - 6x + 8|$.

3.4 Which of the functions $\sin$, $\cos$, Sin^{-1}, Cos^{-1} and Tan^{-1} are even or odd? One of these functions is neither even nor odd. For this function express $f(-x)$ in terms of $f(x)$. Also express Sin^{-1} in terms of Cos^{-1} (consider Fig. 3.3).

3.5 Without using tables or a calculator, evaluate (a) $\sin(\operatorname{Cos}^{-1} 0.8)$, (b) $\sin(\sin^{-1} 0.9)$, (c) $\operatorname{Sin}^{-1}(\sin 4)$, (d) $\operatorname{Sin}^{-1}(\cos 4)$, (e) $\operatorname{Tan}^{-1}(\tan 4)$.

3.6 Sketch the graphs of the functions $\operatorname{Sin}^{-1}(\sin x)$ and $\operatorname{Sin}^{-1}(\cos x)$.

3.7 If $\sinh x = -5/12$, what are the values of $\cosh x$ and $\tanh x$?

3.8 Evaluate (a) $\sinh(\sinh^{-1} 2)$, (b) $\cosh\{\sinh^{-1}(3/4)\}$, (c) $\sinh(\operatorname{Cosh}^{-1}(5/4))$.

3.9 Sketch the graphs of the functions $\sinh \circ \sinh^{-1}$, $\sinh^{-1} \circ \sinh$, $\cosh \circ \operatorname{Cosh}^{-1}$ and $\operatorname{Cosh}^{-1} \circ \cosh$.

3.10 From the definitions of the hyperbolic functions, show that

$$\cosh(x - y) = \cosh x \cosh y - \sinh x \sinh y.$$

3.11 Solve the equations
  (i) $5 \cosh x + \sinh x = 7$;
  (ii) $4 \cosh(\ln x) = 4 \sinh(\ln x) + 7$.

3.12 (i) Express $\tanh x$ in terms of e^{-2x}, and deduce that $\tanh x < 1$, and that $\tanh x \to 1$ as $x \to \infty$.
  (ii) On $[0, \infty)$, $\cosh^2 x$ increases from its minimum value 1. What does this imply for the derivative of $\tanh x$?
  (iii) Use (i) and (ii) to sketch the graph of $\tanh x$ on $[0, \infty)$ and extend this graph onto $(-\infty, \infty)$ after determining whether the function $\tanh$ is even or odd.
  (iv) From the graph obtained in (iii), sketch the graphs of $\tanh(2x)$ and $\tanh(x/2)$.
  (v) Discuss the behaviour of the graph of $\tanh(kx)$ for very large values of k.

3.13 Does the domain of $\tanh$ have to be restricted in order to define an inverse function? Making any necessary restriction, state the domain and range of the resulting function $\tanh^{-1}$, and sketch its graph. Express $\tanh^{-1}$ in terms of $\ln$.

3.14 If $y = \ln\{x + \sqrt{(x^2 - 1)}\}$, show that $\cosh y = x$. (This checks equation (3.19); your result for Exercise 3.13 should be checked in the same way.)

3.15 Obtain the asymptotic behaviour as $x \to -\infty$ of the following functions of x: $\sinh$, $\cosh$, $\tanh$, $\sinh^{-1}$, $\tanh^{-1}$, Cosh^{-1}.

3.16 In this exercise, n denotes a positive integer, x and y are real variables. Consider the following functions:

Function	Domain	Rule
s	positive integers	$s_n = 2n$
t	positive integers	$t_n = 1/n$
u	$x \neq 0$	$u(x) = 1$ if $x > 0$; $u(x) = -1$ if $x < 0$
f	$x \geqslant y \geqslant 0$	$f(x, y) = (x^2 - y^2)^{1/2}$

(More strictly, the domain of f is $\{(x, y): x \geqslant y \geqslant 0\}$, etc.).
  (i) Describe the range of each function.
  (ii) Which of the functions are one-to-one?

(iii) Find the domains of the composite functions

$$u(s) = u \circ s, \ s(u), \ u(f), f(s, t).$$

3.17 By considering their graphs, determine which of the following functions are bounded above and/or below. Give the relevant sup and/or inf in each case, stating whether it is or is not a max or min: (in each case, take the maximal real domain) (i) $f(x) = 3$, (ii) $f(x) = 1/x$,   (iii) $f(x) = 1/(x-2)$,   (iv) $f(t) = 1/|t-2|$,   (v) $f(x) = (1+x^2)^{-1}$, (vi) $f(y) = (y-1)/(y+1)$, (vii) $f(s) = |s+1|$, (viii) $f(x) = x|x|$, (ix)-(xii) the four functions defined in Exercise 3.16.

3.18 Find the intervals, if any, on which the functions defined in Exercises 3.16 and 3.17 are increasing.

3.19 By considering the derivative of the function

$$f(x) = (x^3/3) + ax^2 + bx + c \ (x \text{ real})$$

find conditions on a and b for (i) f to be decreasing in some interval, (ii) f^{-1} to exist.

3.20 Determine the values of a for which the power function a^x is (i) increasing, (ii) decreasing.

3.21 Determine the values of a and r for which the geometric progression sequence $\{ar^n\}$ is (i) decreasing, (ii) neither increasing nor decreasing.

3.22 Consider the function $\cosh(x^2 + 2bx + c)$, considering separately the cases $b^2 > c$, $b^2 = c$ and $b^2 < c$. State
 (i) the domain and range of the function;
 (ii) the intervals in which the function is increasing or decreasing;
 (iii) the values of the sup, max, inf and min (if they exist).

3.23 If $f(x) = 2 \operatorname{Tan}^{-1}(e^x)$, $g(x) = \operatorname{Tan}^{-1}(\sinh x)$, $h(x) = 2 \operatorname{Tan}^{-1}(\tanh \frac{1}{2}x)$, show that

$$g(x) = h(x) = f(x) - \tfrac{1}{2}\pi.$$

3.24 Draw a diagram showing the value of the vector field

$$F(x, y, z) = (y + 2x)i + zj - xk$$

at the points $P(1, 0, 0)$, $Q(0, 1, 0)$, $R(0, 0, 1)$, $A(1, 1, 1)$ and $B(2, 3, 4)$. Give the values of F at any point of the line AB in terms of the parameter t in the equation $r = (i+j+k) + t(i+2j+3k)$ (cf. Example 2.30 on p. 27).

3.25 Find, in terms of the exponential function, the asymptotic form of the following functions (as $x \to \infty$): (i) $F(x) = \frac{1}{2}(1 - \tanh x)$, (ii) $g(x) = \operatorname{sech}^n x$.

3.26 For each of the following functions, give a sketch showing the maximal domain (in the $x - y$ plane), and state the range:
(i) $f(x, y) = (y - x^2)^{1/2}$, (ii) $g(x, y) = \ln(1 - x^2 - y^2)$, (iii) $h(x, y) = \ln(y - x^2)$.

3.27 For each of the following functions, state whether the function has a sup, inf, max or min, and give the values of those which exist:
(i) $f(x) = 1/(x^2 - \frac{1}{4})$ $(x \neq \pm\frac{1}{2}, f(\pm\frac{1}{2})$ undefined$)$, (ii) the sequence $s_n = 1/(n^2 - \frac{1}{4})$.

3.28 The function with value the integer part of x is denoted by $[x]$, for example $[2] = 2$, $[2\frac{1}{2}] = 2$, $[-\frac{1}{2}] = -1$. By considering the graph $y = [x]$, solve the equation $\operatorname{sgn} x = [x]$ (cf. Exercise 3.1).

3.29 Determine whether the function $g(x) = \exp(-|x|)$ has a sup, inf, max or min, giving the values of those which exist.

3.30 What is the natural domain of the function

$$f(x) = \text{Sin}^{-1}(e^{-x})?$$

With this maximal domain, what is the range of the function? State whether the function has an inf, sup, max or min, giving the values of those which exist.

3.31 Determine whether the following functions are even, odd, or neither: (a) $\sinh(x^4 + x^2)$ (b) $\ln\{x + \sqrt{(x^2 + 1)}\}$ (c) $\ln\{x + \sqrt{(x^2 - 1)}\}$.

3.32 Solve the equation $\cosh x + 8 \sinh x = 9$.

3.33 (a) Find the natural domain and range of the function

$$y = -\tfrac{1}{2}\ln(\tanh x)$$

(b) State whether the sequence

$$s_n = 1 - \ln(\tanh n)$$

has a sup, max, inf or min, giving the values of those which exist.

3.34 What is the value of the vector field

$$\mathbf{F}(x, y, z) = (x^2 + y^2 + z^2)\mathbf{i} + (1 - x^2 - y^2)^{1/2}\mathbf{j} + (1 - z^2)^{1/2}\mathbf{k} \qquad (*)$$

at the point $\mathbf{r} = \tfrac{3}{7}\mathbf{i} + \tfrac{4}{7}\mathbf{j} + (2\sqrt{6}/7)\mathbf{k}$. (Square roots need not be evaluated.) Describe geometrically the natural domain of the vector function defined by $(*)$.

3.35 If $f(x) = (x^2 - x)^{1/2}$ and $g(x) = x^2 + 1$, write down formulas for (i) $f(x + 1)$ (ii) $f(2x)$ (iii) $f(-x)$ (iv) $g(-x)$ (v) $g(x^2)$ (vi) $f[g(x)]$.

3.36 For the following functions state the natural domain and range and determine if the function is even, odd, or neither even nor odd.

(i) $\dfrac{1}{x^2 + 1}$,

(ii) $\dfrac{1}{x^3 + 1}$,

(iii) $\sqrt{x^2 + 1}$,

(iv) $\left[\dfrac{1}{1 + (x + \frac{1}{10})^2}\right]$,   (see Exercise 3.28)

(v) $\sqrt{\sin^2 x - \tfrac{1}{4}}$

(vi) $\log\left(\dfrac{1 + x}{1 - x}\right)$,

(vii) $\text{sgn}(x - \sqrt{x})$,

(viii) $\text{sgn}\left(\dfrac{x^2 - 1}{x^2 + 1}\right)$ (see Exercise 3.1).

3.37 What are the natural domain and range of the function

$$f(x, y) = \text{Cos}^{-1}(x^2 + y^2)?$$

3.38 State whether the function $f(x) = \ln(5x - 4 - x^2)$ has a sup, inf, max, or min, giving the values of those which exist.

3.39 Find the natural domain of the function

$$f(x) = \ln(x^2 - 5x + 4) - \ln(x^2 + x - 2).$$

4
Limits

4.1 The Concept of Limit as $x \to a$

Suppose the function f of type $R \to R$ is defined for all numbers in some neighbourhood of a, except possibly at a itself. A **neighbourhood** of a means some open interval (b, c) containing a, so that $b < a < c$.

Example 4.10
$f(x) = (3x+2)/(x-a)^2$ is such a function, its natural domain being $R\backslash\{a\} = (-\infty, a) \cup (a, \infty)$. Similar functions will have a rule $f(x) = n(x)/d(x)$ with $d(a) = 0$. The concept of a limit arises on considering the behaviour of the function near $x = a$, i.e. in some neighbourhood of a. $\square$

Example 4.11
$f(x) = x^{-2} (x \neq 0)$. When x is near 0, $f(x)$ is large. In fact x^{-2} can be made as large as desired by taking x close enough to zero. The function $f(x)$ is said to **tend to infinity** as x approaches 0. This statement is written $f(x) \to \infty$ as $x \to 0$, or $x^{-2} \to \infty$ as $x \to 0$. $\square$

Example 4.12
Consider the function

$$f(x) = |x-2|^{-1} \quad (x \neq 2); \qquad f(2) = 0,$$

illustrated in Fig. 4.1. Here $f(x)$ can be made as large as desired by taking x sufficiently close to 2: $f(x) \to \infty$ as $x \to 2$. In this example $a = 2$ and $f(2)$ is defined, but the statement $f(x) \to \infty$ as $x \to 2$ says nothing about $f(2)$. The statement $x \to 2$, read 'x tends to 2', only involves values of x near 2, and not $x = 2$. $\square$

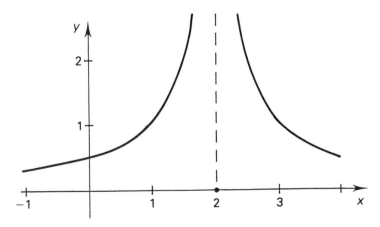

Figure 4.1

The symbol ∞ in a statement means nothing by itself; →∞ is read 'tends to infinity' and means 'takes arbitrarily large values'.

Example 4.13

The following table of $(\sin x)/x$, 0.01(0.01)0.08 (5D)

x	±0.01	±0.02	±0.03	±0.04	±0.05	±0.06	±0.07	±0.08
$\dfrac{\sin x}{x}$	0.99998	0.99994	0.99985	0.99977	0.99958	0.99940	0.99918	0.99893

indicates that as $x \to 0$, the (even) function $(\sin x)/x$ increases and approaches 1. In fact by taking x small enough, $(\sin x)/x$ may be made as near to 1 as desired, and taking x even smaller only produces values even closer to 1. Since the function is even, the same is true as x increases towards 0 through negative values. This behaviour is expressed by the statement $(\sin x)/x$ tends to 1 as x tends to 0, written $(\sin x)/x \to 1$ as $x \to 0$.   □

Example 4.14

$$f(x) = (x^3 - 2x^2)/(x - 2), \qquad (x \neq 2).$$

Then, as $x \neq 2$, a factor $(x - 2)$ common to numerator and denominator can be cancelled, and $f(x) = x^2$ for $x \neq 2$. As $x \to 2$ the values of x^2 approach $2^2 = 4$. Thus $f(x) \to 4$ as $x \to 2$. This means that by taking x near enough to 2 (but not equal to 2), we ensure that all values of $f(x)$ are arbitrarily close to 4.   □

In Example 4.13 the number 1 is called the **limit** of $(\sin x)/x$ as $x \to 0$, and the result is also written $\text{Lim}_{x \to 0} (\sin x/x) = 1$. Similarly the result of Example 4.14 is written $\text{Lim}_{x \to 2} (x^3 - 2x^2)/(x - 2) = 4$. Note again that the function does not have to be defined at $x = a$ to consider the existence of a limit as $x \to a$; and if $f(a)$ is defined this value does not affect the limit in any way. The following results are identical in content to that of Example 4.14. $\text{Lim}_{x \to 2} x^2 = 4$; and if $g(x) = x^2$ for $x \neq 2$, and $g(2) = 0$, then $\text{Lim}_{x \to 2} g(x) = 4$.

The behaviour considered in Examples 4.11 and 4.12 is quite different from that considered in Examples 4.13 and 4.14. The latter examples illustrate the concept of limit. In Example 4.11, $f(x) = x^{-2}$ has no limit as $x \to 0$; in Example 4.12, $f(x)$ has no limit as $x \to 2$. Non-existence of a limit is also possible when the function is bounded.

Example 4.15

Consider the function of Example 3.65 illustrated in Fig. 4.2. This function has no limit L as $x \to -1$, because there is no number L such that all values of $f(x)$ are near L whenever x is near -1. In particular, $f(-1) = -1$ is not a limit, because for values of x slightly greater than -1, $f(x) = x^2$, which takes values near $+1$. Similarly $\text{Lim}_{x \to -1} f(x) \neq +1$, because $f(x) = -1$ when x is slightly less than -1.   □

Example 4.16

$f(x) = \cos(1/x^2)$, $(x \neq 0)$. The function cos is periodic, its values oscillating between -1 and $+1$ for every increase of 2π in its argument. Since $(1/x^2) \to \infty$ as $x \to 0$, $(1/x^2)$ increases through an arbitrarily large number of multiples of 2π. Hence $\cos(1/x^2)$ oscillates between -1 and $+1$ an arbitrarily large number of times as $x \to 0$. There is no single number that

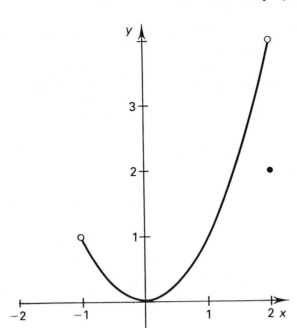

Figure 4.2 $f(x) = -1 \, (-2 \leqslant x \leqslant -1); \; f(x) = x^2 \, (-1 < x < 2)$

the values of $\cos(1/x^2)$ approach, so $\cos(1/x^2)$ has no limit as $x \to 0$. Part of the graph is shown in Fig. 4.3.   □

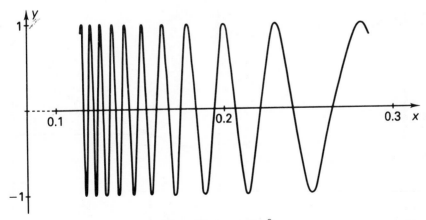

Figure 4.3 $y = \cos(1/x^2)$

In general, the statement $\lim_{x \to a} f(x) = L$ means that for δ small enough, all values of $f(x)$ are as near to L as desired throughout the intervals $(a, a + \delta)$ and $(a - \delta, a)$.

The function f need not be defined at $x = a$, and if $f(a)$ is defined, this value does not affect the existence or value of a limit.

> Similarly $f(x) \to \infty$ as $x \to a$ means that for δ small enough, all values of $f(x)$ throughout the intervals $(a - \delta, a)$ and $(a, a + \delta)$ exceed any desired number.

Example 4.17

Consider the truth of these statements for Example 4.11; $x^{-2} \to \infty$ as $x \to 0$. Since the function is even, only positive x need be considered.

(i) To make x^{-2} greater than a million, one solves this inequality:

$$\frac{1}{x^2} > 10^6 \Leftrightarrow 10^6 x^2 < 1 \Leftrightarrow x^2 < \frac{1}{10^6} \Leftrightarrow x < \frac{1}{10^3}.$$

Thus $x^{-2} > 10^6$ in $(0, 10^{-3})$ (and also in $(-10^{-3}, 0)$, being an even function).

(ii) To make x^{-2} greater than a million million, one solves

$$x^{-2} > 10^{12}$$

to show that this holds for any x in

$$(-10^{-6}, 0) \cup (0, 10^{-6}) = (-10^{-6}, 10^{-6}) \backslash \{0\}.$$

(iii) In general, for *any* positive number X, however large, a neighbourhood $(-\delta, \delta)$ of 0 exists such that $x^{-2} > X$ for all x in $(-\delta, 0) \cup (0, \delta)$ (Fig. 4.4).   □

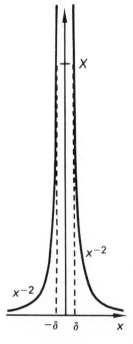

Figure 4.4

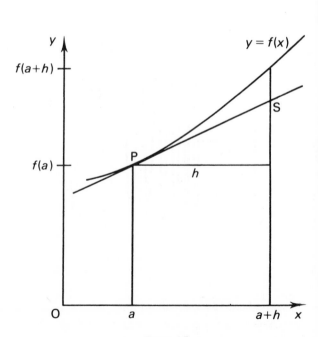

Figure 4.5

An important type of limit appears in the definition of the derivative of a function f:

$$f'(a) = \text{Lim}_{h \to 0}\{f(a+h) - f(a)\}/h.$$

The geometric interpretation (Fig. 4.5) of this limit will be familiar to readers. Its analytic meaning is as stated above: the quotient

$$\{f(a+h) - f(a)\}/h$$

is as close to the number $f'(a)$ as required by taking h in some interval $(-\delta, \delta)\backslash\{0\}$, where δ depends on how close to the limit the quotient is required to be.

Example 4.18
For $f(x) = x^3 + x$,

$$\frac{f(1+h) - f(1)}{h} = h^2 + 3h + 4 \quad \text{if } h \neq 0,$$

so the limit $f'(1)$ has the value 4. In general, for any positive number ε, a neighbourhood $(-\delta, \delta)$ of 0 exists such that

$$4 - \varepsilon < \frac{f(1+h) - f(1)}{h} < 4 + \varepsilon$$

for all h in $(-\delta, 0) \cup (0, \delta)$ (Fig. 4.6).

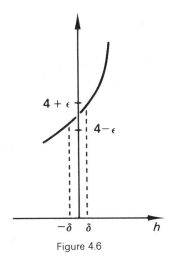

Figure 4.6

Since ε is arbitrarily small, the quotient is as near to 4 as desired throughout the neighbourhood. $\square$

Example 4.19
Since the function ln is defined by $\ln' x = 1/x$,

$$\text{Lim}_{h \to 0} \frac{\ln(1+h)}{h} = \text{Lim}_{h \to 0} \frac{\{\ln(1+h) - \ln 1\}}{h} = \ln' 1 = 1. \quad \square$$

In Example 4.15 $\text{Lim}_{x\to-1} f(x)$ did not exist, because $f(x) = -1$ when $x \leqslant -1$ while $f(x)$ took values near $+1$ when x was slightly greater than -1. The concept of limit could be applied there if one distinguished between x approaching -1 from below, and x approaching -1 from above. If $x \to -1+$ means x approaches -1 from above, the statement $f(x) \to 1$ as $x \to -1+$ has the same significance as a limit statement. (In fact it is sometimes written $\text{Lim}_{x\to 1+} f(x) = 1$, but this notation will not be used in this book.) Similarly $x \to -1-$ means x approaches -1 through values less than -1, and in Example 4.15, $f(x) \to -1$ as $x \to -1-$ (see Fig. 4.8).

Example 4.110

If $f(x) = (x-2)^{-1}$, illustrated in Fig. 4.7, any neighbourhood of 2 contains points giving large positive values of $f(x)$ and points giving large negative values. It is then not correct to write $f(x) \to \infty$ as $x \to 2$. However it is correct to write $f(x) \to \infty$ as $x \to 2+$. We can also write $f(x) \to -\infty$ as $x \to 2-$, indicating the arbitrary large negative values that $f(x)$ assumes in intervals $(2 - \delta, 2)$. $\square$

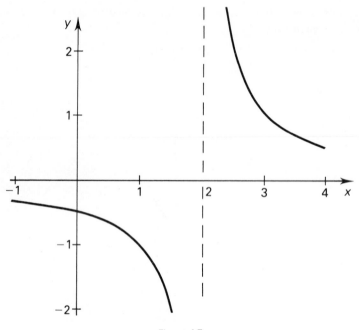

Figure 4.7

If the domain of a function is a bounded interval, say (a, b), then it is meaningless to ask what happens to the function as $x \to a-$ or $x \to b+$. Thus $x \to a$ can only be interpreted as $x \to a+$, and $x \to b$ can only be interpreted as $x \to b-$, and the limit concept and notation is used without ambiguity.

Example 4.111

For the function in Example 4.15 (see Fig. 4.8)

$$f(x) \to -1 \quad \text{as } x \to -2, \qquad \text{or} \qquad \text{Lim}_{x\to-2} f(x) = -1$$

and

$$f(x) \to 4 \quad \text{as } x \to 2, \qquad \text{or} \qquad \operatorname*{Lim}_{x \to 2} f(x) = 4.$$

The value at $x = 2$ again does not affect the existence or value of the limit as $x \to 2$. Other examples, illustrated in Fig. 4.9, are

$$\operatorname{Sin}^{-1} x \to \pi/2 \quad \text{as } x \to 1 \qquad \text{or} \qquad \operatorname*{Lim}_{x \to 1} (\operatorname{Sin}^{-1} x) = \pi/2;$$

$$\operatorname*{Lim}_{x \to -1} (\operatorname{Sin}^{-1} x) = -\pi/2; \qquad \text{and} \qquad \operatorname*{Lim}_{x \to -1} (\operatorname{Cos}^{-1} x) = \pi. \quad \square$$

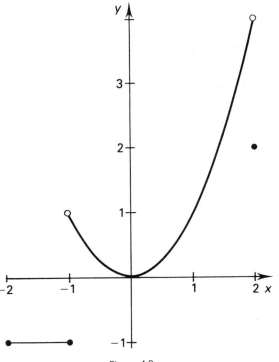

Figure 4.8

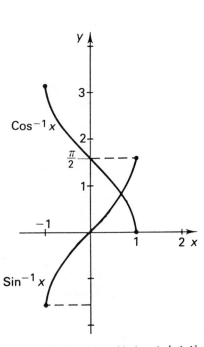

Figure 4.9   Functions with domain $[-1, 1]$

Exercises (answers on p. 91)

4.1.1 Sketch the graphs of the functions (cf. Example 4.14)
  (i) $f(x) = (x^3 - 2x^2)/(x - 2)$, $(x \neq 2)$.
  (ii) $g(x) = x^2$, $(x \neq 2)$; $g(2) = 0$.
  (iii) $y = x^2$.

4.1.2 Sketch the graphs of the following functions, and state whether $\operatorname{Lim}_{x \to 1}$ exists. If it does exist, write down the value of the limit.
  (i) $f(x) = 1/(x - 1)$, $(x \neq 1)$.
  (ii) $f(x) = 1/(x - 1)$, $(x \neq 1)$; $f(1) = 0$.
  (iii) $f(x) = x$, $0 \leqslant x < 1$.
  (iv) $f(x) = x^2$, $(x \neq 1)$; $f(1) = 2$.
  In (ii), is it correct to write $f(x) \to \infty$ as $x \to 1$?

4.1.3 Does $f(x) = x \cos(1/x^2)$, $(x \neq 0)$ have a limit as $x \to 0$?

4.2 The Concept of Limit as $x \to \infty$

So far the behaviour of a function has been considered as $x \to a$, allowing values of x closer and closer to a. Next consider the behaviour of $f(x)$ as $x \to \infty$, which means allowing larger and larger values of x, without any bound.

Example 4.20

If $f(x) = x^2$, then $f(x)$ can be made as large as desired by taking x large enough, and a further increase in x only makes $f(x)$ even larger. Precisely, $x^2 > X$ if $x > \sqrt{X}$, and this is true however large X is. This is written $x^2 \to \infty$ as $x \to \infty$. □

Example 4.21

The function x^{-2} can be made as small as desired by taking x large enough, and a further increase in x only makes x^{-2} even smaller. Precisely, $x^{-2} < \varepsilon$ if $x > 1/\sqrt{\varepsilon}$, and this is true however small ε is ($\varepsilon > 0$). To relate this to the properties of limit already discussed, the statement can be rephrased: x^{-2} can be made as near to 0 as desired, and a further increase in x only makes x^{-2} even nearer to 0. To write this as $x^{-2} \to 0$ as $x \to \infty$, or $\mathrm{Lim}_{x \to \infty}(x^{-2}) = 0$, is quite consistent with the previous discussion of behaviour as $x \to a$. □

Example 4.22

Consider $f(x) = (3x - 2)/x = 3 - (2/x)$. By taking x large enough, $(2/x)$ can be made as small as desired, so $f(x)$ can be made as near to 3 as desired. This is written

$$f(x) \to 3 \quad \text{as } x \to \infty \qquad \text{or} \qquad \mathrm{Lim}_{x \to \infty} \frac{3x - 2}{x} = 3. \quad \square$$

Example 4.23

Since $-1 \leqslant \sin x \leqslant 1$, for positive x the function $(\sin x)/x$ satisfies the inequality $-1/x \leqslant (\sin x)/x \leqslant 1/x$. By taking x large enough, the values of $\pm 1/x$ become as close to 0 as desired, and are as close to 0 for all larger x. From the inequality, $(\sin x)/x$ also becomes as close to 0 as desired, and its values are as close to 0 for all larger x. The important statement here is the second, since $(\sin x)/x$ can be made close to 0 merely by taking x near any integral multiple of π. It is the fact that *all* values of $(\sin x)/x$ are (arbitrarily) close to 0 as $x \to \infty$ that is implied by the statements $(\sin x)/x \to 0$ as $x \to \infty$ or $\mathrm{Lim}_{x \to \infty}(\sin x)/x = 0$. □

Similar considerations apply to the behaviour of functions when the independent variable x decreases to arbitrarily large negative values; then x is said to **tend to minus infinity**, written $x \to -\infty$. Results for the previous examples involving even functions can be written down immediately:

$$x^2 \to \infty \quad \text{as } x \to -\infty;$$

$$x^{-2} \to 0 \quad \text{as } x \to -\infty, \quad \text{or} \quad \mathrm{Lim}_{x \to -\infty}(x^{-2}) = 0;$$

and

$$(\sin x)/x \to 0 \quad \text{as } x \to -\infty, \quad \text{or} \quad \mathrm{Lim}_{x \to -\infty}(\sin x)/x = 0.$$

Also if x is large and negative, then $(-2/x)$ is as small as desired, so

$$[(3x-2)/x] \to 3 \quad \text{as } x \to -\infty \quad \text{or} \quad \lim_{x \to -\infty} (3x-2)/x = 3.$$

If the domain of a function does not contain large values of x, then it is meaningless to speak of its behaviour as $x \to \infty$. Examples of such functions are Sin, Cos, Sin^{-1}, Cos^{-1}, and Tan (see Fig. 3.3 on p. 48). However the idea of a limit as the independent variable gets larger can be applied to a sequence: $s_n \to L$ as $n \to \infty$, or $\text{Lim}_{n \to \infty} s_n = L$, means that by taking a large enough integer N, the Nth term s_N and *all* later terms are as close to L as desired.

Example 4.24

$s_n = n^2 \to \infty$ as $n \to \infty$. The discussion in Example 4.20 remains valid if x is replaced by n, which only takes integral values. Similarly Examples 4.21–23 can also be restricted to sequences:

$$n^{-2} \to 0 \quad \text{as } n \to \infty, \quad \text{or} \quad \lim_{n \to \infty} n^{-2} = 0;$$

$$[(3n-2)/n] \to 3 \quad \text{as } n \to \infty; \quad \text{and} \quad [(\sin n)/n] \to 0 \quad \text{as } n \to \infty. \quad \square$$

On the other hand the concept of limit as $x \to a$ does not extend naturally to sequences, since it involves considering all values of x near a in an open interval $(a, a+\delta)$, where δ is positive. But the domain of a sequence only contains the integers. For a sequence, limits can only exist as $n \to \infty$, and so one can speak of **the limit of a sequence**, with $n \to \infty$ understood. For example, the results in Example 4.24 can also be stated in the following ways: $\{n^2\}$ has no limit; $\{n^{-2}\}$ has the limit 0; $\text{Lim}(3n-2)/n = 3$; and $(\sin n)/n \to 0$.

Example 4.25

The function $\sin(x\pi)$ has no limit as $x \to \infty$, since its values oscillate between -1 and $+1$, and there is no single value L which $\sin(x\pi)$ approaches for all large x. However the sequence $\{\sin n\pi\}$ has every term zero, and therefore its limit is zero. But the sequence $\{\sin(n\pi - \frac{1}{2}\pi)\}$ takes the values ±1 alternately, however large n gets, and so has no limit. $\square$

Since the number of values of $f(x)$ to be considered is not finite, the existence of a limit can never be proved by considering numerical values. Indeed inspection of numerical values may be misleading.

Example 4.26

A certain sequence has values (correct to the number of figures given)

$$s_1 = 1.43, \quad s_2 = 1.91, \quad s_8 = 1.9964, \quad s_{12} = 1.999958,$$

$$s_{16} = 1.9999999795$$

$$s_{17} = 1.99999999914$$

$$s_{18} = 1.9999999999$$

$$s_{19} = 2.00000\,000000$$

$$= s_{20} = s_{21} \quad \text{(correct to 11D)}$$

These numbers might suggest the limit 2 to the unwary. However

$$s_{25} = 2.0000002384$$

$$s_{40} = 3, \qquad s_{60} = 2050.$$

and $s_n = 2 + (-1 + 0.05n)^{11} \to \infty$ as $n \to \infty$. $\square$

Some statements about the **asymptotic behaviour** of functions appeared in Chapter 3, for example $\sinh x \to \frac{1}{2}e^x$ as $x \to \infty$. A formal definition is $f(x) \to g(x)$ as $x \to \infty$ if $f(x) - g(x) \to 0$.

A weaker comparison of asymptotic behaviour is defined by

$$f(x) \sim g(x) \quad \text{as } x \to \infty \quad \text{if } \operatorname*{Lim}_{x \to \infty} \frac{f(x)}{g(x)} = 1. \tag{4.1}$$

Example 4.27

$$(x^2 + 1) \sim x^2 \quad \text{as } x \to \infty.$$

This can be read: $(x^2 + 1)$ behaves asymptotically like x^2, meaning that they get large in a similar way. It would be incorrect to write $(x^2 + 1) \sim x$, because $(x^2 + 1)$ is much larger than x as $x \to \infty$. $\square$

Exercises (answers on p. 91)

4.2.1 Suppose $f(x) \to L$ as $x \to \infty$. Is it true that the sequence $\{f(n)\}$ has the limit L? Does $f(x) \to \infty$ as $x \to \infty \Rightarrow f(n) \to \infty$?

4.2.2 Which of the following statements are correct (for any s_n)?
   (i) If $s_n \to \infty$ as $n \to \infty$, then $s_i \to \infty$ as $i \to \infty$.
   (ii) If $s_n \to \infty$ as $n \to \infty$, then $s_{2k} \to \infty$ as $k \to \infty$.
   (iii) If $s_{2n} \to \infty$ as $n \to \infty$, then $s_n \to \infty$ as $n \to \infty$.
   (iv) If $s_{2n} \to L$ as $n \to \infty$, then $s_i \to L$ as $i \to \infty$.
   (v) If $s_n \to L$ as $n \to \infty$, then $s_{2n+1} \to 2L + 1$ as $n \to \infty$.
   (vi) If $s_{2m} \to L$ as $m \to \infty$, and $s_{2n+1} \to L$ as $n \to \infty$, then $s_r \to L$ as $r \to \infty$.

4.3   Theorems on Limits

Some theorems on limits will now be stated and illustrated by examples. Proofs will not be given, and in fact cannot be given without first giving formal definitions of the meaning of various limiting processes. A discussion of the required definitions is given in Appendix D, but they will not be used in this section.

The discussion of limits in Section 4.1, in particular Examples 4.15, 4.16 and 4.110, implies that the value L of a limit is unique. The absence of formal definitions here may perhaps obscure this fact, so it will be stated as a theorem.

Theorem 4.1
As $x \to a$ (or as $x \to \pm\infty$), the possibilities $f(x) \to L$, $f(x) \to M \neq L$, $f(x) \to \infty$, and $f(x) \to -\infty$ are mutually exclusive.

Results on the limits of sums, products, quotients, and differences are also easy to formulate. The following discussion assumes that $x \to a$, or $x \to \infty$, or $x \to -\infty$, and this will be understood without further mention. If $f(x) \to \infty$ and $g(x) \to L$, what happens to the product $fg(x)$? Now $f(x)$ can be made arbitrarily large, and $g(x)$ can be made arbitrarily close to L. If L is positive, $fg(x)$ must become large and positive; if L is negative, $fg(x)$ must become large and negative. However if $L = 0$, then $f(x)$ gets large, and $g(x)$ gets small, and no general statement can be made about their product.

Example 4.31
To exhibit the different possibilities, suppose $f(x) = x^{-2}$ so that $f(x) \to \infty$ as $x \to 0$.
  (i) If $g(x) = \cos x$, so that $g(x) \to 1 = L$, then $fg(x) = (\cos x)/x^2 \to \infty$.
  (ii) If $g(x) = x^2 - 2$, so that $g(x) \to -2 = L$, then $fg(x) = 1 - (2/x^2) \to -\infty$.
  (iii) If $g(x) = |x|$, so that $g(x) \to 0$, $fg(x) = (1/|x|) \to \infty$. (Note that $f(x) = 1/|x|^2$)
  (iv) If $g(x) = kx^2$, so that $g(x) \to 0$, $fg(x) = k \to k$.
  (v) If $g(x) = x^3$, so that $g(x) \to 0$, $fg(x) = x \to 0$.
  (vi) If $g(x) = -|x|$, so that $g(x) \to 0$, $fg(x) = (-1/|x|) \to -\infty$.
The expressions given for $fg(x)$ are valid for all x near 0, but not at $x = 0$, even in (iv) and (v). Evidently a general theorem on the behaviour of a product fg can be formulated (see Theorem 4.3 below) only if $L = 0$ is excluded. □

(This special case is also naturally excluded in a proof. For example to prove that $fg(x) \to \infty$, one considers the inequality $f(x)g(x) > X$; and if $g(x)$ is close to L this will be reduced to an inequality like $f(x) > X/L$, which is not possible if $L = 0$.)

Similar considerations lead to the following results, in which L and M denote values of limits.

> **Theorem 4.2**
> Suppose as $x \to a$ (or as $x \to \pm\infty$), $f(x) \to L$ and $g(x) \to M$; then
>   (i) $(f + g)(x) \to L + M$,   (ii) $(f - g)(x) \to L - M$,
>   (iii) $fg(x) \to LM$,   (iv) $(f/g)(x) \to L/M$ if $M \neq 0$.
>
> **Theorem 4.3**
> Suppose as $x \to a$ (or as $x \to \pm\infty$), $f(x) \to \infty$ and $g(x) \to L$; then
>   (i) $(f \pm g)(x) \to \infty$
>   (ii) if $L > 0$, $(fg)(x) \to \infty$ and $(f/g)(x) \to \infty$
>   (iii) if $L < 0$, $(fg)(x) \to -\infty$ and $(f/g)(x) \to -\infty$
>   (iv) $(g/f)(x) \to 0$.
> Note that $L = 0$ does not appear in (ii) or (iii) (cf. Example 4.31).
>
> **Theorem 4.4**
> Suppose as $x \to a$ (or as $x \to \pm\infty$), $f(x) \to \infty$ and $g(x) \to \infty$; then
>   (i) $(f + g)(x) \to \infty$, (ii) $(fg)(x) \to \infty$.

Example 4.32
What happens as $x \to 0$ to the functions (i) $(\sin^2 x)/x$, (ii) $(\sin x)/x^2$, (iii) $(\sin^2 x)/x^2$? In each case, the expression is given as a quotient with both numerator and denominator tending to zero. This case $L = M = 0$ is excluded from Theorem 4.2(iv).

However

  (i) $\dfrac{\sin^2 x}{x} = f(x)g(x)$ with $f(x) = \dfrac{\sin x}{x} \to 1$ and $g(x) = \sin x \to 0$.

From Theorem 4.2(iii), with $L = 1$ and $M = 0$, $(\sin^2 x)/x \to 0$ as $x \to 0$.

(ii) $(\sin x)/x^2 = f(x)g(x)$ with $f(x) = (\sin x)/x \to 1$ and $g(x) = 1/x$.

As $x \to 0+$, $g(x) \to \infty$, and so does $f(x)g(x)$; as $x \to 0-$, $g(x) \to -\infty$, and so does $f(x)g(x)$. Thus $(\sin x)/x^2$ has no limit as $x \to 0$.

(iii) $(\sin^2 x)/x^2 = f(x)g(x)$ with $f(x) = g(x) = (\sin x)/x$.

From Theorem 4.2(iii), $(\sin^2 x)/x^2 \to 1$ as $x \to 0$.

The three results can also be stated as (i) $\mathrm{Lim}_{x \to 0} \sin^2 x/x = 0$, (ii) $\mathrm{Lim}_{x \to 0} \sin x/x^2$ does not exist, (iii) $\mathrm{Lim}_{x \to 0} \sin^2 x/x^2 = 1$.   □

Example 4.33

If $f(x) = \ln(2x)$ and $g(x) = \ln x$, then Theorem 4.4 gives (i) $\ln(2x) + \ln x \to \infty$ as $x \to \infty$, (ii) $(\ln 2x)(\ln x) \to \infty$ as $x \to \infty$. As $f(x) = (\ln 2) + (\ln x)$, $f(x) - g(x) = \ln 2$, a constant, and so $\mathrm{Lim}_{x \to \infty}(f - g)(x) = \ln 2$. Similarly $(f/g)(x) = 1 + (\ln 2)/(\ln x) \to 1$ as $x \to \infty$, using Theorems 4.2(i) and 4.3(iv).   □

Statements such as $\mathrm{Lim}_{x \to a} f(x) = L$ or $f(x) \to -\infty$ as $x \to a$ imply certain facts about the values of the function f in neighbourhoods of a. Their meaning certainly does not depend on the label used for the independent (domain) variable, which is thus a 'dummy variable' in such statements.

Example 4.34

(i) $\dfrac{\sin t}{t} \to 1$ as $t \to 0$ (cf. Example 4.13 on p. 74)

(ii) $\dfrac{\cos y}{y^2} \to \infty$ as $y \to 0$ (cf. Example 4.31(i))

(iii) $\mathrm{Lim}_{w \to \infty} \dfrac{3w - 2}{w} = 3$ (cf. Example 4.22 on p. 80)   □

To evaluate a limit, one may need to consider an actual change of variable. This possibility is most obvious in the case $x \to 0$, because if x is in some (small) neighbourhood of 0, so are $-x$ and x^2, implying that $f(-x)$ and $f(x^2)$ have the same behaviour as $f(x)$ as $x \to 0$.

Example 4.35

From Example 4.19 on p. 77

$$\mathrm{Lim}_{x \to 0} \ln(1 + x)/x = 1 \qquad\qquad (*)$$

Then (i) $\mathrm{Lim}_{x \to 0} \ln(1 - x)/(-x) = 1$, or (using Theorem 4.2(iii) with $g(x) = M = -1$),

$$\mathrm{Lim}_{x \to 0} \frac{\ln(1 - x)}{x} = -1;$$

and (ii) $\mathrm{Lim}_{x \to 0} \ln(1 + x^2)/x^2 = 1$.

A straightforward way of getting these results is to convert the required limits (i) and (ii) into (∗) by a change of variable:

(i)
$$\underset{x \to 0}{\text{Lim}}\frac{\ln(1-x)}{x} = \underset{y \to 0}{\text{Lim}}\frac{\ln(1+y)}{-y},$$

where $y = -x$ so that $y \to 0$ as $x \to 0$

$$= -\underset{y \to 0}{\text{Lim}}\frac{\ln(1+y)}{y} = -1 \quad \text{from (∗).}$$

(ii)
$$\underset{x \to 0}{\text{Lim}}\frac{\ln(1+x^2)}{x^2} = \underset{y \to 0}{\text{Lim}}\frac{\ln(1+y)}{y},$$

where $y = x^2$ so that $y \to 0$ as $x \to 0$

$$= 1 \quad \text{from (∗).}$$

(The fact that $y \to 0+$ as $x \to 0$ does not matter, because

$$\underset{y \to 0}{\text{Lim}}\frac{\ln(1+y)}{y} = 1 \Rightarrow \frac{\ln(1+y)}{y} \to 1 \quad \text{as } y \to 0+). \quad \square$$

Example 4.36

(i)
$$\underset{x \to 1}{\text{Lim}}\frac{\sin(\ln x)}{\ln x} = \underset{y \to 0}{\text{Lim}}\frac{\sin y}{y} = 1,$$

(ii)
$$\underset{x \to 0}{\text{Lim}}\frac{\sin(\ln x)}{\ln x} = \underset{y \to -\infty}{\text{Lim}}\frac{\sin y}{y} = 0. \quad \square$$

Exercises (answers on p. 91)

4.3.1 Assuming $\text{Lim}_{x \to 0} \ln(1 \pm x)/x = \pm 1$ (from Example 4.35), evaluate the limits as $x \to 0$ of (i) $[\sin x + \ln(1+x)]/x$, (ii) $\ln^2(1+x)/x$, (iii) $\ln(1+x)^2/x$, (iv) $\ln(1-x^2)/x$. In each case, state which of Theorems 4.2–4.4 you have used.

4.3.2 Use a suitable change of variable to evaluate the limits of the following as $x \to 1$:
  (i) $\{\sin(3x-3)\}/(2x-2)$;
  (ii) $\{\sin(x-1)\}/(x^2-1)$;
  (iii) $(\ln x)/(x^2-1)$.

4.3.3 What happens as $x \to 0$ to the functions defined (for $x \neq 0$) by:
  (i) $\{(\sin x)\ln(1-x)\}/x^2$;
  (ii) $\{\ln(1-x)\}/x^2$;
  (iii) $\{\ln(1-x)\}/\sin x$.

4.4 Techniques for Evaluating Limits

Methods considered at this stage are essentially algebraic manipulations which reduce the given expression to expressions with known limits, combined in ways allowing the use of Theorems 4.2, 4.3 and 4.4. Some known results are collected for reference in the table at the end of this chapter. Note that as $x \to \infty$, the exponential function increases more rapidly than any power of x so that $e^x/x^k \to \infty$ for any k. On the other hand the logarithmic function increases more slowly than any positive power of x, so that $(\ln x)/x^k \to 0$ if $k > 0$. Similarly powers outweigh the logarithmic function as $x \to 0$, i.e. $x^k \ln x \to 0$ as $x \to 0$ if $k > 0$.

Expressions for which the limit is not obvious are sometimes called **indeterminate forms**. The basic type, a quotient with both numerator and denominator tending to zero, may be labelled $0/0$. A quotient $f(x)/g(x)$ with both $f(x)$ and $g(x)$ tending to infinity may be referred to as type ∞/∞, but can always be written $[1/g(x)]/[1/f(x)]$ which is type $0/0$. Similarly a product $f(x)g(x)$ where $f(x) \to \infty$ and $g(x) \to 0$ can be written $g(x)/[1/f(x)]$. The type $\infty - \infty$ includes expressions of the form $f(x) - g(x)$ where both $f(x)$ and $g(x)$ tend to infinity. Finally one can consider expressions of the form $f(x)^{g(x)}$: in type 0^0 both $f(x)$ and $g(x)$ tend to 0, and similarly there are cases of type ∞^0 and 1^∞.

Thus Examples 4.31(iii)–(vi) and 4.32 considered indeterminate forms x/x^2, etc., of type $0/0$, while Example 4.33 considered the expression $\ln 2x - \ln x$, of type $\infty - \infty$ as $x \to \infty$.

Although the symbols classifying indeterminate forms have the form of numerical operations of division, subtraction, or raising to a power, they do not represent such operations, but describe the different situations which can arise when a limit is considered. Parts (iii)–(vi) of Example 4.31 indicate that an indeterminate form of type $0/0$ may have either a (finite) limit, tend to $\pm\infty$, or have no limit. It is this situation which prevents any meaningful definition of division by zero in arithmetic.

If an indeterminate form is a quotient, it is sometimes possible to cancel factors, leaving an expression which is not indeterminate. The value of the limit, if any, is then obvious. This method was used in Example 4.31(iii)–(vi) and in Example 4.14 on p. 74. Cancellation is not valid at the point at which the limit is required, but is valid for all nearby points, and it is values at these points which are the subject of the limit statement.

Example 4.41

Evaluate

$$\lim_{x \to 2} \frac{x^3 - x^2 - 8x + 12}{x^3 - 7x^2 + 16x - 12}.$$

Since both numerator and denominator are zero on substituting $x = 2$, each must contain $(x - 2)$ as a factor:

$$(x^3 - x^2 - 8x + 12) = (x - 2)(x^2 + x - 6),$$
$$(x^3 - 7x^2 + 16x - 12) = (x - 2)(x^2 - 5x + 6).$$

Both quadratic factors also vanish at $x = 2$, showing that a further factorization is required:

$$(x^2 + x - 6) = (x - 2)(x + 3), \qquad (x^2 - 5x + 6) = (x - 2)(x - 3).$$

Hence provided $x \neq 2$,

$$\frac{x^3 - x^2 - 8x + 12}{x^3 - 7x^2 + 16x - 12} = \frac{x + 3}{x - 3},$$

and so the required limit is

$$\lim_{x \to 2} \frac{x + 3}{x - 3} = -5.$$

Any function f with the rule

$$f(x) = \frac{x^3 - x^2 - 8x + 12}{x^3 - 7x^2 + 16x - 12}$$

for all $x \neq 2$ has the property $\text{Lim}_{x \to 2} f(x) = -5$, irrespective of whether $f(2)$ is defined or not, and irrespective of the value of $f(2)$ if it is defined.   □

Example 4.42

(i)
$$\underset{x \to 2}{\text{Lim}} \frac{x^3 - x^2 - 8x + 12}{x^2 - 5x + 6} = \underset{x \to 2}{\text{Lim}} \frac{x^2 + x - 6}{x - 3} = 0.$$

(ii)
$$\frac{x^2 + x - 6}{x^3 - 7x^2 + 16x - 12} = \frac{x + 3}{(x - 2)(x - 3)} \quad \text{for all } x \neq 2,$$

and so a limit as $x \to 2$ does not exist. As $x \to 2+$ (from above), the signs of the factors are $+/+-$; hence

$$\frac{x^2 + x - 6}{x^3 - 7x^2 + 16x - 12} \to -\infty \quad \text{as } x \to 2+.$$

As $x \to 2-$, the signs of the factors are $+/--$; hence

$$\frac{x^2 + x - 6}{x^3 - 7x^2 + 16x - 12} \to \infty \quad \text{as } x \to 2-. \quad □$$

If the vanishing of the numerator or denominator results from a difference of two surd expressions, then $(\sqrt{a} - \sqrt{b})(\sqrt{a} + \sqrt{b}) = (a - b)$ should be used to produce a rational factor more amenable to cancellation.

Example 4.43

(i)
$$\underset{x \to 1}{\text{Lim}} \frac{\sqrt{(x^2 - x + 1)} - \sqrt{(x^2 + 2x - 2)}}{x^2 - 1}$$

$$= \underset{x \to 1}{\text{Lim}} \frac{\{\sqrt{(x^2 - x + 1)} - \sqrt{(x^2 + 2x - 2)}\}\{\sqrt{(x^2 - x + 1)} + \sqrt{(x^2 + 2x - 2)}\}}{(x^2 - 1)\{\sqrt{(x^2 - x + 1)} + \sqrt{(x^2 + 2x - 2)}\}}$$

$$= \underset{x \to 1}{\text{Lim}} \frac{(x^2 - x + 1) - (x^2 + 2x - 2)}{(x^2 - 1)\{\sqrt{(x^2 - x + 1)} + \sqrt{(x^2 + 2x - 2)}\}} \qquad (*)$$

$$= \underset{x \to 1}{\text{Lim}} \frac{-3}{(x + 1)\{\sqrt{(x^2 - x + 1)} + \sqrt{(x^2 + 2x - 2)}\}} = -\frac{3}{4}.$$

(ii) As $x \to \infty$, the expression $f(x) = \sqrt{(x^2 - x + 1)} - \sqrt{(x^2 + 2x - 2)}$ is an indeterminate form of type $\infty - \infty$. Omitting the factor $(x^2 - 1)$ in (i), $(*)$ gives

$$f(x) = (3 - 3x) / \{\sqrt{(x^2 - x + 1)} + \sqrt{(x^2 + 2x - 2)}\}.$$

When $x \to \infty$, the behaviour of a quadratic (or any polynomial) is determined by the highest power, so

$$\sqrt{(x^2 - x + 1)} \sim \sqrt{x^2} = x, \qquad \sqrt{(x^2 + 2x - 2)} \sim x,$$

and

$$f(x) \sim (3 - 3x)/2x = (3/2x) - (\tfrac{3}{2})$$

Hence

$$f(x) \to -\tfrac{3}{2} \quad \text{as } x \to \infty.$$

However replacing a polynomial by its highest power only gives the correct asymptotic behaviour if the terms obtained do not cancel. If this rule had been applied to the original expression for $f(x)$, it would give $f(x) \sim \sqrt{(x^2)} - \sqrt{(x^2)} = x - x = 0$, which is incorrect. □

Expressions containing circular functions may often be transformed to allow the use of the known result $(\sin x)/x \to 1$ as $x \to 0$.

Example 4.44

$$\operatorname*{Lim}_{x \to 0} x \cot x = \operatorname*{Lim}_{x \to 0}(\cos x) \bigg/ \left(\frac{\sin x}{x} \right) = 1,$$

using Theorem 4.2(iv). □

Example 4.45

$$\operatorname*{Lim}_{x \to \pi} \frac{\sin x}{x - \pi} = \operatorname*{Lim}_{y \to 0} \frac{\sin(y + \pi)}{y}, \quad \text{by substituting } y = x - \pi$$

$$= \operatorname*{Lim}_{y \to 0} \frac{-\sin y}{y} = -1. \quad \square$$

Example 4.46

$$\frac{\sin (x - 1)}{x^2 + 2x - 3} = \frac{\sin y}{y(y + 4)} \quad \text{putting } x = y + 1$$

$$\therefore \quad \operatorname*{Lim}_{x \to 1} \frac{\sin(x - 1)}{x^2 + 2x - 3} = \operatorname*{Lim}_{y \to 0} \frac{\sin y}{y} \frac{1}{y + 4} = \frac{1}{4}$$

(Theorem 4.2(iii)). □

When $x \to 0$, the behaviour of a polynomial is determined by the lowest power.

Example 4.47

As $x \to 0$,

$$\frac{\sin x}{x^2 + x} \sim \frac{\sin x}{x} \to 1$$

or

$$\frac{\sin x}{x^2 + x} \sim \frac{x}{x^2 + x} = \frac{1}{x + 1} \to 1. \quad \square$$

The result $\ln(2x) - \ln x \to \ln 2$ as $x \to \infty$, shown in Example 4.33, suggests that all logarithmic terms in an expression should be combined, if possible, before considering the limit.

Example 4.48

$$\lim_{x \to 2} \{\ln|x^2 + x - 6| - \ln|x^2 - 5x + 6|\} \qquad (\text{type} \ -\infty + \infty)$$

$$= \lim_{x \to 2} \ln\left\{\frac{|x^2 + x - 6|}{|x^2 - 5x + 6|}\right\} = \lim_{x \to 2} \ln\left|\frac{x^2 + x - 6}{x^2 - 5x + 6}\right|$$

$$= \lim_{x \to 2} \ln\left|\frac{x + 3}{x - 3}\right| = \ln|-5| = \ln 5.$$

The modulus signs are essential to this example, because the domain of $\ln(x^2 + x - 6) - \ln(x^2 - 5x + 6)$ excludes $[-3, 3]$. The given expression is undefined only at $x = 2$.   □

Similarly, exponential terms may be combined.

Example 4.49

As $x \to \infty$, $f(x) = \exp(x^2 + x)/\exp(x^2 + kx)$ is type ∞/∞. But $f(x) = \exp[(1-k)x]$, so $f(x) \to \infty$ if $k < 1$, $f(x) \to 0$ if $k > 1$, and $f(x) \to 1$ if $k = 1$.   □

Example 4.410

(i) $f(x) = \ln 3x/(4x + 1) - \ln 2x/(2x + 1)$ is type $-\infty + \infty$ as $x \to 0$. But

$$f(x) = \frac{\ln 3}{4x + 1} - \frac{\ln 2}{2x + 1} + \left(\frac{1}{4x + 1} - \frac{1}{2x + 1}\right)\ln x$$

$$= \frac{\ln 3}{4x + 1} - \frac{\ln 2}{2x + 1} - \frac{2x \ln x}{(4x + 1)(2x + 1)}$$

$$\to \ln 3 - \ln 2 - 0 = \ln(\tfrac{3}{2}).$$

(ii) $g(x) = \dfrac{\ln 3x}{4x + 3} - \dfrac{\ln 2x}{2x + 1} = \dfrac{\ln 3}{4x + 3} - \dfrac{\ln 2}{2x + 1} - \dfrac{(2x + 2)\ln x}{(4x + 3)(2x + 1)}$

$$\to \infty \text{ as } x \to 0.$$

(iii) $h(x) = \dfrac{\ln 3x}{4x + 1} - \dfrac{\ln 2x}{2x + 3} = \dfrac{\ln 3}{4x + 1} - \dfrac{\ln 2}{2x + 3} - \dfrac{(2x - 2)\ln x}{(4x + 3)(2x + 1)}$

$$\to -\infty \text{ as } x \to 0.$$

Here it is again valid to write $4x + 1 \sim 1$ and $2x + 1 \sim 1$ before combining the logarithmic terms, e.g.

$$g(x) \sim \tfrac{1}{3}\ln 3x - \ln 2x = \tfrac{1}{3}\ln 3 - \ln 2 - \tfrac{2}{3}\ln x \to \infty.   □$$

Example 4.411

Find the limit of the sequence $\{(1 + a/n)^n\}$.

Here limit means as $n \to \infty$, giving an indeterminate form of type 1^∞. If $s_n = (1 + a/n)^n$, then $\ln s_n = n \ln(1 + a/n)$, and

$$s_n = \exp(\ln s_n) = \exp[n \ln(1 + a/n)]$$

Now

$$\text{Lim}_{n\to\infty}[n\ln(1+a/n)]=\text{Lim}_{x\to\infty}[x\ln(1+a/x)]$$

$$=\text{Lim}_{y\to0}[y^{-1}\ln(1+ay)]\quad\text{by substituting }x=1/y$$

$$=a\,\text{Lim}_{h\to0}[h^{-1}\ln(1+h)]\quad\text{by substituting }y=h/a$$

$$=a,\qquad\text{from Example 4.19 on p. 77.}$$

Hence* $s_n\to\exp a$ as $n\to\infty$. Taking logarithms should always be considered for indeterminate forms of type 0^0, ∞^0 or 1^∞. $\square$

More powerful techniques for evaluating limits will be given in Chapter 16 (see also Exercise 4.16).

Exercises (answers on p. 91)

4.4.1 Find the behaviour as $x\to3$ of functions defined for $x\neq3$ by the following expressions:

(i) $\dfrac{x^2-9}{x^2+2}$,

(ii) $\dfrac{x^2}{x-3}$,

(iii) $\dfrac{x^2-4x+3}{x^2-2x-3}$.

4.4.2 Evaluate

$$\text{Lim}_{x\to2}\frac{\sqrt{(x^2+x-1)}-\sqrt{(x^2+1)}}{x-2}.$$

4.4.3 Evaluate

(i) $\text{Lim}_{x\to0}\dfrac{\sin x}{x^2-x}$,

(ii) $\text{Lim}_{x\to0}\dfrac{\ln(1+x)}{x^2+2x}$.

---

* This step requires continuity of the exponential function. Continuity is discussed in Chapter 5.

Table of Limits

(a) As $x \to 0$,
$$(\sin x)/x \to 1$$
$$x^k \ln x \to 0 \qquad (k>0) \tag{$*$}$$
$$x^k \ln x \to -\infty \qquad (k \leqslant 0)$$
$$x^{kx} \to 1$$

$$P(x) = \sum_{i=m}^{n} a_i x^i = a_m x^m + \cdots + a_n x^n \sim a_m x^m \qquad \text{(lowest power)}.$$

(b) As $x \to \infty$,
$$(\log x)/x^k \to 0 \qquad (k>0) \tag{$*$}$$
$$x^k a^{-x} = x^k/a^x \to 0 \qquad (a>0) \tag{$\dagger$}$$
$$x^{a/x} \to 1$$
$$P(x) \sim a_n x^n \qquad \text{(highest power)}$$
$$P(x) a^{-x} \to 0 \qquad (a>0).$$

(c) Limits of sequences: as $n \to \infty$, $(1+x/n)^n \to e^x$
$$x^n \to \infty \quad \text{if } x>1$$
$$x^n \to 1 \quad \text{if } x=1$$
$$x^n \to 0 \quad \text{if } |x|<1$$

and if $x \leqslant -1$ then x^n has no limit. Other limits of sequences are obtained from (b) on replacing x by n.

($*$) A popular statement of these results is to say that $\log x \to \infty$ more slowly than any power of x.

($\dagger$) This is often used with $a = e$; a popular statement is to say that $e^x \to \infty$ more quickly than any power of x.

Answers to Exercises 4.1.1–4.4.3

4.1.1 The three graphs differ only at $x=2$, where (i) has no point, (ii) has the point $(2,0)$, and (iii) the point $(2,4)$.

4.1.2 (i) No (ii) No (iii) 1 (iv) 1. In (i) $f(x) \to \infty$ as $x \to 1+$, but not as $x \to 1$.

4.1.3 $|f(x)| \leqslant |x| \Rightarrow f(x) \to 0$ as $x \to 0$. **4.2.1** Yes.

4.2.2 (i), (ii), (vi) are true; (iii), (iv), (v) are not true.

4.3.1 (i) 2 using 4.2(i),
(ii) 0 using 4.2(iii),
(iii) 2 using 4.2(iii) with $f(x) = L = 2$,
(iv) 0 using 4.2(i): note that $\ln(1-x^2) = \ln(1-x) + \ln(1+x)$.

4.3.2 (i) $\frac{3}{2}$, (ii) $\frac{1}{2}$, (iii) $\frac{1}{2}$.

4.3.3 (i) limit -1, (ii) no limit, (iii) limit -1.

4.4.1 (i) $\to 0$ (ii) $\to \pm\infty$ as $x \to 3\pm$ (iii) $\to \frac{1}{2}$.

4.4.2 $\sqrt{5}/10$. **4.4.3** (i) -1 (ii) $\frac{1}{2}$.

Further Exercises on Chapter 4

4.1 The **error function** erf has the properties $\mathrm{erf}(0) = 0$, $\mathrm{erf}'(x) = (2/\sqrt{\pi}) \exp(-x^2)$. By considering the definition of $\mathrm{erf}'(0)$, evaluate $\mathrm{Lim}_{h \to 0}(\mathrm{erf}\, h)/h$.

4.2 Find a number Δ such that $x^2 > X$ whenever $x < \Delta$ (cf. the definition of $f(x) \to \infty$ as $x \to -\infty$; because such a Δ can be found for any X, this proves that $x^2 \to \infty$ as $x \to -\infty$).

4.3 Suppose $f(x) \to \infty$ as $x \to a$, and $g(x) \to -\infty$. Consider the behaviour as $x \to a$ of $f + g$, $f - g$, fg and f/g. Either state their behaviour, or give examples showing that a general result cannot be given.

4.4 Find the behaviour as $x \to 1$ of functions defined for $x \neq 1$ by the following expressions:

(i) $\dfrac{x^2 - 1}{x^2 + 2}$,

(ii) $\dfrac{x^2}{x - 1}$,

(iii) $\dfrac{x^2 + x - 2}{x^2 + 2x - 3}$,

(iv) $\dfrac{x^2 + 2x - 3}{x^3 - x^2 - x + 1}$.

4.5 Evaluate

(i) $\mathrm{Lim}_{x \to 2} \dfrac{-3 + \sqrt{(1 + 4x)}}{-2 + \sqrt{(2x)}}$,

(ii) $\mathrm{Lim}_{n \to \infty} \{-n - 2 + \sqrt{(n^2 + 6n + 3)}\}$.

4.6 Find the behaviour as $x \to \infty$ of the functions in Exercise 4.4.

4.7 Evaluate (i) $\mathrm{Lim}_{x \to 0} \sin 2x/3x$, (ii) $\mathrm{Lim}_{x \to \pi} (1 + \cos x)/\sin x$.

4.8 Verify that Example 4.43 (ii) can be evaluated by completing the square, e.g. writing $x^2 + 2x - 2 = (x + 1)^2 - 3 \sim (x + 1)^2$. Note that the resulting expressions do not cancel. Evaluate Exercise 4.5 (ii) in the same way.

4.9 Discuss the behaviour as $x \to a$ of $f(x) = (3x + 2)/(x - a)^2$, distinguishing the cases $a > -\frac{2}{3}$, $a = -\frac{2}{3}$ and $a < -\frac{2}{3}$.

4.10 Discuss the behaviour as $x \to \pm\infty$ of $f(x) = x^n$, where n is an integer.

4.11 Write down the limits as $n \to \infty$ of the sequences with nth terms (i) $1/(3 + 2^n)$, (ii) $2 + 1/n$, (iii) $(n + \cos n)/(2n + 1)$, (iv) $(-1)^n/n$.

4.12 Describe the behaviour as $x \to \infty$ of the following functions: (i) $f(x) = \ln(3x) - \ln(2x + 1)$, (ii) $f(x) = e^{2x} - e^x$, (iii) $f(x) = e^{-x} \sin x$, (iv) $f(x) = e^{-x} \ln x$.

4.13 Describe the behaviour as $x \to 0$ of the following functions:
(i) $f(x) = \ln(3x) - \ln(2x + 1)$, (ii) $f(x) = (\sin x)(\ln x)$, (iii) $f(x) = e^{-x} \ln x$, (iv) $f(x) = ((x + 2)/(x^2 + 1)) \ln 2x$.

4.14 (cf. Exercise 4.6). Suppose $f(x)$ and $g(x)$ are polynomials of degree m and degree n respectively. What can be said about the behaviour of $f(x)/g(x)$ as $x \to \infty$
(i) if $m > n$,
(ii) if $m = n$,
(iii) if $m < n$.

4.15 If

$$\frac{2x-5}{x} < f(x) < \frac{2x^2+7x}{x^2},$$

find $\text{Lim}_{x\to\infty} f(x)$.

4.16 (a) If $f(b) = g(b) = 0$, suppose $f(x) = (x-b)F(x)$ and $g(x) = (x-b)G(x)$, and assume F and G have derivatives in a neighbourhood of b. Then, if $G(b) \neq 0$,

$$\text{Lim}_{x\to b} \frac{f(x)}{g(x)} = \frac{F(b)}{G(b)}.$$

By differentiating f and g (using the product formula), show that $f'(b) = F(b)$ and that

$$\boxed{\text{Lim}_{x\to b} \frac{f(x)}{g(x)} = \frac{f'(b)}{g'(b)}.} \tag{*}$$

(This result will be further discussed in Chapter 16.)

(b) Apply formula (∗) in (a) to Exercises 4.4.2, 4.4.3, and 4.7.

(c) Consider formula (∗) in the four parts of Exercise 4.4. Either apply it, or state why it does not apply.

4.17 By factorizing the polynomials, evaluate the limits as $x \to 2$ of the following rational functions (or, if there is no limit, give the behaviour)

(a) $\dfrac{x^2-x-2}{x^2-2}$,

(b) $\dfrac{x^3+3x+1}{x^3-2x^2-x+2}$,

(c) $\dfrac{x^3+2x^2-7x-2}{x^3-3x^2+x+2}$,

(d) $\dfrac{x^3+2x^2-7x-2}{x^4-5x^3+7x^2-4}$.

4.18 Write down the limits as $n \to \infty$ of the sequences with the following nth terms:

(a) $\dfrac{1}{2+3^n}$,

(b) $\dfrac{2n+\sin(\frac{1}{2}n\pi)}{2n+1}$,

(c) $\dfrac{(-1)^n}{n^2}$,

(d) $\dfrac{\sin(\frac{1}{2}n\pi)}{n}$,

(e) $\dfrac{n+\sin(\frac{1}{2}n\pi)}{n-\cos(n\pi)}$,

(f) $\cos[\ln(\tanh n)]$.

4.19 Evaluate (i) $\text{Lim}_{x\to 2}\{\ln|x^2-6x+8|-\ln|x^2-4|\}$,
(ii) $\text{Lim}_{x\to 1}\{\ln|x^2-5x+4|-\ln|x^2+x-2|\}$.

4.20 (i) Investigate the behaviour of $f(x)=x|x-2|/(x-2)$ as $x\to 2$. (ii) For what values of a does $\text{Lim}_{x\to a} x|x-a|/(x-a)$ exist?

4.21 (i) Investigate the behaviour as $x\to 2$ of $f(x)=x[x-2]/(x-2)$, where $[x-2]$ is the integer part of $(x-2)$ e.g. $[\frac{1}{2}]=0$, $[-\frac{1}{2}]=-1$. (ii) For what values of a does $\text{Lim}_{x\to a} x[x-a]/(x-a)$ exist?

4.22 Describe the behaviour of $f(x)=2(16+2^x)/(8-2^x)$ (i) as $x\to\infty$ (ii) as $x\to-\infty$ (iii) as $x\to 3+$ (iv) as $x\to 3-$.

5
Continuity

5.1 Continuous Functions

Geometrically, a real function is continuous if its graph has no breaks in it. (More generally, if the domain of f is a union of intervals, what is required is continuity in each interval.) The purpose of this section is to give an analytic definition of this concept. To see what is required from a definition, consider first some of the functions already discussed. The functions ln, exp, Sin, Cos, Tan, Sin^{-1}, Cos^{-1}, Tan^{-1}, sinh, cosh, Sinh^{-1}, and Cosh^{-1} (Figs 3.10 on p. 65) are evidently continuous. The function shown in Fig. 5.1

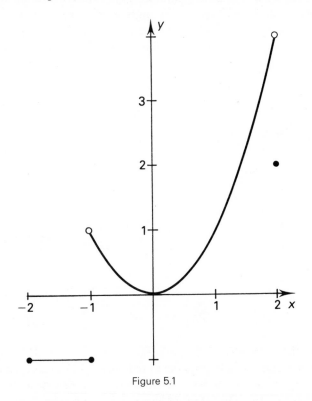

Figure 5.1

is not continuous, evidently being discontinuous at the points $x = -1$ and $x = 2$. Similarly in Fig. 5.2, f is discontinuous at $x = 2$. Since discontinuities occur at particular points, the required definition must fail only at particular points, and must therefore define continuity at a point.

Once this has been done, a function can be defined to be continuous on an interval if it is continuous at every point of the interval. It is sensible to say that the function in Fig. 5.1 is continuous on $[-2, -1)$ and in $(-1, 2)$.

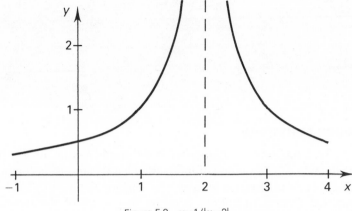

Figure 5.2 $y = 1/|x-2|$

One (trivial) way in which a discontinuity may arise is through the function being undefined at the point. Thus $(\exp x)/x$ is undefined at $x = 0$, and cannot therefore be continuous at $x = 0$ (Fig. 5.3). Similarly $(\sin x)/x$ is undefined at $x = 0$, and is therefore discontinuous at $x = 0$ (Fig. 5.4). So the definition of f continuous at $x = a$ must include the requirement that $f(a)$ is defined.

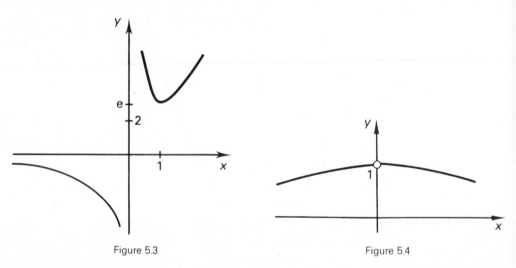

Figure 5.3   Figure 5.4

Consider again the examples of discontinuity. In Fig. 5.1, $f(-1) = -1$ is defined, but f is discontinuous at -1, and it is impossible to redefine $f(-1)$ to give continuity. The same holds at $x = 2$ for the function in Fig. 5.2. Similarly, one cannot assign a value at $x = 0$ in Fig. 5.3 to give continuity. On the other hand, in Fig. 5.4, a continuous function would be obtained if the value 1 were assigned at $x = 0$. Similarly the function in Fig. 5.1 would be continuous at $x = 2$ if the value $f(2)$ was changed to 4.

The distinction between the discontinuities at $x = a$ which could be removed by a suitable definition or redefinition of $f(a)$, and the discontinuities at $x = a$ which are unaffected by the value (if any) of $f(a)$, has already appeared in the discussion of limits. In the first case, $\text{Lim}_{x \to a} f(x)$ exists (see p. 74, Example 4.13 and p. 78, Example 4.111). In the second case, there is no limit (see Examples 4.12 and 4.15). Moreover, in the examples on limits as $x \to a$, if there is no limit, the function is discontinuous at a; while, if there is a limit, it is always possible to define or redefine $f(a)$ to get a function continuous at a.

Example 5.10 (refer to pp. 73–5)

(i) (Example 4.11): x^{-2} has no limit as $x \to 0$, and is discontinuous at $x = 0$.

(ii) (Example 4.13): $(\sin x)/x \to 1$ as $x \to 0$; the function f defined by $f(x) = (\sin x)/x$ $(x \neq 0)$, $f(0) = 1$, is continuous at $x = 0$ (fill in the empty circle in Fig. 5.4).

(iii) (Example 4.14): $(x^3 - 2x^2)/(x-2) \to 4$ as $x \to 2$: the function h defined by $h(x) = (x^3 - 2x^2)/(x-2)$ $(x \neq 2)$; $h(2) = 4$, is continuous at $x = 2$. Then $h(x) = x^2$ for all x. However the function g defined after Example 4.14, by adding $g(2) = 0$ to the rule, would not be continuous at $x = 2$.

(iv) (Example 4.16): $\cos(1/x^2)$ has no limit as $x \to 0$; because of the infinity of oscillations in any neighbourhood of 0, no value at 0 can be chosen so as to give a continuous function.

(v) (Example 4.19): the function $x^{-1} \ln(1+x)$ has a continuous extension f obtained by taking $f(0) = 1$. □

Thus if $f(x)$ is discontinuous at $x = a$, and $\text{Lim}_{x \to a} f(x) = L$, a **continuous extension** of f is obtained by taking $f(a) = L$. Taking any other value for $f(a)$ would give a discontinuous extension. Moreover, if f is continuous at $x = a$, $\text{Lim}_{x \to a} f(x) = f(a)$.

Example 5.11

(i) $x^2 \to 4 = 2^2$ as $x \to 2$.

(ii) $\text{Lim}_{x \to -1}(2x+1)/(x-1) = \frac{1}{2}$, the value of $(2x+1)/(x-1)$ at $x = -1$. □

The examples studied above showing the connection between continuity and the existence and value of a limit suggest the following definition:

> f is continuous at $x = a$ if it is defined throughout $[a - \delta, a]$ or $[a, a + \delta]$ for some positive δ, and $f(a) = \text{Lim}_{x \to a} f(x)$.

To prove that a function is continuous at a point therefore requires solving the inequality appearing in the definition of the relevant limit. Note that the definition covers end-points of the domain of f by requiring the domain to exist on only one side of a (cf. Appendix D).

Theorem 4.2(i)–(iii) implies that **the sum, difference, or product of two continuous functions is continuous**. This means that the continuity of any polynomial function (on any interval) may be deduced from the continuity of the identity function $y = x$ and of the constant functions. Also **the composite of two continuous functions is continuous**.

Example 5.12

The functions $|x^3 + x|$, $\ln(x^2 - 2x)$, $\cos(x^3 + 3x + 1)$, and $\exp(3x^4 + 2)$ are all continuous at any number in their domains. □

Theorem 4.2(iv) implies that **the quotient of two continuous functions is continuous, except at points where the denominator is zero**.

Example 5.13
(i) $(x+2)/(x^2-5x+6)$ is continuous except at $x=2$ and $x=3$;
(ii) $\sin\{(x^3+2x+1)/(x+1)\}$ is continuous except at $x=-1$. □

The fact that $\text{Lim}_{x\to a} f(x) = f(a)$ when f is continuous at a has already been tacitly assumed in most of the examples on evaluation of limits.
   (i) In each part of Example 4.31, the value $g(0)$ was given for $\text{Lim}_{x\to 0} g(x)$. This is correct because each function g is continuous at $x=0$ (see p. 83).
   (ii) In Example 4.41, the last statement $\text{Lim}_{x\to 2}(x+3)/(x-3) = -5$ assumes that $(x+3)/(x-3)$ is continuous at $x=2$ (see p. 86).
   (iii) The solution to Example 4.42(i) assumes that $(x^2+x-6)/(x-3)$ is continuous at $x=2$ (see p. 87).
   (iv) The function in the last line of Example 4.43(i) on p. 87 is assumed continuous at $x=1$.
The continuity of the rational functions in (ii) and (iii) follows from that of polynomials, by applying the quotient theorem. For other cases it will be sufficient to state that **if the derivative $f'(a)$ exists, then f is continuous at $x=a$**. This is further discussed in Section 6.1; it shows that the common transcendental functions ln, sin, etc. are continuous.

Exercise (answer on p. 101)
5.1.1 For each of the following functions give the points, if any, at which the function is not continuous:

(i) $f(x) = \dfrac{x^3-x^2-8x+12}{x^3-7x^2+16x-12}$ $(x\neq 2,3)$; $f(2)=-5,$ $f(3)=0.$

(ii) $f(x) = \dfrac{x^3-x^2-8x+12}{x^3-7x^2+16x-12}$ $(x\neq 2,3)$; $f(2)=f(3)=1.$

(iii) $f(x) = \ln|x|$ (iv) $f(x) = \begin{cases} \ln x & (x>1) \\ 1-x^2 & (-1\leqslant x\leqslant 1) \\ \sin \pi x & (x<-1) \end{cases}$

(v) $f(x) = \dfrac{\sin \pi x}{x^2-x}$ $(x\neq 0,1)$; $f(0) = -\pi = f(1).$

(vi) $f(x) = \begin{cases} (x^2-1)^{-1} & (|x|>1) \\ 1+x^2 & (0<x\leqslant 1) \\ x-1 & (-1\leqslant x\leqslant 0) \end{cases}$

5.2 Properties of Continuous Functions

The definition of continuity allows the following statement:

if $g(x) \to M$ as $x \to a$, and f is continuous at M then $f\{g(x)\} \to f(M)$ as $x \to a$.

This result has already been used in Example 4.48 on p. 88, with $g(x) = (x+3)/(x-3)$, and f the function 'log of modulus of'. It was also used in Example 4.411, with $g(x) = x \ln(1 + a/x)$, and f the exponential function.

The definition of limit implies that if a function is continuous at a point, its values in some neighbourhood of the point form a bounded set with an inf and a sup. It follows that if a function is continuous on an interval, its values in that interval are a bounded set with an inf and a sup. (Actually this step, from a neighbourhood of any point to the interval, is difficult to prove.) Moreover, provided the interval is closed, the inf and sup of the values are a min and max. In other words,

> if a function is continuous on a closed interval, it has both a minimum and a maximum value in that interval.

Example 5.20

(i) The function $(\sin x)/x$ is continuous on $(0, \pi]$. Its values on this interval are bounded with $\sup = 1$ (Fig. 5.5), and $\inf = \min = 0$ (since $\sin \pi = 0$, and $\sin x > 0$ if $0 < x < \pi$). However $(0, \pi]$ is not a closed interval, and the function has no maximum value.

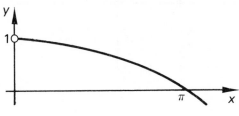

Figure 5.5

(ii) The function f defined by $f(x) = (\sin x)/x \ (x \neq 0); \ f(0) = 1$ is continuous on the closed interval $[0, \pi]$. Its values on this interval have $\inf = \min = 0$, $\sup = \max = 1$.   □

Example 5.21

The function $|x - 2|$ (Fig. 5.6) is continuous on the closed interval $[1, 3]$. Its values on $[1, 3]$ have $\min = 0$, $\max = 1$. Note that the existence of a minimum and maximum does not require the derivative of the function to be zero, or even to exist.   □

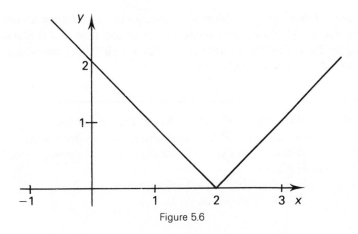

Figure 5.6

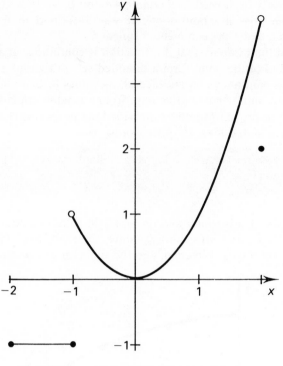

Figure 5.7

If f is continuous on $[a, b]$, its graph goes from $(a, f(a))$ to $(b, f(b))$ without any break, and

must therefore pass through all values between $f(a)$ and $f(b)$.

This can be proved from the definition of continuity, and is known as the **intermediate value theorem**. Figure 5.7 shows why continuity is essential to this theorem. On $[-2, 2]$, the function goes from $f(-2) = -1$ to $f(2) = 2$, but avoids taking any values between -1 and 0 by means of the discontinuity at $x = -1$.

Example 5.22
Show that the polynomial $P(x) = x^5 - 5x + 2$ has at least three roots.
   (i) $P(0) = 2$, $P(1) = -2$. Since P is continuous on $[0, 1]$, by the intermediate value theorem $P(x)$ takes all values between -2 and 2 on $[0, 1]$, including zero. Thus there is a root in $(0, 1)$. (See Fig. 5.8.)
   (ii) Similarly $P(-2) = -20 < 0$, $P(0) = 2 > 0 \Rightarrow$ a root in $(-2, 0)$.
   (iii) $P(1) = -2$, $P(2) = 24 \Rightarrow$ a root in $(1, 2)$. $\square$

A function f continuous on $[a, b]$ may pass through values between $f(a)$ and $f(b)$ more than once, so the argument in the above example does not show that there is only one root in each of the intervals $(0, 1)$, $(-2, 0)$ and $(1, 2)$. The intermediate value theorem could have been applied with the interval $[-2, 2]$:

$P(-2) < 0$, $P(2) > 0 \Rightarrow P(x) = 0$ somewhere in $(-2, 2)$, but this can (and does) happen at more than one point.

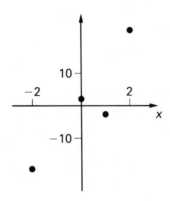

Figure 5.8 $x^2 - 5x + 2$ at $x = -2, 0, 1, 2$

Example 5.23
To discuss solutions of $\ln x = \sin x$, the intermediate value theorem may be applied to $f(x) = \ln x - \sin x$ on any closed subinterval of $(0, \infty)$. The actual end-points of the interval must be chosen so that the signs of $f(a)$ and $f(b)$ are obvious. For example, $f(1) < 0$ and $f(\pi) > 0$. From the intermediate value theorem on $[1, \pi]$, f has a root between 1 and π.   □

Exercise
5.2.1   For each of the following functions state whether the application of intermediate value theorem on $[-1, 1]$ shows that there is a point at which $f(x) = 0$ $(-1 < x < 1)$:
(i) $f(x) = 2x - 1$,
(ii) $f(x) = 2x^5 + 3x^4 + 3x^3 + 3x^2 + 7x + 3$,
(iii) $f(x) = \dfrac{2x - 1}{2x + 1}$,
(iv) $f(x) = \begin{cases} 2x + 1 & (-1 \leqslant x \leqslant 0) \\ 2x - 1 & (0 < x \leqslant 1), \end{cases}$
(v) $f(x) = \sin(\tfrac{1}{2}\pi x)$,
(vi) $f(x) = 4x^2 - x - 1$.

Answers to Exercises 5.1.1, 5.2.1

5.1.1   (i) 3 (cf. Example 4.41), (ii) 2, 3 (cf. Example 4.41), (iii) 0, (iv) continuous, (v) continuous, (vi) 0, ±1.
5.2.1   (i) Yes, (ii) Yes, (iii) No, (iv) No (not continuous), (v) Yes, (vi) No.

Further Exercises on Chapter 5

5.1   Show that the following equations have at least one root in the given intervals.
   (i) $x^3 - 3x + 1 = 0$, $[1, 2]$;
   (ii) $x = 1 + \frac{1}{2} \sin x$, $[0, 2]$;
   (iii) $x^{2n+1} + x = a$, $[a, 0]$ (where $a < 0$, and n is a positive integer).

5.2   In the solutions to Examples 4.46, 4.48 and 4.410, what functions are assumed to be continuous? (See pp. 88 and 89.)

5.3   For the function

$$f(x) = \begin{cases} 2x, & 0 \leqslant x \leqslant 1, \\ k - 2x, & 1 < x \leqslant 2, \end{cases}$$

find the constant k to make f continuous at 1.

   In Exercises 5.4–5.15 various conditions satisfied by a real valued function with domain a closed bounded interval $[a, b]$ with $a < b$ are listed. In each case find an example of a function satisfying all the given conditions or state a theorem showing that such a function cannot exist. (To give an example it is sufficient to give a sketch graph.)

5.4   (i) f is continuous on the open interval (a, b);
   (ii) $f(a) < 0$, $f(b) > 0$;
   (iii) $f(x) \neq 0$, for each x in (a, b).

5.5   (i) f is continuous on the closed interval $[a, b]$;
   (ii) $f(a) < 0$, $f(b) > 0$;
   (iii) $f(x) \neq 0$ for each x in (a, b).

5.6   (i) f is discontinuous at some x_0 in (a, b);
   (ii) f is continuous on $[a, b] \backslash \{x_0\}$ i.e. on $[a, x_0)$ and on $(x_0, b]$;
   (iii) $f(a) < 0$, $f(b) > 0$;
   (iv) $f(x) \neq 0$ for each x in (a, b).

5.7   (i) $f(a) < f(b)$;
   (ii) for any y in $(f(a), f(b))$ there exists an x in (a, b) such that $f(x) = y$;
   (iii) f is discontinuous at some point x_0 in (a, b).

5.8   (i) f is continuous on $[a, b]$;
   (ii) $f(a) < 0$, $f(b) > 0$;
   (iii) there exist infinitely many roots of f in the interval (a, b).

5.9   (i) f is continuous on (a, b);
   (ii) f is bounded on $[a, b]$;
   (iii) f has no maximum value on $[a, b]$.

5.10   (i) f is bounded on $[a, b]$;
   (ii) the set $\{y : y = f(x), x$ in $[a, b]\}$ has a sup.
   (iii) f is continuous on (a, b), but not on $[a, b]$.

5.11   (i) f is continuous on (a, b);
   (ii) f is unbounded on (a, b).

5.12   (i) f is continuous on $[a, b]$;·
   (ii) f is unbounded on $[a, b]$.

5.13   (i) f is continuous on $[a, b]$;
   (ii) f has no maximum value on $[a, b]$.

5.14   (i) f is discontinuous at some x_0 in $[a, b]$;
   (ii) there exists a number c such that cf is continuous on $[a, b]$.

5.15 (i) f is discontinuous at some x_0 in $[a, b]$;

(ii) $(c^2+1)f$ is continuous on $[a, b]$ for some constant real number c.

5.16 For each of the following functions, either find the value of the constant k which makes the function continuous, or give a reason why no such value exists:

(i) $f(x) = \begin{cases} \ln(2-x) & (x<-2) \\ k\ln(x+4) & (x\geqslant-2) \end{cases}$

(ii) $f(x) = \begin{cases} \ln(2-x) & (x<2) \\ k\ln x & (x\geqslant2) \end{cases}$

(iii) $f(x) = \begin{cases} kx & (x\leqslant0, x\geqslant\frac{1}{2}\pi) \\ \tan x & (0<x<\frac{1}{2}\pi) \end{cases}$

(iv) $f(x) = \begin{cases} e^{kx} & (x\geqslant0) \\ k\ln(e-x) & (x<0) \end{cases}$

6

Differentiation, Inequalities, and Curve Sketching

6.1 Definitions, Notation, and Rules

If $\mathrm{Lim}_{h\to 0}\{f(x+h)-f(x)\}/h$ exists, then the function f is said to be **differentiable** at x. If so, then f must also be continuous at x. A formal proof of this will not be given here, but it is evident that for the limit to exist, the expression $\{f(x+h)-f(x)\}/h$ must be an indeterminate form of type $0/0$, so that $f(x+h)\to f(x)$ as $h\to 0$. The value of the limit is called the **derivative** of f at x. The **derived function** f' is defined for all x at which f is differentiable, and its value is the derivative of f. Thus

$$f'(x) = \mathrm{Lim}_{h\to 0}\{f(x+h)-f(x)\}/h. \qquad \textbf{(6.1)}$$

The function f' is also called the **derivative** of f.

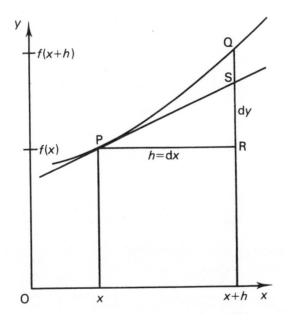

Figure 6.1   Geometrical interpretation of $f'(x)$

An alternative notation for the derivative is suggested by its geometrical interpretation, shown in Fig. 6.1. Since the quotient on the right side of equation (6.1) is QR/PR, which is the slope of the chord PQ, the limit $f'(x)$ is the slope of the tangent at P. If PS is this tangent, its slope is SR/PR. In Fig. 6.1, h can be regarded as a change or increment in the independent variable x. Call this the **differential** of x, and write it dx. Then d$x = $ PR.

If SR is called the differential of the dependent variable y, written dy, then $f'(x) = dy/dx$. In a first course on differential calculus, or in a completely rigorous approach, the derivative notation f' is usually preferred to the Leibniz notation dy/dx. Readers of this book are assumed to have met derivatives before, and to be more interested in the practical applications of the mathematics than in a step-by-step deduction of all results. Differentials will be emphasized here, as the notation has important practical advantages, and the concept is almost essential when considering functions of more than one variable. In this context it is useful to notice the following geometric definitions: f is differentiable at $x = a$ if the graph $y = f(x)$ has a tangent at $x = a$; and then

dx and dy are differentials at $x = a$ if $(a + dx, f(a) + dy)$ is a point on this tangent. However the analytic *definition* of dy is $dy = f'(x)\, dx$,

showing that dy depends both on x and on dx.

Example 6.10

If $y = f(x) = x^n$, then $f'(x) = nx^{n-1}$, and $dy = f'(x)\, dx = nx^{n-1}\, dx$. Substituting x^n for y, this can be written $d(x^n) = nx^{n-1}\, dx$. Similarly

$$d(\sin x) = \cos x\, dx, \qquad d(\ln x) = dx/x, \qquad d(\tan x) = \sec^2 x\, dx, \text{ etc.} \quad \square$$

The notation developed in this example is used in the table of derivatives on p. 154. To obtain the derivative of any other function, one uses the following **rules**, which may be proved by applying the theorems on limits in Chapter 4 to the definition (6.1).

(I)	**sum:**	$(u + v)' = u' + v'$ or $d(u + v) = du + dv$
(II)	**product:**	$(uv)' = uv' + u'v$ or $d(uv) = u\, dv + v\, du$
(III)	**quotient:**	$(u/v)' = (vu' - v'u)/v^2$ or $d(u/v) = (v\, du - u\, dv)/v^2$.

It is also worth noting the special cases which are obtained if $u(x) = c$, a constant:

$$(c + v)' = v'   \text{ or }   d(c + v) = dv$$

$$(cv)' = cv'   \text{ or }   d(cv) = c\, dv$$

$$(c/v)' = -cv'/v^2   \text{ or }   d(c/v) = -c\, dv/v^2.$$

(IV) **composite function:** $(f \circ g)' = (f' \circ g)g'$, or, if $y = f(w)$ and $w = g(x)$ then $dy/dx = f'(w)g'(x) = (dy/dw)(dw/dx)$.

(This last form illustrates the disadvantages of using differentials: the rule is apparently an obvious identity, not requiring proof.) In practice the most convenient formulation is:

if $y = f(w)$ where w is a function of x, then (assuming differentiability) $dy = f'(w)\, dw$.

(V) **inverse function:** $(f^{-1})' = 1/(f' \circ f^{-1})$, or, if $y = f^{-1}(x)$, then $dy/dx = 1/f'(y)$. The second form may be obtained by considering Fig. 6.1. The graph of the inverse function f^{-1} appears on interchanging x and y, or on reflecting in the line $y = x$. Its slope is therefore $PR/SR = 1/f'$, with f' evaluated at y, since x and y have been interchanged. In practice it is easiest to perform the steps

$$y = f^{-1}(x) \quad \Leftrightarrow \quad x = f(y) \quad \Rightarrow \quad dx = f'(y)\, dy, \quad \text{giving } dy/dx.$$

Example 6.11

$$y = e^x \quad \Leftrightarrow \quad x = \ln y \quad \Rightarrow \quad dx = \ln' y\, dy = dy/y.$$

So $dy/dx = y = e^x$. Thus $\exp' = \exp$. $\square$

Example 6.12

(i) $y = \text{Cosh}^{-1} x \Leftrightarrow x = \text{Cosh } y \Rightarrow dx = \sinh y\, dy$, using equation (3.14) on p. 51. Hence $dy/dx = 1/\sinh y$, and this can be written in terms of x using $\cosh^2 y - \sinh^2 y = 1$, $\sinh y = \pm\sqrt{(\cosh^2 y - 1)}$. The sign ambiguity appears because the inverse function Cosh^{-1} can only be defined after restricting the domain of $\cosh$ to $[0, \infty)$, and this condition has not yet been used. If $y > 0$, then $\sinh y > 0$, and the upper sign must be taken. Thus

$$\frac{dy}{dx} = \frac{1}{\sqrt{(\cosh^2 y - 1)}} = \frac{1}{\sqrt{(x^2 - 1)}}.$$

The sign ambiguity could also be resolved by observing that dy/dx must be positive, since the graph (Fig. 6.2) shows that Cosh^{-1} is increasing.

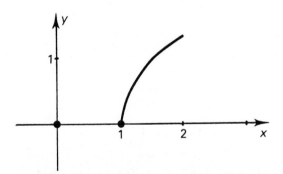

Figure 6.2 $y = \text{Cosh}^{-1} x$

(ii) Alternatively, write $y = \ln\{x + \sqrt{(x^2 - 1)}\}$, and differentiate as a composite function, putting $w = x + \sqrt{(x^2 - 1)} = x + (x^2 - 1)^{1/2}$. Then $y = \ln w$, $dy = dw/w$, and $dw = dx + du$ where $u = v^{1/2}$, $v = x^2 - 1$, giving $du = \frac{1}{2}v^{-1/2}\, dv = xv^{-1/2}$. Thus $dw = \{1 + x/\sqrt{(x^2 - 1)}\}\, dx = \{x + \sqrt{(x^2 - 1)}\}\, dx/\sqrt{(x^2 - 1)} = w\, dx/\sqrt{(x^2 - 1)}$. Finally, $dy = dx/\sqrt{(x^2 - 1)}$ as in (i). $\square$

The process of calculating f' from f is called **differentiation**, although linguistically the term should mean taking a differential, that is calculating dy from y. Checks for differentiation are not always possible. If, as in the previous example, the function can be written in a different form requiring another differentiation rule, the two methods check each other.

Example 6.13

The function $g(x) = \ln|x|$ is defined for all $x \neq 0$.

(i) Since $|x| = |-x|$, the function $\ln|x|$ is even. Its graph is the graph of $\ln x$, plus the reflection of this in the y-axis. Suppose $a > 0$. Then near $x = a$, $\ln|x| = \ln x$, so the slope at a is $1/a$. For an even differentiable function, slopes at $\pm a$ have the same magnitude but opposite sign: at $x = -a$ the slope is $-(1/a) = 1/(-a)$. Hence the slope is $1/x$ for any x in the domain: $g'(x) = 1/x$ $(x \neq 0)$.

(ii) Consider the function as composite: $y = \ln w$, $dy = dw/w$, $w = |x|$.

For $x > 0$, $w = x$, $dw = dx$; for $x < 0$, $w = -x$, $dw = -dx$. However in both cases, $dw/w = dx/x$, again giving $dy/dx = 1/x$.

(iii) A function of the form $y = \ln|f(x)|$ can be considered as a composite $g \circ f$. Then

$$\frac{dy}{dx} = \frac{dg}{df}\frac{df}{dx} = \frac{1}{f}\frac{df}{dx} = \frac{f'(x)}{f(x)}.$$

(iv) As a particular example of (iii), consider $y = \ln|(x-a)/(x+a)|$. Then $y = \ln|w|$ with $w = (x-a)/(x+a)$, which requires rule (III).

$$dy = dw/w, \qquad dw = \frac{(x+a)d(x-a) - (x-a)d(x+a)}{(x+a)^2} = \frac{2a\,dx}{(x+a)^2},$$

since $d(x \pm a) = dx$.

$$\frac{dy}{dx} = \frac{2a}{(x+a)^2 w} = \frac{2a}{x^2 - a^2}.$$

Check:

$$y = \ln\left|\frac{x-a}{x+a}\right| = \ln|x-a| - \ln|x+a|, \qquad \frac{dy}{dx} = \frac{1}{x-a} - \frac{1}{x+a} = \frac{2a}{x^2-a^2}. \quad \square$$

Example 6.14

Differentiate

$$F(x) = \mathrm{Tan}^{-1}\left(\frac{x}{a}\right) + \frac{ax}{x^2 + a^2}.$$

Put $F(x) = y = u + v$, where $u = \mathrm{Tan}^{-1}(x/a)$, $\mathrm{Tan}\,u = x/a$. Then $x = a\,\mathrm{Tan}\,u$, $dx = a\sec^2 u\,du = a(1 + \mathrm{Tan}^2 u)\,du = (a^2 + x^2)\,du/a$. For $v = ax/(x^2 + a^2)$, the quotient rule (III) gives

$$\frac{dv}{dx} = \frac{(a^2 + x^2)a - (ax)(2x)}{(a^2 + x^2)^2} = \frac{a(a^2 - x^2)}{(a^2 + x^2)^2}.$$

Using rule (I),

$$\frac{dy}{dx} = \frac{du}{dx} + \frac{dv}{dx} = \frac{a\{a^2 + x^2 + a^2 - x^2\}}{(a^2 + x^2)^2} = \frac{2a^3}{(a^2 + x^2)^2}.$$

Quick (partial) check: If x is a length, then a must also be a length, since the argument of Tan^{-1} must be dimensionless. Then $F(x)$ is dimensionless, and $dF(x)/dx$ should have dimension $(\text{length})^{-1}$, which it does. $\square$

Example 6.15

Differentiate (i) $\text{Sin}^{-1} x$ (ii) $-\text{Cos}^{-1} x$.

(i) If $y = \text{Sin}^{-1} x$, then $\text{Sin} \, y = x$, $\cos y \, dy = dx$,

$$\frac{dy}{dx} = \frac{1}{\cos y} = \frac{1}{\sqrt{(1 - \sin^2 y)}} = \frac{1}{\sqrt{(1 - x^2)}} = (1 - x^2)^{-1/2}.$$

The positive square root must be chosen, because Sin^{-1} is increasing, (Fig. 6.3) and so has a positive derivative. An alternative argument is that the range of Sin^{-1} is $[-\pi/2, \pi/2]$, and so $\cos y \geqslant 0$. This derivation is not valid for $x = \pm 1$; at these end-points $\text{Sin}^{-1} x$ is not differentiable (tangents exist but are parallel to the y-axis).

(ii) If $w = -\text{Cos}^{-1} x$, $x = \cos(-w) = \cos w$, $dx = -\sin w \, dw$,

$$\frac{dw}{dx} = \frac{-1}{\sin w} = \frac{-1}{-\sqrt{(1 - \cos^2 w)}} = \frac{1}{\sqrt{(1 - x^2)}} \qquad (x \neq \pm 1).$$

The negative square root must be chosen: Cos^{-1} is decreasing (Fig. 6.3) hence $-\text{Cos}^{-1}$ is increasing; alternatively the range of Cos^{-1} is $[0, \pi]$, so the range of $-\text{Cos}^{-1}$ is $[-\pi, 0]$, and $\sin w \leqslant 0$.

The fact that the continuous functions Sin^{-1} and $-\text{Cos}^{-1}$ have the same domain $[-1, 1]$, and the same derivative, means that they can only differ by a constant. In Fig. 6.3, the graph of $-\text{Cos}^{-1}$ would appear by reflecting that of Cos^{-1} in the x-axis. Evidently

$$-\text{Cos}^{-1} x = (\text{Sin}^{-1} x) - (\pi/2). \quad \square$$

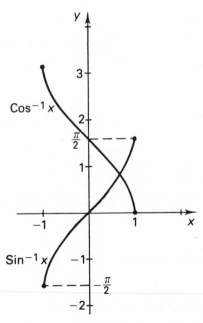

Figure 6.3

Example 6.16

Differentiate $y = \text{Tan}^{-1}(\sqrt{x}) + \sqrt{x}/(1 + x)$.

Put $y = (\mathrm{Tan}^{-1} u) + w$, where $u = \sqrt{x}$, and w is a quotient. Using rule (IV) $d(\mathrm{Tan}^{-1} u) = (1 + u^2)^{-1} du$ and $du = d(x^{1/2}) = \frac{1}{2} x^{-1/2} dx = dx/2u$. Using rule (III) on the quotient $w = u/(1 + x)$,

$$dw = \frac{(1+x)\,du - u\,d(1+x)}{(1+x)^2} = \frac{dx}{(1+x)2u} - \frac{u\,dx}{(1+x)^2}$$

$$\frac{dy}{dx} = \frac{1}{2u(1+u^2)} + \frac{1+x-2u^2}{2u(1+x)^2} = \frac{2}{2u(1+x)^2} \quad \text{since } u^2 = x$$

$$= (1+x)^{-2} x^{-1/2}.$$

This result can be extended as follows:

$$\text{if } y = \mathrm{Tan}^{-1}\!\left(\frac{\sqrt{x}}{a}\right) + \frac{a\sqrt{x}}{a^2 + x}, \quad \text{then } \frac{dy}{dx} = \frac{a^3}{(a^2+x)^2 \sqrt{x}}.$$

Check: if x is a length, a must have dimension $(\text{length})^{1/2}$. dy/dx should have dimension $(\text{length})^{-1}$, which it does. ☐

Example 6.17

Differentiate $y = \sqrt{(a + b/x)}$.

Use the composite function rule with $w = a + b/x$.

$$y = w^{1/2}, \quad dy = \tfrac{1}{2} w^{-1/2}\,dw, \quad dw = (-b/x^2)\,dx$$

$$\therefore \quad \frac{dy}{dx} = \frac{-b}{2x^2 \sqrt{(a+b/x)}} = \frac{-b}{2x\sqrt{(ax^2+bx)}}. \quad ☐$$

Example 6.18

Differentiate $y = \mathrm{Tan}^{-1}\{(4 + 5 \tan \tfrac{1}{2}x)/3\}$.

$$dy = dw/(1+w^2) \quad \text{where } w = (4 + 5 \tan \tfrac{1}{2}x)/3, \qquad dw = 5 \sec^2 \tfrac{1}{2}x\,dx/6.$$

$$\frac{dy}{dx} = \frac{5}{6 \cos^2 \tfrac{1}{2}x\{1 + (4 + 5\tan\tfrac{1}{2}x)^2/9\}}$$

$$= \frac{15/2}{25\cos^2\tfrac{1}{2}x + 40\sin\tfrac{1}{2}x\cos\tfrac{1}{2}x + 25\sin^2\tfrac{1}{2}x} = \frac{3/2}{5 + 4\sin x}. \quad ☐$$

Example 6.19

Differentiate $y = \sin^a x \cos^b x$.

Using rule (II),

$$dy = \sin^a x\,d(\cos^b x) + \cos^b x\,d(\sin^a x),$$

$$= \sin^a x \quad b\cos^{b-1} x\,(-\sin x)\,dx + \cos^b x \quad a\sin^{a-1} x \quad \cos x\,dx,$$

using the composite function rule (IV). Thus

$$dy/dx = -b\sin^{a+1} x \quad \cos^{b-1} x + a\cos^{b+1} x \quad \sin^{a-1} x. \qquad (*).$$

Alternatively, putting $\sin^2 x = 1 - \cos^2 x$ in the first term gives

$$dy/dx = \sin^{a-1} x(-b \cos^{b-1} x + \{a+b\} \cos^{b+1} x).$$

Similarly, using $\cos^2 x = 1 - \sin^2 x$ in the second term of $(*)$ gives

$$dy/dx = \cos^{b-1} x(a \sin^{a-1} x - \{a+b\} \sin^{a+1} x).$$

Check: put $a = 1$ and $b = -1$ so that $y = \tan x$, and dy/dx should be $\sec^2 x = \cos^{-2} x.$ □

Example 6.110
If $y = [x + A\sqrt{(1-x^2)}]/[-Ax + \sqrt{(1-x^2)}]$, show that $dy/dx = (1 + y^2)/\sqrt{(1-x^2)}$.

Since $(d/dx)\sqrt{(1-x^2)} = (-2x)/2\sqrt{(1-x^2)}$, using rule (III) gives

$$\frac{dy}{dx} = \frac{\{-Ax + \sqrt{(1-x^2)}\}\{\sqrt{(1-x^2)} - Ax\} - \{x + A\sqrt{(1-x^2)}\}\{-A\sqrt{(1-x^2)} - x\}}{\{-Ax + \sqrt{(1-x^2)}\}^2 \sqrt{(1-x^2)}}$$

$$= \frac{1 + y^2}{\sqrt{(1-x^2)}}.$$

In this result, A is an **arbitrary constant**. □

If the rule of a function changes to a different expression on different sides of a point a, the derivative at a may or may not exist. This question must usually be investigated by considering the definition (6.1). The derivative certainly does not exist if the function is discontinuous at a.

Example 6.111
(i) The signum function, defined in Exercise 3.1, has no derivative at $x = 0$, because it is discontinuous at the point. Its derivative at any other point is zero.
  (ii) The modulus function $m(x) = |x|$ is continuous at $x = 0$, but has no derivative at $x = 0$. These properties may be ascertained from the graph. Their proof requires the statements:

$$\text{for } x > 0, \quad m(x) = x, \quad \text{so } m(x) \to 0 \quad \text{as } x \to 0+;$$

$$\text{for } x < 0, \quad m(x) = -x, \quad \text{so } m(x) \to 0 \quad \text{as } x \to 0-;$$

these two statements can be combined into $m(x) \to 0$ as $x \to 0$, and $m(0) = 0$, so m is continuous at 0.
  For $h > 0$, $\{m(0+h) - m(0)\}/h = h/h = 1$;   for $h < 0, m(h)/h = -h/h = -1$;   so $\text{Lim}_{h \to 0}\{m(0+h) - m(0)\}/h$ does not exist.
  (iii) The function $f(x) = x|x|$ has derivative zero at $x = 0$. For $h > 0$, $f(h) = h^2$, hence $\{f(0+h) - f(0)\}/h = h \to 0$ as $h \to 0+$. For $h < 0$, $f(h) = -h^2$, hence $\{f(0+h) - f(0)\}/h = -h \to 0$ as $h \to 0-$. The existence of the derivative proves the continuity of f at 0. □

Exercises (answers on p. 152)
6.1.1   Obtain $f'(x)$ for:
  (a) $f(x) = 2 \operatorname{Tan}^{-1}(e^x) + 2$
  (b) $f(x) = -\frac{1}{6}\cos^6 x$
  (c) $f(x) = -1/(2\sin^2 x)$
  (d) $f(x) = \frac{1}{3}\sin^3 x - \frac{1}{5}\sin^5 x$
  (e) $f(x) = \cos x + (\cos x)^{-1}$
  (f) $f(x) = \frac{2}{9}(3x-2)^{3/2}$
  (g) $f(x) = \sqrt{(2x-1)}$
  (h) $f(x) = \frac{2}{27}(3x+2)^{1/2}(6x+19)$

6.1.2   Obtain $g'(t)$ for

(a) $g(t) = -\frac{1}{2}\exp(-t^2)$ (b) $g(t) = \frac{1}{2}\sin(t^2)$

(c) $g(t) = -\frac{1}{2}\cos(t^2+2)$ (d) $g(t) = \frac{1}{3}(t^2+2)^{3/2}$

(e) $g(t) = \sqrt{(t^2+a)}$ (f) $g(t) = \frac{1}{2}\ln(1+t^2)$

6.1.3   Differentiate the following, and express each result as a function of $\cos x$:

(a) $\tan\left(\dfrac{1}{2}x\right)$ (b) $-\cot\left(\dfrac{1}{2}x\right)$ (c) $\dfrac{1}{\sqrt5}\ln\left|\dfrac{\tan(\frac{1}{2}x)+\sqrt{\frac{1}{5}}}{\tan(\frac{1}{2}x)-\sqrt{\frac{1}{5}}}\right|$

(d) $\dfrac{2}{\sqrt5}\,\mathrm{Tan}^{-1}\left[\dfrac{1}{\sqrt5}\tan\left(\dfrac{1}{2}x\right)\right]$

6.1.4   Obtain the derivatives of

(a) $f(x) = \frac{1}{4}x^2(2\ln x - 1)$ (b) $g(x) = x\ln(x^2+1) - 2x + 2\,\mathrm{Tan}^{-1}x$

(c) $h(x) = \frac{1}{2}(x^2+1)\,\mathrm{Tan}^{-1}x - \frac{1}{2}x$ (d) $r(x) = (x^2-1)\sin x + 2x\cos x$

(e) $s(x) = (x^2-2x+2)e^x$ (f) $u(x) = (\cos 3x + 3x\sin 3x)/9$

(g) $v(x) = -[\sin mx + m(\pi - x)\cos mx]/m^2$

6.1.5   Differentiate the two expressions $\frac{1}{2}x\,[\sin(\ln x) \pm \cos(\ln x)]$

6.1.6   Differentiate

(a) $x - 3\ln|x+1|$ (b) $\frac{1}{8}\ln|2x-1| + \frac{1}{2}(2x-1)^{-1} + \frac{13}{16}(2x-1)^{-2}$

(c) $\frac{1}{5}\,\mathrm{Tan}^{-1}\left(\dfrac{x+3}{5}\right)$ (d) $\frac{1}{6}(\ln|x| - \ln|x+6|)$

(e) $2\ln(x^2+2x+3) - \dfrac{11}{\sqrt2}\,\mathrm{Tan}^{-1}\left(\dfrac{x+1}{\sqrt2}\right)$ (f) $\frac{5}{2}\ln|x-3| + \frac{3}{2}\ln|x-1|$

(g) $\frac{1}{2}x^2 - \frac{1}{2}\ln(1+x^2) + \mathrm{Tan}^{-1}x$

and express each result as a rational function.

6.1.7   Obtain $g'(x)$ for

(a) $g(x) = 4\ln|x| + \frac{1}{2}\ln(x^2-2x+2) - 2\,\mathrm{Tan}^{-1}(x-1)$

(b) $g(x) = 2x - \frac{1}{3}\ln|x+1| + 12\ln|x-4| - \frac{5}{3}\ln|x-2|$,

expressing g' as a rational function.

6.1.8   (a) Express the derivative of

$$\frac{3}{8}x + \frac{1}{8}\sin x\cos x(3 + 2\cos^2 x)$$

as a function of $\cos x$.

(b) Express the derivative of

$$\frac{1}{16}x - \frac{1}{48}\sin x\cos x(3 + 2\sin^2 x - 8\sin^4 x)$$

as a function of $\sin x$.

6.2   Logarithmic Differentiation

Suppose the expression giving $f(x)$ contains a product or quotient of functions of x, or an exponent which is a function of x. Then the expression for $\ln\{f(x)\}$ may be simplified using the logarithm properties, and to get $f'(x)$ it is often simpler to differentiate $\ln f(x)$ rather than $f(x)$.

Example 6.20

Differentiate $f(x) = ax/(x^2 + a^2)$.

$$\ln\{f(x)\} = \ln a + \ln x - \ln(x^2 + a^2)$$

$$f'(x)/f(x) = 1/x - 2x/(x^2 + a^2)$$

$$f'(x) = \frac{ax}{x^2 + a^2} \cdot \frac{x^2 + a^2 - 2x^2}{(x^2 + a^2)x} = \frac{a(a^2 - x^2)}{(a^2 + x^2)^2}.$$

This checks part of Example 6.14. The result is valid for negative values of a or x, although the derivation then needs slight modification.   □

Example 6.21

Differentiate $y = \sqrt{(a + b/x)}$.

Since $a + b/x = (ax + b)/x$, $\ln y = \frac{1}{2}\ln(ax + b) - \frac{1}{2}\ln x$, and

$$\frac{1}{y}\frac{dy}{dx} = \frac{a}{2(ax + b)} - \frac{1}{2x} = \frac{-b}{2x(ax + b)}.$$

Multiplying by y gives the result already found in Example 6.17.   □

Example 6.22

Let $f(x) = x^x (x > 0)$. Then $\ln f(x) = x \ln x$, $f'(x)/f(x) = 1 + \ln x$,

$$\boxed{f'(x) = x^x(1 + \ln x).}$$

Check: from equation (3.9), $x^x = \exp(x \ln x)$, so, using rule (IV),

$$d(x^x) = \exp(x \ln x)\, d(x \ln x)$$

$$= \exp(x \ln x)(\ln x + 1)\, dx = x^x(1 + \ln x)\, dx.   □$$

When applied to products and quotients, this 'logarithmic differentiation' is actually only valid when the factors considered are positive. Thus $\ln x$ is used in Examples 6.20 and 6.21, implying $x > 0$. However the same final expressions are always obtained by considering $\ln|f(x)|$ and using the modulus of each factor.

Exercises (answers on p. 153)

6.2.1   Find dy/dx if $y = -(2x + 1)/(2x + 3)^3$

6.2.2   (a) Use logarithmic differentiation to find the derivative of

$$\frac{x(3x^2 + 20)}{(x^2 + 4)^2}$$

(b) Use the result of (a) to differentiate

$$\frac{x(3x^2 + 20)}{128(x^2 + 4)^2} + \frac{3}{256}\mathrm{Tan}^{-1}\left(\frac{1}{2}x\right)$$

6.3 Higher Derivatives

Differentiating the derived function f' gives a function called the **second derivative** of f, denoted by f'' or $f^{(2)}$. Differentiating f'' gives $f^{(3)}$ (or f'''), the third derivative of f. Proceeding thus, the nth derivative of f, denoted by $f^{(n)}$, may be considered.

Again there is an alternative notation using differentials. Since $dy = f'(x)\,dx$ is a function of x, its differential can be taken:

$$d(dy) = d\{f'(x)\,dx\} = \{f'(x)\,dx\}'\,dx.$$

Since dx is independent of x, it is treated as a constant in subsequent differentiations. The derivative of $f'(x)\,dx$ is therefore $f''(x)\,dx$, and $d(dy) = f''(x)(dx)^2$. This is usually written $d^2y = f''(x)\,dx^2$, so that $f''(x) = d^2y/dx^2$.

Example 6.30
If $y = x^n$, $dy = nx^{n-1}\,dx$

$$d^2y = d(dy) = d(nx^{n-1}\,dx) = n\,d(x^{n-1})\,dx = n(n-1)x^{n-2}(dx)^2$$

or $d^2y/dx^2 = n(n-1)x^{n-2}$, or $d^2(x^n)/dx^2 = n(n-1)x^{n-2}$. $\square$

Considering higher derivatives in the same way gives

$d^n y/dx^n = f^{(n)}(x)$,   where $dx^n = (dx)^n$, and $d^n y = d(d \ldots (dy))$ is the nth differential of y.

When the composite function rule is stated in terms of differentials, it appears to be an identity. It was remarked previously that this might be disadvantageous in constructing *proofs*, but it is just this apparent identity which makes first differentials so useful in calculations. However for higher derivatives, a similar application of apparent identities is incorrect. The reason is that if $y = f(w)$ and $w = g(x)$, then dw is not independent of x, and therefore $dy = f'(w)\,dw$ must be differentiated as a product. This means that $f''(w) = d^2y/dw^2$ is incorrect if the right side is actually a quotient of differentials. In practice one can write $dw = g'(x)\,dx$ before the second differentiation.

Example 6.31
If $y = w^3$ where $w = x^2$, find d^2y/dx^2.

$$dy = d(w^3) = 3w^2\,dw \quad \text{and} \quad dw = 2x\,dx,$$

$d^2y = d(3w^2\,dw) = d(6w^2x\,dx) = 6d(w^2x)\,dx$ since x is the independent variable, and so dx is independent of x. Using the product rule II,

$$d(w^2x) = d(w^2)x + w^2\,dx = 2w\,dw\,x + w^2\,dx = 4wx^2\,dx + w^2\,dx = 5x^4\,dx$$

$$\therefore \quad d^2y = 30x^4\,dx^2.$$

(*Check*: $y = x^6$, $dy/dx = 6x^5$, $d^2y/dx^2 = 30x^4$). $\square$

Example 6.32
If $y = A\,e^{-x}\cos 3x + B\,e^{-x}\sin 3x + (\cos 3x + 6\sin 3x)/37$, verify that

$$\frac{d^2y}{dx^2} + 2\frac{dy}{dx} + 10y = \cos 3x.$$

The terms in y containing A and B are differentiated using the product rule II.

$$\frac{dy}{dx} = -A\,e^{-x}\cos 3x - 3A\,e^{-x}\sin 3x - B\,e^{-x}\sin 3x + 3B\,e^{-x}\cos 3x$$

$$+\,3(-\sin 3x + 6\cos 3x)/37$$

$$= (-A+3B)\,e^{-x}\cos 3x - (3A+B)\,e^{-x}\sin 3x + 3(-\sin 3x + 6\cos 3x)/37.$$

$$\frac{d^2y}{dx^2} = (A-3B)\,e^{-x}\cos 3x - 3(-A+3B)\,e^{-x}\sin 3x + (3A+B)\,e^{-x}\sin 3x$$

$$-\,3(3A+B)\,e^{-x}\cos 3x + 9(-\cos 3x - 6\sin 3x)/37.$$

$$\therefore\quad \frac{d^2y}{dx^2} + 2\frac{dy}{dx} + 10y = e^{-x}\cos 3x(A-3B-9A-3B-2A+6B+10A)$$

$$+\,e^{-x}\sin 3x(3A-9B+3A+B-6A-2B+10B)$$

$$+\,(\sin 3x)(-54-6+60)/37 + (\cos 3x)(-9+36+10)/37.$$

The result is true for *arbitrary* values of the constants A and B. $\square$

There are a few functions for which it is possible to obtain a formula for the nth derivative in terms of n. These results are suggested by differentiating the function a number of times, and observing a pattern in the successive derivatives. For example, if $y = x^m$, where m is an integer, then $dy = mx^{m-1}\,dx$, $d^2y = m(m-1)x^{m-2}\,dx^2$, etc., and for $n \leqslant m$ it is apparent that

$$d^n y = m(m-1)(m-2)\cdots(m-n+1)x^{m-n}\,dx^n, \qquad (\dagger)$$

$$\frac{d^n y}{dx^n} = \frac{m!}{(m-n)!}x^{m-n} = n!\binom{m}{n}x^{m-n},$$

where $\binom{m}{n}$ is a binomial coefficient. The form $(\dagger)$ of the result is actually valid for $n > m$, because $m(m-1)\cdots(m-n+1)$ contains a zero factor, and the derivative is zero. It is usual to define $\binom{m}{n} = 0$ if $n > m$, so that the last form of the result is also true for all n. This result and several more are recorded in the table of derivatives on p. 154. They may be proved by induction.

The interpretation of differentials as lengths shows that if x and $y = f(x)$ are lengths, then $f^{(n)}(x)$ has dimension $(length)^{1-n}$, which may allow a check.

Example 6.33

Since $d(\sin u) = \cos u\,du = \sin(u + \tfrac{1}{2}\pi)\,du$,

$$d(\sin x) = \sin(x + \tfrac{1}{2}\pi)\,dx, \qquad d^2(\sin x) = d\{\sin(x + \tfrac{1}{2}\pi)\}\,dx,$$

and

$$d\{\sin(x + \tfrac{1}{2}\pi)\} = d\{\sin u\} \quad \text{with } u = x + \tfrac{1}{2}\pi, \qquad du = dx,$$

so that

$$d^2(\sin x) = \{\sin(u + \tfrac{1}{2}\pi)\,du\}\,dx = \sin(x + \pi)\,dx^2.$$

Similarly

$$d\{\sin(x+\pi)\} = d\{\sin v\} \quad \text{with } v = x + \pi, \qquad dv = dx$$
$$= \sin(v + \tfrac{1}{2}\pi)dv = \sin(x + 3\pi/2)\,dx$$

so that $d^3(\sin x) = \sin(x + 3\pi/2)\,dx^3$.

Continuing demonstrates the result

$$\boxed{d^n(\sin x) = \sin(x + n\pi/2)dx^n. \quad \square}$$

To check a formula for an nth derivative, one obtains the $(n+1)$th derivative firstly by differentiating, and then by replacing n by $n+1$.

Example 6.34

Verify that

$$\boxed{\text{if } f(x) = x^\lambda, \qquad f^{(n)}(x) = \lambda(\lambda - 1) \cdots (\lambda - n + 1)x^{\lambda - n}.} \qquad (*)$$

(i) Differentiating $(*)$ gives $f^{(n+1)}(x) = \lambda(\lambda - 1) \cdots (\lambda - n + 1)(\lambda - n)x^{\lambda - n - 1}$. Here there are $(n+1)$ factors containing λ, one more than in $(*)$.

(ii) Replace n by $n+1$ in $(*)$. The n factors become $(n+1)$ factors, and the formula becomes $f^{(n+1)}(x) = \lambda(\lambda - 1) \cdots (\lambda - n - 1 + 1)x^{\lambda - n - 1}$, which agrees with (i).

This only shows that the formula obtained for $f^{(n)}$ is actually a formula for *some* nth derivative. To show it is the required result, one has also to verify that the formula is correct for $n = 0$ (or $n = 1$ if the formula only holds for $n > 0$).

By defining

$$\binom{\lambda}{n} = \frac{\lambda(\lambda - 1) \cdots (\lambda - n + 1)}{n!} \qquad (n \text{ factors})$$

the result can be written $f^{(n)}(x) = n! \binom{\lambda}{n}x^{\lambda - n}$, valid for any λ. $\square$

These results can be extended by the use of **Leibniz' formula** for the nth derivative of a product. If $f(x) = u(x)v(x)$, then the product rule II is $f'(x) = u(x)v'(x) + u'(x)v(x)$. Differentiating again, applying the product rule to uv' and to $u'v$, gives

$$f'' = uv'' + u'v' + u'v' + u''v = uv'' + 2u'v' + u''v.$$

Next, after three applications of the product rule, and collecting terms, one obtains

$$f''' = uv''' + 3u'v'' + 3u''v' + u'''v$$

or

$$f^{(3)} = uv^{(3)} + 3u^{(1)}v^{(2)} + 3u^{(2)}v^{(1)} + u^{(3)}v.$$

Similarly $f^{(4)} = uv^{(4)} + 4u^{(1)}v^{(3)} + 6u^{(2)}v^{(2)} + 4u^{(3)}v^{(1)} + u^{(4)}v$. The numerical coefficients that have appeared are just the binomial coefficients $\binom{n}{m} = n!/m!(n - m)!$, suggesting that

$$f^{(n)} = uv^{(n)} + nu^{(1)}v^{(n-1)} + \tfrac{1}{2}n(n - 1)u^{(2)}v^{(n-2)} + \cdots + u^{(n)}v.$$

Or, writing $u^{(0)} = u$ and $v^{(0)} = v$,

$$f^{(n)} = \sum_{r=0}^{n} \binom{n}{r} u^{(r)} v^{(n-r)}. \tag{6.2}$$

Leibniz' formula is useful provided the general form of the higher derivatives of the factors u and v are known. In the simplest applications, one factor has all except a few derivatives zero.

Example 6.35
Give an expression for the nth derivative of $x^2 e^{2x}$.

If $u(x) = x^2$, then $u'(x) = 2x$, $u''(x) = 2$, and all higher derivatives of u are zero. Hence the sum in equation (6.2) reduces to three terms:

$$(x^2 e^{2x})^{(n)} = x^2 v^{(n)} + 2nx v^{(n-1)} + n(n-1) v^{(n-2)}$$

with $v(x) = e^{2x}$.
But then $v'(x) = 2 e^{2x}$, $v''(x) = 4 e^{2x}$, $v'''(x) = 2^3 e^{2x}$, and evidently $v^{(r)}(x) = 2^r e^{2x}$ for any r. So the nth derivative of $x^2 e^{2x}$ is

$$\{x^2 2^n + nx2^n + n(n-1)2^{n-2}\} e^{2x}. \tag{*}$$

Check: Differentiating gives $\{x^2 2^{n+1} + 2^{n+1}x + 2^{n+1}nx + 2^n n + n(n-1)2^{n-1}\} e^{2x}$. Since $2^n n + n(n-1)2^{n-1} = (2n + n^2 - n)2^{n-1}$, this is (*) with n replaced by $n+1$. And (*) is correct for $n = 0$. □

Example 6.36
If $f(x) = x^{15} \sin 3x$, calculate $f^{(24)}(0)$.

Let $u(x) = x^{15}$ and $v(x) = \sin 3x$. Although u has 15 non-zero derivatives, only one is non-zero at $x = 0$:

$$u'(x) = 15x^{14}, \qquad u''(x) = 15.14x^{13}, \qquad u^{(3)}(x) = 15.14.13x^{12}, \ldots$$

$$u(0) = 0 = u'(0) = u''(0) = u^{(3)}(0) = \cdots.$$

At $x = 0$, all derivatives of u are zero until x has disappeared at $u^{(15)}(x) = 15!$. After that all higher derivatives of u are identically zero, so on putting $x = 0$ the sum in equation (6.2) reduces to the single term with $r = 15$:

$$f^{(n)}(0) = \binom{n}{15} u^{(15)}(0) v^{(n-15)}(0).$$

$$f^{(24)}(0) = \frac{24!}{15!9!} 15! v^{(9)}(0).$$

Now $v = \sin t$ with $t = 3x$, $dt = 3\,dx$.

$$d^9 v = d^9(\sin t) = \sin(t + 9\pi/2)\,dt^9, \quad \text{using Example 6.33,}$$

$$= \sin(3x + 9\pi/2)3^9\,dx^9 \quad \text{(since } dx/dt \text{ is constant).}$$

$$\therefore \quad v^{(9)}(0) = \frac{d^9 v}{dx^9}\bigg|_{x=0} = 3^9 \sin(9\pi/2) = 3^9 \sin(4\pi + \pi/2)$$

$$= 3^9.$$

$$f^{(24)}(0) = \frac{24!3^9}{9!} = 33653\ 786076\ 155621\ 376000. \quad \square$$

Exercises (answers on p. 153)

6.3.1 Find $d^2 y/dx^2$ when $y = 2x(1-x^2)^{1/2}$.

6.3.2 Evaluate $d^2 y/dx^2 + 2a\ dy/dx + a^2 y$ for
(i) $y = e^{-ax}$, (ii) $y = x\ e^{-ax}$, (iii) $y = bx^2\ e^{-ax}$.

6.3.3 If $y = e^x \sin(x\sqrt{5})$, show that

$$\frac{d^2 y}{dx^2} - 2\frac{dy}{dx} + 6y = 0.$$

6.3.4 If $f(x) = \frac{1}{2}x \sin 2x$, show that $f''(x) = -4f(x) + 2\cos 2x$.

6.3.5 Evaluate

$$(\cos x)\frac{d^2 y}{dx^2} + (\sin x)\frac{dy}{dx} + (4\cos^3 x)y$$

for
(i) $y = \sin(2 \sin x)$, (ii) $y = 3 - 2\sin^2 x$.

6.3.6 Evaluate $(1-x^2)f''(x) - 2xf'(x) + 2f(x)$ for

$$f(x) = 1 + \tfrac{1}{2}x\ \ln\left|\frac{x-1}{x+1}\right|.$$

6.3.7 Show that $\binom{-1}{n} = (-1)^n$. If m is a positive integer, express $\binom{-m}{n}$ in terms of factorials. Apply this result to the nth derivative of x^{-m}.

6.3.8 Write down the first five derivatives of $\cos x$ and of e^{-x}, and hence the 5th derivative of $e^{-x} \cos x$. What is the value of this 5th derivative at $x = 0$?

6.4 Vector Functions

For a vector function of type $R \to R^3$, say

$$r(t) = f(t)i + g(t)j + h(t)k \tag{2.12}$$

the definition (6.1) of derivative gives

$$r'(t) = \text{Lim}_{h\to 0}\{r(t+h) - r(t)\}/h \tag{6.3}$$

$$= \text{Lim}_{p\to 0}\{r(t+p) - r(t)\}/p \quad \text{(to avoid confusion with } h(t)\text{)}$$

$$= \text{Lim}_{p\to 0}\frac{f(t+p)i + g(t+p)j + h(t+p)k - f(t)i - g(t)j - h(t)k}{p}$$

$$= i\ \text{Lim}_{p\to 0}\frac{f(t+p) - f(t)}{p} + j\ \text{Lim}_{p\to 0}\frac{g(t+p) - g(t)}{p} + k\ \text{Lim}_{p\to 0}\frac{h(t+p) - h(t)}{p}$$

$$= if'(t) + jg'(t) + kh'(t). \tag{6.4}$$

This shows that to evaluate the derivative of a vector function, it is only necessary to differentiate the three component functions.

Example 6.40
If $r(t) = (\cos t)i + (\cos t)j + (\sin t)k$, then

$$r'(t) = (-\sin t)i - (\sin t)j + (\cos t)k. \quad \square$$

In general, geometrically $r(t)$ represents a space curve, as discussed in Section 2.6. In equation (6.3), $r(t+p)$ is then the vector from the origin to the point Q with parameter $t+p$, $r(t)$ is the vector $\overrightarrow{OP}$ to the point with parameter t, and their difference is $\overrightarrow{PQ}$ (Fig. 6.4). The geometrical interpretation of the limiting process is only slightly different from

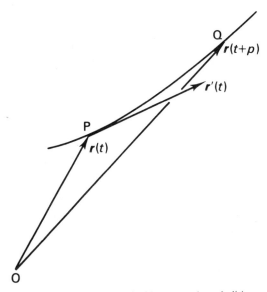

Figure 6.4   Geometrical interpretation of $r'(t)$

that considered in Fig. 6.1 on p. 105. In both diagrams, as h or $p \to 0$, $Q \to P$: in Fig. 6.1 the chord $\overrightarrow{PQ}$ tends to a tangent in the limit;

in Fig. 6.4 the vector $\vec{PQ}$ tends to a tangent vector at P.

This is true both for a plane curve and a space curve in three dimensions.

Example 6.41
The vector $r'(t)$ found in the previous example is the tangent vector (at the point with parameter t) to the ellipse described in Example 2.62 on p. 36 and illustrated in Fig. 2.11. Figure 6.5 shows the ellipse in the plane $x = y$. The point A(1, 1, 0) has parameter $t = 0$, and $r'(0) = k$ is a tangent vector at A; similarly $r'(\pi/2) = -i - j$ is a tangent vector at B(0, 0, 1). $\square$

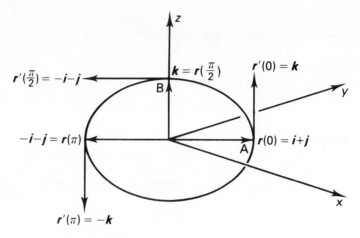

Figure 6.5   Tangent vectors to ellipse in the plane $x=y$

It is often necessary to normalize such tangent vectors.

Example 6.42
Find a unit tangent vector to the parabola

$$r(t) = t^2(i+j) + 2tk$$

at the point P(4, 4, −4).

The derivative $r'(t) = 2t(i+j) + 2k$ gives a tangent vector at any point with parameter t. The parameter of P satisfies $t^2 = 4$, $2t = -4$, and so is −2. Thus $-4i - 4j + 2k$ is a tangent vector at P. This has length $\sqrt{[(-4)^2 + (-4)^2 + 2^2]} = \sqrt{36} = 6$, so

$$(-4i - 4j + 2k)/6 = (-2i - 2j + k)/3$$

is a unit tangent vector at P.

Check: Is it a unit vector? Are the signs of the components consistent with the geometry? (Fig. 2.12). (Unless the curve is already known, or very simple, this geometrical check will involve too much work to be worthwhile.)

   Note that $(2i + 2j - k)/3$, which has the opposite sense, is also a solution to the example. □

Exercises (answers on p. 153)
6.4.1   If $r(t) = 3ti - (\cos t)j + (t + \sin t)k$, calculate

(a) dr/dt,   (b) d^2r/dt^2,   (c) $|dr/dt|$,   (d) $d|r|/dt$.

6.4.2   Find the unit tangent vector at the general point of the space curve

$$r(t) = (bt \cos at)i + (bt \sin at)j + ctk.$$

6.5   Functions Defined Parametrically

Substituting a value of t into the equations

$$x = f(t), \qquad y = g(t) \tag{6.5}$$

will give a pair (x, y), and so equations (6.5) define a relation between x and y. This relation is a function if f is one-to-one, so that no two pairs (x, y) can have the same x. The relation or function is said to be **defined parametrically** by equations (6.5), t being the parameter.

Example 6.50

$$x = \sin t, \qquad y = \sin 2t \qquad (-\pi/2 < t < \pi/2).$$

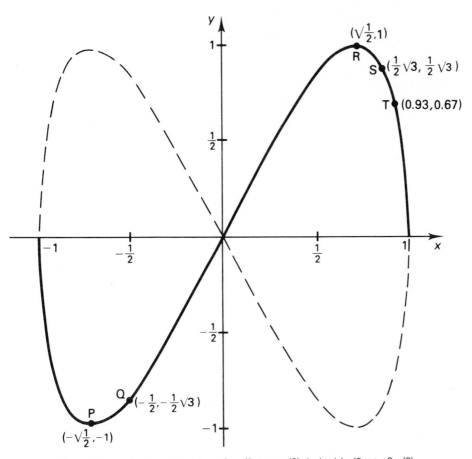

Figure 6.6 $x = \sin t$, $y = \sin 2t$. Solid $(-\pi/2 < t < \pi/2)$ dashed $(\pi/2 < t < 3\pi/2)$
Parameter t has values $-\pi/4$, $-\pi/6$, $\pi/4$, $\pi/3$, 1.2 at P, Q, R, S, T.

The resulting graph, shown as the solid curve in Fig. 6.6, is evidently the graph of a function. (In practice, the graph is more easily drawn after the derivative has been calculated.) Its slope dy/dx at any point may be obtained by taking the differentials of the parametric equations:

$$dx = \cos t \, dt, \qquad dy = 2 \cos 2t \, dt$$

$$dy/dx = 2 \cos 2t / \cos t, \quad \text{since } \cos t > 0.$$

When parametric equations are being used, it is usually convenient to have the slope (or any higher derivatives) in terms of the parameter t rather than in terms of x.

To obtain the graph the sign of the slope should be considered. The function $\cos t$ changes sign at $\pm\pi/2$, so $\cos 2t$ (and hence dy/dx) is positive for $-\pi/4 < t < \pi/4$.   □

This method for calculating the derivative of a function defined parametrically may be justified by rewriting equations (6.5) as $y = g(t)$ where $t = f^{-1}(x)$. Thus the function is the composite $g \circ f^{-1}$ and its derivative can be calculated using rule IV: $dy = g'(t)\,dt$ where dt must be expressed in terms of dx by differentiating the inverse function f^{-1}. By rule V, $dx = f'(t)\,dt$ gives the appropriate differentials.

This argument also shows how to obtain the higher derivatives. $dy/dx = g'(t)/f'(t)$ is a function of t, where $t = f^{-1}(x)$, and so to differentiate again requires the composite function rule.

Example 6.51

If y is defined as a function of x by the parametric equations

$$x = \sin t, \quad y = \sin 2t \,(-\pi/2 < t < \pi/2), \text{ find } d^2y/dx^2.$$

Put $y' = dy/dx$, so that dy'/dx is required. The previous example obtained

$$y' = 2\cos 2t/\cos t. \text{ Using the quotient rule III,}$$

$$dy' = \frac{\cos t \, d(2\cos 2t) - 2\cos 2t \, d(\cos t)}{\cos^2 t}$$

$$= \frac{\cos t(-4\sin 2t \, dt) - 2\cos 2t \,(-\sin t \, dt)}{\cos^2 t}.$$

As in the previous example, $dx = \cos t \, dt$. Hence the composite function rule IV gives

$$\frac{dy'}{dx} = \frac{-4\cos t \sin 2t + 2\cos 2t \sin t}{\cos^3 t}$$

$$= \frac{-6\sin t \cos^2 t - 2\sin^3 t}{\cos^3 t}.$$

Check: the graph (Fig. 6.6) has a maximum at $t = \pi/4$ and a minimum at $t = -\pi/4$. Hence the second derivative should be negative or positive at $t = \pm\pi/4$. However, at $t = \pm\pi/4$, $\cos 2t = 0$, and $\cos t > 0$, so this only checks the sign of the first term in the numerator.   □

An alternative method (Exercise 6.3.1) is to differentiate after expressing y in terms of x by eliminating the parameter. In general this is either impossible, or too complicated to be of use as a check.

In the example, the values of the parameter were restricted by $-\pi/2 < t < \pi/2$ so that $x = \sin t$ was one-to-one, and the pairs (x, y) form a function. If the pairs (x, y) form a relation, then dy/dx (and higher derivatives) at any point of the graph may be obtained by the same method. The values of t can be divided into subsets in each of which $x = f(t)$ is one-to-one, giving several functions of x.

Example 6.52

$$x = \sin t, \quad y = \sin 2t \quad (-\pi/2 < t \leq 3\pi/2).$$

The values of t can be divided into the sets $(-\pi/2, \pi/2)$ and $[\pi/2, 3\pi/2]$, in each of which $x = \sin t$ is one-to-one. For the first set, $t = \mathrm{Sin}^{-1} x$, and the pairs (x, y) form the function considered in the previous two examples. For the second set, an inverse function may also be defined, and the pairs (x, y) form another function. Its graph is indicated by the dashed curve in Fig. 6.6. Its first two derivatives are given by the formulas derived in Example 6.51, except when $t = \pi/2$ and $t = 3\pi/2$ for which $\cos t = 0$ and the derivatives do not exist. In this example, these points have been included so that the graph of the relation is a closed curve. □

The graph of the relation defined parametrically by $x = f(t)$, $y = g(t)$ is also the curve represented by the vector function $r(t) = f(t)i + g(t)j$.

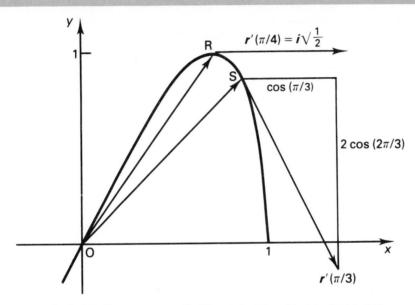

Figure 6.7   Tangent vectors $r'(\pi/4)$ and $r'(\pi/3)$ to $r(t) = (\sin t)i + (\sin 2t)j$
$\overrightarrow{OR} = r(\pi/4)$, $\overrightarrow{OS} = r(\pi/3) = \frac{1}{2}\sqrt{3}(i + j)$

This is illustrated in Fig. 6.7, which should be compared with Fig. 6.6, for the function $r(t) = (\sin t)i + (\sin 2t)j$ $(-\pi/2 < t < \pi/2)$. One advantage of using the vector function is that it remains a function if the domain (the values of t) is extended, for example to $(-\pi/2, 3\pi/2]$ so that the dashed curve is also included. Although the vector function, and the function consisting of the pairs (x, y) defined parametrically, represent the same curve, they are not equivalent. The independent variable of the vector function is t, and its range is a set of vectors (or points); the function defined parametrically has independent variable x, and its range is the set of values of y.

Example 6.53
The solid curve in Fig. 6.6 is represented by the vector function $r(t) = (\sin t)i + (\sin 2t)j$ with domain $(-\pi/2, \pi/2)$ and range the set of points of the curve, or the set of vectors from the origin to these points. The curve is also represented by the function $y = 2x\sqrt{(1 - x^2)}$, with domain $(-1, 1)$ and range $[-1, 1]$. This function may be defined parametrically by $x = \sin t$, $y = \sin 2t$. □

When using differentials for second derivatives it was necessary to specify which variable was independent, whereas for first differentials and derivatives this did not matter. Because of this, there is a relationship between the first derivatives of $r(t)$ and of the function defined parametrically, but not between their corresponding higher derivatives. In the previous section the vector $r'(t)$ was shown to be a tangent vector at the point with parameter t. From Fig. 6.1, the components of a tangent vector to a plane curve are differentials, e.g. $\overrightarrow{PS} = PR\mathbf{i} + RS\mathbf{j}$. Their ratio is the slope. Since $r'(t) = f'(t)\mathbf{i} + g'(t)\mathbf{j}$, this geometric argument shows that the slope is $g'(t)/f'(t)$, and confirms the validity of the procedure used in Example 6.50. Figure 6.7 illustrates $r'(\pi/3)$ and $r'(\pi/4)$ for that example.

In that example, the slope was actually obtained as the quotient of the differentials $2\cos 2t\, \mathrm{d}t = g'(t)\, \mathrm{d}t$ and $\cos t\, \mathrm{d}t = f'(t)\, \mathrm{d}t$. The $\mathrm{d}t$, however, does not alter the fact that the differentials are components of a tangent vector, because $r'(t)$ and $f'(t)\, \mathrm{d}t\,\mathbf{i} + g'(t)\, \mathrm{d}t\,\mathbf{j} = r'(t)\, \mathrm{d}t$ have the same (or opposite) direction.

Now for $y = f(x)$, the differential $\mathrm{d}y$ is defined as $f'(x)\, \mathrm{d}x$. The natural extension of this to a vector function $r(t)$ is to define $\mathrm{d}r = r'(t)\, \mathrm{d}t$. Then the above argument shows that $\mathrm{d}r$ is a vector along the tangent at t to the curve represented by the function. Moreover this is true for a space curve, i.e. for $r(t) = f(t)\mathbf{i} + g(t)\mathbf{j} + h(t)\mathbf{k}$. Also $r'(t) = \mathrm{d}r/\mathrm{d}t$.

In discussing functions of several variables in Chapter 3, it was observed that the function is often denoted by the same symbol as the independent variable. Denoting f, g, and h by x, y, and z gives

$$r(t) = x(t)\mathbf{i} + y(t)\mathbf{j} + z(t)\mathbf{k}, \ r'(t) = x'(t)\mathbf{i} + y'(t)\mathbf{j} + z'(t)\mathbf{k}$$
$$\mathrm{d}r = \mathrm{d}x\,\mathbf{i} + \mathrm{d}y\,\mathbf{j} + \mathrm{d}z\,\mathbf{k} = r'(t)\, \mathrm{d}t.$$

Exercise (answer on p. 153)

6.5.1   Suppose x and y are related by the parametric equations

$$x = t^3 + 3t + 1, \qquad y = t^4 - t^2 + 3.$$

Express $\mathrm{d}y/\mathrm{d}x$ and $\mathrm{d}^2y/\mathrm{d}x^2$ in terms of the parameter and calculate their values at the point $(-3, 3)$.

6.6   Functions Defined Implicitly

Given an equation connecting two variables x and y, it may be solved for y after inserting some particular value of x, say $x = a$. The solutions $y = y_1, y_2, \ldots$ may be used to construct pairs (a, y_1), $(a, y_2), \ldots$, which define a relation. A function is defined if a domain is stated (or implied) and only one solution y is obtained from each value x in this domain.

Example 6.60

If $x = \sin t$ and $y = \sin 2t = 2x\cos t$, then $y/2x = \cos t$, and so $x^2 + y^2/4x^2 = 1$ and $4x^4 + y^2 = 4x^2$.

Conversely, given the equation $4x^4 + y^2 = 4x^2$ (*), any particular value $x = a$ gives the equation $y^2 = 4a^2(1 - a^2)$ for y. Provided $-1 \leqslant a \leqslant 1$, there are two solutions $\pm 2a\sqrt{(1 - a^2)}$, giving two points on the curve in Fig. 6.6 on p. 121, one on the solid part and one on the dashed part. The relation representing the whole curve is **implicitly defined** by the equation (*).   □

Example 6.61

If $a^3y^5 - 5ay + 2 = 0$, there is no explicit formula giving y in terms of a, but for each given a the values of y could be obtained numerically. Thus the equation $x^3y^5 - 5xy + 2 = 0$ implicitly defines a relation. The relation is certainly not a function if the domain includes $x = 1$, because Example 5.22 showed that the equation $y^5 - 5y + 2 = 0$ is satisfied by at least three values of y (see p. 100). □

Example 6.62

Consider $xy = e^y$.

The equation can be solved to give x explicitly in terms of y, so x can be plotted against y (see also Example 6.81). On interchanging the axes (Fig. 6.8) there is evidently one value of y for each value of x in $(-\infty, 0) \cup \{e\}$. This is the largest domain possible if $xy = e^y$ is to define an implicit **function**.

A function is also defined if the domain is any subset of $(-\infty, 0) \cup \{e\}$, but if $x > e$ is allowed, then $xy = e^y$ defines an implicit **relation**.

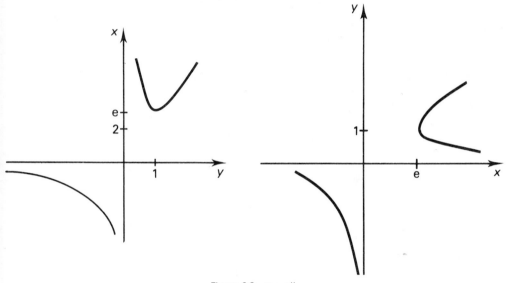

Figure 6.8 $xy = e^y$

□

As with functions defined parametrically, the slope of the curve represented by the function or relation is usually required before sketching the graph, and the problem of finding the derivatives has to be considered. Again, the rule is just to differentiate the given equation, but in this case the justification cannot be given yet, but must be deferred to Chapter 18.

Example 6.63

Find the first and second derivatives of functions defined implicitly by the equation $4x^4 + y^2 = 4x^2$.

Differentiate:

$$d(4x^4) + d(y^2) = d(4x^2).$$

$$16x^3 \, dx + 2y \, dy = 8x \, dx$$

so

$$2y\,dy = (8x - 16x^3)\,dx, \qquad dy/dx = 4x(1 - 2x^2)/y.$$

This procedure is certainly justifiable in this example, because on substituting $y = \sin 2t = 2\sin t\cos t$, $x = \sin t$, $1 - 2x^2 = \cos 2t$, the previous result of Example 6.26 is obtained. Note that the present method fails to determine the slope at $x = y = 0$; this is consistent with there being no unique slope at $(0, 0)$ for the relation. In general the appearance of y in the formula for dy/dx distinguishes between points having the same x.

Next differentiate $y' = (4x - 8x^3)/y$ using the quotient rule III:

$$dy' = \frac{y\,d(4x - 8x^3) - (4x - 8x^3)\,dy}{y^2} = \frac{y(4 - 24x^2)\,dx - \{(4x - 8x^3)^2/y\}\,dx}{y^2},$$

using the first derivative to substitute for dy in terms of dx. So

$$\frac{d^2y}{dx^2} = \frac{dy'}{dx} = \frac{4y^2(1 - 6x^2) - 16x^2(1 - 2x^2)^2}{y^3},$$

which agrees with Exercise 6.3.1 on putting $y = 2x(1 - x^2)^{1/2}$.   □

Example 6.64

Find the second derivative of a function defined by $xy = e^y$.

$$\ln x + \ln y = y$$

$$\frac{dx}{x} + \frac{dy}{y} = dy,$$

$$\frac{dx}{x} = dy\frac{(y-1)}{y}, \qquad y' = \frac{dy}{dx} = y/x(y-1)$$

$$\ln y' = \ln y - \ln x - \ln(y-1)$$

$$\frac{dy'}{y'} = \frac{dy}{y} - \frac{dx}{x} - \frac{dy}{y-1} = \frac{-dx}{x} - \frac{dy}{y(y-1)} = -\frac{dx}{x} - \frac{dx}{x(y-1)^2}$$

$$\frac{d^2y}{dx^2} = \frac{dy'}{dx} = -\frac{y\{(y-1)^2 + 1\}}{x^2(y-1)^3}.$$

Check: From Fig. 6.8, d^2y/dx^2 is negative when $y < 0$, or when $y > 1$, and d^2y/dx^2 is positive if $0 < y < 1$. The formula obtained agrees with these signs.   □

Example 6.65

Find the derivative of the function defined implicitly by

$$(2x - 3y + 1)^2(x + 2y - 2) = C \quad \text{(a constant)}.$$

Since $dC = 0$, differentiating gives

$$0 = d\{(2x - 3y + 1)^2(x + 2y - 2)\}$$
$$= d\{(2x - 3y + 1)^2\}(x + 2y - 2) + (2x - 3y + 1)^2 d(x + 2y - 2),$$

using the product rule II. From the composite function rule IV,

$$d\{(2x - 3y + 1)^2\} = 2(2x - 3y + 1)d(2x - 3y + 1),$$

giving

$$2(2\,dx - 3\,dy)(x + 2y - 2) + (2x - 3y + 1)(dx + 2dy) = 0$$

$$(6x + 5y - 7)\,dx = 2\,dy(x + 9y - 7), \qquad dy/dx = (6x + 5y - 7)/2(x + 9y - 7).$$

In this work there was a division by $(2x - 3y + 1)$, so the result is not valid if $2x - 3y + 1 = 0$. However, from the given equation, this is only possible if $C = 0$, and in this special case the graph consists of the two straight lines $2x - 3y + 1 = 0$ and $x + 2y - 2 = 0$, with slopes $\frac{2}{3}$ and $-\frac{1}{2}$ respectively.

Check: the general result is valid for $C = 0$ and $2x - 3y + 1 \neq 0$ and so should give $-\frac{1}{2}$ when $x + 2y - 2 = 0$. Substituting $x = 2 - 2y$ gives $dy/dx = (5 - 7y)/2(7y - 5) = -\frac{1}{2}$ unless $y = 5/7$. The point $(4/7, 5/7)$ is the intersection of the two lines, and so is not expected to yield a value for the slope. □

Exercise (answer on p. 153)
6.6.1 Find dy/dx and d^2y/dx^2 if $xy^2 = ax + b$.

6.7 The Mean Value Theorem

In Fig. 6.9 it is evident that at some point between P and Q there is a tangent that has

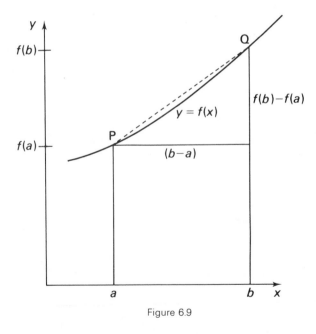

Figure 6.9

the same slope as the chord PQ. Similarly, in Fig. 6.10, consider the chord OP joining the origin with parameter $t = 0$ to P with parameter $t = 1.2$. Somewhere near the maximum at $t = \pi/4$ there is a tangent parallel to OP. The reader should consider other examples. In general it appears that given any chord PQ, between P and Q there is a point on the curve where the tangent is parallel to the chord PQ. However the following example

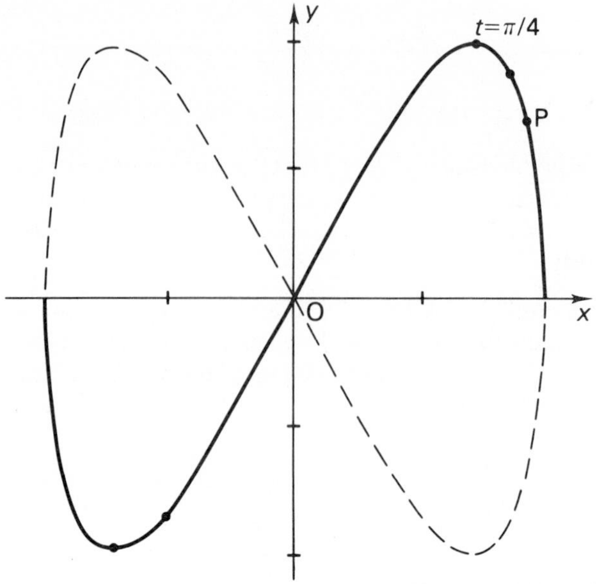

Figure 6.10

shows it is necessary to impose some conditions on the function $y = f(x)$ representing the curve.

Example 6.70
(i) Consider $|x|$ on any interval $[a, b]$ with $a < 0$ and $b > 0$ (Fig. 6.11(a)). There is no point in (a, b) where the derivative (i.e. the slope of the tangent) is equal to the slope of the chord joining $P(a, -a)$ and $Q(b, b)$. This is evidently because the graph has a kink at $x = 0$, enabling the curve to pass from P to Q without its slope taking that of the chord PQ. Thus $f'(x)$ must exist at all interior points of the interval, giving a smooth curve, to ensure a tangent parallel to the chord.

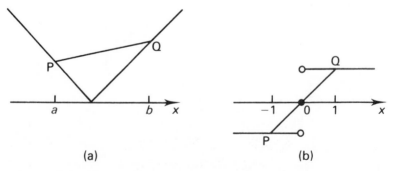

(a)   (b)

Figure 6.11   Mean value theorem inapplicable (a) $|x|$ (b) sgn x

(ii) Consider sgn x on the interval $[0, 1]$ (Fig. 6.11(b)). Although the chord OQ has slope 1, the slope is zero in the interval. The result evidently fails because of the discontinuity at $x = 0$. Thus $f(x)$ must be **continuous** throughout the interval.   □

For $y = f(x)$, the slope of the chord in the interval $[a, b]$ is $\{f(b) - f(a)\}/(b - a)$.

> The **mean value theorem** (of the differential calculus) states that if f **is continuous on the closed interval** $[a, b]$, and f **is differentiable on the open interval** (a, b), then there is a point c in (a, b) where $f'(c) = \{f(b) - f(a)\}/(b - a)$.

The proof, which will not be given here, usually starts by taking the special case in which $f(a) = f(b)$; this case is called **Rolle's theorem** (Fig. 6.12(i)). The mean value theorem

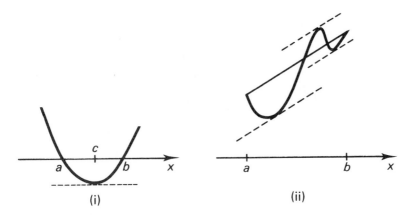

Figure 6.12 (i) Rolle's theorem (ii) Mean value theorem

does not provide an algorithm for calculating c; this could be done when the formula for $f'(x)$ is known, but applications of the theorem do not require c to be found. In fact there may be more than one point in (a, b) at which the derivative is the slope of the chord (Fig. 6.12(ii)). The mean value theorem ensures that there is at least one. It is most useful in theoretical work applying to a general function f. Its application to some particular examples allows inequalities to be derived. Rolle's theorem is important when considering the number of roots of the function f.

Example 6.71
Show that the polynomial $P(x) = x^5 - 5x + 2$ has exactly three roots.

In Example 5.22, the application of the intermediate value theorem (see p. 100) showed that there is at least one root in each of the intervals $(0, 1)$, $(-2, 0)$ and $(1, 2)$. Since $P'(x) = 5x^4 - 5$ exists at all points, the mean value theorem can be applied to P on any closed interval.

Suppose there are two roots r and s in $(0, 1)$, with $r < s$. Then $P(r) = P(s) = 0$, so Rolle's theorem on $[r, s]$ implies there is a point c in (r, s) where $P'(c) = 0$. Since $r < c < s$, $0 < c < 1$. However $P'(x) < 0$ for $0 < x < 1$, so there is no such point c. The contradiction shows that there cannot be two roots in $(0, 1)$.

As $P'(x)$ is zero only at $x = \pm 1$, the same argument shows that there cannot be more than one root in $(-\infty, -1]$, or in $[-1, 1]$, or in $[1, \infty)$. Thus there are just three roots; and since there is a root in $(0, 1)$, the root in $(-2, 0)$ must be in $(-2, -1)$.

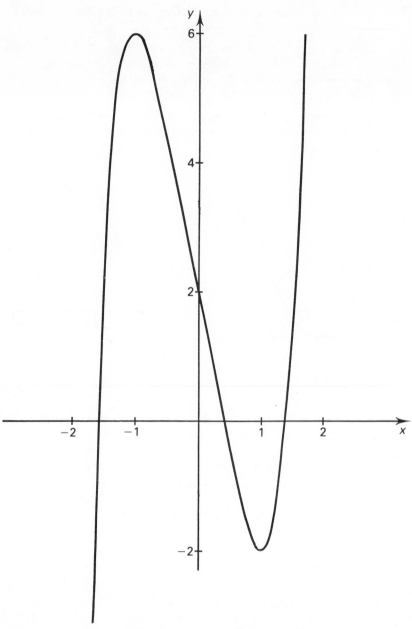

Figure 6.13 $y = P(x) = x^5 - 5x + 2$

The method used in this example is obvious geometrically (Fig. 6.13). Thus in $(0, 1)$, $P'(x) < 0$ and so P is decreasing. Hence $P(x)$ cannot pass through zero more than once (since it is continuous). However Rolle's theorem provides the formal proof of the results.   □

The mean value theorem can also be used to get an inequality for $f(x)$ from any known inequality or bound on $f'(x)$.

Example 6.72

Let $f(x) = x - \sin x$. For any $b > 0$, f is continuous and differentiable on $[0, b]$, with $f'(x) = 1 - \cos x$. By the mean value theorem, there is a number c in $(0, b)$ such that $[(b - \sin b) - 0]/(b - 0) = 1 - \cos c$.

Then $\sin b/b = \cos c \le 1$.

Similarly for any $b < 0$, the mean value theorem can be applied on $[b, 0]$ with the same result, which can be written $\sin x/x \le 1$ if $x \ne 0$. $\square$

In this example, the fact that $f'(c) \ge 0$ allows the deduction $f(b) \ge f(0)$. This type of application of the mean value theorem is required for a formal proof of the statement (at the end of Chapter 3) that the sign of the derivative indicates whether the function is increasing or decreasing. If $f'(x)$ is positive on (a, b), then $f'(c) > 0 \Rightarrow f(b) > f(a)$, while if $f'(x)$ is negative on (a, b), then $f'(c) < 0 \Rightarrow f(b) < f(a)$. These statements hold for any pair of numbers $a < b$ provided f' exists on (a, b) and f is continuous on $[a, b]$.

Exercises (answers on p. 153)

6.7.1   Let $f(x) = 1 - x^{2/3}$, so that $f(1) = f(-1) = 0$. Show that $f'(x)$ is never zero on the interval $[-1, 1]$. Which of the conditions for Rolle's theorem does not hold?

6.7.2   A function f has domain $[0, 4]$ and rule

$$f(x) = \frac{(x^2 - 4x + 3)\sin x}{x - 2} \qquad (x \ne 2), \qquad f(2) = 0.$$

Consider the intervals

(i) $[0, 1]$, (ii) $[0, \frac{1}{2}\pi]$, (iii) $[1, 2]$, (iv) $[2, 3]$, (v) $[3, \pi]$. For each interval, state

(a) whether Rolle's theorem is applicable, and

(b) whether the mean value theorem is applicable.

For those cases where a theorem is not applicable, give the condition which f fails to satisfy.

6.7.3   Sketch the graph of the function $y = g(x) = |x^2 - 1|$. State whether or not the mean value theorem is applicable to g on any of the following intervals:

(i) $[-2, -1]$, (ii) $[-2, 0]$, (iii) $[-2, 1]$.

Is there any interval on which Rolle's theorem can be applied to g?

6.8   Curve Sketching

This section will make various general remarks relating to sketching the graph of a given function or relation. The objective should be to show the important qualitative features, especially those relevant to the problem at hand. Properties likely to be of interest are:

---

domain and range;

any symmetry or periodicity in the graph;

points where the slope is zero (turning points);

sign of slope between turning points;

asymptotic behaviour as $x \to \pm\infty$, or $y \to \pm\infty$; (see equation (4.1) on p. 82)

special values—in particular, points where x or y is zero.

Example 6.80

Sketch the curve $y = P(x) = x^5 - 5x + 2$.

$$P'(x) = 5(x^4 - 1), \text{ so } P'(\pm 1) = 0, \ P'(x) < 0 \text{ for } -1 < x < 1,$$

and otherwise $P'(x) > 0$; for large x (positive or negative), $y \sim x^5$, so $y \to \pm\infty$ as $x \to \pm\infty$. This is sufficient to show that the graph increases from large negative values to $y = 6$ at $x = -1$, then decreases to $y = -2$ at $x = 1$, then increases to arbitrarily large positive values (Fig. 6.13 on p. 130).

The inferences about the graph depend on the fact that P is continuous and P' exists for all x, as discussed in Example 6.71.   □

Example 6.81

Sketch the curve $y = \exp x / x$.

The domain excludes only $x = 0$. y always has the same sign as x. From (†) in the table of limits on p. 91, $1/y = x/e^x \to 0$ as $x \to \infty$, so $y \to \infty$, and also

$$\text{Lim}_{x \to -\infty} x^{-1} e^x = \text{Lim}_{t \to \infty} -t^{-1} e^{-t} = 0. \text{ As } x \to 0\pm, \ y \to \pm\infty.$$

$$\frac{dy}{dx} = \frac{(x-1)e^x}{x^2} > 0 \ \text{ if } x > 1, \quad \text{and} \quad \frac{dy}{dx} < 0 \ \text{ if } x < 1,$$

so the function is decreasing on $(-\infty, 0)$ and $(0, 1)$, and increasing on $(1, \infty)$. The information obtained is shown in Fig. 6.14.   □

It is useful to be familiar with the qualitative behaviour of the common elementary functions.

The following table shows what properties are meant by the term qualitative behaviour.

Table 6.1   (Refer to Fig. 6.15)

Function	Range	Symmetry	Slope	Asymptotic Behaviour	Special Values
exp	$(0, \infty)$		>0	$\to \infty$ as $x \to \infty$ $\to 0$ as $x \to -\infty$	$\exp 0 = 1$ $\exp 1 = e$
ln domain $(0, \infty)$			>0	$\to \infty$ as $x \to \infty$ $\to -\infty$ as $x \to 0$	$\ln 1 = 0$ $\ln e = 1$
sin	$[-1, 1]$	odd, period 2π	zero at $\frac{1}{2}\pi + n\pi$		$\sin n\pi = 0$ $\sin(\frac{1}{2}\pi + n\pi) = (-1)^n$
Tan^{-1}	$(-\pi/2, \pi/2)$	odd	>0	$\to \pm\pi/2$ as $x \to \pm\infty$	$\text{Tan}^{-1} 0 = 0$
cosh	$[1, \infty)$	even	same sign as x	$\to \infty$ as $x \to \pm\infty$	minimum at $(0, 1)$

Sketches showing these features are often sufficient (i.e. the point-by-point accuracy of Fig. 6.15 is not required). Such 'rough' sketches not only take less time than actually writing down the properties as in the table, but may also give a clearer idea of the behaviour of the function than the results in the table.

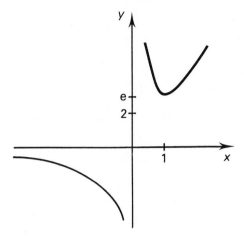

Figure 6.14 $y=(\exp x)/x$

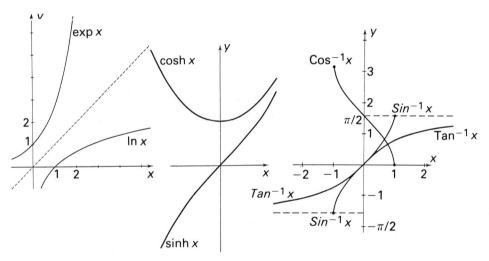

Figure 6.15   Graphs of common functions

There are obvious relations between the curve $y=f(x)$ and the curves $y=k+f(x)$ or $y=cf(x)$. Also $y=f(x+b)$ is $y=f(x)$ moved a distance b in the x-direction (to the left if $b>0$, to right if $b<0$).

Example 6.82

The graph of

$$y=\frac{2x+1}{x-1}=2+\frac{3}{x-1}$$

may be obtained from the graph of $y=1/x$ by the operations $(b=1,\ c=3,\ k=2)$

$$\frac{1}{x}\to\frac{1}{x-1}\to\frac{3}{x-1}\to 2+\frac{3}{x-1},$$

as in Fig. 6.16.

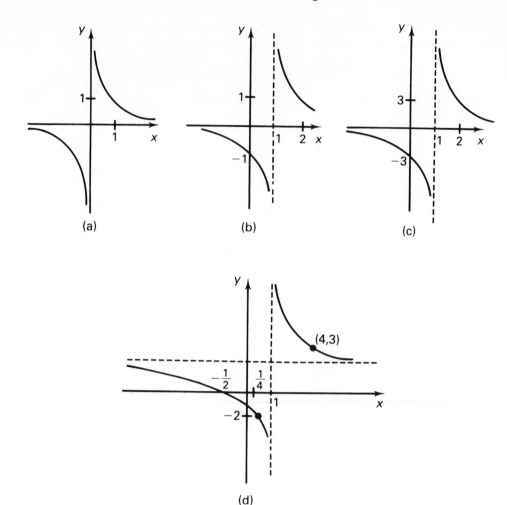

Figure 6.16   (a) $y=1/x$ (b) $y=1/(x-1)$ (c) $y=3/(x-1)$ (d) $y=2+3/(x-1)$

If $b>0$, $y=f(bx)$ is $y=f(x)$ compressed (or stretched) in the x-direction by a factor $1/b$. Since $y=f(-x)$ is the reflection in the y-axis of $y=f(x)$, $y=f(-bx)$ is $y=f(x)$ after scaling and reflection. $\square$

Example 6.83
The curves $y=\ln(3x)$ and $y=\ln(\frac{1}{2}x)$ are obtained from the curve $y=\ln x$ by scaling in the x-direction (Fig. 6.17). The curve $y=\ln(-x)$ is the reflection in the y-axis of the curve $y=\ln x$; the curve $y=\ln(-\frac{1}{2}x)$ is the reflection in the y-axis of the curve $y=\ln(\frac{1}{2}x)$. Note that $y=\ln 3x$ and $y=\ln(\frac{1}{2}x)$ can also be obtained from $y=\ln x$ by the addition of a constant, because $\ln bx=\ln b+\ln x$. $\square$

The graph of $y=|f(x)|$ is obtained by reflecting in the x-axis those parts of the graph of $y=f(x)$ with y negative.

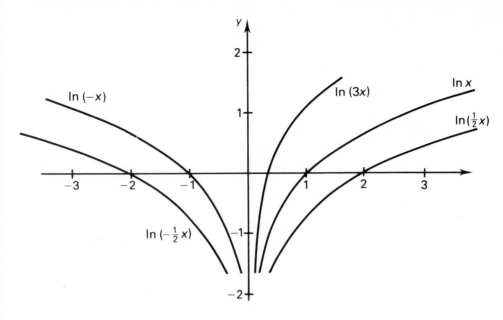

Figure 6.17 $y=\ln(bx)$ for $b=-\frac{1}{2}, -1, 3, 1, \frac{1}{2}$

Example 6.84

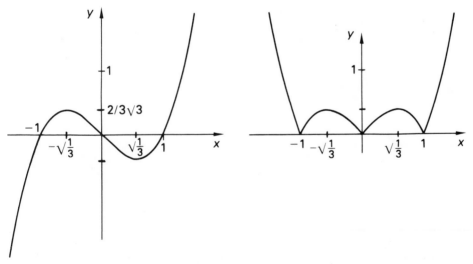

Figure 6.18   (a) $y=x^3-x$ (b) $y=|x^3-x|$

□

The graph of $y=1/f(x)$ is also easily obtained from that of $y=f(x)$.

Example 6.85

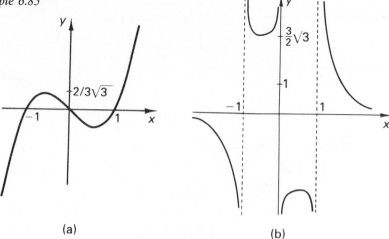

(a)   (b)

Figure 6.19   (a) $y = x^3 - x$ (b) $y = 1/(x^3 - x)$

The use of odd or even symmetry has already been illustrated in obtaining Fig. 3.5 from Fig. 3.4 (reproduced as Figs 6.20 and 6.21).

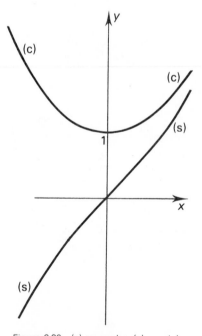

Figure 6.20   (c) $y = \cosh x$ (s) $y = \sinh x$

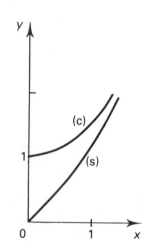

Figure 6.21   (c) $y = \cosh x$ (s) $y = \sinh x$

Example 6.86

Sketch the curve

$$y = \frac{x + a\sqrt{(1-x^2)}}{-ax + \sqrt{(1-x^2)}},$$

considering different values of the constant a when necessary.

(i) The domain is restricted to $[-1, 1]$, to avoid square roots of negative numbers. Then $y = -1/a$ at both end-points ($x = \pm 1$), provided $a \neq 0$, which is evidently a value of a requiring special consideration.

(ii) For any a, $dy/dx = (1 + y^2)/\sqrt{(1 - x^2)}$ (see Example 6.110 on p. 111). For a sketch, the most important deductions are that the function is always increasing, and that $dy/dx \to \infty$ as $x \to \pm 1$.

(iii) For $a \neq 0$, it turns out to be convenient to define $b = 1/a$, so that

$$y = \frac{bx + \sqrt{(1 - x^2)}}{-x + b\sqrt{(1 - x^2)}} = -b + \frac{1 + b^2}{b - x/\sqrt{(1 - x^2)}}. \tag{6.6}$$

This shows that the general case (arbitrary a) is a simple composite of the special case $y = x/\sqrt{(1 - x^2)}$ obtained when $a = 0$. This case will therefore be considered first.

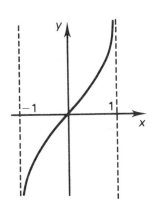

Figure 6.22 $\quad y = x/\sqrt{(1 - x^2)}$

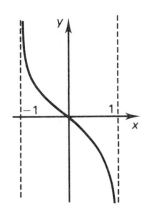

Figure 6.23 $\quad y = -x/\sqrt{(1 - x^2)}$

Since $y = x/\sqrt{(1 - x^2)}$ is an odd, increasing function, and $y \to \infty$ as $x \to 1$, Fig. 6.22 can now be sketched from the known information. In Fig. 6.23, the sign is changed in preparation for the general case (6.6), which is obtained by sketching the following in succession: $y_1 = b - (x/\sqrt{(1 - x^2)})$, $y_2 = 1/y_1$, $y_3 = (1 + b^2)y_2$ and $y = -b + y_3$. These stages are shown in Fig. 6.24, the sketches on the left being for a and b positive, and those on the right for a and b negative. Since $(dy/dx) \to \infty$ as $x \to \pm 1$, the derivatives dy_2/dx and dy_3/dx must also have this property. To show the intercepts of the curve with the x-axis, it is convenient to also introduce the quantity $c = 1/\sqrt{(1 + b^2)}$, satisfying $0 < c < 1$. The dotted lines always show vertical asymptotes. $\square$

The properties listed in Table 6.1 may be considered also for parametric equations. Thus for

$$x = \sin t, \qquad y = \sin 2t \qquad (-\pi/2 < t < \pi/2)$$

(i) the domain and range are restricted to $(-1, 1)$;

(ii) x and y both change sign when t changes sign, so the function is odd;

(iii) $dy/dx = 2 \cos 2t/\cos t$ (see Example 6.50) has the same sign as $\cos 2t$. This is positive for $-\pi/4 < t < \pi/4$, so on the interval $-\sqrt{\frac{1}{2}} < x < \sqrt{\frac{1}{2}}$, y increases from -1 to 1. Similarly y decreases from 0 to -1 on $-1 < x < -\sqrt{\frac{1}{2}}$, and y decreases from 1 to 0 on $\sqrt{\frac{1}{2}} < x < 1$. The main features of Fig. 6.25 are thus obtained (see p. 139).

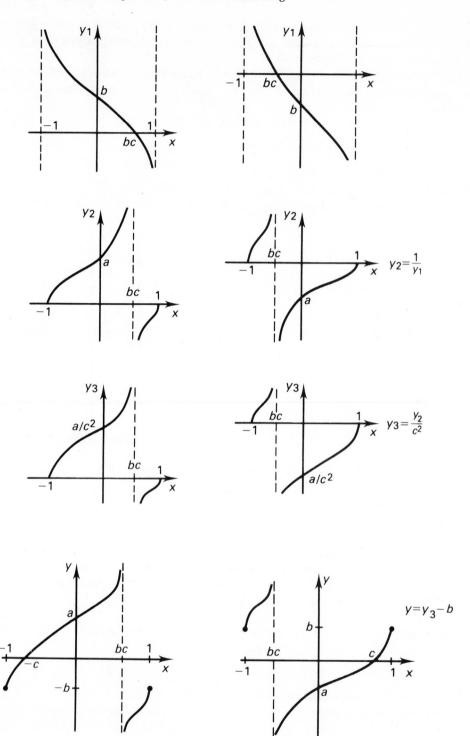

Figure 6.24 $y_1 = b - \dfrac{x}{\sqrt{(1-x^2)}}; \quad c = \dfrac{1}{\sqrt{(1+b^2)}}, \quad a = \dfrac{1}{b}; \quad a, b > 0$ on left; $a, b < 0$ on right

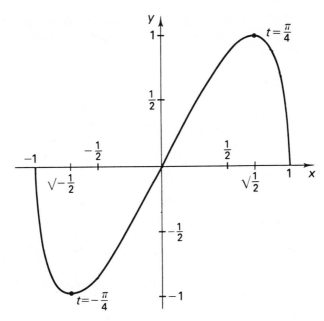

Figure 6.25 $x = \sin t, y = \sin 2t$

Exercises (answers on p. 153)

6.8.1 Sketch the following curves, each pair on the same diagram
    (a) $y = e^x$ and $y = 1 + e^x$
    (b) $y = e^x$ and $y = 6e^x$
    (c) $y = e^x$ and $y = ee^x = e^{x+1}$
    (d) $y = e^x$ and $y = e^{2x}$
    (e) $y = e^x$ and $y = e^{-x} = 1/e^x$
    (f) $y = e^x$ and $y = e^{-2x+3}$.

6.8.2 If $y = \sqrt{(a + b/x)}$, then (Examples 6.17 and 6.21 on p. 110 and p. 113)

$$\frac{dy}{dx} = \frac{-by}{2x(ax+b)} = \frac{-b}{2x\sqrt{(ax^2+bx)}}.$$

Sketch the curve for the case when a and b are positive.

6.8.3 If $y = x^x = \exp(x \ln x)$, then (Table of limits and Example 6.22 on p. 113)

$$y \to 1 \quad \text{as } x \to 0, \quad \text{and} \quad dy/dx = y(1 + \ln x).$$

Sketch the curve.

6.9 Inequalities

In general, solving an **inequality** means finding the values of x for which $f(x) < b$ (or $f(x) > b$), where f is a given function and b a given number. The algebraic and graphical processes used are similar to those used for solving equations (i.e. equalities: inequalities are also called **inequations**). When f is a polynomial, it is sufficient to factorize $f(x) - b$, and argue from the fact that the product of two quantities of the same sign is positive while the product of two quantities of opposite sign is negative. Factorization requires finding the roots of the polynomial $f(x)-b$; once these are known simple graphical considerations are also sufficient.

Example 6.90

Solve the inequality $x^3-6x^2+3x+12>2$.

The required values of x are those satisfying

$$P(x)=x^3-6x^2+3x+10>0.$$

Obviously -1 is a root of the polynomial P, so $(x+1)$ is a factor:

$$P(x)=(x+1)(x^2-7x+10)>0$$

$$\Leftrightarrow (x+1)(x-2)(x-5)>0.$$

The roots -1, 2, 5 are the values of x where the factors may change sign. In $(-\infty, -1)$, their signs are $---$, implying $P(x)<0$. Similarly $-1<x<2$ gives $+--$ and $P(x)>0$; $2<x<5$ gives $++-$, $P(x)<0$; and $x>5$ gives $P(x)>0$. The given inequality is satisfied in $\{x: -1<x<2$ or $x>5\}=(-1,2)\cup(5,\infty)$.

Alternatively the necessary features of the graph of P are known from its roots -1, 2, 5 which are the points where the graph crosses the x-axis, and the sign of the derivative $P'(x)=3x^2-12x+3$. Thus $P'(-1)=18>0$, so P is increasing at -1: $P(x)$ changes sign from negative to positive as x increases through -1. Similarly P changes sign from positive to negative as x increases through 2, and finally to positive again as x increases through 5 (Fig. 6.26). These are the only sign changes of $P(x)$, since P has no other roots. This

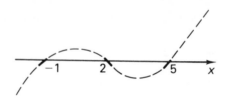

Figure 6.26   Sign changes of $P(x)=x^3-6x^2+3x+10$

argument assumes that the graph of the polynomial is continuous. Then the sign of $P(x)$ is known in the dashed portions of Fig. 6.26. No other details of the curve are required in order to solve the inequality.

Checks: if $f(x)=x^3-6x^2+3x+12$, then $f(0)=12>2$, $f(6)=30$ and $f(-1)=f(2)=f(5)=2$.   □

In general the following three procedures may be used to check a solution of an inequality $f(x)<b$:

(i) substitute one or two values which allow a simple evaluation of the given function f;

(ii) at the end-points of the intervals obtained as the solution, one expects either $f(x)=b$, or the graph of f to have some discontinuity, often because $f(x)\to \pm\infty$;

(iii) a graphical argument may be used to check an algebraic deduction, and perhaps vice-versa.

There is one important difference between the algebraic methods used for solving inequalities and equations. Although

$$a < b \Leftrightarrow a \pm c < b \pm c \text{ corresponding to } a = b \Leftrightarrow a \pm c = b \pm c$$

the result analogous to $a = b \Leftrightarrow ac = bc$ is:

$$a < b \Leftrightarrow ac < bc \text{ if } c > 0 \quad \text{while } a < b \Leftrightarrow ac > bc \text{ if } c < 0.$$

In other words, multiplying an inequality through by a **negative** quantity **reverses** the inequality.

If $a < b$, then $b - a > 0$. If $c > 0$, then $c(b - a) > 0$ so $ca < cb$; but if $c < 0$, $c(b - a) < 0$ so $ca > cb$.

Example 6.91
Solve the inequality $-4x^2 - 7x + 2 \geqslant 0$.

To factorize it is usually convenient to make the highest power have positive coefficient. Multiplying the given inequality by -1 reverses it:

$$4x^2 + 7x - 2 \leqslant 0 \tag{$*$}$$

$$\Leftrightarrow (4x - 1)(x + 2) \leqslant 0$$

$$\Leftrightarrow -2 \leqslant x \leqslant 1/4.$$

Here $(*)$ can also be obtained from the given inequality by adding $(4x^2 + 7x - 2)$ to each side. $\square$

A **rational function** is a quotient of two polynomials. The inequality $P(x)/Q(x) < b$ may be solved either by factorizing the numerator and denominator of the rational function $\{P(x)/Q(x)\} - b$, or by converting to the polynomial inequalities $P(x) < bQ(x)$ and $P(x) > bQ(x)$, with the two different cases according to the sign of $Q(x)$.

Example 6.92
Solve $1/(x - 4) \leqslant \frac{1}{2}$,

(i)
$$\frac{1}{x - 4} - \frac{1}{2} \leqslant 0 \Leftrightarrow \frac{(6 - x)}{(x - 4)} \leqslant 0 \text{ (multiplying by 2).}$$

Considering the signs of the numerator and denominator, which change at $x = 6$ and 4 respectively, shows that the inequality holds in $(-\infty, 4)$ and $(6, \infty)$ but not in $(4, 6)$. The equality holds at $x = 6$, but $x = 4$ is excluded since the given expression is then meaningless. Thus the solution set is $(-\infty, 4) \cup [6, \infty)$.

(ii) The other way to solve the equality would be to multiply each side by $(x - 4)$. This operation on the inequality requires the consideration of two cases.

(a) suppose $x - 4 > 0$, i.e. $x > 4$. Then, multiplying by $2(x - 4) > 0$,

$$\frac{1}{x - 4} \leqslant \frac{1}{2} \Leftrightarrow 2 \leqslant x - 4 \Leftrightarrow x \geqslant 6$$

and all these values are consistent with the condition $x > 4$ defining this case.

(b) If $x - 4 < 0$, i.e. $x < 4$, then the inequality reverses on multiplying by $2(x - 4)$, leading to $x \leqslant 6$. This conclusion, together with the defining condition $x < 4$ of this case, gives $x < 4$.

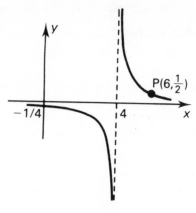

Figure 6.27

(iii) The simplest method is to graph $y = 1/(x - 4)$ (Fig. 6.27), and determine the point P at which $1/(x - 4) = \frac{1}{2}$. The solution is then obvious.   □

In the above example, multiplication by $2(x - 4)$ has the same effect as taking the reciprocal of each side of the inequality. In general the effect of this operation also depends on the sign, for example $2 < 3$ and $\frac{1}{2} > 1/3$, but $-2 < 3$ and $-\frac{1}{2} < \frac{1}{3}$.

The check to the previous example involved sketching the graph of a function and then observing that the inequality must hold in certain intervals bounded by solutions of the equality. This is often the only feasible method.

Example 6.93
Solve $\ln x < \sin x$.

Since $\ln x > 1 \geqslant \sin x$ when $x > e$, and $e < 5\pi/2$, it is clear that the graphs of $\ln$ and $\sin$ intersect in only one point, say $x = a$, and that the inequality is true in $(0, a)$. A numerical procedure for determining a, the solution of the equality $\ln x = \sin x$, will be given in Chapter 7. The graphs show that $\pi/2 < a < e$, and inspection of tables gives $a \simeq 2.22$ ($\sin 2.22 \simeq \sin 0.92 = 0.7956$, $\ln 2.22 = 0.7975$).   □

Example 6.94
Solve $(\exp x)/x < 2$.

The graph of $f(x) = (\exp x)/x$ is sketched in Fig. 6.28 (see also p. 132). Obviously the inequality holds in $(-\infty, 0)$ only.   □

In general before sketching any graphs to solve an inequality (or equation), one should consider whether the inequality can be rearranged so as to simplify the graphs which are required. For example to solve $x^3 < \exp(\sin x)$ it is easiest to rewrite it as $\ln(x^3) < \sin x \Leftrightarrow 3 \ln x < \sin x$. This particular rearrangement depends on the fact that exp is an increasing function, so that $\ln x < f(x) \Leftrightarrow x < \exp\{f(x)\}$. Also it is only valid for $x > 0$, so that $\ln(x^3)$ is defined. The given inequality is obviously true for $x \leqslant 0$, since $\exp(\sin x) > 0$.

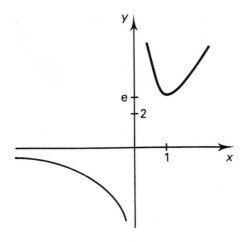

Figure 6.28

If the expressions in an equation involve square roots or moduli, it is tempting to remove them by squaring. In general, this leads to an incorrect result, because the squaring operation changes the solution set. For example the solution set of $x^2 = a^2$ is not just $x = a$ but also $x = -a$. Similarly $|x| = x$ is true only if $x \geqslant 0$, but $|x|^2 = x^2$ is true for all x. The next two examples show that inequalities have the same feature.

Example 6.95
Solve $|x - 2| < 1 - x$.

Squaring removes the modulus sign, and apparently simplifies the inequality to

$$x^2 - 4x + 4 < 1 - 2x + x^2 \Leftrightarrow 3 < 2x \Leftrightarrow x > 3/2.$$

Check: the graph of $|x - 2|$ was shown in Fig. 3.12. Evidently there are no values of x for which $|x - 2| < 1 - x$ (see p. 67).

A correct algebraic procedure is to remove the modulus sign by considering two separate cases:

(i) if $x \geqslant 2$, $|x - 2| = x - 2$ and $x - 2 < 1 - x$ if $x < 3/2$, but this is inconsistent with the assumption $x \geqslant 2$ defining this first case.
(ii) if $x \leqslant 2$, $|x - 2| = 2 - x$ and $2 - x < 1 - x \Rightarrow 2 < 1$ and so is impossible. □

Example 6.96
Solve $x + \sqrt{(x^2 - 1)} > -1$.

(i) Again an incorrect result may be obtained by squaring:

$$\sqrt{(x^2 - 1)} > -1 - x \qquad \text{gives} \qquad x^2 - 1 > 1 + 2x + x^2 \Leftrightarrow 2x < -2 \Leftrightarrow x < -1.$$

This is certainly not the full solution, because if $x \geqslant 1$ then $x + \sqrt{(x^2 - 1)} \geqslant 1 > -1$.

(ii) If $f(x) = x + (x^2-1)^{1/2}$, then (cf. dw in Example 6.12(ii) on p. 107)

$$f'(x) = 1 + \tfrac{1}{2}(x^2-1)^{-1/2}(2x) = 1 + \{x/\sqrt{(x^2-1)}\} = f(x)/\sqrt{(x^2-1)}$$

(a) On $(1, \infty)$, $f(x) > 1$ so $f'(x) > 0$, and f is increasing from the value $f(1) = 1$.

(b) On $(-\infty, -1)$, $x = -|x|$. Since $0 < \sqrt{(x^2-1)} < |x|$, $f(x)$ and $f'(x)$ are negative, and f is decreasing to the value $f(-1) = -1$.

Hence the inequality is true on $(-\infty, -1)$ and $[1, \infty)$. (An alternative graphical solution is to compare the line $y = -x - 1$ with the upper half of Fig. 3.6 on p. 52.) $\square$

The squaring operation can be used only to remove modulus signs from *each* side of an inequality: $x^2 < y^2 \Leftrightarrow |x| < |y|$.

Since complex numbers are not ordered, it is meaningless to write $z_1 < z_2$. However the modulus of a complex expression may satisfy an inequality, and the solution of such an inequality may be specified as a region of the complex plane.

Example 6.97

(i) The inequality $|z| < 2$ is satisfied by the complex numbers represented by all points of the interior of the circular disc of radius 2 centred on the origin.

(ii) If α is complex and nonzero, and c is real and positive, consider $|\alpha z| \le c$. Since $|\alpha z| = |\alpha||z|$, and $|\alpha| > 0$, the given inequality is satisfied for $|z| \le c/|\alpha|$, i.e. all points of a circular disc of radius $c/|\alpha|$. (If $\alpha = 0$, then $|\alpha z| = 0$ and $|\alpha z| \le c$ is true for all z.)

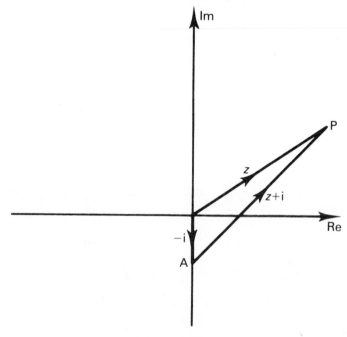

Figure 6.29 $|z+i| = AP$

(iii) Consider $|z+i| \le c$. Now $|z+i| = |z-(-i)|$ is the distance between the points representing z and $-i$ (Fig. 6.29). Hence $|z+i| \le c$ is satisfied by points P of a circular disc of radius c centred on A $(0, -1)$.

Check: Is the equality satisfied on the boundary of this disc? If $z = x + yi$, then $|z + i|^2 = |x + (y + 1)i|^2 = x^2 + (y + 1)^2$, and $x^2 + (y + 1)^2 = c^2$ is the equation of the circle centre $(0, -1)$ and radius c. □

For other examples with complex numbers, see Appendix A, Section A.7.

Exercises (answers on p. 154)

6.9.1 Solve the inequality $1/(x + 1) < 2$ by multiplying by $(x + 1)$ and considering two cases. Check the result graphically.

6.9.2 Verify that the solution of $x^3 < \exp(\sin x)$ is $x < b$, where b is a positive number smaller than $\frac{1}{2}\pi$.

6.9.3 Solve $x \leqslant e \ln x$.

6.9.4 Show that $\{x: x < 2\}$ is not the solution to $x^2 < 4$. What is the solution set? Which of the following are correct solutions:
  (i) $\{x: |x| < 2\}$, (ii) $\{x: -x < 2\}$
  (iii) $\{x: -x < 2\} \cup \{x: x < 2\}$, (iv) $\{x: -x < 2\} \cap \{x: x < 2\}$?
  Write down the solution set to $x^2 > 4$,
  (a) using an inequality for $|x|$ as in (i)
  (b) using only inequalities for x, and an intersection or union as in (iii) or (iv).

6.9.5 Verify the result of Example 6.96 using the suggested graphical method.

6.9.6 Solve the inequality $|x + 1| < |x + 2|$ by squaring. Check your result graphically.

6.9.7 Write down an inequality which represents, in the complex plane, the points of a circular disc of radius 3 centred on $(-1, 2)$.

6.9.8 Each of the following inequalities defines an interval of real numbers. Find the interval in each case.
  (i) $|x - 5| \leqslant |x + 1| - 5$, (ii) $|x + 1| \leqslant x + 1$,

  (iii) $\dfrac{|x + 3| + 15}{4 - x} > 2$, (iv) $|x^2 - 1| \leqslant 1$.

6.9.9 Each of the following inequalities defines a set of real numbers which can be expressed as the union of two disjoint intervals. Find such an expression in each case.
  (i) $x^{-1} < 2$, (ii) $x/(x - 5) \geqslant 0$,
  (iii) $1/(2x - 3) < 1$, (iv) $x - 1/x \geqslant 0$,
  (v) $|x^2 - 2| \leqslant 1$.

6.10 Partial Derivatives

The definition $f'(x) = \mathrm{Lim}_{h \to 0}\{f(x + h) - f(x)\}/h$ is extended to a function $f(x, y)$ of two variables by defining

$$f_x(x, y) = \mathrm{Lim}_{h \to 0}\{f(x + h, y) - f(x, y)\}/h \qquad (6.7)$$

$$f_y(x, y) = \mathrm{Lim}_{h \to 0}\{f(x, y + h) - f(x, y)\}/h. \qquad (6.8)$$

If the limit exists, then (6.7) is called the **partial derivative** (of f) with respect to x. Since the value of y in equation (6.7) is not varied, f_x is also called the partial derivative with respect to x keeping y constant. This also shows that

> all formulas and theorems for the evaluation of derivatives are applicable to the evaluation of equation (6.7):

just differentiate $f(x, y)$ as a function of x, regarding y as a constant, using the differentiation rules (p. 106) as necessary. Similarly to evaluate equation (6.8), the partial derivative with respect to y keeping x constant, differentiate f as a function of y, treating x as a constant.

Example 6.100
$$f(x, y) = x^3 + 3x^2y^2 + 2y^2$$
$$f_x(x, y) = 3x^2 + 6xy^2 + 0 \quad \text{(keeping } y \text{ constant)}$$
$$f_y(x, y) = 0 + 6x^2y + 4y \quad \text{(keeping } x \text{ constant)}. \quad \square$$

Example 6.101
$$f(x, y) = (2x - 3y + 1)^2(x + 2y - 2) \text{ (cf. Example 6.65)}.$$

Let $w(x, y) = 2x - 3y + 1$, $u = w^2$, and $v(x, y) = x + 2y - 2$. The product rule II gives $f_x = u_x v + u v_x$, and the composite function rule IV gives $u_x = 2ww_x$. Similarly $f_y = 2ww_y v + u v_y$. Taking derivatives with respect to x, treating y as a constant:
$$w_x(x, y) = 2, \ v_x(x, y) = 1,$$
hence
$$f_x(x, y) = 4w(x, y)v(x, y) + u(x, y) = (2x - 3y + 1)(6x + 5y - 7).$$
Taking derivatives with respect to y, treating x as a constant:
$$w_y(x, y) = -3, \ v_y(x, y) = 2,$$
hence
$$f_y(x, y) = -6w(x, y)v(x, y) + 2u(x, y) = (2x - 3y + 1)(-2x - 18y + 14).$$
In practice, this work is better set out as follows:
$$f_x(x, y) = \{(2x - 3y + 1)^2\}_x(x + 2y - 2) + (2x - 3y + 1)^2(x + 2y - 2)_x \quad \text{(rule II)}$$
$$= 2(2x - 3y + 1)(2x - 3y + 1)_x(x + 2y - 2) + (2x - 3y + 1)^2 \quad \text{(rule IV)}$$
etc. $\square$

A function of two variables has four different **second partial derivatives**:

> f_{xx} denotes the derivative of f_x with respect to x, keeping y constant
> f_{xy} denotes the derivative of f_x with respect to y, keeping x constant
> f_{yx} denotes the derivative of f_y with respect to x, keeping y constant
> f_{yy} denotes the derivative of f_y with respect to y, keeping x constant.

Example 6.102

$f(x, y) = x^4 y^2 + x^3 - y^2$.

$$f_x(x, y) = 4x^3 y^2 + 3x^2, \qquad f_{xx}(x, y) = 12x^2 y^2 + 6x, \qquad f_{xy}(x, y) = 8x^3 y$$

$$f_y(x, y) = 2x^4 y - 2y, \qquad f_{yx}(x, y) = 8x^3 y, \qquad f_{yy}(x, y) = 2x^4 - 2. \quad \Box$$

In this example,

$$\boxed{f_{xy} = f_{yx}.}$$

Subject to some conditions involving continuity, this is true for any function f. Since continuity of a function of two variables has not been defined here, the conditions will not be stated, and the result will be assumed for all functions encountered in this book. It affords a simple check on the expressions obtained for f_x and f_y.

The above considerations extend in an obvious way to functions of more than two variables.

Example 6.103

$g(x, y, z, t) = xy^2 z^2 + yz^3 t^2 + xt$.

$$g_x(x, y, z, t) = y^2 z^2 + t, \qquad g_y(x, y, z, t) = 2xyz^2 + z^3 t^2,$$

$$g_z(x, y, z, t) = 2xy^2 z + 3yz^2 t^2, \qquad g_t(x, y, z, t) = 2yz^3 t + x.$$

There are ten different second partial derivatives, for example

$$g_{ty}(x, y, z, t) = 2z^3 t = g_{yt}(x, y, z, t). \quad \Box$$

Various alternative notations will now be discussed. It is sometimes advantageous to think of differentiating with respect to the *first* variable keeping the *second* constant, or vice-versa. Then f_x is denoted by f_1, f_y by f_2, etc. The second derivative given in Example 6.103 would be written

$$g_{42}(x, y, z, t) = 2z^3 t.$$

Once again the symbol denoting the function may be eliminated in favour of the dependent variable. For instance (rewriting part of Example 6.102), if $w = x^4 y^2 + x^3 - y^2$, then $w_y = 2x^4 y - 2y$, $w_{xy} = 8x^3 y$, etc.

Example 6.104

Suppose $w = f(x, y) = x^4 y^2 + x^3 - y^2$ (Example 6.102). Then

$$\frac{\partial w}{\partial x} = \frac{\partial f}{\partial x} = 4x^3 y^2 + 3x^2, \qquad \frac{\partial w}{\partial y} = \frac{\partial f}{\partial y} = 2x^4 y - 2y,$$

$$\frac{\partial^2 w}{\partial x^2} = \frac{\partial^2 f}{\partial x^2} = 12x^2 y^2 + 6x = \frac{\partial}{\partial x}\left(\frac{\partial w}{\partial x}\right) = \frac{\partial}{\partial x}\left(\frac{\partial f}{\partial x}\right),$$

and similarly

$$\frac{\partial^2 f}{\partial y^2} = \frac{\partial}{\partial y}\left(\frac{\partial f}{\partial y}\right) = f_{yy} = w_{yy} = \frac{\partial}{\partial y}\left(\frac{\partial w}{\partial y}\right) = \frac{\partial^2 w}{\partial y^2},$$

$$\frac{\partial^2 f}{\partial x \partial y} = \frac{\partial}{\partial x}\left(\frac{\partial f}{\partial y}\right) = f_{xy} = w_{xy} = \frac{\partial}{\partial x}\left(\frac{\partial w}{\partial y}\right) = \frac{\partial^2 w}{\partial x \partial y}$$

$$= \frac{\partial^2 f}{\partial y \partial x} = \frac{\partial^2 w}{\partial y \partial x}. \quad \square$$

Also $\partial f / \partial x$ may be enclosed in brackets, and the variables kept constant written as subscripts outside the brackets. Thus (Example 6.103) if $w = g(x, y, z, t)$, then $\partial w / \partial x = \partial g / \partial x$ could be written

$$\left(\frac{\partial w}{\partial x}\right)_{y,z,t} \quad \text{or} \quad \left(\frac{\partial g}{\partial x}\right)_{y,z,t}; \quad \text{similarly } w_{ty} = \left(\frac{\partial}{\partial t}\right)_{x,y,z}\left(\frac{\partial w}{\partial y}\right)_{x,z,t}.$$

Here $(\partial/\partial t)_{x,y,z}$ denotes the **operation** of differentiating with respect to t, keeping x, y, and z constant. Although this notation was invented by analogy with the ordinary derivative being written as a quotient of two differentials, there is no analogous interpretation. The symbol $\partial w / \partial x$ should *not* be interpreted as a quotient. Differentials for functions of more than one variable will be discussed in Chapters 14 and 18, where it will be seen that the general relation between partial derivatives and differentials does not allow the partial derivative to be regarded as a quotient.

The notation $\partial w / \partial x|_P$ or $\partial w / \partial x|_{2,3}$ indicates the value of the partial derivative at the point P(2, 3). If $w = f(x, y)$, the same value could be written $f_x(2, 3)$ or $f_x(\text{P})$.

Exercise (answers on p. 154)

6.10.1 Suppose $w = f(x, y, z) = x^2 y + xz^3 - xyz$.
Find
(i) $f_x(x, y, z)$, (ii) $\partial w / \partial y$, (iii) $\partial f / \partial z$, (iv) $f_3(x, y, z)$
(v) f_{xy}, (vi) w_{yz}, (vii) $f_{zz}(1, 2, -1)$, (viii) $\partial^2 w / \partial x \partial z|_{2,3,-1}$.

6.11 Complex Functions

Section 6.4 showed that the derivative of a vector function may be evaluated by differentiating the component functions. The analogy between the complex number $x + iy$ and the vector $x\mathbf{i} + y\mathbf{j}$, discussed in Appendix A, means that a complex function $(R \to C)$ and a vector function $(R \to R^2)$ can be represented by the same plane curve. Parts (ii) and (iii) of Example 3.47 were illustrations of this (see p. 59).

The work leading from equation (6.3) to equation (6.4) may evidently be repeated for a complex function, with the functions f and g defined by its real and imaginary parts (cf. p. 118):

$$z'(t) = \lim_{h \to 0}\{z(t+h) - z(t)\}/h$$

and if

$$z(t) = f(t) + ig(t),$$

$$z'(t) = f'(t) + ig'(t). \tag{6.9}$$

Moreover the geometrical interpretation will be the same: in the complex plane (Argand diagram) $z'(t)$ is represented by the tangent vector at t to the curve representing $z(t)$. The complex differential $dz = f'(t)\,dt + ig'(t)\,dt$ is also represented by a tangent vector.

Example 6.112

Figure 6.6 may be interpreted as an Argand diagram in which the curve represents the complex function

$$z(t) = \sin t + i \sin 2t \qquad (0 \leqslant t < 2\pi)$$

with the derivative

$$z'(t) = \cos t + 2i \cos 2t.$$

Then Fig. 6.7 shows the representation of $z(\pi/4)$, $z'(\pi/4)$, $z(\pi/3)$ and $z'(\pi/3)$ (cf. pp. 121 and 123).   □

Example 6.113

Obtain the derivative of the function z of type $R \to C$, where $z(t) = (t+i)^{-1}$.

According to equations (6.9), one should obtain the real and imaginary parts, and differentiate them. Since

$$z(t) = \frac{1}{t+i} = \frac{t-i}{(t+i)(t-i)} = \frac{t-i}{t^2+1}$$

the real and imaginary parts are the functions $(R \to R)$

$$u(t) = t/(t^2+1) \quad \text{and} \quad v(t) = -1/(t^2+1).$$

Then

$$u'(t) = \frac{(t^2+1)-2t^2}{(t^2+1)^2}, \qquad v'(t) = \frac{2t}{(t^2+1)^2}$$

so

$$z'(t) = u'(t) + iv'(t) = \frac{1-t^2+2it}{(t^2+1)^2}. \quad \square \tag{6.10}$$

In this work, the differentiation of $u(t) + iv(t)$ to get $u'(t) + iv'(t)$ could proceed in exactly the same way if i was a real constant, and the function z was real. In that situation, one would certainly obtain the same result by differentiating the original expression $(t+i)^{-1}$. This means that

> to differentiate a complex function $(R \to C)$, it is not necessary to separate the real and imaginary parts explicitly; the expression for the function is simply differentiated with i a constant.

It is easy to verify that $z(t) = (t+i)^{-1}$, for example, has derivative

$$z'(t) = -(t+i)^{-2}. \tag{6.11}$$

Since equation (6.10) can be factorized to give

$$z'(t) = \frac{(1+it)^2}{\{(1+it)(1-it)\}^2} = \frac{1}{(1-it)^2} = \frac{1}{\{(t+i)(-i)\}^2} = \frac{1}{-(t+i)^2},$$

it is the same as equation (6.11).

However this does not necessarily mean that differentiating any complex function of type $(R \to C)$ is a trivial extension of the work on real functions. At the present stage, none of the results in the table of derivatives at the end of the chapter can be said to be true when w is complex, because the functions sin, cos, etc. have not been defined on a complex domain. Any functions defined directly in terms of algebraic operations on complex numbers can be considered, but this only leads to polynomials in t with complex coefficients, and rational functions given by quotients of such polynomials. Other complex functions may be defined as in equations (6.9) and Example 6.112, but this gives nothing really new, because the results could be expressed by considering two real functions f and g without using i. On the other hand if it was possible, for complex k, to define sin kt and cos kt in such a way that equations (6.9) gave $z'(t) = k \cos kt$ for the derivative of $z(t) = \sin kt$, this would be a new result.

It would also be feasible to define sin kt in such a way that its derivative, defined by (6.9), was not $k \cos kt$. If possible, it is obviously more convenient for derivatives of complex functions to have the same form as the results for the corresponding real functions.

As an example consider $z(t) = \exp(it)$, which has not yet been defined. Since it would be very confusing to have to distinguish between $\exp(i0)$ and $\exp(0)$, a desirable property is

$$\exp(it) = 1 \quad \text{when } t = 0, \quad \text{i.e. } z(0) = 0 \tag{6.12}$$

Another desirable property would be

$$\frac{dz}{dt} = z'(t) = i \exp(it), \tag{6.13}$$

so that the differentiation rule is familiar.

It will now be shown that these two properties fix the required definition. Suppose $\exp(it) = f(t) + ig(t)$, where f and g are real functions to be determined so that equations (6.12) and (6.13) are true. Then (6.12) requires $f(0) + ig(0) = 1 \Rightarrow f(0) = 1, g(0) = 0$. Using equations (6.9), (6.13) requires

$$f'(t) + ig'(t) = i\{f(t) + ig(t)\} = -g(t) + if(t).$$

Equating real and imaginary parts:

$$f' = -g \tag{6.14}$$

$$g' = f. \tag{6.15}$$

Differentiating equation (6.14), $f'' = -g' = -f$, using equation (6.15).
Also (6.14) requires $f'(0) = -g(0) = 0$.
The real functions sin and cos both satisfy $f'' = -f$, and $f = \cos$ also gives $f(0) = 1, f'(0) = 0$. From equation (6.14) $g = -f' = \sin$. Hence $z(t)$ satisfies equations (6.12) and (6.13) if (and only if)

$$\exp(it) = \cos t + i \sin t \tag{6.16}$$

is taken as the **definition** of $\exp(it)$.

To check equation (6.13) differentiate (6.16) using (6.9):

$$z'(t) = \cos' t + i \sin' t = -\sin t + i \cos t;$$

and

$$i \exp(it) = i (\cos t + i \sin t) = i \cos t - \sin t.$$

The function defined by equation (6.16) is often denoted by cis. Thus cis is an $\mathbf{R} \to \mathbf{C}$ type function with domain R. Its range is the set of complex numbers of unit modulus, so that it is represented in the complex plane by the unit circle (the circle of unit radius centred on the origin). The properties (6.12) and (6.13) can be written cis $0 = 1$, and $\text{cis}'(t) = i \, \text{cis}(t)$. However it seems preferable to use $\exp(it)$, because it may also be shown that (see Exercise 6.11.3):

$$\boxed{\exp(it)\exp(is) = \exp(it+is).} \qquad \textbf{(6.17)}$$

It is now possible to explain why the circular and hyperbolic functions have analogous algebraic properties.

Define $\sinh(it)$, $\cosh(it)$ and $\tanh(it)$ by the same equations (3.10) as the real functions:

$$\sinh(it) = \tfrac{1}{2}\exp(it) - \tfrac{1}{2}\exp(-it), \quad \text{etc.,}$$

where

$$\exp(-it) = \exp[i(-t)] = \cos(-t) + i \sin(-t) = \cos t - i \sin t. \qquad (6.18)$$

The algebraic relations satisfied by the real hyperbolic functions are all consequences of properties of the real exponential function. See on p. 51 for instance, the working of Examples 3.30 and 3.31. Since $\exp(it)$ has the properties of e^x which are used, especially equation (6.17), the same algebraic relations between hyperbolic functions remain true when the variable is it. For instance, the results $\cosh^2(it) - \sinh^2(it) = 1$ and $\sinh(2it) = 2 \sinh(it) \cosh(it)$ may be written down from the results on p. 51 of Example 3.30 and may be demonstrated by writing out the working of that example with $\exp(it)$ and $\exp(-it)$ replacing e^x and e^{-x}.

But equations (6.16) and (6.18) allow the complex hyperbolic functions to be expressed in terms of circular functions:

$$\cosh(it) = \tfrac{1}{2}\exp(it) + \tfrac{1}{2}\exp(-it) = \cos t, \quad \text{and} \quad \sinh(it) = i \sin t. \qquad \textbf{(6.19)}$$

Thus any algebraic relation between the functions **cosh** and **sinh** also holds between **cos** and **i sin**.

The factor i leads to the sign change before a product of two sines, since this contains $i^2 = 1$.

Example 6.114
(i) $\cosh^2(it) - \sinh^2(it) = \cos^2 t + \sin^2 t.$ (ii) $\sinh(2it) = i \sin(2t)$ and $2 \sinh(it) \cosh(it) = 2i \sin t \cos t.$ (iii) $3 \sinh(it) + 4 \sinh^3(it) = 3i \sin t + 4i^3 \sin^3 t = i(3 \sin t - 4 \sin^3 t)$ and $\sinh(3it) = i \sin 3t$ (cf. Example 3.31 on p. 52). $\square$

The hyperbolic functions of a complex variable have been discussed here only to illuminate the analogy between the circular functions and the real hyperbolic functions. In practice, because of equations (6.19), one usually works with the circular functions rather than the complex hyperbolic functions.

The usual notation for the complex exponential function appears by defining $e^{it} = \exp(it)$. In this notation, the results obtained above are as follows:

$$\frac{d}{dt}(e^{it}) = i\, e^{it} \tag{6.13}$$

$$e^{it} = \cos t + i \sin t \tag{6.16}$$

$$\cos t = \frac{e^{it} + e^{-it}}{2}, \qquad \sin t = \frac{e^{it} - e^{-it}}{2i} \tag{6.19}$$

The results $e^{i\pi/2} = i$, $e^{-i\pi/2} = -i$ and $e^{i\pi} = -1$ are special cases of equation (6.16).

Exercises (answers on p. 154)

6.11.1   Evaluate
(a) $\exp(i\pi/4)$, (b) $\exp(3i\pi/2)$, (c) $\exp(2i\pi)$.

6.11.2   Illustrate the number $r\, e^{i\theta}\,(r>0)$ in an Argand diagram. What are the modulus and argument of $r\, e^{i\theta}$?

6.11.3   Assuming the addition formulas (A19) for cos and sin, verify equation (6.17).

6.11.4   Check the formulas (6.19) for sin and cos by differentiating.

6.11.5   Write de Moivre's theorem

$$(\cos \theta + i \sin \theta)^n = \cos n\theta + i \sin n\theta$$

in terms of the exponential function.

Answers to Exercises 6.1.1–6.11.5

6.1.1   (a) $1/\cosh x$, (b) $\cos^5 x \sin x$, (c) $\sin^{-3} x \cos x$, (d) $\sin^2 x \cos^3 x$,
(e) $\sin^3 x \cos^{-2} x$, (f) $(3x-2)^{1/2}$, (g) $1/\sqrt{(2x-1)}$, (h) $(2x+3)/\sqrt{(3x+2)}$.

6.1.2   (a) $t \exp(-t^2)$, (b) $t \cos(t^2)$, (c) $t \sin(t^2+2)$, (d) $t\sqrt{(t^2+2)}$,
(e) $t/\sqrt{(t^2+a)}$, (f) $t/(1+t^2)$.

6.1.3   (a) $(1+c)^{-1}$, (b) $(1-c)^{-1}$, (c) $(3c-2)^{-1}$, (d) $(3+2c)^{-1}$,
where $c = \cos x = 2\cos^2(\tfrac{1}{2}x) - 1$.

6.1.4   (a) $x \ln x$, (b) $\ln(x^2+1)$, (c) $x \operatorname{Tan}^{-1} x$, (d) $(x^2+1)\cos x$,
(e) $x^2 e^x$, (f) $x \cos 3x$, (g) $(x-\pi)\sin mx$.

6.1.5 $\cos(\ln x)$ and $\sin(\ln x)$.

6.1.6   (a) $(x-2)/(x+1)$, (b) $(x^2-3x-2)/(2x-1)^3$,
(c) $(x^2+6x+34)^{-1}$, (d) $(x^2+6x)^{-1}$, (e) $(4x-7)/(x^2+2x+3)$,
(f) $(4x-7)/(x^2-4x+3)$, (g) $(x^3+1)/(x^2+1)$.

6.1.7   (a) $\dfrac{5x^2-11x+8}{x^3-2x^2+2x}$ (b) $\dfrac{2x^3-x-4}{(x+1)(x-4)(x-2)}$.

6.1.8   (a) $\cos^4 x$, (b) $\sin^4 x - \sin^6 x$

6.2.1 $8x/(3+2x)^4$.   **6.2.2** (a) $(80-24x^2-3x^4)/(x^2+4)^3$, (b) $1/(x^2+4)^3$.

6.3.1 $(4x^3-6x)(1-x^2)^{-3/2}$.   **6.3.2** (i) 0, (ii) 0, (iii) $2b\,e^{-ax}$.

6.3.5 (i) 0, (ii) $8\cos^5 x$.   **6.3.6** 0.

6.3.7 $(-1)^n(m+n-1)!/(m-1)!n!$; $\dfrac{d^n}{dx^n}(x^{-m})=(-1)^n\dfrac{(m+n-1)!}{(m-1)!}x^{-m-n}$.

6.3.8 (iii) From Leibniz formula (6.2)

$$(e^{-x}\cos x)^{(5)}=4\,e^{-x}(\cos x+\sin x).$$

6.4.1 (a) $3i+(\sin t)j+(1+\cos t)k$, (b) $(\cos t)j-(\sin t)k$,

(c) $\sqrt{(11+2\cos t)}$, (d) $\dfrac{10t+\sin t+t\cos t}{\sqrt{(1+10t^2+2t\sin\cdot t)}}$.

6.4.2 $\pm(c^2+b^2+a^2b^2t^2)^{-1/2}[(b\cos at-abt\sin at)i+(b\sin at+abt\cos at)j+ck]$.

6.5.1 $\dfrac{dy}{dx}=\dfrac{2t(2t^2-1)}{3(t^2+1)}$, $\dfrac{d^2y}{dx^2}=\dfrac{4t^4+14t^2-2}{9(t^2+1)^3}$

with values $-\tfrac{1}{3}$ and $\tfrac{2}{9}$ at $(-3,3)$ where $t=-1$.

6.6.1 $y'=dy/dx=-\tfrac{1}{2}b/x^2y$ (cf. Examples 6.17 and 6.21)

$$\dfrac{d^2y}{dx^2}=\dfrac{dy'}{dx}=bx^{-3}y^{-1}-\tfrac{1}{4}b^2x^{-4}y^{-3}.$$

Note the dimensional check: a is $(length)^2$, b is $(length)^3$.

6.7.2 (a) Rolle's theorem does not apply
on (ii) because $f(0)\neq f(\tfrac{1}{2}\pi)$
on (iii) or (iv) because f is not continuous at $x=2$.
(b) For the same reason, the mean value theorem does not apply on (iii) or (iv).

6.7.3 Since g' does not exist at $x=-1$, the mean value theorem cannot be used on $[-2,0]$ or $[-2,1]$, but it does apply on $[-2,-1]$ since g' exists on the open interval $(-2,-1)$. Rolle's theorem applies on $[-1,1]$.

6.8.1

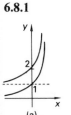 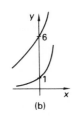 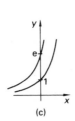 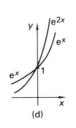 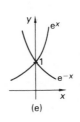 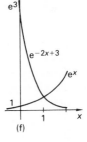

(a)   (b)   (c)   (d)   (e)   (f)

6.8.2   **6.8.3**

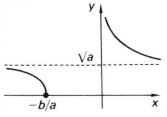   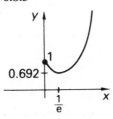

Figures 6.8.1–6.8.3

6.9.1 $(-\infty, -1) \cup (-\frac{1}{2}, \infty)$; consider $x > -1$ and $x < -1$.
6.9.2   Compare graphs of $\sin x$ and $3 \ln x$.   **6.9.3** $x = 1$.
6.9.4   (i) and (iv) are correct, being equivalent to $(-2, 2)$.
6.9.5   **6.9.6**

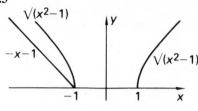

Figure 6.9.5

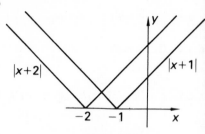

Figure 6.9.6

6.9.7 $|x + 1 - 2i| \le 3$.
6.9.8   (i) $[4\frac{1}{2}, \infty)$ (ii) $[-1, \infty)$ (iii) $(-4, 4)$ (iv) $[-\sqrt{2}, \sqrt{2}]$
6.9.9   (i) $(-\infty, 0) \cup (0, \frac{1}{2})$ (ii) $[0, 5) \cup (5, \infty)$ (iii) $(-\infty, 1) \cup (2, \infty)$
      (iv) $(-1, 0) \cup (1, \infty)$ (v) $[-\sqrt{3}, -1] \cup [1, \sqrt{3}]$.
6.10.1   (i) $2xy + z^3 - yz$, (ii) $x^2 - xz$, (iii) $3xz^2 - xy$, (iv) $3xz^2 - xy$,
      (v) $2x - z$, (vi) $-x$ (vii) 6, (viii) 0.
6.11.1   (a) $(1 + i)/\sqrt{2}$, (b) $-i$, (c) 1.
6.11.2 $|r\,e^{i\theta}| = r$; $\arg(r\,e^{i\theta}) = \theta$ (if $r > 0$).   **6.11.5** $(e^{i\theta})^n = e^{in\theta}$.

Table of Derivatives

The results below are given in the differentials notation:

$$d\{f(x)\} = f'(x)\,dx,$$

using w instead of x, to emphasize that the formulas hold for any real variable. Any symbol other than w denotes a constant.

$d(w^a) = aw^{a-1}\,dw$
$d(\sin w) = \cos w\,dw, d(\cos w) = -\sin w\,dw$
$d(\tan w) = \sec^2 w\,dw = (1 + \tan^2 w)\,dw$
$d(\cot w) = -\mathrm{cosec}^2 w\,dw = -(1 + \cot^2 w)\,dw$
$d(\sec w) = \tan w \sec w\,dw,$ $d(\mathrm{cosec}\ w) = -\cot w\ \mathrm{cosec}\ w\,dw$
$d(\sinh w) = \cosh w\,dw,$ $d(\cosh w) = \sinh w\,dw$
$d(\tanh w) = \mathrm{sech}^2 w\,dw = (1 - \tanh^2 w)\,dw$
$d(\mathrm{sech}\ w) = -\tanh w\ \mathrm{sech}\ w\,dw$
$d(e^w) = e^w\,dw,$ $d(\ln w) = d(\log w) = dw/w$
$d(a^w) = a^w \ln a\,dw$ $(a > 0)$
$d(w^w) = w^w(1 + \ln w)\,dw$ $(w > 0)$
$d(\mathrm{Sin}^{-1} w) = (1 - w^2)^{-1/2}\,dw$ $(-\pi/2 < \mathrm{Sin}^{-1} w < \pi/2, |w| < 1)$
$d(\mathrm{Cos}^{-1} w) = -(1 - w^2)^{-1/2}\,dw$ $(0 < \mathrm{Cos}^{-1} w < \pi, |w| < 1)$
$d(\mathrm{Tan}^{-1} w) = (1 + w^2)^{-1}\,dw$ $(-\frac{1}{2}\pi < \mathrm{Tan}^{-1} w < \frac{1}{2}\pi)$
$d(\sinh^{-1} w) = d(\ln\{w + \sqrt{(1 + w^2)}\}) = (1 + w^2)^{-1/2}\,dw$
$d(\mathrm{Cosh}^{-1} w) = d(\ln\{w + \sqrt{(w^2 - 1)}\}) = (w^2 - 1)^{-1/2}\,dw$ $(\mathrm{Cosh}^{-1} w > 0, w > 1)$
$d(\mathrm{Tanh}^{-1} w) = d(\frac{1}{2} \ln\{(1 + w)/(1 - w)\}) = (1 - w^2)^{-1}\,dw$ $(|w| < 1)$

Further Exercises on Chapter 6

6.1   For each of the following functions f, with domain R,
   (a) sketch the graph;
   (b) determine whether $f'(1)$ exists, and if so calculate its value;
   (c) find the rule and domain of the function f';
   (d) sketch the graph of f'.

   (i) $f(x) = x^2$
   (ii) $f(x) = x^2$ if $x \leqslant 1$; $f(x) = -x^2 + 4x - 2$ if $x \geqslant 1$
   (iii) $f(x) = x^2$ if $|x| \leqslant 1$; $f(x) = |x|$ if $|x| \geqslant 1$.

6.2   Use the definition (6.1) to show that the function f given by

$$f(x) = x^2 \quad \text{if } x > 0; \qquad f(x) = 0 \quad \text{if } x \leqslant 0$$

   is differentiable at 0. Sketch the graphs of f, f' and f''.
   What are the domain and range of f''?

6.3   Determine whether $f'(0)$ exists for

$$f(x) = x \sin(1/x) \text{ if } x \neq 0; \ f(0) = 0.$$

6.4   Differentiate

   (a) $y = \sqrt[3]{\dfrac{(x-1)(x+2)}{(x+1)(x-2)}}$, (b) $y = x^{\cos x}(x > 0)$.

6.5   Use logarithmic differentiation to check the result of Example 6.19.

6.6   Find, in terms of n, the nth derivatives of
   (a) $\log|1 - x|$, (b) $\cos x$ (log means ln).
   Verify the results (as in Example 6.34).

6.7   Find $f^{(n)}(x)$ when $f(x) = (x^2 + 1)\log|1 + x|$.

6.8   Find $f^{(20)}(0)$ when $f(x) = (x^7 + 2)e^x$.

6.9   Show that a tangent vector at a general point P of the curve represented by

$$r(t) = (2 \cos t - \sin t)i - (\cos t - 2 \sin t)j + 2(\cos t + \sin t)k$$

   is perpendicular to the radius vector $\overrightarrow{OP} = r(t)$.
   Show that $|\overrightarrow{OP}|$ and $r \times dr/dt$ are independent of t.
   Interpret these results geometrically.

6.10 Let dots denote derivatives with respect to t, and suppose A, B, ω, and h are constants.
   (i) if $r \times \dot{r} = h$, show that $r \times \ddot{r} = 0$
   (ii) if $r(t) = A(\omega t - \sin \omega t)i + A(1 - \cos \omega t)j + Bt\, k$, show that $\ddot{r} = A\omega^2 j - \omega(k \times \dot{r})$.

6.11 Show that the parametric equations (cf. Exercise 6.5.1)

$$x = t^3 + 3t + 1, \qquad y = t^4 - t^2 + 3$$

   define y as a function of x. Find the turning points of this function, and determine whether they are local maxima or minima.

6.12 Find d^2y/dx^2 for the spiral represented by

$$x = t \cos \pi t, \qquad y = t \sin \pi t.$$

   Find the slope of the curve at the points where it crosses the axes.

6.13 Use logarithmic differentiation to check the result of Example 6.65.

6.14 If x and y are related by $x^2 + xy + y^2 = 7$, find dy/dx and d^2y/dx^2 in terms of x and y.

6.15 Use Rolle's theorem to prove that, regardless of the value of b, there is at most one point x in the interval $[-1, 1]$ for which $x^3 - 3x + b = 0$.

6.16 Find the conditions on p and q for the equation

$$x^3 - px + q = 0$$

to have one, two or three distinct (real) solutions.

6.17 Suppose f is differentiable everywhere (and hence continuous)

(i) If f has m distinct real zeros, what can be said about the number of zeros of f'? (Use Rolle's theorem $m - 1$ times).

(ii) If f' has k distinct zeros, what can be said about the number of zeros of f?

(iii) Suppose f'' exists everywhere, and has k distinct real zeros. What can be said about the number of zeros of f'? What can then be said about the number of zeros of f?

(iv) How does (iii) extend to higher derivatives?

6.18 As an application of Exercise 6.17, show the following:

(i) $x^n + ax + b = 0$ (a, b real; n a positive integer) has at most 2 distinct real roots if n is even and at most 3 distinct real roots if n is odd.

(ii) $x^4 + 30x^2 + 84x + 108$ has at most 2 distinct real zeros.

(iii) $x^5 + 10x^4 + 50x^3 + 9x^2 + 7x + 10 = 0$ has at most 3 distinct real roots.

(iv) $x^5 + 7x + 20 = 0$ has at most 1 distinct real root.

6.19 Use the mean value theorem to show that

(a) $e^x - ex > 0$ if $x > 1$

(b) $e^x - ex > 0$ if $x < 1$.

Illustrate the results with a sketch showing $y = e^x$ and $y = ex$.

6.20 Use the mean value theorem and the result (Example 6.72)

$$\sin x \leq x \quad \text{if } x > 0$$

to show that $1 - \frac{1}{2}x^2 \leq \cos x$ if $x > 0$. Illustrate the result with a sketch.

6.21 (i) If $0 < c < b$, show that $(1 + b^2)^{-1} < (1 + c^2)^{-1} < 1$. Deduce that $b/(1 + b^2) < \mathrm{Tan}^{-1} b < b$, by using the mean value theorem.

(ii) If $0 < a < 1$ show, using the mean value theorem, that

$$\frac{\pi}{4} - \frac{1-a}{1+a^2} < \mathrm{Tan}^{-1} a < \frac{\pi}{4} - \tfrac{1}{2}(1-a).$$

6.22 For $f(x, y) = e^{xy} \cos(x + y)$ find $\partial f/\partial x$ and $\partial f/\partial y$, and evaluate them at the point $(\pi, 0)$.

6.23 Consider the symmetry of the graphs of even and odd functions, and determine the resulting relation between the slopes at $\pm x$. What can be said about the derivative of an even or odd function? What can be said about the nth derivative? What can be said about $f^{(n)}(0)$? (Assume f differentiable at 0, and hence continuous.)

Note: in Exercises 6.24–6.30 a solution is a statement of the intervals on which the inequality holds.

6.24 Solve the inequality $3x^4 - 3x^3 - 8x^2 + 4 \geq -4$.

6.25 Solve (i) $-2 < 1/(x - 1) \leq 1$ (ii) $x/(x - 5) \geq 0$.

6.26 Solve (i) $x e^{-x} < \frac{1}{2}$ (ii) $x^2 e^x > 0$ (iii) $(\exp x)/x^2 > 1/e$.

6.27 Solve (i) $|x^2 - 2| \leq 1$ (ii) $|x - 5| < |x + 1|$ (iii) $1/|x - 2| < 3$.

6.28 Solve $x^2 + 6x + 19 > |5x + 5|$.

6.29 Solve $2x^3 - 3x^2 - 5x + 12 < |3x^2 + 3x - 12|$.

6.30 Solve $x - \sqrt{(x^2 - 1)} < 1$ (i) graphically (ii) analytically.

6.31 Solve the following inequalities, expressing your answer as a geometrical description of a set of points in the Argand diagram:

(i) $|3z + 4iz| > 10$, (ii) $|z - 1| < 1$, (iii) $|z + 1| > 1$,
(iv) $|2z + 3| \leq 4$, (v) $|2z - 1 - i| \leq 2$, (vi) $|iz + 1| \leq 2$.

6.32 Show that, if x is in the neighbourhood $(2 - \varepsilon/5, 2 + \varepsilon/5)$ of 2, where $\varepsilon < 5$, then x^2 is in the neighbourhood $(4 - \varepsilon, 4 + \varepsilon)$ of 4.

6.33 Solve the inequality $b/x \geq a$, considering the six cases corresponding to b positive or negative, and a positive, negative, or zero.

6.34 If

$$A(x) = \begin{cases} x + 2 & (x \leq -1) \\ (x^3 + 4)/3 & (x \geq -1), \end{cases}$$

determine whether $A'(-1)$ exists.

6.35 (i) For the function in Example 6.86, calculate the second derivative, and show that this has the same sign as y when $x = 0$, and the same sign as x when $y = 0$.

(ii) From (i), Fig. 6.24, and the intermediate value theorem (Section 5.2) deduce that there is a point where the second derivative is zero. Show that the slope is a minimum at this point, and that the minimum slope is less or equal to 1.

(iii) Show that the function has an inverse if one of the points $x = \pm 1$ is removed from the domain. Give sketches showing the form of the graph of the inverse function. Obtain formulas for the rule of the inverse function, and state its domain and range.

6.36 (i) Show that the slope of the curve represented by the parametric equations $x = t - \sin t$, $y = 1 - \cos t$ is given by $dy/dx = \cos \frac{1}{2}t$.

(ii) Sketch that part of the curve corresponding to $0 \leq t \leq 2\pi$.

(iii) Use the periodicity of sin and cos to give the form of the complete curve. (This is a **cycloid**—the path of a point on the rim of a rolling wheel of unit radius.)

6.37 Evaluate $f^{(5)}(x)$ for $f(x) = e^{-x^2}$, and hence determine the intervals on which $f^{(4)}(x)$ is decreasing or increasing. Find the minimum and maximum values of $f^{(4)}(x)$ on the interval $[0, 1]$.

6.38 Sketch the curves represented by the following relations:

(i) $y^2 = 6 \sin x + 8$ (ii) $y^2 = 6 \sin x + 3$.

Discuss how the form of the curve represented by $y^2 = 6 \sin x + b$ depends on b.

6.39 Discuss how the form of the curve $y = \sin x + b/\sin x$ depends on b.

6.40 Find $(1/y) \, dy/dx$ if $y = [(x + 5)^2 \sin 2x]/(2x + 3)^7$.

6.41 Find $f^{(10)}(0)$ when $f(x) = (x^3 - 1)e^x$.

6.42 Find dy/dx at the point $(\frac{1}{2}, 1)$ if $y^3 + 2x^2y = 1 + x$.

6.43 Find a unit tangent vector to the curve

$$r(t) = \sqrt{2} \cos t \, \mathbf{i} + \sqrt{2} \sin t \, \mathbf{j} + \sqrt{7} \, t \, \mathbf{k}$$

at the point $(1, 1, 7\frac{1}{2}\pi/4)$.

Find the point P of the curve where the tangent vector is perpendicular to the vector $\overrightarrow{OP}$.

6.44 Solve the following inequalities:

(a) $\dfrac{2x}{3x - 1} < 1$ (b) $|(x - 1)e^x| < e^2$.

6.45 Determine whether

$$f(x) = \begin{cases} (2-x^2)/x & (x \leqslant -1) \\ x^2 & (-1 < x < 2) \\ (2x^2+8)/x^2 & (x \geqslant 2) \end{cases}$$

has a sup, inf, max or min, giving the values of those which exist. Giving reasons, state whether f is (a) continuous (b) even (c) differentiable.

6.46 Solve the inequality $|x^2 - 17| \leqslant 8$.

6.47 For $y = x^{\ln x}$ $(x > 0)$, express dy/dx in terms of x.

6.48 If x and y are related by the parametric equations

$$x = t^3 - 2t^2, \qquad y = t^4 + 5t^2 + 1,$$

express d^2y/dx^2 in terms of t.

6.49 Find $f^{(5)}(0)$ when $f(x) = (x^3 - 1)e^x$.

6.50 Let $g(x) = x - x^{1/3}$. Discuss whether Rolle's theorem is applicable to g on the interval $[-1, 1]$. Is there an x in $(-1, 1)$ for which $g'(x) = 0$?

6.51 For $w = f(x, y, z) = xy^2 + x^2z$, obtain expressions for w_{yz} and $\partial^2 f/\partial x\, \partial z$, and evaluate $f_x(3, 1, 4)$ and $\partial^2 w/\partial y^2|_{2,7,8}$.

6.52 Find the intervals on which the following inequalities are true:

(i) $\dfrac{x}{2x-3} > 1$ (ii) $|x^2 - 10| < 6$ (iii) $|(x+1)e^x| < 1$

6.53 Find a unit tangent vector to the curve

$$r = (2 \sin 2t)i + (2 \cos 2t)j + 6tk$$

at the point $(\sqrt{3}, 1, \pi)$.

6.54 For $f(x) = (x^3 - 1) \sin x$, find $f^{(5)}(0)$.

6.55 Consider the function f with domain $[0, 3]$ and rule

$$f(x) = (x^2 - 3x + 2)\tan x.$$

For each of the following intervals, state whether Rolle's theorem can be applied (giving reasons):
(a) $[0, 1]$ (b) $[1, 2]$ (c) $[2, 3]$ (d) $[2, \pi]$.

6.56 Use Rolle's theorem to show that

$$x^5 + 5x^4 + 60x^3 - 21x^2 + 11x + 2 = 0$$

has at most 3 distinct real roots.

6.57 Show that, if

$$x^5 + ax^4 + bx^3 + cx^2 + dx + e = 0$$

has 5 real roots, then $2a^2 > 5b$.

6.58 If $w = f(x, y, z) = x^3y^2 - yz^3 + x^2z$, find an expression for $\partial^2 w/\partial y^2$, and evaluate $f_{xx}(1, 2, -1)$.

6.59 Find $f^{(n)}(x)$ for $f(x) = (x^2 + 2x + 4)e^x$.

6.60 Solve $|(2x+1)/(x-1)| > 3$.

6.61 If $w = f(x, y) = \cos(x^2 + xy + y^2)$, find an expression for w_{xy}, and evaluate $f_{yy}(\sqrt{\pi}, \sqrt{\pi})$.

6.62 Solve the inequality $|x^2 - 10| < 5x - 14$.

6.63 Find $(1/y)\,dy/dx$ for $y=[(x+3)^3(2x-1)^4\cos 3x]/(3x+1)^5\,e^x$.

6.64 If x and y are related by the parametric equations

$$x=t^4-2t, \qquad y=t^3+t^2+1,$$

express d^2y/dx^2 in terms of t.

6.65 For $f(x)=(x^2+2x+2)\,e^x$, calculate $f^{(12)}(x)$.

6.66 Show that the point $P(-1,-2,0)$ is on the curve

$$r=\cos 2t\,i+2\sin t\,j+\cos 3t\,k.$$

Find a tangent vector to the curve at P.

6.67 A function f has domain $[0,3]$ and rule

$$f(x)=\frac{\tan x}{x^2-3x+2} \qquad (x\neq 1,\tfrac{1}{2}\pi,2)$$

$$f(1)=1, \qquad f(\tfrac{1}{2}\pi)=0, \qquad f(2)=2$$

For each of the intervals
(a) $[0,1]$ (b) $[1.5,1.6]$ (c) $[2.5,3.0]$
state whether the mean value theorem (of differentiation) is applicable. If the theorem is not applicable, give the condition(s) which f fails to satisfy.

6.68 Find the intervals on which $y=e^{-x}/x$ is decreasing. Sketch the curve, and hence solve the inequality $e^{-x}/x<1/e$.

6.69 How many distinct third partial derivatives are there
   (i) for a function of two independent variables?
   (ii) for a function of three independent variables?

6.70 Express $(d^n/dx^n)\,(x\sin x)$ in terms of n and x.

6.71 Find (in terms of n) the value at $x=0$ of $(d^n/dx^n)\,\{x^n(1-x)^n\}$.

6.72 Show that, for the relation $\sqrt{x/y}+2\sqrt{y/x}=3$, $dy/dx=1$ or $\tfrac{1}{4}$.

6.73 If $x^n+y^n=c^n$, express d^2y/dx^2 in terms of x, c and n.

6.74 Find the derivatives of (i) $y=x^{\cos x}$ (ii) $y=(\cos x)^x$.

6.75 Find (in terms of t) a unit normal vector at any point of the cycloid represented by

$$r(t)=(t-\sin t)i+(1-\cos t)j.$$

7
Numerical Solution of Equations

7.1 Newton's Method

Any equation with one unknown x can be written in the form $f(x) = 0$, so that the solutions are the values of x where the graph of f cuts the x-axis. Suppose that the number of solutions and their approximate locations are known. If $x = x_r$ is an approximation to one of the solutions, Newton's method of calculating a better approximation x_{r+1} is illustrated in Fig. 7.1. Geometrically, take the point Q where the tangent at $P(x_r, f(x_r))$

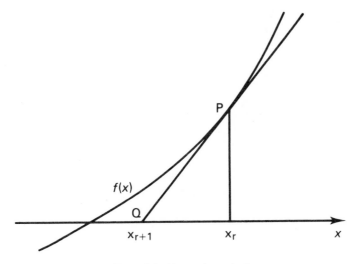

Figure 7.1   Newton's method

cuts the x-axis. The slope at P is $f'(x_r) = PM/QM = f(x_r)/(x_r - x_{r+1})$. Rearranging this equation gives

$$x_{r+1} = x_r - f(x_r)/f'(x_r). \tag{7.1}$$

Then, starting from an initial approximation x_0, repeated use of equation (7.1) gives $x_1 = x_0 - f(x_0)/f'(x_0)$, $x_2 = x_1 - f(x_1)/f'(x_1)$, etc. This **iteration** of formula (7.1) may be continued until sufficient accuracy is attained. The iteration is illustrated geometrically in Fig. 7.2

Example 7.10
Find the solution of $x^5 - 5x + 2 = 0$ satisfying $0 < x < 1$.

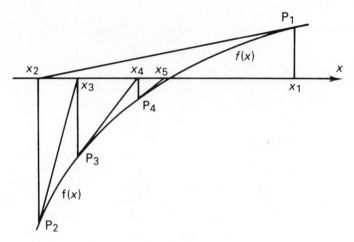

Figure 7.2   Iteration of Newton's formula

The polynomial $P(x) = x^5 - 5x + 2$ has just one root r in $(0, 1)$. (Examples 5.22 on p. 100 and 6.71 on p. 129.) Take $x_0 = \frac{1}{2}$ as the initial approximation, and use equation (7.1) with $f = P$.

Then

$$P(\tfrac{1}{2}) = \tfrac{1}{32} - \tfrac{1}{2} = -\tfrac{15}{32},$$
$$P'(\tfrac{1}{2}) = 5(\tfrac{1}{16} - 1) = -\tfrac{75}{16},$$

and

$$x_1 = \tfrac{1}{2} - P(\tfrac{1}{2})/P'(\tfrac{1}{2}) = \tfrac{1}{2} - \tfrac{1}{10} = 0.4.$$

The next iteration requires $P(0.4) = 0.4^5 = 0.01024$, and $P'(0.4) = 5(0.4^4 - 1) = -4.872$, giving the next approximation

$$x_2 = 0.4 - P(0.4)/P'(0.4) = 0.4021 \quad (4S)$$

where (4S) signifies that the **arithmetic** is correct to 4 significant figures.

Assuming that the figures which are unchanged in an iteration are correct gives $r = 0.40$ (2S). The precise meaning of this statement is that r lies between 0.395 and 0.405, which is easily verified. Since $P(x)$ decreases through zero at $x = r$ (Fig. 7.3), and $P(0.4) > 0$, $r > 0.4$. As $P(0.405) = 0.011 - 2.025 + 2. < 0$, $r < 0.405$. Thus $r = 0.40$ is correct to two decimal places (or significant figures). □

Example 7.11
Find, correct to 3S, all the roots of $P(x) = x^5 - 5x + 2$.

The first step is to proceed as in Examples 6.71 and 5.22, to show that there are just three roots r, s, t with $-2 < s < -1$, $0 < r < 1$, and $1 < t < 2$ (or find some other approximate locations of the three roots). Then proceed as in the previous example, which determined r. The following table shows results obtained using $x_0 = -1.5$ as the initial approximation to s, and using $x_0 = 1.2$ as the initial approximation to t.

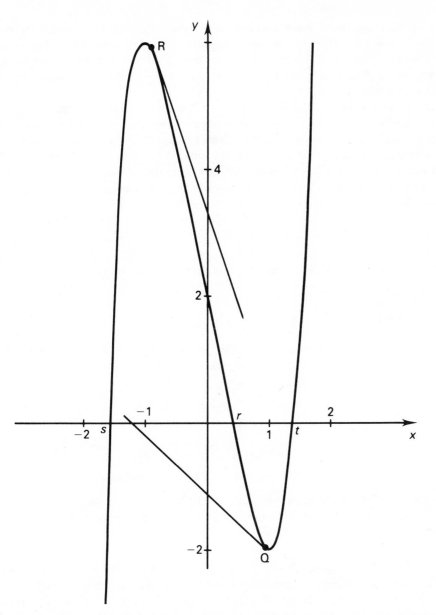

Figure 7.3 Unsatisfactory initial approximations for roots of $x^5 - 5x + 2$

Table 7.1

x	$P(x)$	$P'(x)$	$-P(x)/P'(x)$	$(4x/5) + (4x-2)/P'(x)$
-1.5	$61/32$	$325/16$	-0.0938	-1.5938
-1.5938	-0.3152	27.2630	0.0115	-1.5822
-1.5823	-0.0071			
1.2	-1.5117	5.3680	0.2816	1.4816
1.4816	1.7311	19.0925	-0.0906	1.3909
1.3910	0.2526	13.7190	-0.0184	1.3725
1.3726	0.0090			

These calculations have been stopped when the value of $P(x)$ indicates that the next correction $-P(x)/P'(x)$ will not change the second decimal place. The results are $s = -1.58(3S)$ and $t = 1.37$ (3S). In the last column, the next approximation $x - (x^5 + 5x + 2)/(5x^4 - 5)$ is calculated as $(4x/5) + \{(4x - 2)/5(x^4 - 1)\}$, providing a check on the arithmetic.

From the graph (Fig. 7.3) of $P(x) = x^5 - 5x + 2$, the effect of different initial approximations x_0 can be seen. If $x_0 < -1$, then all subsequent approximations are less than s, and an approximation to s will be obtained. Similarly $x_0 > 1$ results in an approximation to t. However if x_0 is just greater than -1, the tangent (at R in Fig. 7.3) may cut Ox at a point with $x > 1$, leading to t when the iteration is continued. Similarly an initial approximation to r which is too close to 1 will result in the root s being obtained (tangent at Q in Fig. 7.3).   □

Calculations using Newton's method involve the iteration of a single formula (7.1), and are therefore easily programmed for computer use. BASIC and FORTRAN programs are given in Appendix C, based on the flow diagram given on p. 176.

Example 7.12
Solve the equation $\ln x = \sin x$.

In Example 6.93 it was observed that this equation has only one solution a, satisfying $\pi/2 < a < e$. To apply Newton's method, take $f(x) = \ln x - \sin x$, $f'(x) = x^{-1} - \cos x$, and $x_0 = 2$. Iterating equation (7.1) gives

$$f(2) = -0.216150, \qquad x_1 = 2.235934$$

$$f(x_1) = 0.178273\text{E} - 1, \qquad x_2 = 2.219186$$

$$f(x_2) = 0.826436\text{E} - 4, \qquad x_3 = 2.219107$$

$$f(x_3) = 0.187720\text{E} - 8. \qquad \text{(where E}n \text{ means} \times 10^n)$$

With the computer program in Appendix C, the iteration then stops because $|x_3 - x_4| < 1\text{E} - 6$. The result $a = 2.219107$ also provides a more accurate solution of the inequality in Example 6.93.   □

In the discussion of the result $r = 0.40$ (2S) in Example 7.10, the accuracy was measured by the difference between the true root r and the approximate root x_2. This concept of accuracy is reflected in the computer program by the stopping condition—that successive approximations differ by less than a prescribed amount E. However a discussion of accuracy should consider the purpose for which the solution is required. For example, the important point may be that the value of $f(x)$ should be in a prescribed neighbourhood of zero. It is easy to alter the stopping condition to depend on the smallness of $|f(x)|$.

In Example 7.11 it was shown that it is possible to choose an initial approximation x_0 which will lead to the wrong root. Even when the desired root is obtained, a poor choice of x_0 can greatly increase the number of iterations which are necessary. It is also possible to construct examples for which the method fails to obtain any solution.

Example 7.13
Find the larger solution of $1.035x = \exp(0.03431x)$.

A sketch shows that the line $y = 1.035x$ cuts the curve $y = \exp(0.03431x)$ in two points, one near $x = 1$, and one at a much larger value of x. Note that $y = \exp(0.03431x)$, being an exponential function, tends to infinity faster than $y = 1.035x$.

With $f(x) = 1.035x - \exp(0.03431x)$, the computer program gives the following results:

	i	x_i	$f(x_i)$
(i) $x_0 = 50$	0	50	46.19
	1	−4.71	−5.727
	2	0.98	−0.0173
	3	1.00	−1.8E−7
(ii) $x_0 = 100$	0	100	72.59
	1	2954	−1E44
	20	2400	−6E35
	40	1817	−1E27
	60	1234	−2E18
	80	651	−5E9
	100	146.34	−0.0102
	102	146.3184798	0
(iii) $x_0 = 200$	0	200	−748
	1	176	−243
	2	159	−66
	3	149	−11
	4	146.5	−0.56
	5	146.3189	−0.0016
	6	146.3184798	0

The first choice of x_0 gives the wrong root; the second gives the larger root, but only after 102 iterations, whch is excessive compared to the 6 iterations required in the third calculation.

These results appear because f has a maximum when x is just less than 100 (Fig. 7.4 shows the tangents corresponding to the first approximation in each iteration (i), (ii) and (iii)).   □

Example 7.14
The equation $0.03431x = \exp(1.035x)$ has no solution, and the values of $f(x) = 0.03431x - \exp(1.035x)$ are all negative, with a maximum value of -0.146 at $x = -3.3$. If an attempt is made to find a solution, using Newton's method, the first few values of x_i oscillate about the position of the maximum:

i	0	1	2	3	4	5	6	7	8	9	10	11	12	13	14
x_i	0	−1	−2	−5	2	1	0.1	−1	−2	−4	4	3	2	1	0.3

Further values ($i = 12, 24, 36, \ldots$) are shown in Fig. 7.5.   □

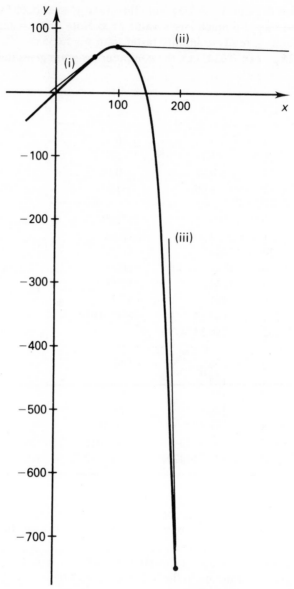

Figure 7.4 $y = 1.035x - \exp(0.03431x)$

Example 7.15

If $f(x) = \sqrt[3]{(x-r)}$, then

$$x - f(x)/f'(x) = r - 2(x-r) = r + 2(r-x).$$

This means that equation (7.1) always gives a point on the opposite side of the root r, and twice as far away:

(i) $x > r$: ⊢———+——+——+   (ii) $x < r$: ——+———+———+

$r - 2(x-r)$ r x x r $r + 2(r-x)$

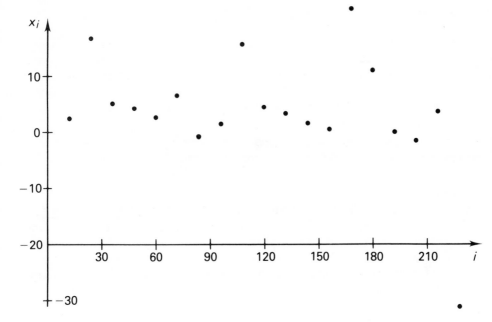

Figure 7.5   Values of x_i obtained after i iterations; $i = 12(12)216$

For example, $x_0 = r + 1$ gives $x_1 = r - 2$, $x_2 = r + 4$, $x_3 = r - 8, \ldots$

The root $x = r$ cannot be obtained by Newton's method.   □

In Newton's method, each application of equation (7.1) usually improves the approximation. In a hand calculation, it is therefore unnecessary to retain a large number of significant figures during the first few iterations. For instance, in calculation (iii) of Example 7.13 three significant figures are sufficient until x_5 is calculated. Some labour may thus be avoided. Also any undetected mistake will automatically be rectified in Newton's method. Obviously arithmetic mistakes will sometimes occur, unless a programmed calculator is being used.

Exercises (answers on p. 177)

7.1.1   Show that the equation

$$f(x) = 32x^3 - 72x^2 + 48x - 9 = 0$$

has three roots. Choose three starting values for Newton's method which will give the three different roots on iteration. In each case calculate the first iteration.

7.1.2   Show that the equation $x^3 + x = 1$ has just one solution. Apply Newton's method, starting from $x_0 = 1$, and stopping (i) when $|x_i - x_{i+1}| < 0.1$, (ii) when $|x^3 + x - 1| < 0.1$. What estimates for the root are thereby obtained?

7.2   Errors

Using Newton's method, after n iterations one obtains a number x_n which is an approximate solution of the equation $f(x) = 0$. Suppose the iterations are producing numbers that get closer and closer to the required root r, and that no arithmetical mistakes have been made. Then $x_n - r$ may be called the error in the approximation x_n. The purpose of the present section is to distinguish two different causes of this error.

> Since the accuracy increases as n gets larger, one source of error is simply taking too small a value for n. This is called **truncation error**.

Example 7.20
Consider Example 7.12 and work to 5 significant figures (5S). Then the root is $a = 2.2191 = x_3$, while $x_2 = 2.2192$, $x_1 = 2.2359$. The truncation error in x_1 is $x_1 - a = 0.0168$, and the truncation error in x_2 is $1\mathrm{E} - 4$. For x_3 the truncation error is negligible; but note that the truth of this statement depends on the accuracy required or stated. Here $(x_3 - a) < 0.5\mathrm{E} - 4$, so that any further reduction in the truncation error (by increasing n) does not alter the 5th significant figure.   □

> The other source of error in a numerical calculation lies in the fact that the arithmetical operations can only be performed to a certain number of decimal places. Products or quotients are rounded off, and the resulting error is called **rounding error**.

Example 7.21
If the calculation in Example 7.12 is made using 4-figure tables to get the values of ln, sin, and cos, and rounding-off quotients to four decimal places (4D), one obtains $x_2 = 2.2192$, $f(x_2) = 0.0000$. Another iteration then makes no difference ($x_3 = x_2$). Thus working to 4D only gives the root correct to 3D. Unless more accurate values of ln, sin and cos are available, this error is not reduced by further iteration, so it is quite distinct from truncation error. (Similarly, any n-figure calculator gives limited accuracy.)

The above statement, that $x_2 = 2.2192$ is correct to 3D, was made by comparison with the previous calculation in Example 7.12. It can also be deduced from the calculation to 4D, for which the maximum error in any rounding-off is 5 in the 5th decimal place, which is $\frac{1}{2}$ in the 4th decimal place. The sign of the rounding error is unknown, since it is not known whether the numbers in the 4-figure tables are rounded down or rounded up. Hence the maximum rounding error in the 4th decimal place of $\ln x_2$ and $\sin x_2$ is $\pm\frac{1}{2}$. Assuming the worst, that both errors are maximum and have opposite sign, the maximum rounding error in $f(x_2) = 0.0000$ is ± 1 in the 4th place. So $|f(x_2)| < 0.0001$, and in Fig. 7.6, the $x = x_2$ point of the graph is somewhere on AB. If CA and BD are lines through A and B with the slope $f'(x_2)$, the tangent at x_2 is parallel to and between AC and BD. The next approximation x_3 is somewhere on CD. Since $f'(x_2) = 1$ (1S), CD $= 0.0002$ and $|x_3 - x_2| \leq 0.0001$: the next approximation gives a change of at most 1 in the 4th place. Therefore the 3rd place in x_2 is correct.

In this argument, rounding errors in the calculation of x_2 do not have to be considered, because the way in which x_2 is obtained is not relevant. The fact that the next iteration always improves the approximation in Newton's method means that the consideration of rounding error can be confined to the last iteration.   □

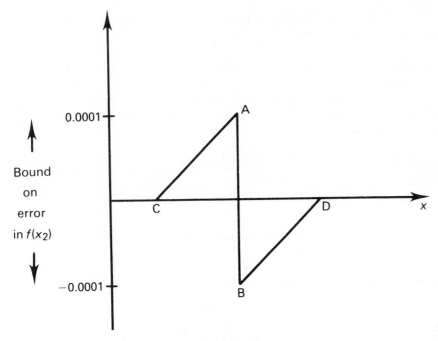

Figure 7.6   Rounding error in $f(x) = \ln x - \sin x$

The next example illustrates how the rounding error can depend on the way that a quantity is evaluated.

Example 7.22
Comparing the first and last columns of Table 7.1 (p. 163), one sees a difference in the last decimal place of three of the values. This will now be shown to result from rounding errors.

Suppose ε and δ are the rounding errors introduced when P and P' are calculated. Then the quotient actually evaluated is

$$\frac{P+\varepsilon}{P'+\delta} = \frac{P+\varepsilon}{P'(1+y)}, \quad \text{where } y = \delta/P'.$$

As y is small, y^2 is negligible compared to 1 ($y^2 \ll 1$), and $(1 \pm y)$ can be taken to be reciprocals of each other. Then the quotient becomes

$$\frac{(P+\varepsilon)(1-y)}{P'} = \frac{P}{P'} + \frac{\varepsilon}{P'} - \frac{\delta P}{P'^2},$$

also neglecting the $\varepsilon\delta$ product term. At the values of x considered, P is small, and P'^2 large, so ε/P' is an estimate of the rounding error in P/P'. This is the rounding error in the first column of Table 7.1.

Similarly, the rounding error in $(4x-2)/P'$ is $-\delta(4x-2)P'^2$, which is negligible for the values of P' considered. The rounding error in the last column of Table 7.1 therefore comes from the evaluation of $4x/5$.

Thus the rounding errors in columns 1 and 5 of Table 7.1 arise in different ways, which explains the discrepancy between the results.   □

The significance of errors can only be judged by distinguishing between **absolute error** and **relative error**. In 2.2192 ± 0.0001, the absolute error is ± 0.0001, and the relative error 1 part in 22192, or 0.0045%. On the other hand, with $f(x_2) = 0.0001$, the approximate value 0.0000 (obtained in Example 7.21) has the same absolute error -0.0001, but the relative error is 100%.

> Whenever two nearly equal numbers are subtracted there is always a loss of significant figures, and this may greatly increase the relative error.

Example 7.23
Find the solutions of $x^2 + 10x + 0.02 = 0$ correct to 4S, given 5-figure tables of square roots and reciprocals.

The usual formula (A.2) for the roots of a quadratic gives

$$x = -5 \pm \sqrt{24.98} = -5 \pm 4.9981 = -9.9981 \text{ and } -0.0019.$$

To 4S, one solution is evidently -9.998, but the other has only two significant figures. However the product of the roots has to be 0.02, so the second root can also be calculated as $0.02/-9.998 = -0.02 \times 0.10002$ (using the table of reciprocals). This gives -0.002000 (4S). Note that, because of rounding errors in nearly equal numbers which are subtracted, the previous result -0.0019 was not even correct to 2S.   □

In Newton's method, as the iteration proceeds, calculated values of $f(x)$ get smaller, and often are naturally obtained by the subtraction of nearly equal quantities. The resulting error can be reduced by evaluating $x - f(x)/f'(x)$ in a way that does not require the evaluation of $f(x)$, for example the form used in the last column of Table 7.1 on p. 163.

Rounding error is usually insignificant when each iteration improves the approximation, or when only a few iterations are required. Otherwise rounding errors build up as a calculation proceeds, until the numbers obtained are meaningless as far as the original objective is concerned. An example of this has already been illustrated in Fig. 7.5, which shows values of x_i obtained by applying Newton's iteration formula (7.1) on p. 161 to an equation with no root (Example 7.14). These values were calculated on a Control Data 3200 computer. Performing the same calculation on a Burroughs 6700 computer gave

$$x_{60} = 2.616 \ (2.620), \qquad x_{72} = 5.58 \ (6.19),$$

$$x_{84} = -1.6 \ (-1.0), \qquad x_{96} = -4.05 \ (1.26), \qquad x_{168} = -2 \ (22).$$

The numbers in brackets are those obtained from the 3200 computer, and the difference between the two sets of results can only be attributed to the fact that the two computers round-off to different approximations. After about 70 iterations, rounding errors have built up to the extent that the subsequent calculations are meaningless. It should be stressed that, with Newton's method, this only happens when there is no root to be found, so that the calculation is meaningless anyway. However it provides an illustration of the way in which rounding error might invalidate other numerical processes.

In principle, the maximum possible rounding error can always be calculated as in Example 7.21 using the fact that in each round-off the maximum error in the last decimal place is $\frac{1}{2}$. This is also true for computer calculations provided one remembers that computers use base 2 arithmetic. The actual rounding error is usually much less than the possible maximum owing to cancellations of errors of opposite sign. This is because rounding is sometimes down (e.g. $0.322 \rightarrow 0.32$ with rounding error -0.002) and sometimes up (e.g. $0.327 \rightarrow 0.33$ with rounding error $+0.003$). To encourage such cancellations, a number with last figure 5 can be rounded to the nearest even number, for example $0.325 \rightarrow 0.32$ and $0.335 \rightarrow 0.34$.

Subtracting nearly equal numbers has already been mentioned as an operation to avoid if possible. If it cannot be avoided, the calculation should be arranged so that the numbers are subtracted at an early stage, before rounding errors have built up. Another arithmetic operation that should always be done as soon as possible is multiplication by a large number, or, equivalently, division by a small number. This is because the accumulated rounding error gets multiplied by the large number.

Exercises (answers on p. 177)

7.2.1 Compare the result of rounding-off 1.23455 to 2D (i) in a single operation, (ii) digit by digit, using the rule of rounding 5 to an even number.

7.2.2 For the five numbers 0.333
$$0.905$$
$$0.033$$
$$0.493$$
$$0.122$$
compare the results of (i) adding and then rounding to 2D, (ii) rounding to 2D and then adding.

7.2.3 To evaluate a quadratic expression, either side of
$$(x^2) + (ax) + b = \{x(x+a)\} + b$$
may be used. How many arithmetic operations are used in the alternative methods? Which method is likely to have least rounding error?

7.3   The Bisection Method

Suppose there is a solution of $f(x) = 0$ in (a, b). Assume that f is continuous on $[a, b]$, and that $f(a)$ and $f(b)$ have opposite sign (Fig. 7.7). If $a < c < b$, then the sign of $f(c)$ shows whether the solution lies in (a, c) or (c, b) (Fig. 7.7). Taking $c = \frac{1}{2}a + \frac{1}{2}b$ for simplicity, so that c is the midpoint of (a, b), means that the size of the interval in which the solution is known to lie has been halved (bisected).

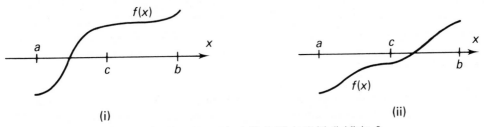

(i)   (ii)

Figure 7.7   Bisection method: (i) $f(a)f(c) < 0$ (ii) $f(a)f(c) > 0$

If the process is repeated, each iteration halves the size of the interval containing the solution. After n iterations this interval has length $(b-a)/2^n$, and so whatever accuracy is required can be obtained.

Example 7.30
Find the smallest solution of $e^{-x} = \sin(\frac{1}{2}\pi x)$.

A sketch shows that all solutions are positive, and that the smallest, say $x = r$, is in the interval $(0, 1)$ (Fig. 7.8). If $f(x) = e^{-x} - \sin(\frac{1}{2}\pi x)$, then $f(0) = 1 > 0$, $f(1) = e^{-1} - 1 < 0$, and

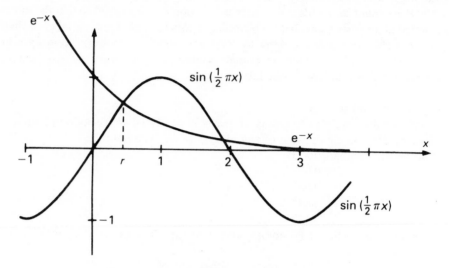

Figure 7.8   Intersections of graphs of e^{-x} and $\sin(\frac{1}{2}\pi x)$

the first five iterations of the bisection method give:

Iteration	a	b	c	$f(c) = e^{-c} - \sin(\frac{1}{2}\pi c)$
1	0	1	$\frac{1}{2}$	$0.6065 - 0.7071 < 0$
2	0	$\frac{1}{2}$	$\frac{1}{4}$	$0.7788 - 0.3827 > 0$
3	$\frac{1}{4}$	$\frac{1}{2}$	$\frac{3}{8}$	$0.6873 - 0.5556 > 0$
4	$\frac{3}{8}$	$\frac{1}{2}$	$\frac{7}{16}$	$0.6456 - 0.6344 = 0.0112 > 0$
5	$\frac{7}{16}$	$\frac{1}{2}$	$\frac{15}{32}$	$0.6258 - 0.6716 = -0.0458 < 0$

At this stage it is known that $0.4375 = \frac{7}{16} < r < \frac{15}{32} = 0.46875$; and comparing the last 2 values of $f(c)$ shows that r is closer to $\frac{7}{16}$, so that $r = 0.4$ (1S). With the alternative criterion of $|f(x)| < 0.01$ (say), the results suggest $x = 0.44$, and $f(0.44) = 0.0066$ can be verified. For higher accuracy the iteration can be continued; for example iteration 12 gives $f(0.4436) = -5.66E - 5$. □

Figure 7.7 showed the situation when $f(a) < 0$ and $f(b) > 0$. To write a computer program which also allows the alternative signs it is convenient to test the sign of $f(a)f(c)$ rather than that of $f(c)$. In other words instead of asking for the sign of $f(c)$, ask whether

$f(c)$ and $f(a)$ have the same sign. If so, the solution is in (c, b); if not, it is in (a, c). The resulting flow chart is given in Section 7.5 at the end of the chapter. FORTRAN and BASIC programs are given in Appendix C.

The main advantage of the bisection method over Newton's method is that f' does not have to be obtained or programmed. In fact, f need not be differentiable. However, provided the derivative is not too small, Newton's method requires fewer iterations. Whether differentiation or a larger number of iterations is more formidable will depend both on the particular example and on the available computational facilities.

The bisection method is sometimes called either the **half interval search** method, or the **binary search** method.

Exercises (answers on p. 177)

7.3.1 Apply the bisection method to the equation $\ln x = \sin x$, starting with the interval $(2.0, 2.4)$, and stopping when $\ln$ and $\sin$ differ by less than 0.01. Deduce that $x = 2.2$ is correct to 2S.

7.3.2 In Example 7.10, the root in $(0, \frac{1}{2})$ of $x^5 - 5x + 2 = 0$ was found correct to 2D with two iterations using Newton's method. Show that, starting from $(0, \frac{1}{2})$, the bisection method requires 6 iterations to get 2D accuracy.

7.4 Direct Iteration

The Newton-Raphson procedure for solving $f(x) = 0$ iterates a formula of the form $x_{n+1} = g(x_n)$, with $g(x) = x - f(x)/f'(x)$. It is possible to obtain other iteration formulas by directly rearranging $f(x) = 0$ into the form $x = g(x)$.

Example 7.40 (cf. Example 7.10 on p. 162)
(i) The equation

$$f(x) = x^5 - 5x + 2 = 0$$

can be rearranged to

$$x = \tfrac{1}{5}(x^5 + 2) = g(x). \tag{7.2}$$

Taking $x_0 = \frac{1}{2}$ as an initial approximation to the root in $(0, 1)$, iteration of equation (7.2) gives

$$x_1 = g(x_0) = \tfrac{1}{5}(x_0^5 + 2) = \tfrac{13}{32} = 0.406$$

$$x_2 = g(x_1) = \tfrac{1}{5}(x_1^5 + 2) = 0.4022$$

$$x_3 = g(x_2) = 0.402105$$

$$x_4 = g(x_3) = 0.402102,$$

showing a satisfactory convergence towards the root.
(ii) Taking $x_0 = -1.5$ as a first approximation to the root in $(-2, -1)$ leads to $x_1 = -1.12$, $x_2 = 0.05$, $x_3 = 0.4$, which is evidently converging onto the wrong root.
(iii) Taking $x_0 = -2$ does not give convergence: $x_1 = 6$, $x_2 = -1555, \ldots$
(iv) An alternative rearrangement of $x^5 - 5x + 2 = 0$ is

$$x = \sqrt[5]{(5x - 2)} = g_1(x). \tag{7.3}$$

Iterating (7.3) from the initial approximation $x_0 = -1.5$ now gives a sequence converging to the required root:

$$x_1 = g_1(x_0) = \sqrt[5]{(5x_0 - 2)} = \sqrt[5]{(-9.5)} = -1.56,$$

$$x_2 = g_1(x_1) = \sqrt[5]{(-9.8)} = -1.579,$$

$$x_3 = g_1(x_2) = \sqrt[5]{(-9.9)} = -1.582, \ldots \quad \Box$$

The two useless calculations (ii) and (iii) in the previous example can be avoided by using the following result:

the iteration of $x_{n+1} = g(x_n)$ converges to the required root r (i.e. $r = g(r)$) if x_0 and r lie in an interval in which $|g'(x)|$ has an upper bound which is less than 1, say $|g'(x)| \leq \alpha < 1$.

Example 7.41
The behaviour of the iterations in Example 7.40 can now be predicted in advance.
 (i) If $g(x) = \frac{1}{5}(x^5 + 2)$, then $g'(x) = x^4$. There is a root in $(0, \frac{1}{2})$. On this interval $|g'(x)| \leq \frac{1}{16} < 1$, so starting from $x_0 = \frac{1}{2}$ convergence is assured ($\alpha = \frac{1}{16}$).
 (ii) and (iii) In $(-2, -1)$, $g'(x) = x^4 > 1$, so no choice of x_0 will give convergence to the root in $(-2, -1)$.
 (iv) If $g_1(x) = (5x - 2)^{1/5}$, $g_1'(x) = (5x - 2)^{-4/5}$, and on $(-2, -1)$

$$(\tfrac{1}{12})^{4/5} < |g_1'(x)| < (\tfrac{1}{7})^{4/5} = 0.21$$

Thus $\alpha = (\frac{1}{7})^{4/5} < 1$ bounds $|g_1'(x)|$, and convergence to the root is assured from any x_0 in $(-2, -1)$. $\Box$

To use the result, it is sufficient to decide that $\alpha < 1$ exists, without actually finding $\sup|g'(x)|$.

The above convergence condition may be deduced by applying the mean value theorem (see Section 6.7) to the function g on the interval $[x_n, r]$ (or $[r, x_n]$): for some number c between x_n and r, $(x_n - r)g'(c) = g(x_n) - g(r)$.

Since $g(r) = r$, and the iteration formula is $g(x_n) = x_{n+1}$, this can be written $x_{n+1} - r = g'(c)(x_n - r)$, giving

$$|x_{n+1} - r| = |g'(c)||x_n - r|$$

Hence, if $g'(c) \leq \alpha$,

$$|x_{n+1} - r| \leq \alpha|x_n - r|. \tag{7.4}$$

This inequality is true for any n, for example

$$|x_1 - r| \leq \alpha|x_0 - r|.$$

If $\alpha < 1$, this means that x_1 is nearer to r than x_0. Similarly

$$|x_2 - r| \leq \alpha|x_1 - r| \leq \alpha^2|x_0 - r|$$

$$|x_3 - r| \leq \alpha|x_2 - r| \leq \alpha^3|x_0 - r|$$

leading to

$$|x_n - r| \leqslant \alpha^n |x_0 - r|. \tag{7.5}$$

As $\alpha < 1$, $\alpha^n \to 0$ as $n \to \infty$, and so $|x_n - r| \to 0$, $x_n \to r$. The sequence $\{x_i\}$ of iterations converges to the required root.

This proof shows that the smaller the value of α, the faster the convergence. It also shows how to get an upper bound on the truncation error at any stage.

Example 7.42

In Example 7.40(i), the x_n are in $(0, \frac{1}{2})$, and on this interval $|g'(x)| = x^4 < \frac{1}{16}$. In equation (7.5), $|x_0 - r| < \frac{1}{2}$, so the equation gives $|x_n - r| \leqslant \frac{1}{2}(\frac{1}{16})^n$. Thus $\frac{1}{2}(\frac{1}{16})^n$ is an upper bound on the truncation error in x_n. For example $n = 4$ gives

$$|x_4 - r| \leqslant (\tfrac{1}{2})^{17} < 10^{-5}.$$

This means that the 4th figure in x_4 is certainly correct $(r = 0.4021(4S))$, and that the 5th figure is at most one out.

Similarly in Example 7.40(iv), $|x_0 - r| < 1$, and $\alpha = \frac{1}{4}$ is an upper bound on $|g_1'(x)|$ in $(-2, -1)$. From (7.5),

$$|x_n - r| < (\tfrac{1}{2})^{2n}.$$

For instance if the final approximation should satisfy

$$|x_n - r| < 0.005 = \tfrac{1}{200},$$

the bound $(\frac{1}{2})^{2n}$ gives this if $n = 4$. So x_4 should be calculated. $\square$

The iteration method is presented here mainly to give an example of the theoretical evaluation of the efficiency of a numerical method. In practice Newton's method would usually be more convenient, since the iteration method requires not only an approximation to the root, but also an appropriate (and perhaps non-obvious) rearrangement of the given equation.

The general convergence result also indicates that Newton's method is usually efficient. If $g(x) = x - f(x)/f'(x)$, then

$$g'(x) = 1 - \frac{f'^2 - ff''}{f'^2} = \frac{f(x)f''(x)}{[f'(x)]^2}$$

Since $f(r) = 0$, $g'(r) = 0$ unless $f'(r) = 0$. If $g'(r) = 0$, then $|g'(x)|$ should remain quite small in some interval containing the root r, and iterations in such an interval will converge rapidly.

Exercises (answers on p. 177)

7.4.1   Which of the two iteration formulas

$$x = g(x) = \tfrac{1}{5}(x^5 + 2), \qquad x = g_1(x) = (5x - 2)^{1/5}$$

should be used to find the root in $(1, 2)$ of $x^5 - 5x + 2 = 0$? Show that $\alpha = 0.4$ can be used in the convergence result, with the interval $(1, 2)$; deduce that, starting from $x_0 = 1.5$, 5 iterations should give $|x_n - r| < 0.005$.

7.4.2   Find the larger root of the equation (cf. Example 7.13)

$$1.035x = \exp(0.03431x)$$

by direct iteration, and give an upper bound for the truncation error in the result.

7.5   Summaries of Methods for Finding a Root *r* of *f*(*x*)=0

Newton's Method
1   Select one of the alternative criteria in 4.
2   Choose initial approximation x_0 and accuracy parameter ε.

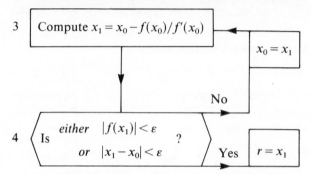

See Appendix C for BASIC and FORTRAN programs.

Bisection Method (Half-interval search, Binary search)
1   Select one of the alternative criteria in 5.
2   Choose accuracy parameter ε.

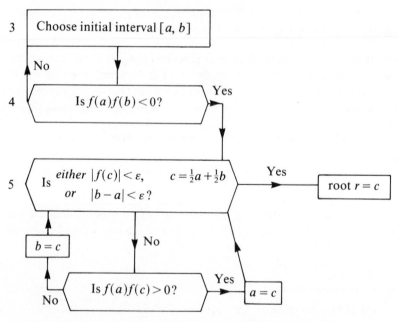

See Appendix C for BASIC and FORTRAN programs.

Iteration Method
1   Select one of the alternative accuracy criteria in 6.
2   Choose initial approximation x_0 and accuracy parameter ε.

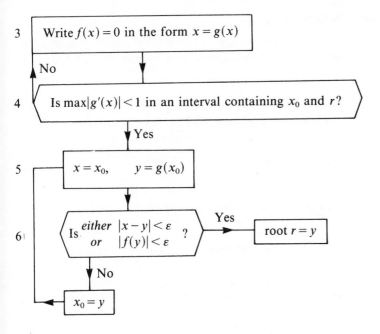

3   Write $f(x) = 0$ in the form $x = g(x)$

No

4   Is $\max |g'(x)| < 1$ in an interval containing x_0 and r?

Yes

5     $x = x_0, \qquad y = g(x_0)$

6   Is $\begin{array}{l} either \ \ |x-y| < \varepsilon \\ or \ \ \ \ \ |f(y)| < \varepsilon \end{array}$?   Yes   root $r = y$

No

$x_0 = y$

See Appendix C for BASIC and FORTRAN programs.

Answers to Exercises 7.1.1–7.4.2

7.1.1 From the sign of $f'(x)$, $f(x)$ is increasing for $x < \frac{1}{2}$ or for $x > 1$, and decreases from 1 to -1 on $[\frac{1}{2}, 1]$. So there are three roots, $r < \frac{1}{2}$, $\frac{1}{2} < s < 1$, and $t > 1$. To obtain r, choose $x_0 < \frac{1}{2}$; to obtain t choose $x_0 > 1$; to obtain s, choose x_0 so that $64x_0^3 - 120x_0^2 + 72x_0 < 15$ and $64x_0^3 - 168x_0^2 + 144x_0 > 37$, for example $x_0 = 3/4$.

7.1.2 (i) and (ii) both stop at $x_2 = 0.69$ (2S), giving an estimate 0.7 (1S) for the root.

7.2.1 (i) 1.23, (ii) 1.24.   **7.2.2** (i) 1.89, (ii) 1.87.

7.2.3 Left expression requires 2 multiplications and 2 additions; right expression requires 1 multiplication less and so is likely to have less rounding error, except perhaps for large x, since the rounding error in $(x + a)$ is multiplied by x.

7.3.1 $x = 2.225$; $x = 2.2$ (2S) as $\ln 2.225 > \sin 2.225$ (cf. Example 7.12).

7.4.1 Use $g_1(x)$. Taking $\alpha = 0.4$ as the bound on g_1' in (1, 2) leads to $|x_5 - r| < 0.00512$, so that 5 iterations should be sufficient. (In fact, 3 are sufficient, because $r > 1.5$ and $\alpha = 0.26$ is a bound on g_1' in (1.5, 2)).

7.4.2 Take

$$g(x) = \frac{\log(1.035x)}{0.03431}, \qquad g'(x) = \frac{30.2}{x}.$$

Then, for example, $x_0 = 100$ gives $\alpha = 0.3$, and after 7 iterations evidently $r < 147$, so $|x_0 - r| < 47$. An upper bound on $|x_7 - r|$ is $47(0.3)^7 = 0.01$.

Further Exercises on Chapter 7

7.1   Show that the equation $x^2 \ln x = 6$ has just one solution. Find an interval, of length not greater than 0.1, which contains the root. Also find a value of x such that

$$5.95 \leqslant x^2 \ln x \leqslant 6.05.$$

7.2   A cubic expression can be evaluated numerically either as $(x^3) + (ax^2) + (bx) + c$ or as $[x\{x(x+a) + b\} + c]$. Which method is likely to have least rounding error?

7.3   Evaluate the following expressions for $x = \frac{1}{3}$ and $y = \frac{1}{9}$, working to 7D:

$$x + (\tfrac{1}{3}xy) + (\tfrac{1}{5}xy^2) + \tfrac{1}{7}(xy^3) + \tfrac{1}{9}(xy^4) + \tfrac{1}{11}(xy^5)$$

and

$$x[1 + \{\tfrac{1}{3} + (\tfrac{1}{5} + [\tfrac{1}{7} + \{\tfrac{1}{9} + \tfrac{1}{11}y\}y]y)y\}y].$$

What is the actual value, correct to 6D?

7.4   Derive the inequalities on x_0 given in the answer to Exercise 7.1.1 which ensure that the root s is obtained.

7.5   Suppose a quartic expression is to be evaluated. Compare the number of arithmetic operations involved in the alternative forms $(((ax + b)x + c)x + d)x + e$, $a[x(x + \alpha) + \beta] [x(x + \alpha) + x + \gamma] + \delta$.

7.6   Consider the equation $\sin x = (x+1)/(x-1)$.

(i) Use the intermediate value theorem to show that there is a solution in the interval $(-1, 0)$.

(ii) Use the bisection method to find a value of $x(-1 < x < 0)$ such that the two sides of the equation differ by less than 10^{-4}.

(iii) Could the iteration method be used to find the solution in $(-1, 0)$?

8
Series

8.1 Convergence of Series

On pp. 62–3 Examples 3.52 and 3.51 showed sequences consisting of the successive decimal approximations to the fractions $\frac{3}{7}$ and $\frac{7}{3}$. The nth approximation s_n could be regarded as the sum of n terms v_k, where v_k is (the correction) obtained when the kth decimal place is evaluated:

(i) rounding-down to 4D, $\frac{3}{7} = 0.4285$

$$= 0.4 + 0.02 + 0.008 + 0.0005 = v_1 + v_2 + v_3 + v_4;$$

(ii) $2.333\ldots33\ (n\mathrm{D}) = 2 + (3/10) + (3/10^2) + \cdots + (3/10^{n-1}) + (3/10^n)$

$$= v_0 + v_1 + v_2 + \cdots + v_{n-1} + v_n \text{ with } v_k = (3/10^k).$$

Another example of the same type of process is Newton's method for solving $f(x) = 0$, considered in Section 7.1. If $v_n = -f(x_{n-1})/f'(x_{n-1})$ the successive approximations are x_0, $x_1 = x_0 + v_1$, $x_2 = x_1 + v_2 = x_0 + v_1 + v_2$, $x_3 = x_2 + v_2 = x_0 + v_1 + v_2 + v_3$

$$\ldots\ldots\ldots x_n = x_{n-1} + v_n = x_0 + \sum_{k=1}^{n} v_k.$$

The object of this chapter is to study such sequences $\{s_n\}$ or $\{x_n\}$, using the ideas on limits discussed in Chapter 4. Example 3.64 on p. 66 indicated the approach: the decimal approximations 2.3, 2.33, 2.333, ... can be made as close to $\frac{7}{3}$ as desired by taking the number of decimal places large enough, and a further increase in the number of places only takes the approximation even closer. Thus $s_n \to \frac{7}{3}$ as $n \to \infty$; the **limit** of the sequence $\{s_n\}$ is $\frac{7}{3}$. Similarly in Example 3.52, the limit of either sequence $\{s_n\}$ is $\frac{3}{7}$. In Newton's method for solving $f(x) = 0$, the limit of the sequence $\{x_n\}$ is the required root, unless the derivative is very small near the root.

Given a sequence $\{s_n\}$ of approximations of the type $s_1 = v_1$, $s_2 = v_1 + v_2$, $s_3 = s_2 + v_3 = v_1 + v_2 + v_3$, ..., i.e. a series, the following questions obviously arise:

(i) does $\{s_n\}$ have a limit L?

(ii) if so, is L the number that the approximation procedure is supposed to calculate?

(iii) if so, how many terms v_k need be summed to achieve a prescribed accuracy? (i.e. how many repetitions of the approximation process will be necessary.) In other words, how quickly does s_n approach the limit L? Note that the existence of a limit implies that any accuracy is possible in principle: s_n can be obtained in an arbitrarily small neighbourhood of L by taking n sufficiently large.

Example 8.10

(i) In Example 7.14, the sequence generated by Newton's method has no limit (see p. 165).

(ii) In Example 7.13(i), the sequence generated has a limit 1, but this is not the required root (see p. 165).

(iii) In Example 7.13(ii), the sequence generated has a limit which is the required root, but an undesirably large number of terms have to be computed to get reasonably close to the limit. ☐

A sequence $\{s_n\}$ of the type $\{s_n = v_1 + v_2 + \cdots + v_n = \sum_{k=1}^{n} v_k\}$ is referred to as a **series**, and denoted by $\sum v_k$ or $\sum v_n$. The numbers v_k are called the **terms** of the series. To discuss the questions raised above, the following definitions are introduced.

> The series is said to be **convergent** if $\{s_n\}$ has a limit, and the limit is then called the **sum of the series**. A convergent series is said to **converge to its sum**.

Example 8.11

Let $v_k = (0.428571)(1/10^6)^{k-1}$ (cf. Example 3.52 on p. 63). Then the series $\sum v_k$ converges to sum $\frac{3}{7}$. ☐

Example 8.12

Let $v_k = k$. Then $s_n = (1 + 2 + \cdots + n) = \frac{1}{2}n(n+1)$, and $\{s_n\}$ has no limit. Thus the series $\sum k$ is not convergent. ☐

Example 8.13

If $\{v_k\}$ is a geometric progression, say $v_k = ar^{k-1}$, then $\sum v_k$ is called a **geometric series**. Then

$$s_n = a + ar + ar^2 + \cdots + ar^{n-1}$$

$$rs_n = ar + ar^2 + \cdots + ar^{n-1} + ar^n.$$

Subtracting, and dividing by $(1-r)$ gives

$$\boxed{s_n = a(1 - r^n)/(1 - r) \qquad (r \neq 1).} \tag{8.1}$$

Whether the series converges, i.e. the existence or otherwise of $\mathrm{Lim}_{n \to \infty} s_n$, depends on the behaviour of r^n as $n \to \infty$. The different possibilities are collected in the table at the end of Chapter 4. Thus

(i) if $-1 < r < 1$, $r^n \to 0$ as $n \to \infty$, and $s_n \to a/(1-r)$. The series is convergent and its sum is $a/(1-r)$. Example 8.11 is the special case with $a = 0.428571$ and $r = 10^{-6}$.

(ii) if $r > 1$, or $r \leqslant -1$, r^n does not tend to a limit as $n \to \infty$, and so $\{s_n\}$ has no limit. The series does not converge.

(iii) if $r = 1$, $v_k = a$, $s_n = na \to \pm\infty$ as $n \to \infty$. The series is not convergent.

> Thus the geometric series $\sum (ar^{n-1})$ does not converge if $|r| \geqslant 1$, and converges to sum $a/(1-r)$ if $|r| < 1$. ☐

Example 8.14

Suppose a calculating machine (or a person) can add, subtract and multiply decimal numbers, but not divide. Use this machine to calculate a/b.

A possible procedure is to use the geometric series. Put $r = 1 - b$, so that $a/(1-r)$ is required. This is $\mathrm{Lim}_{n \to \infty} s_n$ where $s_n = \sum_{k=1}^{n} (ar^{k-1})$, so that a, $a + ar$, $a + ar + ar^2 = s_3$,

$s_3 + ar^3$, etc. are successive approximations. However this is only true for $-1 < r < 1$, or $0 < b < 2$, since otherwise the series does not converge. This would not really restrict the calculations. For example, to calculate $\frac{7}{3}$ it would be incorrect to take $a = 7$ and $r = -2$ giving the sequence 7, -7, 21, $-35,\ldots$. However it would be feasible to take $a = 0.7$, $b = 0.3$, $r = 0.7$ giving the sequence of approximations

$$s_1 = 0.7$$

$$s_2 = 0.70 + 0.49 = 1.19$$

$$s_3 = 1.190 + 0.343 = 1.533$$

$$s_4 = 1.5330 + 0.2401 = 1.7731 \tag{8.2}$$

$$s_5 = 1.77310 + 0.16807 = 1.94117$$

$$s_6 = 1.941170 + 0.117649 = 2.058819$$

because the result of Example 8.13 ensures the convergence to the required quotient. The terms shown suggest that the convergence is slow—many terms of the series must be summed to get close to the limit. The alternative calculation of 7/3 as 2.1/0.9 uses $a = 2.1$, $r = 0.1$, giving the sequence 2.1, $2.1 + 0.21 = 2.31$, $2.31 + 0.021 = 2.331, \ldots$. Then

$$s_n = \frac{2.33\ldots 31}{\underbrace{}_{n-1 \text{ 3's}}}$$

is actually correct to $(n-1)$ decimal places. (cf. Exercise 8.2)   □

The three questions posed previously on p. 179 can be rephrased in the terminology since introduced:

(i) does a given series converge?
(ii) if so, is its sum the number that is the object of the calculation? and
(iii) how many terms of the series must be summed to get within a given neighbourhood of the sum?

Clearly answers to these questions must not involve knowing the value of the sum, since if this were known the procedure would not be required. It should be emphasized that the word sum refers to the limit of the sequence $\{s_n\}$, and not to the result s_n of any particular addition $v_1 + v_2 + \cdots + v_n$. In fact the sum, being the limit, cannot be obtained by any addition process. Any s_n can only be an approximation to the sum.

Example 8.15
The series with terms $v_n = 1/n$ is called the **harmonic series**. Then, rounding-off to 3D,

$$s_1 = 1, \ s_2 = 1 + \tfrac{1}{2} = 1.5$$

$$s_3 = 1.5 + \tfrac{1}{3} = 1.833$$

$$s_4 = s_3 + \tfrac{1}{4} = 2.083$$

$$s_5 = s_4 + \tfrac{1}{5} = 2.283 \tag{8.3}$$

$$s_6 = s_5 + \tfrac{1}{6} = 2.450$$

$$s_7 = s_6 + \tfrac{1}{7} = 2.593$$

$$s_8 = s_7 + \tfrac{1}{8} = 2.718$$

Does the harmonic series converge? The following argument shows that s_n can be made as large as desired by taking n large enough. Consider s_n when n is a power of 2: $s_1 = 1$,

$$s_2 = 1 + \tfrac{1}{2},$$

$$s_4 = 1 + \tfrac{1}{2} + \tfrac{1}{3} + \tfrac{1}{4} > 1 + \tfrac{1}{2} + \tfrac{1}{4} + \tfrac{1}{4} = 1 + \tfrac{1}{2} + \tfrac{1}{2}$$

$$s_8 = s_4 + \tfrac{1}{5} + \tfrac{1}{6} + \tfrac{1}{7} + \tfrac{1}{8} > s_4 + \tfrac{1}{8} + \tfrac{1}{8} + \tfrac{1}{8} + \tfrac{1}{8}$$

i.e.
$$s_8 > s_4 + \tfrac{1}{2} \quad \text{and} \quad s_4 + \tfrac{1}{2} > (1 + \tfrac{1}{2} + \tfrac{1}{2}) + \tfrac{1}{2} = 1 + \tfrac{3}{2}$$

$$s_{16} = s_8 + \tfrac{1}{9} + \tfrac{1}{10} + \cdots + \tfrac{1}{15} + \tfrac{1}{16} > s_8 + \tfrac{8}{16} = s_8 + \tfrac{1}{2} > 1 + \tfrac{4}{2}.$$

$$\longleftarrow \text{8 terms} \longrightarrow$$

Thus when $n = 2^2$, $s_n > 1 + \tfrac{2}{2}$;
 when $n = 2^3$, $s_n > 1 + \tfrac{3}{2}$;
 when $n = 2^4$, $s_n > 1 + \tfrac{4}{2}$; continuing leads to
 when $n = 2^m$, $s_n > 1 + m/2$. This result means s_n can be made arbitrarily large: given any number Δ, however large, choose an integer $m > 2\Delta - 2$, and take $n = 2^m$; then $s_n > 1 + m/2 > \Delta$, and since all terms of the harmonic series are positive, taking n larger only increases s_n still further. Thus $s_n \to \infty$ as $n \to \infty$:

the harmonic series does not converge. $\square$

The numbers shown in equations (8.2) and (8.3) are displayed mainly to indicate that their calculation gives no information on whether the series converges or not. Comparing (8.2) and (8.3), it is not obvious that (8.2) gives the first six terms of a sequence with a limit, while those in (8.3) eventually get larger than any desired value Δ. Extending these calculations within practical limits does not indicate the eventual behaviour of (8.3) for large n:

$$s_{40} = 4.28, \qquad s_{49} = 4.48, \qquad s_{50} = 4.50, \ldots. \qquad \text{(cf. (8.3))}.$$

The inequality $s_n > 1 + m/2$, derived above for the harmonic series, also suggests the very slow increase of $\{s_n\}$. Using this inequality to ensure that $s_n > 100$, one would take $m = 198$ and $n = 2^{198}$. Although the results (cf. (8.2))

$$s_{40} = 2.33333229, \qquad s_{49} = 2.33333329,$$

for $v_k = 0.7^k$ are more encouraging, Example 8.16 (below) is a warning against deducing the existence of a limit from numerical computations. Once some non-numeric argument has established convergence, it is somewhat safer to use numerical results to estimate the value of the limit, but the actual accuracy then remains unknown.

Numerical evaluation of any number of the s_n can neither prove or disprove convergence. For instance, the values shown on p. 181 give no indication of any limit, but might approach some limit at higher values of n; and whatever s_n had been calculated, one could never be sure on the basis of such calculations whether for larger n the values s_n clustered around a limit or not. Alternatively, if the s_n apparently have a limit, one can never be sure they do not deviate from it at some larger n.

Example 8.16
(i) if $s_k = 2 + (-1 + 0.5k)^{11}$, then $s_{12} = 1.999958$, $s_{19} = s_{20} = s_{21} = 2$ (correct to 11D), but $s_{60} = 2050$ and $\sum v_k$ is not convergent. (Other values of s_n for this example were given in Example 4.26 on p. 81.)

(ii) If a new series is constructed from the harmonic series by omitting all terms containing a particular digit, it can be shown that the new series converges. For instance, omitting all terms containing zero, so that $v_{10} = \frac{1}{11}$, $v_{19} = \frac{1}{21}$, etc., then

$$s_8 = 2.72, \qquad s_{36} = 4.07, \qquad s_{45} = 4.27,$$

again giving little indication of convergence and certainly not indicating the actual value 23.10345 (5D) of the limit. $\square$

The harmonic series is an example where the behaviour of s_n as $n \to \infty$ cannot be investigated by the methods of Section 4.4, which require a formula for s_n, such as (8.1). The theory of series is designed to deal with the situation in which a formula is given for v_n, but the equation $s_n = v_1 + v_2 + \cdots + v_n$ cannot be simplified. It would be rather arduous to have to devise a different special method, such as that for the harmonic series, to discuss the convergence of each different series that might be required. General tests and theorems are needed. A useful test will be considered in Section 8.3. For the moment two theorems will be stated without proof:

Theorem 8.1
The series $\sum v_n$ cannot converge unless $v_n \to 0$ as $n \to \infty$.

This theorem follows from the properties of a limit. Convergence implies that n can be chosen so that the sum of n terms ($\sum_{k=1}^{n} v_k$) is within some given neighbourhood of the limit, and remains in this neighbourhood however many more terms are added. This is only possible if $v_n \to 0$, so that any additional term is as small as necessary. (This is not a formal proof of Theorem 8.1, but is intended to make it plausible, and to indicate how a proof could be constructed).

Note that if $v_n \to 0$ as $n \to \infty$, the theorem gives no information.

For example, $1/n \to 0$, and the harmonic series is not convergent.

From the point of view of convergence properties, the simplest series are those in which all the terms v_n are positive. Then $\{s_n\}$ is an increasing sequence, and either must have a limit or must tend to infinity. This is a special case of the statement in Section 3.6 regarding a set B in which the number of elements is not finite. Taking $B = \{s_n\}$, either the sequence has a sup, or the sequence contains arbitrarily large numbers. Therefore if the sequence does not contain arbitrarily large numbers, it has a sup. Because the sequence $\{s_n\}$ is increasing, this sup is a limit and cannot be a max. This suggests (although it is not a proof) the following result:

Theorem 8.2
If all terms of a series $\sum v_n$ are positive, and $s_n = \sum_{k=1}^{n} v_k$ is bounded, then $\{s_n\}$ has a limit, i.e. $\sum v_n$ converges.

To show that $\{s_n\}$ is bounded, it is not necessary to know the sup (which is the limit), but only to find some number M such that $s_n \leq M$ for all n. This ensures that s_n cannot tend to infinity.

The method used in Example 8.15 for the harmonic series may be described as showing that s_n is *not* bounded.

Theorems on limits also lead to some general results. If $\sum v_n$ is a convergent series, so is $\sum (cv_n)$, for any constant c; if $\sum v_n$ is not convergent, then neither is $\sum (cv_n)$, except in the trivial case $c = 0$. $\sum (u_n + v_n)$ is convergent if both $\sum u_n$ and $\sum v_n$ are convergent.

Example 8.17

Consider the series $\sum 1/n^3$.

An inequality can be established for s_n when n has the form $2^m - 1$ (cf. the treatment of the harmonic series in Example 8.15).

$$s_1 = 1, \qquad s_3 = 1 + 1/2^3 + 1/3^3 < 1 + 1/2^3 + 1/2^3 = 1 + \tfrac{1}{4}$$

$$s_7 = s_3 + 1/4^3 + 1/5^3 + 1/6^3 + 1/7^3$$

$$< s_3 + 1/4^3 + 1/4^3 + 1/4^3 + 1/4^3$$

$$s_7 < s_3 + 4/4^3 = s_3 + 1/4^2 < 1 + \tfrac{1}{4} + 1/4^2$$

$$s_{15} = s_7 + 1/8^3 + 1/9^3 + \cdots + 1/15^3 < s_7 + 8/8^3 = s_7 + 1/4^3.$$

$$\longleftarrow \quad \text{8 terms} \quad \longrightarrow$$

Thus, when $n = 2^2 - 1$, $s_n < 1 + \tfrac{1}{4}$;

when $n = 2^3 - 1$, $s_n < 1 + \tfrac{1}{4} + 1/4^2$;

when $n = 2^4 - 1$, $s_n < 1 + \tfrac{1}{4} + 1/4^2 + 1/4^3$; continuing gives

when $n = 2^m - 1$, $s_n < 1 + \tfrac{1}{4} + 1/4^2 + \cdots + 1/4^{m-1}$.

The right side of this inequality is a geometric progression with m terms, first term $a = 1$, and ratio $\tfrac{1}{4}$. From equation (8.1) this can be summed, to give

$$s_n < \frac{1 - (\tfrac{1}{4})^m}{1 - \tfrac{1}{4}} = \tfrac{4}{3}\{1 - (\tfrac{1}{4})^m\} < \tfrac{4}{3}.$$

Thus, if n is one less than a power of 2, then $s_n < \tfrac{4}{3}$. If n is any other integer, there is a larger integer N which is one less than a power of 2. Then $s_n < s_N$, since the terms are positive, and so $s_n < \tfrac{4}{3}$, since $s_N < \tfrac{4}{3}$.

By Theorem 8.2, with the upper bound $M = \tfrac{4}{3}$, the series $\sum 1/n^3$ converges.

Note that the above work does not determine the sum. (This is not $\tfrac{4}{3}$, because the inequality for s_3 adds $(\tfrac{1}{8}) - (\tfrac{1}{27}) = \tfrac{19}{216}$, and so s_n certainly cannot get larger than $\tfrac{4}{3} - \tfrac{19}{216}$.) □

The same procedure shows that $\sum 1/n^p$ converges for any $p > 1$. (The case $p = 1$ is the harmonic series, which does not converge).

Exercises (answers on p. 191)

8.1.1 The work in Example 7.13(iii) defines two sequences:

$$s_0 = 200, \qquad s_1 = 176, \qquad s_2 = 159, \ldots.$$

$$t_0 = -748, \qquad t_1 = -243, \qquad t_2 = -66, \ldots. \qquad \text{(see p. 165)}$$

(i) Is $\{s_n\}$ a series? If so, what are the terms of the series?

(ii) Is $\{t_n\}$ a series? If so, what are the terms of the series?

(iii) What are the limits, if any, of the sequences $\{s_n\}$ and $\{t_n\}$?

8.1.2 Evaluating 2/9 as a decimal gives $0.2222\ldots$. What values of a and r in the geometric series give $s_1 = 0.2$, $s_2 = 0.22$, etc.? Verify that equation (8.1) does give the nth decimal approximation.

8.1.3 For each of the following series, $\sum v_n$, state whether Theorem 8.1 shows that they are convergent or not convergent.
  (i) $v_n = n+2$, (ii) $v_n = 1/\sqrt{n}$, (iii) $v_n = n^2$, (iv) $v_n = 1/(2-n)$.

8.1.4 (i) What inequality is obtained by continuing the following argument (to $k!$):
  $2! \geqslant 2$, $3! = 2!3 > 2!2 = 2^2$,

$$4! = 3!4 > 3!2 > 2^2 2 = 2^3, \ldots..$$

  (ii) Deduce an inequality for $1/k!$, and hence show that

$$s_n = \frac{1}{1!} + \frac{1}{2!} + \frac{1}{3!} + \cdots + \frac{1}{n!} < \sum_{k=1}^{n} (\tfrac{1}{2})^{k-1}.$$

  (iii) Use equation (8.1) to find an upper bound for s_n in (ii). What can be concluded from Theorem 8.2?

8.1.5 State whether the following series are convergent or not:

  (i) $\sum[(\tfrac{1}{2})^k + (\tfrac{1}{3})^k]$, (ii) $\sum\left[\dfrac{1}{k^3} + (-\tfrac{3}{4})^k\right]$,

  (iii) $\sum \dfrac{4}{k^3}$ (iv) $\sum \dfrac{1}{4k}$.

8.2 Notation

In the summation notation $\sum_{k=1}^{n} v_k = v_1 + v_2 + \cdots + v_n$ the index k is a **'dummy variable'** which merely takes the values from 1 to n. Any convenient symbol may be used for a dummy variable, for example $\sum_{k=1}^{n} v_k = \sum_{p=1}^{n} v_p$. The only symbol that should not be used in $\sum_{k=1}^{n} v_k$ is n, which is already denoting the final value of the dummy variable.

If the series is convergent, its sum, that is $\mathrm{Lim}_{n\to\infty} \sum_{k=1}^{n} v_k$, is written $\sum_{k=1}^{\infty} v_k$. When the limit is being considered, n becomes a dummy variable, that is $\mathrm{Lim}_{n\to\infty} s_n = \mathrm{Lim}_{m\to\infty} s_m$, etc. Since n has disappeared from the notation in $\sum_{k=1}^{\infty} v_k$, it may now replace the dummy variable k. Thus the sum of a convergent series with terms v_n is often written $\sum_{n=1}^{\infty} v_n$.

Example 8.20
For the geometric series with terms ar^{n-1} (cf. Example 8.13 on p. 180)

$$\sum_{k=1}^{n} ar^{k-1} = a(1-r^n)/(1-r) = \sum_{m=1}^{n} ar^{m-1} \qquad (8.1)$$

and if $|r| < 1$,

$$\sum_{k=1}^{\infty} ar^{k-1} = a/(1-r) = \sum_{m=1}^{\infty} ar^{m-1} = \sum_{n=1}^{\infty} ar^{n-1}. \quad \square$$

Sometimes the formula giving v_n is simplified by considering the next term or the previous term instead of the nth term. For example, a geometric series is most conveniently specified by giving the $(n+1)$th term, namely ar^n. When this is done, the sums under consideration no longer start with $n=1$, and this must be indicated in the notation.

Example 8.21

$\sum_{k=0}^{n} ar^k$ is the sum of $(n+1)$ terms of the geometric series. Thus

$$\sum_{k=0}^{n} ar^k = a(1-r^{n+1})/(1-r) = \sum_{m=1}^{n+1} ar^{m-1}.$$

This is a change in notation only, and so does not affect the behaviour as $n \to \infty$. Thus $\text{Lim}_{n\to\infty} \sum_{k=0}^{n} ar^k = a/(1-r)$, which can be written $\sum_{k=0}^{\infty} ar^k$ or $\sum_{n=0}^{\infty} ar^n$. □

In considering series, the only type of limit involved is $\text{Lim}_{n\to\infty} s_n$, and if $s_n \to L$, then so does s_{n+1}, s_{n+2}, or s_{n+m} for any fixed m. For example $r^{n+1} \to 0$ if $|r| < 1$ may be written by writing $r^{n+1} = rr^n$). The general case is related to Theorem 8.1 (on p. 183): $s_{n+1} - s_n = v_{n+1} \to 0$ if the series converges.

The addition or removal of a finite number of terms at the beginning of a series will not affect *whether* it converges or not. If it converges then the *sum is changed* according to the terms put in or deleted.

Example 8.22

(i) The series with terms 3, 2, 1, 0, 1, $\frac{1}{2}, \frac{1}{3}, \frac{1}{4}, \ldots 1/n, \ldots$ does not converge.

(ii) The series with terms $a, b, c, cr, cr^2, cr^3, \ldots, cr^n, \ldots$ converges if $|r| < 1$. Then its sum is

$$a + b + \sum_{n=0}^{\infty} cr^n = a + b + c/(1-r).$$

(iii) The series with terms $a, ar^2, ar^4, ar^5, ar^6, \ldots, ar^n, \ldots$ also converges if $|r| < 1$, to the sum

$$\frac{a}{1-r} - ar - ar^3 = -ar - ar^3 + \sum_{n=0}^{\infty} ar^n = a + ar^2 + \sum_{n=4}^{\infty} ar^n. □$$

In this example, dots were used to indicate terms of a sequence, defined for all positive integer n. The series, or their sums, are also commonly referred to using a similar notation. Thus, in the previous example,

(i) $3 + 2 + 1 + 0 + 1 + \frac{1}{2} + \cdots + 1/n + \cdots$ does not converge;

(ii) $a + b + c + cr + \cdots + cr^n + \cdots = a + b + c/(1-r)$;

(iii) $a + ar^2 + ar^4 + ar^5 + \cdots + ar^n + \cdots = -ar - ar^3 + a/(1-r)$.

In (ii) and (iii), the symbol $=$ implies that the series converges, to the sum on the right. The **general term** of the series is the one written as a function of $n(v_n$, or perhaps $v_{n\pm1})$. This is sometimes omitted if the first few terms unambiguously indicate the general term. The harmonic series could be denoted by

$$1 + \tfrac{1}{2} + \tfrac{1}{3} + \tfrac{1}{4} + \cdots,$$

and similarly the sum of a convergent geometric series could be shown by

$$a + ar + ar^2 + ar^3 + \cdots = a/(1-r) \qquad (|r| < 1).$$

Exercises (answers on p. 191)

8.2.1   By considering exactly what terms appear on each side of the following equations, determine which equations are true for any v_i (note that (ii) defines s_n).

(i) $\displaystyle\sum_{r=1}^{3} \frac{1}{r} = \frac{11}{6}$

(ii) $\displaystyle s_n = \sum_{i=1}^{n} v_i$

(iii) $\displaystyle s_n = v_1 + \sum_{r=1}^{n-1} v_{r+1}$

(iv) $\displaystyle s_{n+1} = \sum_{r=0}^{n+1} v_r$

(v) $\displaystyle s_{n+1} = \sum_{r=0}^{n} v_{r+1}$

(vi) $\displaystyle s_n = \sum_{r=0}^{n-1} v_{n-r}$

(vii) $\displaystyle s_n = \sum_{k=1}^{n} v_{n+1-k}$

(viii) $\displaystyle \sum_{r=1}^{n} v_t v_r = v_t s_n$

(ix) $\displaystyle s_n^2 = \sum_{t=1}^{n} \left(\sum_{r=1}^{n} v_t v_r \right)$

(x) $\displaystyle s_n^2 = 2 \sum_{t=1}^{n} \sum_{r=1}^{t} v_t v_r$

(xi) $\displaystyle s_n^2 = - \sum_{r=1}^{n} v_r^2 + 2 \sum_{t=1}^{n} \sum_{r=1}^{t} v_t v_r$

(xii) $\displaystyle \sum_{i=1}^{n} \sum_{j=1}^{n} a_i b_j = \sum_{i=1}^{n} \sum_{j=1}^{n} a_j b_i$

(xiii) $\displaystyle s_n^2 = \sum_{t=1}^{n} v_t^2 + 2 \sum_{r=2}^{n} \sum_{t=1}^{r-1} v_t v_r$

(xiv) $\displaystyle \sum_{r=1}^{2n} a_r = \sum_{k=1}^{n} (a_{2k} + a_{2k+1})$.

8.2.2   Comment on the following statements, each of which purports to show that the sum of a series is 2:

(i) $1 + \frac{1}{2} + \frac{1}{4} + \frac{1}{8} + \cdots + \dfrac{1}{2^n} = 2$

(ii) $1 + \frac{1}{2} + \frac{1}{4} + \frac{1}{8} + \cdots + \dfrac{1}{2^n} + \cdots = 2$

(iii) $1 + \frac{1}{2} + \frac{1}{4} + \frac{1}{8} + \cdots = 2$

(iv) $\displaystyle\sum_{n=1}^{\infty} (1/2^n) = 2$.

8.3   The Comparison Tests

Suppose $\sum v_n$ is a series of positive terms, and another series $\sum c_n$ is convergent, and has all its terms larger than those of $\sum v_n$. Thus $0 < v_k < c_k$ for all k, and for any n, $\sum_{k=1}^{n} v_k < \sum_{k=1}^{n} c_k$. If S is the sum of $\sum c_k$, then $\{\sum_{k=1}^{n} c_k\}$ approaches the limit S from below (since $c_k > 0$), and so $\sum_{k=1}^{n} c_k < S$, for any n. Hence $\sum_{k=1}^{n} v_k < S$. By Theorem 8.2, $\sum v_k$ converges. In applying this to a given series $\sum v_k$, one compares with a series $\sum c_k$ which is known to be convergent and with terms greater than those of $\sum v_k$. The table at the end of this chapter should be consulted for possible comparison series $\sum c_k$.

Example 8.30
(i) If $v_n = (1/2^n) \sin^2 n$, choose $c_n = 1/2^n$. Then, as $\sin^2 n < 1$, $v_n < c_n$; and $\sum c_n = \sum (\frac{1}{2})^n$ is a convergent geometric series. So $\sum (\sin^2 n)/2^n$ converges by comparison with $\sum 1/2^n$.

(ii) If $v_n = (\sin n)/2^n$, then $v_n < 1/2^n$, but the comparison test does not apply because $\sum v_n$ is not a series of positive terms.

(iii) If $v_n = (1/n) \sin^2 n$, then $\sum v_n$ is a series of positive terms, and $v_n < 1/n$, but this does not give an application of the comparison test because $\sum(1/n)$ is not convergent.   □

On the other hand, if the terms v_k are all larger than those of a series $\sum d_k$ which is not convergent, then $\sum v_k$ cannot converge either. For $\sum_{k=1}^{n} v_k > \sum_{k=1}^{n} d_k$, which can be made arbitrarily large. Hence $\{\sum_{k=1}^{n} v_k\}$ cannot have a limit.

Example 8.31

(i) If $v_n = 1/\sqrt{n}$, then $v_n > 1/n$, and hence $\sum v_n$ does not converge, by comparison with the harmonic series $\sum 1/n$.

(ii) If $v_n = 1/n^p$, for any $p < 1$, again $\sum v_n$ does not converge, by comparison with the harmonic series $\sum 1/n$.   □

Whether a series converges or not depends on the nature of its terms for large values of n. This has two consequences for comparison tests.

Firstly, the comparison is not affected if there are a few terms (in fact any finite number of terms) for which the condition $0 < v_k < c_k$ (or $v_k > d_k$) does not hold.

Example 8.32

(i) $\sum (n-4)/n^3$ converges by comparison with $\sum 1/n^2$ although the first 4 terms are not positive.

(ii) If

$$v_n = \frac{2n-4}{n\sqrt{n}} = \frac{2-4/n}{\sqrt{n}},$$

then $\sum v_n$ is not convergent, by comparison with $\sum 1/\sqrt{n}$. Here v_1 and v_2 are not positive, $v_3 < 1/\sqrt{3}$, and $v_4 = 1/\sqrt{4}$, but $v_n > 1/\sqrt{n}$ for all $n > 4$.   □

Secondly, whether a series converges or not can sometimes be determined from the asymptotic form of v_n as $n \to \infty$.

Example 8.33

(i) $v_n = (n-4)/n^3 \to n/n^3 = 1/n^2$. Hence $\sum v_n$ converges because $\sum (1/n^2)$ converges.

(ii) $v_n = (2n-4)/n\sqrt{n} \to 2n/n\sqrt{n} = 2/\sqrt{n}$. Hence $\sum v_n$ has the same behaviour as $\sum 2/\sqrt{n}$ and $\sum 1/\sqrt{n}$, i.e. $\sum v_n$ is not convergent.   □

Comparing Examples 8.32 and 8.33 shows that the asymptotic form of v_n may indicate a suitable comparison series.

There are other tests which can be applied to v_n in order to determine whether the series $\sum v_k$ is convergent or not. These tests are described in books on series, which may be referred to if necessary. Because of Theorem 8.2, many of the tests only apply to series of positive terms. The comparison test is presented above as a simple example of the many tests which have been devised (see Exercise 8.25 for the ratio test, and also Exercises 10.42-4 on pp. 257-8).

Exercises (answers on p. 192)
8.3.1 Use a comparison test to show that the following series $\sum v_n$ are convergent:

(i) $v_n = \dfrac{\cos^2 n}{3^n}$, (ii) $v_n = \dfrac{1}{n2^n}$, (iii) $v_n = \dfrac{n-1}{n^4}$,

(iv) $v_n = \dfrac{2n-1}{n^4}$, (v) $v_n = \dfrac{n+1}{n^4}$.

8.3.2 Use a comparison test to show that the following series $\sum v_n$ are not convergent:

(i) $v_n = \dfrac{n^2+1}{n^3}$, (ii) $v_n = \dfrac{n^2-1}{n^3}$, (iii) $v_n = \dfrac{1}{\sqrt{(2n^2-1)}}$.

8.3.3 Use a comparison test to determine whether series $\sum v_n$, with the following terms, are convergent or not.

(i) $v_n = \dfrac{1}{n^2+n+1}$, (ii) $v_n = \dfrac{1}{n!}$, (iii) $v_n = \dfrac{n^2+n+1}{n^3-n^2+n+1}$,

(iv) $v_n = \dfrac{2^n}{n!}$, (v) $v_n = \dfrac{1}{\ln n}$ $(n > 1)$, (vi) $v_n = n^{-\ln n}$.

8.4 Absolute Convergence

Starting from any series $\sum v_n$, one can form the related series $\sum |v_n|$, which is a series of positive terms.

> **Theorem 8.3**
> If $\sum |v_n|$ converges, then so does $\sum v_n$.

Example 8.40
If $v_n = (\sin n)/2^n$, then $0 < |v_n| < 1/2^n$. Hence $\sum |v_n|$ converges by comparison with the convergent geometric series $\sum (\frac{1}{2})^n$. By Theorem 8.3, $\sum v_n$ also converges. □

If $\sum |v_n|$ does not converge, then this gives no information on the behaviour of $\sum v_n$.

Example 8.41
If $v_n = (-1)^n/n$, then it can be shown (see Exercise 8.20) that $\sum v_n$ converges. However $|v_n| = 1/n$, and $\sum |v_n|$ is the harmonic series which does not converge. □

A series like $\sum (-1)^n/n$ is called an **alternating series**, because the terms are alternately positive and negative. The general term of an alternating series contains either the factor $(-1)^n$ or the factor $(-1)^{n+1}$, according as the $n = 1$ term is negative or positive. These factors, which have the values ± 1, are often written $(-)^n$ and $(-)^{n+1}$, as they only determine the sign.

Example 8.42
The series $\sum (-)^n/n$ is $-1 + \frac{1}{2} - \frac{1}{3} + \frac{1}{4} - \frac{1}{5} + \cdots$. The series $1 - \frac{1}{2} + \frac{1}{3} - \frac{1}{4} + \frac{1}{5} \cdots$ is $\sum (-)^{n+1}/n$. □

Suppose $\sum |v_n|$ converges. Then, according to Theorem 8.3, $\sum v_n$ converges. Now suppose $\sum u_n$ is any series obtained from $\sum v_n$ by changing the sign of some of the terms. Then $u_n = \pm v_n$, and $|u_n| = |v_n|$. So $\sum |u_n|$ converges, and so does $\sum u_n$, from Theorem 8.3.

Hence $\sum v_n$ is a series with the following property: it is convergent, and so is any series obtained by changing the sign of any of the terms (this actually includes $\sum |v_n|$, obtained by making all the signs positive). Any such series is called **absolutely convergent**. From Theorem 8.3, a series $\sum v_n$ is absolutely convergent if $\sum |v_n|$ converges.

Example 8.43

(i) The series

$$1 + \tfrac{1}{2} - \tfrac{1}{4} + \tfrac{1}{8} + \tfrac{1}{16} - \tfrac{1}{32} + \tfrac{1}{64} + \tfrac{1}{128} - \tfrac{1}{256} + \tfrac{1}{512} \cdots$$

(with every 3rd term negative) is absolutely convergent, because the geometric series $1 + \tfrac{1}{2} + \tfrac{1}{4} + \tfrac{1}{8} + \tfrac{1}{16} + \tfrac{1}{32} + \cdots$ is convergent.

(ii) The series $\sum (-)^n / n^3$ is absolutely convergent, because $\sum (1/n^3)$ converges (Example 8.17 on p. 184).

(iii) The series in Example 8.42 are convergent, but not absolutely convergent. □

> The sum of an absolutely convergent series may be obtained using any convenient rearrangement of the terms. However for a series which is convergent, but *not absolutely convergent, a rearrangement may change the sum*. This emphasizes the fact that the sum is actually a limit.

Example 8.44

(i) The sum in Example 8.43 (i) is correctly given by the rearrangement

$$(1 + \tfrac{1}{2} + \tfrac{1}{4} + \tfrac{1}{8} + \cdots) - 2(\tfrac{1}{4} + \tfrac{1}{32} + \cdots) = \frac{1}{1 - \tfrac{1}{2}} - 2\left(\frac{\tfrac{1}{4}}{1 - \tfrac{1}{8}}\right) = \tfrac{10}{7},$$

because the series is absolutely convergent.

(ii) Grouping the terms in pairs shows that the sum of the series

$$1 - \tfrac{1}{2} + \tfrac{1}{3} - \tfrac{1}{4} + \cdots = (1 - \tfrac{1}{2}) + (\tfrac{1}{3} - \tfrac{1}{4}) + \cdots$$

is positive (in fact greater than $\tfrac{1}{2}$). Thus the following manipulation

$$1 - \tfrac{1}{2} + \tfrac{1}{3} - \tfrac{1}{4} + \cdots = 1 + \tfrac{1}{2} - \tfrac{2}{2} + \tfrac{1}{3} + \tfrac{1}{4} - \tfrac{2}{4} + \cdots$$

$$= (1 + \tfrac{1}{2} + \tfrac{1}{3} + \cdots) - (\tfrac{2}{2} + \tfrac{2}{4} + \tfrac{2}{6} + \cdots) \qquad (\dagger)$$

$$= 0$$

is *incorrect*. In ($\dagger$) the terms have been rearranged, and this is not possible (without changing the sum) because the series is not absolutely convergent. □

Example 8.45

Another rearrangement (cf. Example 8.44(ii)) of the series $\sum (-1)^{n+1} / n$ is

$$1 + \tfrac{1}{3} - \tfrac{1}{2} + \tfrac{1}{5} + \tfrac{1}{7} - \tfrac{1}{4} + \tfrac{1}{9} + \tfrac{1}{11} - \tfrac{1}{6} + \cdots$$

This series is convergent (see Exercise 8.21), but not absolutely convergent. Suppose its sum is *T*. By grouping the terms in threes,

$$T = \sum_{n=0}^{\infty} w_n, \quad \text{where } w_n = \frac{1}{4n+1} + \frac{1}{4n+3} - \frac{1}{2n+2}.$$

Suppose the sum of

$$1 - \tfrac{1}{2} + \tfrac{1}{3} - \tfrac{1}{4} + \tfrac{1}{5} - \tfrac{1}{6} + \cdots$$

is *S*.

By grouping the terms in pairs, $S = \sum_{n=0}^{\infty} u_n$ with

$$u_n = \frac{1}{2n+1} - \frac{1}{2n+2},$$

and by grouping the terms in fours,

$$S = \sum_{n=0}^{\infty} v_n, \quad \text{with } v_n = \frac{1}{4n+1} - \frac{1}{4n+2} + \frac{1}{4n+3} - \frac{1}{4n+4}.$$

Since $w_n = \tfrac{1}{2}u_n + v_n$, $T = \tfrac{3}{2}S$. This shows directly that the rearrangement changes the sum. (This example is taken (with permission) from *Infinite Series and Sequences* by K. Knopp (Dover, 1956).) □

Exercises

8.4.1 Show that
   (i) the terms of a geometric series are either all the same sign or alternating;
   (ii) any convergent geometric series is absolutely convergent.

8.4.2 Find the sum of the series

$$1 - \tfrac{1}{2} - \tfrac{1}{4} + \tfrac{1}{8} - \tfrac{1}{16} - \tfrac{1}{32} + \tfrac{1}{64} - \tfrac{1}{128} - \tfrac{1}{256} + \tfrac{1}{512} - \tfrac{1}{1024} - \tfrac{1}{2048} + \tfrac{1}{4096} - \cdots.$$

8.4.3 If *S* is the sum of the series $1 - \tfrac{1}{2} + \tfrac{1}{3} - \tfrac{1}{4} + \cdots$, show that the sum of the rearrangement

$$1 - \tfrac{1}{2} - \tfrac{1}{4} + \tfrac{1}{3} - \tfrac{1}{6} - \tfrac{1}{8} + \tfrac{1}{5} - \tfrac{1}{10} - \tfrac{1}{12} + \cdots.$$

is $\tfrac{1}{2}S$. [Hint: $(1 - \tfrac{1}{2}) = \tfrac{1}{2}$, $(\tfrac{1}{3} - \tfrac{1}{6}) = \tfrac{1}{6}$, etc.].

Answers to Exercises 8.1.1–8.4.2

8.1.1 (i) Yes. Series with general term $v_n = -f(x_{n-1})/f'(x_{n-1})$ $(n \neq 0)$, i.e. the terms are

$$v_0 = 200, \quad v_1 = -24 = -f(x_0)/f'(x_0),$$

$$v_2 = -17 = -f(x_1)/f'(x_1) \text{ etc.}$$

   (ii) No, because t_n is not obtained by adding a term to t_{n-1}.
   (iii) $s_n \to L$, where *L* is the larger root of $f(x) = 0$; $t_n \to 0$.

8.1.2 $a = 0.2$, $r = 0.1$.

8.1.3 Theorem 8.1 shows that (i) and (iii) are not convergent, but gives no information for (ii), (iv) or (v).

8.1.4 (i) $k! > 2^{k-1}$, (ii) $1/k! < 1/2^{k-1}$, (iii) $s_n < 2$, so s_n is bounded, and $\sum (1/k!)$ converges.

8.1.5 From the results given before Example 8.17, (iv) does not converge, while (i), (ii) and (iii) do converge.

8.2.1 All correct except (iv), (x) and (xiv).

8.2.2 (i) and (iv) not true; (iii) true if the context implies a geometric series.
8.3.1   (i) $v_n < c_n = (1/3)^n$, (ii) $v_n < c_n = (1/2)^n$,

(iii) $v_n < c_n = 1/n^3$, (iv) $v_n < c_n = 2/n^3$, (v) $v_n < c_n = 2/n^3$.
8.3.2   (i) $v_n > d_n = 1/n$, (ii) $v_n > d_n = 1/2n$ $(n > 1)$,
(iii) $v_n > d_n = 1/n\sqrt{2}$.
8.3.3   (i) $v_n < c_n = 1/n^2$ ($\sum v_n$ convergent)
(ii) $v_n < c_n = 1/2^{n-1}$ ($\sum v_n$ convergent; see Exercise 8.1.4)
(iii) $v_n > d_n = 1/n$ ($\sum v_n$ not convergent)
(iv) $v_n < c_n = 2(2/3)^{n-1}$ $(n > 4)$ ($\sum v_n$ convergent)
(v) $v_n > d_n = 1/n$ ($\sum v_n$ not convergent)
(vi) $v_n < c_n = 1/n^{\ln 3}$ $(n > 2)$ ($\sum v_n$ convergent).
Note that other comparison series are possible for Exercises 8.3.1–3.
8.4.2 $\frac{2}{7}$.

Further Exercises on Chapter 8

8.1 Show that, for any initial value x_0, the sequence generated in Example 7.15 is a geometric series which does not converge.

8.2 From equation (8.1) write down an expression for the **truncation error** (cf. Section 7.2) in s_n for the geometric series. Show that for Example 8.14 this error is $e_n = \frac{7}{3}E - n$. [In the circumstances of Example 8.14, where division is generally an inadmissible operation, e_n cannot be evaluated exactly. However $\frac{7}{3} < \frac{7}{2} = 7(0.5) = 3.5$ gives an upper bound on e_n which is sufficient to show that s_n is correct to $(n-1)$D].

8.3 Write down the nth term v_n of a series for which s_6 is the expression given in Exercise 7.3 on p. 178.

8.4   (i) Show that if the formula

$$s_n = 1 + 2 + 3 + \cdots + n = \tfrac{1}{2}n(n+1) \tag{*}$$

is true for some integer n, then it is true for the next integer $(n+1)$. What further statement is necessary in order to prove (*)?

(ii) Use (*) to show that if the terms of a series are in arithmetic progression, i.e. $v_k = a + kd$, then $\sum v_k$ does not converge. Which theorem would show this without using (*)?

8.5 If $v_k = 1/(a+k)(a+k+1)$, verify that

$$\frac{1}{a+k} - \frac{1}{a+k+1} = v_k$$

and use this to show that $\sum_{k=1}^{\infty} v_k$ converges, and find its sum. (Assume a is not a negative integer).

8.6 If $v_k = 1/(a+k)(a+k+2)$, find numbers b and c so that

$$v_k = \frac{b}{a+k} - \frac{c}{a+k+2} \quad \text{for any } k.$$

Deduce that the series $\sum_{k=1}^{\infty} v_k$ converges, and find its sum. (Assume a is not a negative integer.)

8.7 Use the result $\ln(a/b) = \ln a - \ln b$ to evaluate

$$\sum_{k=1}^{n} \ln\left(\frac{k}{k+2}\right) = \ln(\tfrac{1}{3}) + \ln(\tfrac{2}{4}) + \cdots + \ln\left(\frac{n}{n+2}\right)$$

in terms of n. Deduce that the series $\sum \ln(k/(k+2))$ does not converge.

8.8 Use the result $\exp(ab) = (\exp a)^b$ to show that series $\sum_{n} e^{-nk}$ is a geometric series which converges for any fixed positive k. What are the sums of the series

(i) $\displaystyle\sum_{n=0}^{\infty} e^{-nk} = 1 + e^{-k} + e^{-2k} + \cdots$ $(k > 0)$

(ii) $\displaystyle\sum_{n=1}^{\infty} e^{-nk} = e^{-k} + e^{-2k} + \cdots$ $(k > 0)$

(iii) $\displaystyle\sum_{n=2}^{\infty} e^{-n} = \frac{1}{e^2} + \frac{1}{e^3} + \frac{1}{e^4} + \cdots$

(iv) $\displaystyle\sum_{n=0}^{\infty} e^{-2nk} = 1 + e^{-2k} + e^{-4k} + \cdots$ $(k > 0)$?

8.9 Consider the series $\sum_{n=1}^{\infty} n^{-2}$.
Show that $s_3 < 1 + \tfrac{1}{2}$, $s_7 < 1 + \tfrac{1}{2} + (\tfrac{1}{2})^2$, and $s_{15} < 1 + \tfrac{1}{2} + (\tfrac{1}{2})^2 + (\tfrac{1}{2})^3$, and deduce the corresponding inequality for s_n when $n = 2^m - 1$. Hence show that $s_n < 2$ for any n. Can Theorem 8.2 now be applied?

Each of the following Exercises 8.10–8.19 gives a set of conditions involving the terms v_n of a series $v_1 + v_2 + v_3 + \cdots$, $s_n = \sum_{i=1}^{n} v_i$, and the sum $S = \mathrm{Lim}_{n \to \infty} s_n$ of the series. In each exercise, either give a specific example of v_n for which the series satisfies the given conditions, or give reasons why such a series cannot exist. The symbol r denotes a constant, independent of n. Unless otherwise stated, the given conditions are true for all n:

8.10 (i) $v_{n+1} = r v_n$ $(0 < r < 1)$, (ii) $s_n < 1$, (iii) $S = 1$.
8.11 (i) $v_{n+1} = r v_n$ $(0 < r < 1)$, (ii) $S < 0$.
8.12 (i) $v_{n+1} = r v_n$ $(0 < r < 1)$, (ii) $s_{10} > 1$, (iii) $S = 1$.
8.13 (i) $v_{n+1} = r v_n$ $(r > 1)$, (ii) $S = 2$.
8.14 (i) $v_{n+1} = r v_n$ $(-1 < r < 0)$, (ii) $S < \tfrac{1}{2} v_1$.
8.15 (i) $1 \leqslant v_n \leqslant 2$, (ii) $100 \leqslant S \leqslant 200$.
8.16 (i) $v_{n+1}/v_n < 0$, (ii) $S > 0$.
8.17 (i) $s_n < 2$, (ii) S does not exist.
8.18 (i) $n v_n > 1$, (ii) $S = 2$.
8.19 (i) $0 < n^3 v_n < 1$, (ii) $S = 3/2$.
8.20 Show that, if $v_n = 1/(2n+1) - 1/(2n+2)$, then $v_n < 1/4n^2$.

Deduce that the series

$$\tfrac{1}{3} - \tfrac{1}{4} + \tfrac{1}{5} - \tfrac{1}{6} + \tfrac{1}{7} - \tfrac{1}{8} + \cdots$$

converges, and that the series in Example 8.42 converge (p. 189).

8.21 Show that, if $v_n = (8n+5)/(4n+1)(4n+3)(2n+2)$, then $v_n < 1/2n^2$. Deduce that the series (cf. Example 8.45 on p. 190).

$$1 + \tfrac{1}{3} - \tfrac{1}{2} + \tfrac{1}{5} + \tfrac{1}{7} - \tfrac{1}{4} + \tfrac{1}{9} + \tfrac{1}{11} - \tfrac{1}{6} + \cdots$$

is convergent.

8.22 Find the sums of the following series:

(i) $1 - \dfrac{1}{3^2} + \dfrac{1}{3^4} - \dfrac{1}{3^6} + \cdots + \dfrac{(-1)^n}{3^{2n}} + \cdots .$

(ii) $1 + \frac{1}{2} - \frac{1}{4} + \frac{1}{8} + \frac{1}{16} - \frac{1}{32} + \frac{1}{64} + \frac{1}{128} - \frac{1}{256} + \cdots .$ (with every 3rd term negative)

8.23 For each of the following conditions on the terms of a series $\sum v_n$ state whether the condition implies that the series converges, or does not converge, or whether no conclusion on the behaviour can be inferred:

(a) $v_n \rightarrow 0$ as $n \rightarrow \infty$

(b) $0 < v_n < 1/n$ for all n

(c) $-1/n^2 < v_n < 1/n^2$ for all n

(d) $v_n > 1/n$ for all n.

8.24 For each of the following series

(a) $\sum \dfrac{(-1)^n}{n}$ (b) $\sum \dfrac{1}{n^2}$ (c) $\sum \dfrac{1}{\sqrt{n}}$

either state what can be deduced by comparison with the harmonic series $\sum 1/n$, or state why this comparison test does not apply.

8.25

> If $\sum_{n=1}^{\infty} v_n$ is a series of positive terms, the **ratio test** states that the series converges if $\mathrm{Lim}_{n \to \infty}\, v_{n+1}/v_n < 1$, and that the series does not converge if $\mathrm{Lim}_{n \to \infty}\, v_{n+1}/v_n > 1$. ($\mathrm{Lim}_{n \to \infty}\, v_{n+1}/v_n = 1$ allows no inference).

For the series with the following general terms, write down v_{n+1}, $\mathrm{Lim}_{n \to \infty}\, v_{n+1}/v_n$, and the conclusion of the ratio test:

(i) $v_n = \dfrac{1}{n}$ (ii) $v_n = \dfrac{n^2}{2^n}$ (iii) $v_n = \dfrac{1}{n!}$ (iv) $v_n = \dfrac{3^n}{n^3}$.

8.26 (i) (a) for what values of p is $\sum_{n=1}^{\infty} 1/n^p$ a convergent series of positive terms?

(b) For what values of a and r is $\sum ar^{n-1}$ a convergent series of positive terms?

(ii) Use the results of (i) and a comparison test to determine whether the following series converge:

(a) $\sum \dfrac{1}{n^3 + n^2 + 1}$ (b) $\sum \dfrac{3^n}{n!}$ (c) $\sum \dfrac{n^2 + 2n + 1}{n^3 + 2n + 1}$

Table of Series

Unless otherwise stated, $\sum$ means $\sum_{n=1}^{\infty}$.

I Series of Positive terms

$$\sum \frac{1}{n^2} = \frac{\pi^2}{6}, \qquad \sum \frac{1}{n^4} = \frac{\pi^4}{90}, \qquad \sum \frac{1}{n^6} = \frac{\pi^6}{945}$$

$$\sum_{n=2}^{\infty} \frac{1}{n^2 - 1} = \frac{3}{4}, \qquad \sum \frac{1}{4n^2 - 1} = \frac{1}{2}, \qquad \sum \frac{1}{(4n^2 - 1)^2} = \frac{\pi^2 - 8}{16}$$

$$\sum \frac{1}{(4n^2 - 1)^3} = \frac{32 - 3\pi^2}{18}, \qquad \sum \frac{1}{(4n^2 - 1)^4} = \frac{\pi^4 + 30\pi^2 - 384}{768}$$

$$\sum \frac{1}{n(4n^2 - 1)} = 2 \ln 2 - 1, \qquad \sum \frac{1}{n(9n^2 - 1)} = \frac{3}{2}(\ln 3 - 1)$$

$$\sum \frac{1}{n(36n^2 - 1)} = -3 + \frac{3}{2} \ln 3 + 2 \ln 2$$

$$\sum \frac{n}{(4n^2 - 1)^2} = \frac{1}{8}, \qquad \sum \frac{1}{n(4n - 1)^2} = \frac{3}{2} - 2 \ln 2$$

$$\sum_{n=0}^{\infty} \frac{1}{n!} = e, \qquad \sum_{n=0}^{\infty} \frac{1}{(2n)!} = \cosh 1, \qquad \sum_{n=0}^{\infty} \frac{1}{(2n+1)!} = \sinh 1.$$

II Alternating Series

$$\sum \frac{(-)^n}{n} = \ln \frac{1}{2}, \qquad \sum \frac{(-)^n}{n^2} = -\frac{\pi^2}{12}, \qquad \sum \frac{(-)^n}{n^4} = -\frac{7\pi^4}{720}$$

$$\sum \frac{(-)^n}{2n+1} = \frac{\pi}{4} - 1, \qquad \sum \frac{(-)^n}{(2n+1)^3} = \frac{\pi^3}{32} - 1$$

$$\sum \frac{(-)^n}{3n+1} = \frac{1}{3} \ln 2 + \frac{\pi}{3\sqrt{3}} - 1, \qquad \sum \frac{(-)^n}{3n+2} = \frac{\pi}{3\sqrt{3}} - \frac{1}{3} \ln 2 - 1$$

$$\sum_{n=2}^{\infty} \frac{(-)^n}{n^2 - 1} = \frac{1}{4}, \qquad \sum \frac{(-)^n}{4n+1} = \frac{\pi + 2 \ln (1 + \sqrt{2})}{4\sqrt{2}} - 1$$

$$\sum_{n=0}^{\infty} \frac{(-)^n}{n!} = \frac{1}{e}, \qquad \sum_{n=0}^{\infty} \frac{(-)^n}{(2n)!} = \cos 1, \qquad \sum_{n=0}^{\infty} \frac{(-)^n}{(2n+1)!} = \sin 1.$$

III Other Series

Provided a is not a negative integer,

$$\sum \frac{1}{(a + n)(a + n + 1)} = \frac{1}{a + 1}$$

$$\sum \frac{1}{(a + n)(a + n + 2)} = \frac{2a + 3}{2(a + 1)(a + 2)}$$

$$\sum \frac{1}{(a+n)(a+n+1)(a+n+2)} = \frac{1}{2(a+1)(a+2)}$$

$$\sum \frac{1}{(a+n)(a+n+1)(a+n+2)(a+n+3)} = \frac{1}{3(a+1)(a+2)(a+3)}$$

$$\sum \frac{\sin n\theta}{n} = (\pi - \theta)/2 \qquad\qquad (0 < \theta < \pi)$$

$$\sum (-)^n \frac{\sin n\theta}{n} = \theta/2 \qquad\qquad (-\pi < \theta < \pi)$$

$$\sum \frac{\cos n\theta}{n} = -\ln\left(2 \sin \frac{\theta}{2}\right) \qquad\qquad (0 < \theta < 2\pi)$$

$$\sum (-)^n \frac{\cos n\theta}{n} = -\ln\left(2 \cos \frac{\theta}{2}\right) \qquad\qquad (-\pi < \theta < \pi)$$

$$\sum \frac{\cos n\theta}{n^2} = \tfrac{1}{4}\theta^2 - \tfrac{1}{2}\theta\pi + \tfrac{1}{6}\pi^2 \qquad\qquad (0 \leqslant \theta \leqslant 2\pi)$$

Numerous other results, especially with terms involving sin or cos, may be found in references on series, for example

Handbook of Series for Scientists and Engineers, by V. Mangulis (Academic Press, 1965); *A Table of Series and Products*, by E. R. Hansen (Prentice-Hall, 1975).

9

The Integral Calculus

9.1 Definition of the Riemann Integral

In the previous chapter sequences of the type $\{s_n : s_n = v_1 + v_2 + \cdots + v_n\}$ were studied, and conditions were obtained for the existence of a limit (i.e. for the convergence of the series $\sum v_k$). This chapter considers similar questions for a different type of sequence. Although the structure of this sequence $\{R_n\}$ is more complicated than $\{s_n = v_1 + v_2 + \cdots + v_n\}$, the existence or nonexistence of a limit can usually be decided without difficulty, and there are rather general methods for evaluating the limit. In this section, the mathematical nature of the sequence will be described. The following sections give some practical examples, and then various properties of the limit, emphasizing those which allow its evaluation. Specific techniques for obtaining the limit form the subject of Chapters 10, 11 and 15.

The sequence $\{R_n\}$ is constructed from a given function f and a given subset of the domain of f. Unless otherwise stated, f will be type $R \to R$, and the subset a given interval $[a, b]$ in the domain of f. To get R_n, first divide $[a, b]$ into n subintervals of equal length $\delta = (b-a)/n$:

$$
\begin{array}{ccccccc}
\vert & \vert & \vert & \cdots\cdots\cdots\cdots & \vert & & \vert \\
a & x_1 & x_2 & & x_{n-1} & & b
\end{array}
$$

The points of subdivision are denoted by $x_1, x_2, \ldots, x_{n-1}$. Choose a set of points $c_1, c_2, \ldots, c_n$, one in each closed subinterval:

$$
\begin{array}{ccccccc}
& c_1 & & c_2 & & c_{n-1} & & c_n \\
\vert & \vert & \vert & \vert & \cdots\cdots\cdots & \vert & \vert & \vert & \vert \\
a & & x_1 & & x_2 & & x_{n-1} & & b
\end{array}
$$

$a \le c_1 \le x_1,\ x_1 \le c_2 \le x_2, \ldots, x_{i-1} \le c_i \le x_i$ in the ith subinterval.

Then R_n is obtained by summing the values $f(c_i)$ and multiplying by the subinterval length:

$$R_n = \delta \sum_{i=1}^{n} f(c_i) \tag{9.1}$$

Example 9.10

Suppose $f(x) = x^2$, $a = 0$ and $b = 1$, and the points c_i are always chosen at the midpoints of the subintervals. Then when $n = 1$, $c_1 = \frac{1}{2}$, and $R_1 = (b-a)f(c_1) = (\frac{1}{2})^2$.

For $n = 2$, the subdivision is

and

$$R_2 = \tfrac{1}{2}f(\tfrac{1}{4}) + \tfrac{1}{2}f(\tfrac{3}{4}) = \tfrac{1}{2}(\tfrac{1}{4})^2 + \tfrac{1}{2}(\tfrac{3}{4})^2.$$

For $n = 3$, the three subintervals have length $\tfrac{1}{3}$:

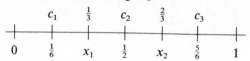

Thus

$$R_3 = \tfrac{1}{3}f(\tfrac{1}{6}) + \tfrac{1}{3}f(\tfrac{1}{2}) + \tfrac{1}{3}f(\tfrac{5}{6}) = \tfrac{1}{3}(\tfrac{1}{6})^2 + \tfrac{1}{3}(\tfrac{1}{2})^2 + \tfrac{1}{3}(\tfrac{5}{6})^2. \quad \square$$

This prescription for R_n does not lead to a unique sequence, because the way in which the points c_i are to be chosen was left indefinite.

Example 9.11

Consider the previous example again.

(i) Taking the c_i at the left end-points of the subintervals gives

$$R_1 = 0^2, \quad R_2 = \tfrac{1}{2}0^2 + \tfrac{1}{2}(\tfrac{1}{2})^2, \quad R_3 = \tfrac{1}{3}0^2 + \tfrac{1}{3}(\tfrac{1}{3})^2 + \tfrac{1}{3}(\tfrac{2}{3})^2, \quad \ldots.$$

(ii) Taking $c_i = x_i$ (the right end-point of each subinterval) gives

$$R_1 = 1^2, \quad R_2 = \tfrac{1}{2}(\tfrac{1}{2})^2 + \tfrac{1}{2}(1)^2, \quad R_3 = \tfrac{1}{3}(\tfrac{1}{3})^2 + \tfrac{1}{3}(\tfrac{2}{3})^2 + \tfrac{1}{3}(1)^2, \quad \ldots \quad \square$$

The statements above thus define many sequences $\{R_n\}$. However, in cases of interest, all such sequences have *the same limit*, and it is always the limit which is the object of the calculation. The limit is denoted by $R_a^b(f)$, indicating that it depends on the function f, and on the interval $[a, b]$. It is called the **Riemann integral of f from a to b.**

The existence or otherwise of the limit is not obvious, because $\sum_{i=1}^{n} f(c_i) \to \infty$ as $n \to \infty$, while $\delta = (b - a)/n \to 0$. For the time being its existence will be assumed.

Although the different sequences $\{R_n\}$ have the same limit, some may approach the limit more quickly than others. This could be significant for estimating the limit numerically.

Example 9.12

The following table shows terms from three of the sequences for $f(x) = \exp(-x^2)$ on $[0, 1]$. The sequences labelled L_n, U_n, and M_n were obtained by choosing the points c_i in the subintervals at the right end-points, left end-points and midpoints respectively.

n	L_n	M_n	U_n
2	0.57	0.755	0.89
10	0.71	0.7471	0.78
50	0.740	0.746836	0.753
500	0.7462	0.746824	0.7476

This table indicates that the different sequences $\{L_n\}$, $\{M_n\}$ and $\{U_n\}$ do have the same limit $R_0^1(e^{-x^2})$, but $\{L_n\}$ and $\{U_n\}$ approach the limit more slowly than the sequence $\{M_n\}$. The values M_{50} and M_{500} suggest that $R_0^1(e^{-x^2}) = 0.7468$ (4S).

Since e^{-x^2} is decreasing, the value at the right end-point of a subinterval is the least value in this subinterval. This means that $L_n < R_n$ where R_n is any other sequence obtained with a different choice of the points c_i. Similarly $U_n > R_n$ since U_n uses the greatest value in each subinterval. □

If the limit $R_a^b(f)$ does exist, then f is said to be **Riemann-integrable** on $[a, b]$.

Exercises (answers on p. 218)

9.1.1 Evaluate the 4th term for each of the sequences in Examples 9.10, 9.11(i) and 9.11(ii).
  Why does the sequence in 9.11(i) give the sequence $\{R_n\}$ having the smallest terms? What can be said about the sequence in 9.11(ii)?

9.1.2 Suppose the interval $[0, 1]$ is divided into n subintervals of equal length. For the ith subinterval $[x_{i-1}, x_i]$, express in terms of i and n
  (i) the right end-point x_i
  (ii) the left end-point x_{i-1}, and
  (iii) the midpoint.

9.1.3 Sketch $f(x) = x^2$ on the interval $[-1, 1]$. Give a prescription for choosing $(i = 1, 2, \ldots, n)$ the c_i in $[x_{i-1}, x_i]$ so that the sequence R_n has the smallest terms. (Hint: if necessary, the prescriptions for n even and n odd can be different.)

9.1.4 (i) For $f(x) = k$, a constant, use equation (9.1) to show that R_n is independent of n. What is the value of $R_a^b(f)$?
  (ii) If $g(x) = k + f(x)$, use equation (9.1) to express $R_a^b(g)$ in terms of $R_a^b(f)$.

9.2 Applications

Example 9.20
If a particle is moved along the straight path AB by a force having the constant value F, the work done by the force is $AB \cdot F$.

Consider the work done by a variable force $F(x)$, where x measures distance along the line AB.

Suppose A and B are given by $x = a$ and $x = b$.
  Divide $[a, b]$ into n subintervals $[x_{i-1}, x_i]$ of length δ. If W_i is the work done during motion through the ith subinterval, then the total work is $W = \sum_{i=1}^{n} W_i$. If m_i is the minimum value of the force in $[x_{i-1}, x_i]$, then $W_i \geq m_i \delta$, since this would be the work done by a constant force m_i. Similarly, if M_i is the maximum force at any point in $[x_{i-1}, x_i]$, then $W_i \leq M_i \delta$. Writing out these inequalities for each of the n subintervals gives

$$m_1 \delta \leq W_1 \leq M_1 \delta$$
$$m_2 \delta \leq W_2 \leq M_2 \delta \qquad \qquad (9.2)$$
$$\cdots\cdots\cdots\cdots$$
$$\cdots\cdots\cdots\cdots$$
$$m_n \delta \leq W_n \leq M_n \delta.$$

The result of adding the n inequalities will be written $L_n \leq W \leq U_n$. Since the numbers m_i and M_i are values in the ith subinterval of the force function F, L_n and U_n are sums of the type (9.1). If F is Riemann-integrable on $[a, b]$, then $\{L_n\}$ and $\{U_n\}$ have the same limit, and the inequality $L_n \leq W \leq U_n$ shows that this limit is W. (Since $L_n \leq W$, then $\mathrm{Lim}\{L_n\} \leq W$; similarly $\mathrm{Lim}\{U_n\} \geq W$).

Hence the required work is $W = R_a^b(F)$.   □

If the force function F is not Riemann-integrable on $[a, b]$, then the limits of $\{L_n\}$ and $\{U_n\}$ either do not exist, or are unequal. There is then no consistent way of defining the work done by the force, so the calculation is not required.

In most examples, the function f has a minimum and a maximum value in any subinterval. Either may be chosen for $f(c_i)$, giving two special cases of R_n. These will be denoted by L_n and U_n. Since $L_n \leq R_n \leq U_n$ for any other R_n, if the sequences $\{L_n\}$ and $\{U_n\}$ have the same limit, so do all the other sequences $\{R_n\}$.

Example 9.21
A function consisting of the n pairs (x_i, y_i) has an average value $(\sum_i y_i)/n$. If the function is not one-to-one, and the value y_i appears t_i times, the average value can be written $\sum (t_i/n)y_i$, where the sum is over distinct y_i only. The factor (t_i/n) is a **weighting factor** proportional to the number of times y_i occurs.

Consider now the analogous calculation for a function f defined at every point of an interval $[a, b]$. Divide $[a, b]$ into n subintervals, and choose typical values of f in each subinterval, say $f(c_1), f(c_2), \ldots, f(c_n)$. Corresponding to the weighting factor

$$\frac{t_i}{n} = \frac{\text{number of points giving the value } y_i}{\text{total number of points in domain}}$$

take

$$\frac{\text{length of subinterval in which value } f(c_i) \text{ is typical}}{\text{total length of domain}} = \frac{\delta}{b-a}.$$

Summing over the chosen typical values gives

$$\sum_{i=1}^{n} \frac{\delta}{b-a} f(c_i) = \frac{\delta}{b-a} \sum_{i=1}^{n} f(c_i).$$

The remaining sum is just that occurring in equation (9.1), so on letting $n \to \infty$, the limit $R_a^b(f)$ is obtained.

Thus if f is Riemann-integrable on $[a, b]$, then its **average value** on $[a, b]$ is $R_a^b(f)/(b-a)$.

This can be regarded as a **definition** of the average value of f on $[a, b]$ for the case where the independent variable takes all values on this interval.   □

Example 9.22
Consider the length of the curve $y = f(x)$ in the interval $[a, b]$.

Divide $[a, b]$ into n subintervals by points $x_1, x_2, \ldots, x_i \ldots$, and suppose $P_0, P_1, \ldots, P_n$ are the corresponding points of the curve. In each subinterval, take the chord length $P_{i-1}P_i$ (Fig. 9.1).

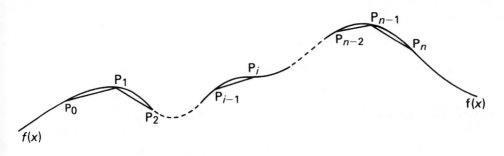

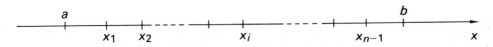

Figure 9.1 Chords $P_{i-1}P_i$ used to obtain length of curve P_0P_n.

A reasonable **definition** of length of the curve P_0P_n is to add all these chord lengths, and take the limit as $n \to \infty$,

since the smaller the subintervals, the more closely the chords approximate the curve.

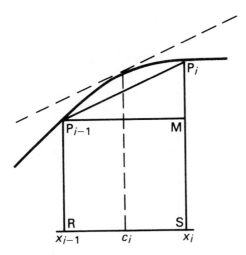

Figure 9.2 Chord length using mean value theorem

From Fig. 9.2, which shows the curve and chord in the ith subinterval

$$(P_{i-1}P_i)^2 = (MP_{i-1})^2 + (MP_i)^2, \quad \text{and} \quad MP_{i-1} = (x_i - x_{i-1}) = \delta.$$

Also MP_i/MP_{i-1} is the slope of the chord. According to the mean value theorem of Section 6.7, there is a point c_i in the subinterval where $f'(c_i) = MP_i/MP_{i-1}$.

$$MP_i = f'(c_i)(MP_{i-1}) = f'(c_i)\delta$$

and

$$(P_{i-1}P_i)^2 = \delta^2[1+\{f'(c_i)\}^2].$$

Define a function $g = \sqrt{(1+f'^2)}$. Then $P_{i-1}P_i = g(c_i)\delta$, and $\sum_{i=1}^{n}(P_{i-1}P_i)$ is equation (9.1), with g replacing f. Taking the limit as $n \to \infty$ shows that

the Riemann integral $R_a^b(g) = R_a^b(\sqrt{(1+f'^2)})$ is the required length.

The use of the mean value theorem requires that f is continuous on $[a, b]$, and that f' exists on (a, b). Further conditions on f' may be required for the limit $R_a^b(g)$ to exist. $\square$

Example 9.23
Suppose f is positive and increasing on $[a, b]$.

Consider the area A bounded by the x-axis, the ordinates $x = a$ and $x = b$, and the curve $y = f(x)$.

Divide (a, b) into n subintervals as in the previous example. In the ith subinterval (Fig. 9.3), evidently
area rectangle RSMP$_{i-1}$ < area A_i in subinterval < area rectangle QRSP$_i$.
    Since RP$_{i-1} = f(x_{i-1})$ and SP$_i = f(x_i)$,

$$\delta f(x_{i-1}) < A_i < \delta f(x_i) \tag{9.3}$$

or

$$\delta m_i < A_i < \delta M_i, \tag{9.4}$$

again using m_i and M_i for the least and greatest values of f in the subinterval.

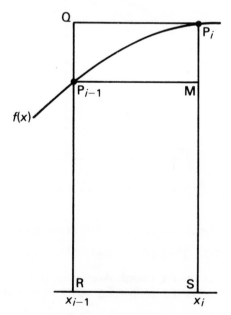

Figure 9.3   Areas in subinterval

There are n inequalities of this type, one for each subinterval, exactly as in Example 9.20. Summing these n inequalities gives

$$L_n = \delta \sum_{i=1}^{n} m_i \leq A \leq \delta \sum_{i=1}^{n} M_i = U_n$$

and a repetition of the argument in Example 9.20 shows that

$$A = R_a^b(f),$$

provided the limit $R_a^b(f)$ exists.

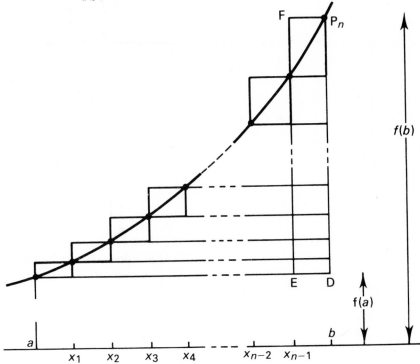

Figure 9.4   Riemann sums U_n and L_n

The contribution to L_n from the ith subinterval is the area $RSMP_{i-1}$ in Fig. 9.3, and $SRQP_i$ is the contribution to U_n. The difference $U_n - L_n$ is the area of the rectangles shown in Fig. 9.4. The rectangles could all be slid along horizontally into the last subinterval, so their total area is just that of the rectangle $DEFP_n$. Thus

$$U_n - L_n = \{f(b) - f(a)\}\delta$$
$$= \{f(b) - f(a)\}(b-a)/n. \tag{9.5}$$

Therefore $\text{Lim}_{n\to\infty}(U_n - L_n) = 0$: if $(\text{Lim}_{n\to\infty} U_n)$ and $(\text{Lim}_{n\to\infty} L_n)$ exist, they must be equal. □

The argument showing that $A = R_a^b(f)$ has exactly the same mathematical content as the argument in Example 9.20 showing that $W = R_a^b(F)$. Only the interpretation is different.

However Example 9.20 was more general because the force function F was not assumed positive and increasing. For the area application these restrictions may also be removed. In fact (9.4) holds in all cases, provided area A_i below the x-axis is considered negative.

Example 9.24

The function $l(x) = mx$ represents a straight line, so that areas between the curve and the x-axis are known geometrically. In Fig. 9.5, for example $(m > 0)$, area $OAB = \frac{1}{2}m$.

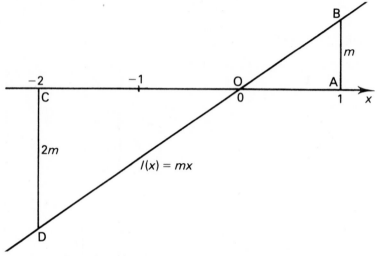

Figure 9.5   Triangular areas between x-axis and line $y = mx$

From the result of the previous example, $R_0^1(l) = \frac{1}{2}m$. However in area CDO $(= 2m)$, all values of $l(x)$ are negative, so $R_{-2}^0(l) = -2m$. On $[-2, 1]$ $R_{-2}^1(l)$ represents the area between the x-axis, the line, and the ordinates CD and AB provided area is taken negative in OCD and positive in OAB, so that $R_{-2}^1(l) = -2m + \frac{1}{2}m = -3m/2$.   □

Exercises (answers on p. 218)

9.2.1   Consider the function which assigns to each month the number of days in the month, a set of 12 pairs such as (February, 28). Write down the range of this function, and for each element of the range the weighting factor defined in Example 9.21. What is the average value of the function?

9.2.2   Given the calculation of $R_0^1(e^{-x^2})$ on p. 198, write down
(i) the work done by a force $F(x) = e^{-x^2}$ in motion from $A(x = 0)$ to $B(x = 1)$;
(ii) the average value of $\exp(-x^2)$ on the interval $[0, 1]$;
(iii) the area bounded by the axes, the line $x = 1$, and the curve $y = e^{-x^2}$.

9.2.3   Draw diagrams which interpret as areas the three values of R_3 given in Examples 9.10 and 9.11, and the two results in Exercise 9.1.4.

9.2.4   Evaluate $R_a^b(|x|)$ by computing an area geometrically.

9.2.5   Suppose P and Q are points on the semi-circle of radius r and centre $(r, 0)$, and $M(a, 0)$ and $N(b, 0)$ are the feet of the perpendiculars from P and Q onto the x-axis.
(i) Find geometrically (in terms of r, a and b) the area PQMN and the arc-length PQ. (See Fig. 9.2.5.)
(ii) Find the equation representing the semi-circle in the explicit form $y = f(x)$.
(iii) Find the two functions f and g for which the values of $R_a^b(f)$ and $R_a^b(g)$ are given by (i).

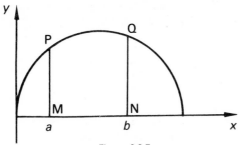

Figure 9.2.5

9.3 Properties of the Riemann Integral

Consider first an alternative notation for the Riemann integral

$$R_a^b(f) = \operatorname*{Lim}_{n \to \infty} \sum_{i=1}^{n} f(c_i)\delta.$$

Since c_i can be any point in $[x_{i-1}, x_i]$, $f(c_i)$ may well be replaced by $f(x)$. Also δ can be regarded as an increment in the independent variable x, and so written as a differential dx:

$$R_a^b(f) = \operatorname*{Lim}_{n \to \infty} \sum_{1}^{n} \{f(x)\, dx\}.$$

The $\sum$ notation is not very appropriate after i has been dropped, so $\sum$ is replaced by S. For the same reason, the sum is now better considered as a sum from x_1 to x_n. When the limit is taken, n is a dummy variable; on dropping this it is better to replace x_n by b, and correspondingly x_1 by a:

$$R_a^b(f) = \operatorname{Lim} S_a^b f(x)\, dx.$$

If changing S to $\int$ denotes that the limit has been taken,

then $R_a^b(f)$ is written $\int_a^b f(x)\, dx$. This can be read 'the integral of f from a to b'.

Since $\int_a^b f(x)\, dx$ is a limit, some of the limit theorems can be applied. If $f = g + h$, then the sum can be divided into two sums:

$$\int_a^b f(x)\, dx = R_a^b(f)$$

$$= \lim_{n \to \infty} \delta \sum_{i=1}^{n} \{g(c_i) + h(c_i)\} = \lim_{n \to \infty} \left[\delta \sum_{i=1}^{n} g(c_i) + \delta \sum_{i=1}^{n} h(c_i) \right]$$

$$= \lim_{n \to \infty} \delta \sum_{i=1}^{n} g(c_i) + \lim_{n \to \infty} \delta \sum_{i=1}^{n} h(c_i)$$

by using Theorem 4.2(i) on p. 83, assuming both limits exist. Thus, when

$$f = g + h, \quad R_a^b(f) = R_a^b(g) + R_a^b(h)$$

or

$$\int_a^b f(x)\, dx = \int_a^b g(x)\, dx + \int_a^b h(x)\, dx. \tag{9.6}$$

If kf replaces f, where k is a constant, then k can be factored out of the sum, and out of the limit (Theorem 4.2(iii) with $g(x) = k = M$). Thus

$$\int_a^b (kf)\,\mathrm{d}x = k \int_a^b f\,\mathrm{d}x \quad \text{or} \quad R_a^b(kf) = kR_a^b(f). \tag{9.7}$$

In Example 9.23, the area under the curve $y = f(x)$ in $[a, b]$ was shown to be $R_a^b(f)$. Conversely, if f represents a curve, then $R_a^b(f)$ can be interpreted as an area between this curve and the x-axis. Any Riemann integral, however it arises, can be considered in some sense as an area. In Example 9.20, a curve may be obtained from $F(x)$, by plotting force against distance. The work done by the force is the 'area' under this curve. This 'area' has the appropriate dimensions, since any abscissa is a length, and any ordinate represents a force. Similarly, in Example 9.22, a curve may be obtained by plotting $g(x) = \sqrt{[1 + \{f'(x)\}^2]}$ against x. The 'area' under this curve gives the length of the curve $y = f(x)$. Again the dimensions are correct: $f'(x)$ is the quotient of two length differentials, and so dimensionless. Thus $g(x)$ is dimensionless, and $g(x)\,\mathrm{d}x$ or $g(c_i)(x_{i+1} - x_i)$ is a length.

Properties of the Riemann integral may therefore be seen by considering properties of area. This approach will be adopted in the rest of this section. For actual proofs of the results, which will not be given here, one must proceed from the definition of R_a^b.

If $0 < g(x) < f(x)$, then the curve $y = f(x)$ lies above the curve $y = g(x)$, and the area below $y = f(x)$ is greater than the corresponding area below $y = g(x)$. Thus

$$0 < g(x) < f(x) \quad \text{on } (a, b) \quad \Rightarrow \quad \int_a^b f(x)\,\mathrm{d}x > \int_a^b g(x)\,\mathrm{d}x. \tag{9.8}$$

In Example 9.24, on p. 204, $R_{-2}^1(l)$ was calculated by adding the areas corresponding to $R_{-2}^0(l)$ and $R_0^1(l)$. Adding the area under a curve in $[a, b]$ to that in $[b, c]$ will always give the area under the curve in $[a, c]$. Thus

$$R_a^b(f) + R_b^c(f) = R_a^c(f) \quad \text{or} \quad \int_a^b f(x)\,\mathrm{d}x + \int_b^c f(x)\,\mathrm{d}x = \int_a^c f(x)\,\mathrm{d}x. \tag{9.9}$$

So far conditions for the existence of $R_a^b(f)$ have not been discussed. In view of the area interpretation, if it is geometrically sensible to talk about the area, then $R_a^b(f)$ must exist. On the other hand, if the equivalent area does not appear on geometrical considerations to be defined, then $R_a^b(f)$ is not expected to exist.

If f is continuous on $[a, b]$, then it is natural to suppose that the area under the curve is well-defined. So if f is continuous on $[a, b]$, the Riemann integral $R_a^b(f)$ must exist.

Example 9.30

(i) Consider $f(x) = |x|$, illustrated in Fig. 9.6(i). The area under the curve in $[a, b]$ is defined, so $R_a^b(|x|) = \int_a^b |x|\,\mathrm{d}x$ exists. Thus f need not be differentiable for $R_a^b(f)$ to exist. ($|x|$ has no derivative at $x = 0$).

(ii) Consider sgn x in $[-1, 1]$, illustrated in Fig. 9.6(ii). The area in $[-1, 0]$ between the curve and the x-axis is a square of unit side below the axis, giving a contribution -1. Similarly the area under the curve in $[0, 1]$ is $+1$; and so the area in $[-1, 1]$ is zero. This suggests that $R_{-1}^1(\text{sgn})$ exists, having the value zero.

Similarly $R_a^b(\text{sgn})$ exists on any interval, in spite of the discontinuity at $x = 0$. Thus continuity, although a **sufficient** condition for the existence of the Riemann integral, is not **necessary**.

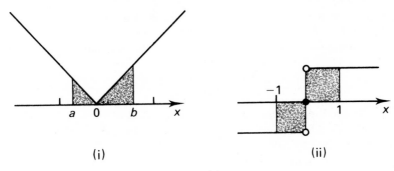

(i)   (ii)

Figure 9.6   (i) $f(x) = |x|$ (ii) $f(x) = \text{sgn } x$

(iii) Consider $f(x) = 1/x$ on $(0, 1]$, illustrated in Fig. 9.7. Because $1/x \to \infty$ as $x \to 0+$, it does not seem sensible to speak of the area under the curve. Thus $R_0^1(1/x)$ or $\int_0^1 (1/x)\, dx$ is not expected to exist. In fact the sequence $\{U_n\}$ cannot be formed because $1/x$ has no maximum on the first subinterval; the sequence $\{L_n\}$ can be written down, but has no limit as $n \to \infty$ (cf. Exercise 9.3.4). $\square$

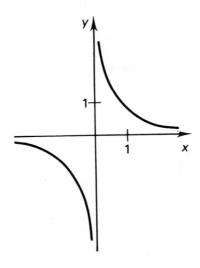

Figure 9.7

This shows that continuity on the **open** interval (a, b) is insufficient to ensure the existence of $R_a^b(f)$, and that in general f must be **bounded** on (a, b).

In practice,

the most useful criterion for the existence of the Riemann integral is as follows:
$\int_a^b f \, dx = R_a^b(f)$ exists if f is bounded and continuous on (a, b).

In conjunction with (9.9), this should cover all cases of interest. For example $\int_{-1}^1 \text{sgn}(x) \, dx$ can be written $\int_{-1}^0 \text{sgn}(x) \, dx + \int_0^1 \text{sgn}(x) \, dx$, and the function is bounded and continuous on both $(-1, 0)$ and $(0, 1)$.

The next property is most easily obtained from the fact that $\int_a^b f(x) \, dx/(b-a)$ is the average value of f on $[a, b]$. (See Example 9.21 on p. 200.) The average value must lie between the minimum and maximum values, giving the inequality

$$m \leqslant \frac{1}{b-a} \int_a^b f(x) \, dx \leqslant M$$

where m and M are the minimum and maximum values of f on $[a, b]$. (This inequality could also be obtained from the area interpretation, since it is just (9.4) on p. 202 for the whole interval $[a, b]$).

When f is continuous, the intermediate value theorem of Section 5.2 says that f must take every value between m and M somewhere on $[a, b]$. Thus at some point c it must take the average value:

$$f(c) = \left[\int_a^b f(x) \, dx \right] / (b-a)$$

This result is called the **mean value theorem of integration:** if f is continuous on (a, b), then there is a point c $(a < c < b)$ such that

$$\int_a^b f(x) \, dx = (b-a)f(c). \tag{9.10}$$

The definition of R_n and $R_a^b(f)$ evidently requires $a < b$. However it is consistent to define $R_a^a(f) = 0$ for any f. If the interval length becomes zero, so do the lengths of all subintervals, and $R_n = 0$.

Exercises (answers on p. 219)

9.3.1 Write out the results of the following examples and exercises, using the notation $\int_a^b f(x) \, dx$ instead of $R_a^b(f)$: Example 9.12, Exercise 9.1.4, Examples 9.20, 9.21, 9.22, 9.23 and 9.24, and Exercises 9.2.4 and 9.2.5.

What is the value of $\int_{1/2}^{3/2} (2x - x^2)^{-1/2} \, dx$?

9.3.2 Evaluate (i) $\int_0^1 2e^{-x^2} \, dx$, (ii) $\int_0^1 (x + e^{-x^2}) \, dx$ (use Example 9.12 on p. 198).

9.3.3 Draw diagrams to illustrate equations (9.8) and (9.9) in terms of areas. Show from similar diagrams that (9.8) holds for the cases

$$g(x) < 0 < f(x) \quad \text{and} \quad g(x) < f(x) < 0.$$

For the cases of (9.8) where g or f changes sign, use (9.9) to divide (a, b) into intervals in which neither f nor g change sign. Does (9.8) hold whenever $g(x) < f(x)$ on (a, b)?

9.3.4   Use the result of Exercise 9.1.2 to show that for $f(x) = 1/x$ on $[0, 1]$, L_n is the sum of the first n terms of the harmonic series. (This verifies that $\{L_n\}$ has no limit—see Example 8.15 on p. 181.)

9.3.5   Verify equation (9.10), the mean value theorem of integration, for $\int_0^1 e^{-x^2}\, dx$, by obtaining the value of c (use Example 9.12 on p. 198.)

9.3.6   Is the definition $R_a^a(f) = 0$ consistent with the results in Examples 9.20, 9.22 and 9.23 on work, arc-length, and area?

9.4   The Fundamental Theorem

As with the general results of the previous section, methods of evaluating the limit $\int_a^b f(x)\, dx$ can be discussed in terms of the problem of determining an area under the curve $y = f(x)$. Numerical methods will be deferred to Chapter 15. Note that Example 9.12 (p. 198) indicates that direct use of the defining sequences $\{R_n\}$ is inefficient. The amount of calculation in S_{500} is not justified by the 4 significant figures apparently obtained, and in any case presumably involves substantial rounding error. The truncation error is known only to the extent that the required limit must lie between L_n and U_n (for any n). Thus the only *certain* conclusion (from the values for L_{500} and U_{500}) is that $\int_0^1 e^{-x^2}\, dx = 0.75$ (2S).

To derive the general analytic method, it is convenient to define an area function A which measures the area under the curve $y = f(x)$ from the ordinate at $x = a$. Then $A(x)$ is the area under the curve in the interval $[a, x]$. This is illustrated in Fig. 9.8. Evidently

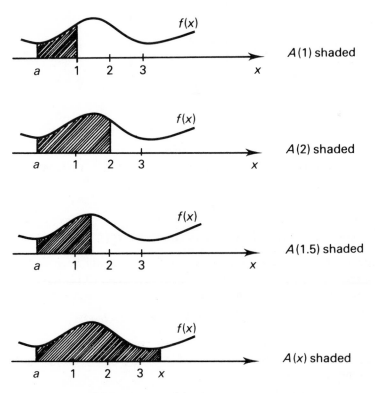

Figure 9.8   Function $A(x)$ giving area under $y = f(x)$

$A(a) = 0$, and the domain of A is $x \geqslant a$. The function A can take negative values, since area below the x-axis is regarded as negative.

The use of calculus to determine areas is based on a result concerning the derivative $A'(x)$. If this exists, it will be

$$\operatorname*{Lim}_{h \to 0} \{A(x + h) - A(x)\}/h.$$

Now $A(x + h)$ is the area in $[a, x + h]$, and $A(x)$ is the area in $[a, x]$ so the difference is the area in $[x, x + h]$. Call this area A_h. Then inequalities such as (9.3) on p. 202 can be derived for A_h, by the same geometrical argument. For example, Fig. 9.9 illustrates the

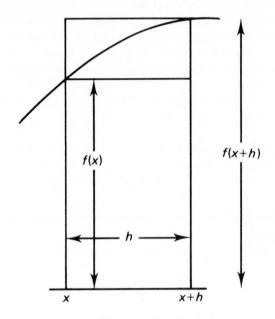

Figure 9.9   Area $A(x + h) - A(x)$

case where f is positive and increasing, and is merely Fig. 9.3 relabelled. So

$$hf(x) < A_h < hf(x + h)$$

and

$$f(x) < \{A(x + h) - A(x)\}/h < f(x + h). \tag{9.11}$$

The division by h requires h positive, which has evidently been assumed anyway in considering an interval $[x, x + h]$. As $h \to 0+$, the inequality (9.11) remains true. Provided f is continuous, $f(x + h) \to f(x)$. The quotient in between must therefore also tend to $f(x)$:

$$\{A(x + h) - A(x)\}/h \to f(x) \quad \text{as} \quad h \to 0+.$$

The behaviour of $\{A(x + h) - A(x)\}/h$ as $h \to 0-$ may be considered by putting $p = -h$, and letting $p \to 0+$ in the quotient $\{A(x) - A(x - p)\}/p$. Relabelling Fig. 9.9 so that the interval becomes $[x - p, x]$, one obtains

$$pf(x - p) < A(x) - A(x - p) < pf(x).$$

Again divide by $p>0$, and let $p\to 0+$. Provided f is continuous, $f(x-p)\to f(x)$, and so must the quotient. Thus

$$\{A(x+h)-A(x)\}/h\to f(x) \quad\text{as } h\to 0-.$$

Together with the previous result as $h\to 0+$, this shows that

$$A'(x)=f(x). \tag{9.12}$$

As in the previous discussion of area, the restriction that f is positive and increasing can be removed by a separate consideration of the other geometric cases, using (9.4) rather than (9.3) when necessary. However f must be assumed continuous at x.

Example 9.40
Consider again the area AOB in Fig. 9.10, and take $a=0$ in defining $A(x)$, so that $A(0)=0$, and $A(1)=$ area OAB. From equation (9.12), $A'(x)=l(x)=mx$: A is a function whose derivative is mx. So $A(x)=\frac{1}{2}mx^2$, which also satisfies $A(0)=0$. Finally $A(1)=\frac{1}{2}m$.

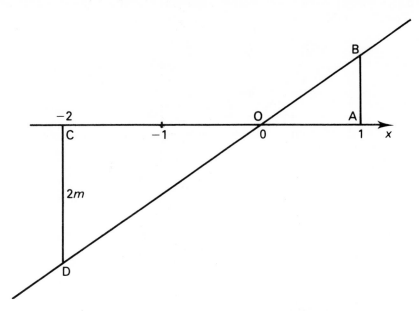

Figure 9.10   Area between x-axis and line $l(x)=mx$

Note that the equation $A'(x)=mx$ has no **unique** solution, being true for $A(x)=\frac{1}{2}mx^2+C$, where C is any constant. However here C is determined by the condition $A(0)=0$. In general, the arbitrary constant C should be included at the stage of writing down the solution of equation (9.12).

To find the area CDO in Fig. 9.10, redefine $A(x)$ by taking $a=-2$. Then $A(0)$ is the required area. Equation (9.12) is still $A'(x)=l(x)=mx$ but $A(x)\neq\frac{1}{2}mx^2$, since now $A(0)\neq 0$. The required argument is

$$A'(x)=mx\Rightarrow A(x)=\tfrac{1}{2}mx^2+C \quad\text{(where C is arbitrary)}$$

and

$$0=A(-2)=2m+C\Rightarrow C=-2m.$$

Hence $A(x) = \frac{1}{2}mx^2 - 2m$, and $A(0) = -2m$. Also the area between CD and AB is $A(1) = 3m/2$. □

The result (9.12) remains true when the area function $A(x)$ is expressed as a Riemann integral.

> It is then called **the fundamental theorem of the calculus:**
> Suppose f is continuous on $[a, b]$, and a function A is defined by $A(x) = R_a^x(f)$.
> Then $A'(x) = f(x)$.

The assumption of continuity ensures that $R_a^x(f)$ exists for $a \le x \le b$, so that $[a, b]$ is in the domain of A. Also $A(a) = 0$.

When the fundamental theorem is stated using the notation $\int_a^b f(x)\,dx$, b is replaced by x. Since $R_a^b(f)$ depends only on a, b and f, and not on the variable x, the x in $\int_a^b f(x)\,dx$ is a dummy variable which can be replaced by an alternative symbol if necessary. To avoid confusion this is necessary if x is replacing b.

> So **the fundamental theorem is written**, provided f is continuous on $[a, x]$,
>
> if
> $$A(x) = \int_a^x f(u)\,du, \quad \text{then } A'(x) = f(x).$$

For a proof of the fundamental theorem, it is neater, and more general, to apply the mean value theorem (9.10) than to develop the procedure which led to equation (9.12). If $A(x) = \int_a^x f(u)\,du$, then

$$A(x+h) - A(x) = \int_x^{x+h} f(u)\,du, \quad \text{from equation (9.9) on p. 206}$$

$$= hf(c), \quad \text{from equation (9.10) on p. 208.}$$

Since $x \le c \le x + h$, $c \to x$ as $h \to 0+$, and $f(c) \to f(x)$ if f is continuous. The case $h \to 0-$ may be treated in the same way.

Exercises (answers on p. 219)

9.4.1 Obtain inequalities like (9.11) on p. 201 for $h > 0$ and
   (i) f positive and decreasing
   (ii) f negative and decreasing.

9.4.2 (i) From Example 9.11 write down numbers λ and μ for which $\lambda < \int_0^1 x^2\,dx < \mu$. (See p. 198.)
   (ii) If $A(x)$ denotes the area under the curve $y = x^2$ in the interval $[0, x]$, write down $A'(x)$, and find $A(x)$.
   (iii) If $f(x) = x^2$, and $A(x) = R_0^x(f)$, write down $A'(x)$ and $A(x)$.
   (iv) If $f(x) = x^2$ and $A(x) = \int_0^x u^2\,du$, write down $A'(x)$ and $A(x)$.
   Check that your answer is consistent with your answer in (i).

9.4.3 (i) If $A(x)$ denotes the area under the curve $y = \cos x$ in the interval $[-\frac{1}{2}\pi, x]$, where $x \le \frac{1}{2}\pi$, write down $A'(x)$ and find $A(x)$.
   (ii) If $A(x) = \int_{-\pi/2}^x \cos u\,du$, write down $A'(x)$ and $A(x)$.

9.4.4   If $A(x) = \int_0^x e^{-t^2} \, dt$, write down $A'(x)$, and $A(0)$.

9.4.5   If

$$F(x) = \int_1^x \frac{2u^2 \sin u - 3 \cos u}{1 + u^2} \, du,$$

write down $F'(x)$ and $F(1)$.

9.5   Evaluation of Riemann Integrals

The importance of the fundamental theorem lies in the fact that it relates integration to differentiation, giving a general method of evaluating $\int_a^b f(x) \, dx$ by using known results on derivatives. This procedure has already been illustrated in Example 9.40 on p. 211 which required the knowledge that the derivative of $\frac{1}{2}mx^2$ is mx.

The general method depends on the following converse of the fundamental theorem: if A is a function such that $A' = f$ and $A(a) = 0$, then $A(x) = R_a^x(f)$. This again requires f to be **continuous** on $[a, x]$.

Example 9.50
Since $\ln' x = 1/x$ and $\ln 1 = 0$, taking $A = \ln$ and $a = 1$ shows that $\ln x = \int_1^x (1/u) \, du$ $(x \geqslant 1)$.   □

Example 9.51
If $l(x) = mx$, find an expression for

$$R_0^x(l) = \int_0^x mt \, dt.$$

The required expression $A(x)$ is determined by $A'(x) = mx$ and $A(0) = 0$.

$$A'(x) = mx \Rightarrow A(x) = C + \tfrac{1}{2}mx^2 \quad \text{(where } C \text{ is arbitrary)},$$

and $0 = A(0) \Rightarrow 0 = C$. Hence $\int_0^x mt \, dt = \frac{1}{2}mx^2$.
(This work is the same as in Example 9.40, except for the area interpretation.)   □

The functions satisfying $A' = f$ only differ in the choice of the arbitrary constant. If $P(x)$ is any function satisfying $P' = f$, then $A(x) = C + P(x)$ for some constant C. This constant is determined by

$$A(a) = 0 \quad \Rightarrow \quad C = -P(a).$$

Hence
$$A(x) = P(x) - P(a) \text{ and}$$

$$\int_a^b f(x) \, dx = R_a^b(f) = A(b) = P(b) - P(a). \tag{9.13}$$

The prescription for evaluating $\int_a^b f(x) \, dx$ then becomes: find any function P satisfying $P' = f$; then evaluate $P(b) - P(a)$,

which is usually written $[P(x)]_a^b$ or $P(x)|_a^b$. Any such function P is called a **primitive** or **antiderivative** of f. The function $C + P(x)$, which contains the arbitrary constant, is called the **indefinite integral** of f, and denoted by $\int f(x) \, dx$.

To stress that the use of equation (9.13) implies the determination of the arbitrary constant, it will be retained in the following examples. Thus Example 9.51 could be written

$$\int_0^x mt \, dt = \tfrac{1}{2}mt^2\big|_0^x = \tfrac{1}{2}mx^2 - 0 = \tfrac{1}{2}mx^2$$

using $P(t) = \tfrac{1}{2}mt^2$. Alternatively,

$$\int_0^x mt \, dt = (C + \tfrac{1}{2}mt^2)\big|_0^x = \tfrac{1}{2}mx^2,$$

any constant C cancelling. Note that the first step in evaluating $R_a^b(f)$, finding the primitive or indefinite integral, can be performed using any symbol for the independent variable, since in the following step one substitutes values b and a for this variable. (In other words, it is a dummy variable.) When $b = x$ (as above), x should not be used for the dummy integration variable.

Example 9.52
Find the length of the curve $y = \cosh x$ in the interval $[0, 2]$.

Take $f(x) = \cosh x$, and determine the function $g = \sqrt{(1 + f'^2)}$. (See Example 9.22 on p. 201.) Since $f'(x) = \sinh x$, $g(x) = \sqrt{(1 + \sinh^2 x)} = \cosh x$. From Example 9.22, the required length is $R_0^2(\cosh)$, i.e. $\int_0^2 \cosh x \, dx$.
The indefinite integral required for $R_0^2(\cosh)$ is

$$\int \cosh x \, dx = C + \sinh x.$$

Hence $\int_0^2 \cosh x \, dx = (C + \sinh x)\big|_0^2 = C + (\sinh 2) - C - (\sinh 0)$.
Thus the required length is $\sinh 2 = \tfrac{1}{2}(e^2 - 1/e^2) = 3.627$ (4S).   □

Example 9.53
Calculate $R_{-2}^1(f)$ for the function $f(x) = -1$ if $-2 \leqslant x \leqslant -1$; $f(x) = x^2$ if $-1 < x \leqslant 1$ (see Fig. 9.11).

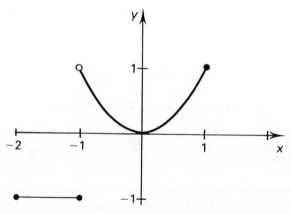

Figure 9.11   Integral of discontinuous function $f(x)$

Because of the discontinuity in f at $x = -1$ this integral must be calculated as $R_{-2}^{-1}(f) + R_{-1}^{1}(f)$. First

$$R_{-2}^{-1}(f) = \int_{-2}^{-1} (-1)\,dx = (C - x)|_{-2}^{-1} = 1 - 2 = -1.$$

From the area interpretation, this is obviously correct, the area in $[-2, -1]$ between the curve and the x-axis being a square of unit side below the x-axis.

$$R_{-1}^{1}(f) = \int_{-1}^{1} x^2\,dx = (C + x^3/3)|_{-1}^{1} = (\tfrac{1}{3}) - (-\tfrac{1}{3}) = \tfrac{2}{3},$$

which looks reasonable when considered as an area.

$$R_{-2}^{1}(f) = R_{-2}^{-1}(f) + R_{-1}^{1}(f) = -\tfrac{1}{3}. \quad \square$$

The indefinite integral $\int f(x)\,dx$ is an expression containing an arbitrary constant. The Riemann integral $\int_a^b f(x)\,dx$ is a number; in particular, $\int_a^x f(u)\,du$ is a value of a function. With the introduction of the term indefinite integral for $\int f(x)\,dx$, the Riemann integral may be called the **definite integral.**

The Riemann integral $R_a^b(f)$ has been defined only for $a \leqslant b$. As the right side of equation (9.13) changes sign when a and b are interchanged it is useful to define $R_b^a(f) = -R_a^b(f)$. Then (9.13) is true for any a and b. Similarly there are no restrictions on a, b or c in equation (9.9) on p. 206 and equation (9.10) on p. 208.

Exercises (answers on p. 219)

9.5.1 For each of the following f, find expressions for $R_0^x(f)$ and $R_1^x(f)$: (i) $f(x) = 5x^4$, (ii) $f(x) = (x^2 + 1)^{-1}$, (iii) $f(u) = 3u^2$, (iv) $f(\theta) = \sec^2 \theta$.
   (If necessary, refer to the table of derivatives at the end of Chapter 6).

9.5.2 For each of the following g, find expressions for $\int_0^x g(t)\,dt$ and $\int_1^x g(t)\,dt$: (i) $g(t) = 5t^4$, (ii) $g(x) = (x^2 + 1)^{-1}$, (iii) $g(u) = 3u^2$, (iv) $g(\theta) = \sec^2 \theta$.

9.5.3 Find an antiderivative of $f(x) = 5x^4 + \sec^2 x$.

9.5.4 Find a primitive of $g(t) = \sinh t$.

9.5.5 Give an expression for $\int 1/\sqrt{(1 - x^2)}\,dx$.

9.5.6 Evaluate the following definite integrals:

(i) $\displaystyle\int_{-1/2}^{1/2} \frac{dx}{\sqrt{(1 - x^2)}}$,   (ii) $\displaystyle\int_0^1 \frac{du}{1 + u^2}$,   (iii) $\displaystyle\int_2^0 x^3\,dx.$

9.5.7 Comment on the following argument:

$$\frac{1}{x^2} \geqslant 1 \quad \text{on } [-1, 1], \quad \text{so} \quad \int_{-1}^{1} \frac{1}{x^2}\,dx \geqslant \int_{-1}^{1} dx = x|_{-1}^{1} = 2.$$

$$\int_{-1}^{1} \frac{1}{x^2}\,dx = -\frac{1}{x}\bigg|_{-1}^{1} = -1 - (+1) = -2.$$

Hence $-2 \geqslant 2.$

9.6   Vector Functions and Complex Functions

Suppose the function f is one of the types $R \to R^2$, $R \to R^3$ or $R \to C$. Then the sum

$$R_n = \delta \sum_{i=1}^{n} f(c_i) \tag{9.1}$$

is still defined, and $\{R_n\}$ becomes a sequence of vectors, or a sequence of complex numbers.

In Section 6.4 it was shown that the derivative of a vector function may be evaluated by differentiating the component functions. To derive this it was only necessary to separate the quotient $\{r(t+h) - r(t)\}/h$ into components before taking the limit as $h \to 0$. Similarly, in Section 6.11 the derivative of a complex function was obtained by differentiating the real and imaginary parts. If f is a vector function, then R_n in equation (9.1) may also be separated into components before taking the limit. Exactly as for derivatives, this leads to the result that the integral of a vector function $(R \to R^3)$ may be obtained by integrating the component functions. Similarly the integral of a complex function $(R \to C)$ may be obtained by integrating the real and imaginary parts.

Example 9.60
If $r(t) = 2ti + (\cos t)j + (1/t)k$, evaluate $\int_1^2 r(t)\, dt$.

$$\int_1^2 r(t)\, dt = i \int_1^2 2t\, dt + j \int_1^2 \cos t\, dt + k \int_1^2 (1/t)\, dt$$

$$= i[A + t^2]_1^2 + j[B + \sin t]_1^2 + k[C + \ln t]_1^2$$

in which A, B, and C are arbitrary constants.

$$\int_1^2 r(t)\, dt = 3i + (\sin 2 - \sin 1)j + (\ln 2)k. \quad \square$$

Example 9.61
Evaluate $\int_1^2 z(t)\, dt$, where $z(t) = 3t^2 + 2it$

$$\int_1^2 (3t^2 + 2it)\, dt = \int_1^2 3t^2\, dt + i \int_1^2 2t\, dt$$

$$= [A + t^3]_1^2 + i[B + t^2]_1^2 = 7 + 3i. \quad \square$$

Since vectors or complex numbers cannot satisfy inequalities, not many of the previous results can be directly applied to vector or complex functions. However proofs of equations (9.6), (9.7) and (9.9) do not require inequalities, and in equation (9.7) the constant k can be complex. The fundamental theorem does hold, provided the components (or real and imaginary parts) are continuous. This is because the derivative of a vector function is just obtained by differentiating the component functions, to which the fundamental theorem can be applied. The direct application of the fundamental theorem to complex functions may be of practical value, since some results on differentiation need not be expressed in terms of the real and imaginary parts.

Example 9.62

From Example 6.113 and equation (6.11), the derivative of $z(t) = -1/(t+i)$ is $1/(t+i)^2$ (see p. 149). Hence

$$\int_a^b \frac{1}{(t+i)^2} \, dt = \left[C + \frac{-1}{t+i} \right]_a^b = -\frac{1}{b+i} + \frac{1}{a+i}.$$

In this work the arbitrary constant C must be complex, because (cf. Example 9.61) if the real and imaginary parts had been integrated separately, two real arbitrary constants would appear in the form $A + iB$. Equation (6.10) indicates how much more complicated the integration would be by the latter method.   □

Example 9.63

Evaluate $\int_0^\pi e^{it} \, dt$.

$$\int_0^\pi e^{it} \, dt = -i \int_0^\pi (i \, e^{it}) \, dt \quad \text{using equation (9.7) on p. 206}$$

$$= -i[C + e^{it}]_0^\pi \quad \text{using equation (6.13) on p. 150}$$

$$= -i(e^{i\pi} - e^{i0}) = 2i, \quad \text{using equation (6.16) on p. 150.}$$

Note that C is complex.

Check:

$$\int_0^\pi e^{it} \, dt = \int_0^\pi \cos t \, dt + i \int_0^\pi \sin t \, dt$$

$$= [\sin t]_0^\pi + i[-\cos t]_0^\pi = 0 - 0 + i(1 - -1) = 2i.   □$$

Exercises (answers on p. 219)

9.6.1   If $r(t) = t^2 i + (t - 2\sqrt{t})j + (2t^3 - 7)k$,

$$\text{find } \int r(t) \, dt, \text{ and hence evaluate } \int_1^3 r(t) \, dt$$

9.6.2   By (i) equating real parts, and (ii) equating imaginary parts, (cf. equation (6.10)) of the result in Example 9.62, evaluate

$$\text{(i) } \int_a^b \frac{t^2 - 1}{(t^2 + 1)^2} \, dt, \quad \text{and (ii) } \int_a^b \frac{2t}{(t^2 + 1)^2} \, dt.$$

9.6.3   (i) If k is a nonzero integer, show that $\int_{-\pi}^\pi e^{ikx} \, dx = 0$.

(ii) Define a sequence of functions $f_n(x) = e^{inx}$ $(n = 0, 1, 2, \ldots)$.

$$\text{Show that } \int_{-\pi}^\pi \overline{f_m(x)} f_n(x) \, dx = \begin{cases} 0 & \text{if } m \neq n, \\ 2\pi & \text{if } m = n. \end{cases}$$

Answers to Exercises 9.1.1–9.6.2

9.1.1 $\frac{1}{4}\{0^2 + (\frac{1}{4})^2 + (\frac{2}{4})^2 + (\frac{3}{4})^2\} = \frac{14}{64}$ (left end-points)

$\frac{1}{4}\{(\frac{1}{8})^2 + (\frac{3}{8})^2 + (\frac{5}{8})^2 + (\frac{7}{8})^2\} = \frac{21}{64}$ (midpoints)

$\frac{1}{4}\{(\frac{1}{4})^2 + (\frac{2}{4})^2 + (\frac{3}{4})^2 + (\frac{4}{4})^2\} = \frac{30}{64}$ (right end-points)

$f(x) = x^2$ is increasing on $[0, 1]$, so the least and greatest values of f in any subinterval are at the left and right end-points. The sequence in Example 9.11(ii) gives the largest possible terms.

9.1.2 $x_i = i/n$, $x_{i-1} = (i-1)/n$, midpoint $(i-\frac{1}{2})/n$.

9.1.3 $c_i = x_i$ if $x_i < 0$; $c_i = x_{i-1}$ if $x_{i-1} > 0$; otherwise $c_i = 0$. In other words: take the right end-point of a subinterval contained in $[-1, 0]$; take the left end-point of a subinterval contained in $[0, 1]$; and (odd n only) take the midpoint 0 of $[-1/n, 1/n]$.

9.1.4   (i) $R_a^b(k) = k(b-a)$, (ii) $R_a^b(g) = R_a^b(f) + k(b-a)$.

9.2.1   Range is $\{28, 30, 31\}$; weights are $\frac{1}{12}, \frac{1}{3}, \frac{7}{12}$; average $\frac{365}{12}$.

9.2.2   (i) (ii) (iii) 0.7468 (4S).

9.2.3

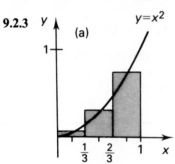 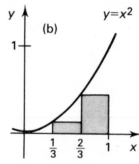 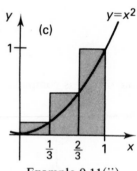

Example 9.10   Example 9.11(i)   Example 9.11(ii)

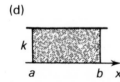 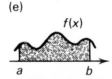 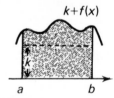

9.2.4 $\frac{1}{2}(b|b| - a|a|)$ (or consider 3 cases with different signs of a, b).

9.2.5   (i) area PQMN $= \frac{1}{2}r^2\psi + \frac{1}{2}(r-a)(2ar - a^2)^{1/2} + \frac{1}{2}(b-r)(2br - b^2)^{1/2}$,

arc PQ $= r\psi$ where $\psi = \text{Sin}^{-1}\left(\dfrac{b-r}{r}\right) + \text{Sin}^{-1}\left(\dfrac{r-a}{r}\right)$.

(ii) $y = (2xr - x^2)^{1/2}$

(iii) $f(x) = (2xr - x^2)^{1/2}$, $g(x) = r(2xr - x^2)^{-1/2}$ ($0 < x < 2r$).

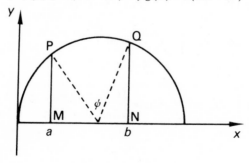

9.3.2 (i) 1.4936 (5S), (ii) 1.2468 (5S).

9.3.5 $c = 0.540$.

9.4.1 For (i) and (ii) $f(x+h) < \{A(x+h) - A(x)\}/h < f(x)$.
(For (ii), the three quantities are all negative).

9.4.2 (i) $(\lambda, \mu) = (0, 1)$ or $(1/8, 5/8)$ or $(5/27, 14/27)$, because the $\{R_i\}$ in Examples 9.11(i) and (ii) are $\{L_i\}$ and $\{U_i\}$.
(ii), (iii) and (iv) $A'(x) = x^2$, $A(x) = x^3/3$.
Check: $\lambda < A(1) = 1/3 < \mu$.

9.4.3 $A'(x) = \cos x$, $A(x) = 1 + \sin x$, for both (i) and (ii).

9.4.4 e^{-x^2}; 0.

9.4.5 $\dfrac{2x^2 \sin x - 3 \cos x}{1 + x^2}$; 0.

9.5.1 and 9.5.2

	(i)	(ii)	(iii)	(iv)	
$R_0^x(f)$	x^5	$\mathrm{Tan}^{-1}x$	x^3	$\tan x$	$\displaystyle\int_0^x g(t)\,dt$
$R_1^x(t)$	$x^5 - 1$	$(\mathrm{Tan}^{-1} x) - \dfrac{\pi}{4}$	$x^3 - 1$	$(\tan x) - (\tan 1)$	$\displaystyle\int_1^x g(t)\,dt.$

9.5.3 $x^5 + \tan x$ (answer not unique).

9.5.4 $1 + \cosh t$ (answer not unique).

9.5.5 $C + \mathrm{Sin}^{-1}x$ or $B - \mathrm{Cos}^{-1}x$, where C or B denotes an arbitrary constant.

9.5.6 (i) $\pi/3$, (ii) $\pi/4$, (iii) -4.

9.5.7 $\int_{-1}^1 dx/x^2 = R_{-1}^1(1/x^2)$ does not exist, since $1/x^2 \to \infty$ as $x \to 0$; the sequences $\{R_n\}$ have no limit.

9.6.1 $\frac{1}{3}t^3 i + (\frac{1}{2}t^2 - \frac{4}{3}t\sqrt{t})j + (\frac{1}{2}t^4 - 7t)k + A$ where A denotes an arbitrary vector; $\frac{26}{3}i + (\frac{16}{3} - 4\sqrt{3})j + 26k$.

9.6.2 (i) $\dfrac{a}{a^2+1} - \dfrac{b}{b^2+1}$, (ii) $\dfrac{1}{a^2+1} - \dfrac{1}{b^2+1}$.

Further Exercises on Chapter 9

9.1 Show that the general term of the sequence in Example 9.11(i) is $R_n = (1/n^3)\sum_{i=0}^{n-1} i^2$.
Verify that, if $t_i = 2i^3 - 3i^2 + 1$, then

$$t_{i+1} - t_i = 6i^2.$$

Hence express R_n in terms of t_n, and evaluate $R_0^1(x^2)$. Similarly, evaluate $R_0^1(x^2)$ using the sequence in Example 9.11(ii).

9.2 Suppose R_n is formed as in equation (9.1), but with subintervals that need not be of equal length. Verify that the argument of Example 9.23 is unaltered except that (using Fig. 9.5) equation (9.5) is replaced by

$$U_n - L_n = \{f(b) - f(a)\}\Delta_n$$

where Δ_n is the width of the largest subinterval. [This shows that $\{L_n\}$, $\{U_n\}$ (and hence any $\{R_n\}$) have the same limit provided $\Delta_n \to 0$, i.e. the lengths of all subintervals tend to zero as $n \to \infty$].

9.3   What is the average value of a function defined at a single point $x = a$? Show that this value is obtained for

$$\text{Lim}_{b \to a} \{\text{average of } f \text{ on } [a, b]\}$$

on using the fundamental theorem to evaluate the limit, after putting $b = a + h$.

9.4   Define $A(x)$ for $-2 \leqslant x \leqslant 2$ as the area in the interval $[-2, x]$ under the curve (Fig. 9.12)

$$y = f(x) = \begin{cases} 1 & \text{if } -2 \leqslant x \leqslant -1 \\ x^2 & \text{if } -1 \leqslant x \leqslant 2. \end{cases}$$

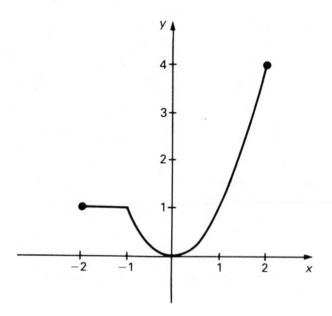

Figure 9.12 $f(x)$ in Exercise 9.4

(i) Write down the values $A(-2)$ and $\dot{A}(-1)$.

(ii) Is A continuous?

(iii) Is f continuous?

(iv) Is it true that $A' = f$?

(v) Obtain from $A'(x)$ the rule for $A(x)$ when $-2 \leqslant x \leqslant -1$, checking the consistency with (i).

(vi) Obtain from $A'(x)$ the rule for $A(x)$ when $-1 \leqslant x \leqslant 2$.

(vii) At what stage(s) does this procedure fail for Example 9.53?

9.5   Define $A(x)$ as the area under the semi-circle $y = (2xr - x^2)^{1/2}$ in the interval $[a, x]$, and $s(x)$ as the arc-length in $[a, x]$ $(0 \leqslant a \leqslant x \leqslant 2r)$.

(i) Write down the rules of the functions $A(x)$ and $s(x)$, using the results of Exercise 9.2.5(i).

(ii) Use the results of Exercise 9.2.5(iii) to verify the fundamental theorem for $R_a^x(f)$ and $R_a^x(g)$.

9.6   Show that $d/dx \int_x^a f(u)\, du = -f(x)$.

9.7 (i) If $G(w) = \int_a^w f(u)\,du$, what is dG/dw?

(ii) If $G(x) = \int_a^{x^2} f(u)\,du$, find dG/dx by using (i) and the rule for differentiating a composite function (with $w = x^2$).

9.8 If l is the length of the curve $y = b\cosh(x/b)$ in the interval $[-b, b]$, express b in terms of l and e.

9.9 Find the length of the curve

$$y = \frac{x^3}{a^2} + \frac{a^2}{12x}$$

from $x = \tfrac{1}{2}a$ to $x = a$ $(a > 0)$.

9.10 Find the length of the curve $y = x^4/a^3 + a^3/32x^2$ from $x = a$ to $x = 2a$ $(a > 0)$.

9.11 To derive inequalities for functions of x, it is convenient to write (9.8) in the form

$$\int_a^x f(u)\,du > \int_a^x g(u)\,du \quad \text{if } f(u) > g(u) \text{ on } (a, x).$$

(i) Take $a = 0$, $f(u) = 1$, $g(u) = (1 + u^2)^{-1}$.

Show that $f(u) > g(u)$ on $(0, x)$, for any positive x, and deduce that $\text{Tan}^{-1} x < x$.

(ii) Show that $(1 + u^2)^{-1} > (1 + x^2)^{-1}$ for $0 < u < x$.

Taking $a = 0$, $f(u) = (1 + u^2)^{-1}$, $g(u) = (1 + x^2)^{-1}$ (a constant function of u), deduce that $\text{Tan}^{-1} x > x/(1 + x^2)$.

9.12 (i) If $1 < u < x$, then $1/x < 1/u < 1$. Deduce that

$$\frac{x-1}{x} < \ln x < x - 1. \tag{$*$}$$

(ii) Change x to y in $(*)$, so that $y > 1$. By substituting $y = 1/x$, show that $(*)$ is true for $0 < x < 1$.

What happens when $x = 1$?

9.13 Suppose that on (a, b) $g(x) \geq 0$, and that $f(x)$ has a minimum value m and a maximum value M. Use (9.8) and (9.7) to obtain

$$m \int_a^b g(x)\,dx \leq \int_a^b f(x)g(x)\,dx \leq M \int_a^b g(x)\,dx.$$

If f is continuous, deduce that there is a number c in (a, b) such that $\int_a^b f(x)g(x)\,dx / \int_a^b g(x)\,dx = f(c)$.

9.14 Use the result of Exercise 9.13 to show that there are numbers c_1 and c_2 in $(0, 1)$ such that

$$\int_0^1 \frac{\sin \pi x}{x^2 + 1}\,dx = \frac{2}{\pi(c_1^2 + 1)} = \frac{\pi}{4}\sin \pi c_2.$$

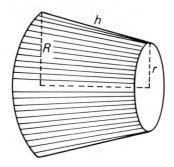

Figure 9.13 Frustrum of a cone

9.15 The surface area of a frustrum of a cone is $\pi(r+R)h$, where h is the slant height, and r and R are the radii of the circular faces (Fig. 9.13). Now suppose the curve and chords in Fig. 9.14 are rotated about the x-axis.

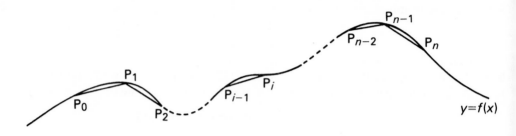

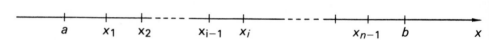

Figure 9.14   Generation of solid by rotating curve $y = f(x)$

(i) Express the volume of the frustrum generated by the rotation of $P_{i-1}P_i$ in terms of the length $P_{i-1}P_i$ and values of f.

(ii) Defining c_i and $g(x)$ as in Example 9.22, show that the surface area of the solid generated by the rotation of all the chords is

$$\pi\delta \sum_{i=1}^{n} f(x_{i-1})g(c_i) + \pi\delta \sum_{i=1}^{n} f(x_i)g(c_i),$$

where $\delta = (b-a)/n$.

(iii) Assuming that all sequences R_n have the same limit (Section 9.1), deduce that

the surface area of the solid generated by rotating the curve $y = f(x)$ is

$$2\pi R_a^b(fg) = 2\pi \int_a^b f(x)g(x)\, dx = 2\pi \int_a^b f(x)[1+\{f'(x)\}^2]^{1/2}\, dx$$

(iv) Verify that this result gives the formula $\pi(r+R)h$ for the surface area of a frustrum of a cone.

9.16 For the following functions $f(x)$ and intervals $[a, b]$, use the result of Exercise 9.15(iii) to calculate the surface area of the solids obtained by rotating about the x-axis the section of the curve $y = f(x)$ in $[a, b]$:

(i) $f(x) = \cosh x$, $[0, 1]$ (ii) $y = \frac{1}{4}x^3 + 1/3x$, $[1, 2]$

(iii) $y = \frac{1}{3}x^3 + 1/4x$, $[1, 3]$ (iv) $f(x) = x^4/a^3 + a^3/32x^2$, $[a, 2a]$

(v) $y = (a^2 - x^2)^{1/2}$, $[-a, a]$.

9.17 Find the following derivatives:

(i) $\dfrac{d}{dt} \displaystyle\int_0^t \sin(x^2)\,dx$ (ii) $\dfrac{d}{dx} \displaystyle\int_{x^2}^9 (1+u^3)^{1/2}\,du$ (iii) $\dfrac{d}{dx} \displaystyle\int_x^{x^2} \sin(1+t^2)\,dt$

9.18 If $u \geqslant 1$, show that $u^{-3/2} \leqslant u^{-1} \leqslant u^{-1/2}$. Use this to obtain bounds on $\log(\sqrt{e})$ (cf. Exercise 9.11). Deduce that $\frac{5}{4} \leqslant e^{1/4} \leqslant \frac{4}{3}$.

9.19 Use the inequality $\sec^2 u > 1$ $(0 < u < \frac{1}{2}\pi)$ to show that $\tan x > x$ $(0 < x < \frac{1}{2}\pi)$.

10
Antiderivatives

10.1 Standard Results

The fundamental theorem of the calculus leads to the evaluation of a Riemann integral of a continuous function f by means of the equation

$$\int_a^b f(x)\, \mathrm{d}x = R_a^b(f) = P(b) - P(a) \tag{9.13}$$

in which P is any antiderivative of f. This chapter discusses methods of finding P from the given function f, which is often called the **integrand**.

Any discussion of this problem has to take some set of functions as known, and consider only integrands f and antiderivatives P which can be expressed in terms of this set. Some of the integrands f may not have antiderivatives which can be composed from the known set of functions. The simplest example of this is when the known set of functions are the powers of x. Then $\mathrm{d}(x^m) = mx^{m-1}\,\mathrm{d}x$ implies the inverse result $\int x^n\, \mathrm{d}x = x^{n+1}/(n+1)$, provided $n \neq -1$. However $f(x) = x^{-1} = 1/x$ does not have an antiderivative which can be explicitly written in terms of powers of x. Because of its many applications, it is then convenient to introduce a new function ln and to develop the properties of this new function.

This chapter regards as known the functions already used in this book: polynomials, irrational powers, exponential and logarithmic functions, trigonometric and hyperbolic functions and their inverses. The problem is not: find an antiderivative of any given function f expressed in terms of these known functions. It is rather:

> decide whether the given integrand f has an antiderivative P which can be expressed in the known functions, and if so, obtain the expression for $P(x)$.

The only practical approach to this question is to tabulate a set of antiderivatives which are regarded as known, and then to discuss ways of expressing any other integral in terms of these standard results. What is considered as known, standard and tabulated is somewhat arbitrary, but does determine the subsequent treatment. Here the list of results at the end of the chapter are regarded as known. The problem to be discussed is therefore:

> given an integrand f, can the integral be reduced to the use of the standard results given at the end of the chapter?

These results, often called standard forms, will be referred to using the label SFn as shown in the table. There are basically only two techniques available for this reduction—substitution, and integration by parts, which are discussed in the next two sections.

Any differentiation rule may be inverted to give a rule relevant to finding antiderivatives. For this purpose it is useful to interpret the indefinite integration symbol $\int$ as converting a differential back into a function: $\int dP = P$. If $P'(x) = f(x)$, then $dP = f(x) \, dx$, so this interpretation gives just $\int f(x) \, dx = P(x)$, which is correct (except for the arbitrary constant). Then, for example, applying the symbol $\int$ to each side of the differentiation rule $du + dv = d(u + v)$ gives $\int (du + dv) = u + v$. This may be written

$$\int \{u'(x) + v'(x)\} \, dx = u(x) + v(x)$$

$$= \int u'(x) \, dx + \int v'(x) \, dx.$$

Any antiderivative which is obtained may be checked by differentiating to recover the given integrand. As a preliminary check it is sometimes possible to use the dimensions of the quantities involved, as in Example 6.14 on p. 108.

Example 10.10
In $\int e^{au} \sin bu \, du$, if u is a length, then so is du, and an antiderivative must also be a length. Since a and b must be inverse lengths, the expressions SF16 and SF17 (see the table on p. 253) do have the proper dimension. $\square$

Exercises (answers on p. 252)
10.1.1   If c is constant $c \, dv = d(cv)$. What is the corresponding rule when integrating?
10.1.2   Use the table of antiderivatives at the end of the chapter to write down expressions for the following indefinite integrals:
      (i) $\int (4 - x^2)^{-1/2} \, dx$, (ii) $\int (9 + x^2)^{-1} \, dx$, (iii) $\int e^{-2t} \cos t \, dt$.

10.2   Substitution, or Change of Variable

This technique applies the inverse of the rule for differentiating a composite function.

Example 10.20
Suppose $y = w^4$ where $w = \sin x$. Then $dy = 4w^3 \, dw = 4 \sin^3 x \cos x \, dx$, and so $P(x) = \sin^4 x$ is an antiderivative of $f(x) = 4 \sin^3 x \cos x$.
      The reverse of the differentiation procedure requires guessing that $w = \sin x$ is a useful change of variable for evaluating $\int 4 \sin^3 x \cos x \, dx$, and knowing that w^4 is an antiderivative of $4w^3$(SF1). The correct guess for the change of variable, or substitution, is inspired by the observation that if $w = \sin x$ then $dw = \cos x \, dx$. Thus

$$\int 4 \sin^3 x \cos x \, dx = \int 4w^3 \, dw \quad \text{where } w = \sin x$$

$$= w^4 + C = \sin^4 x + C. \quad \square$$

To evaluate a definite integral, it is not even necessary to convert back to the original variable x, since

$$P(b) - P(a) = Q(b') - Q(a')$$

where $Q(w)$ is $P(x)$ in terms of w, and a' and b' are the values of w corresponding to $x = a$ and $x = b$. For these to be unique, the variables x and w must be related by a one-to-one function. This condition, and certain other restrictions on allowable changes of variable $w = g(x)$, may also be derived from the definition of a definite integral as a sequence limit (see Appendix E).

Example 10.21

$$\int_0^{\pi/2} 4 \sin^3 x \cos x \, dx = [\sin^4 x]_0^{\pi/2} = 1.$$

or

$$\int_0^{\pi/2} 4 \sin^3 x \cos x \, dx = \int_0^1 4w^3 \, dw \quad \text{where } w = \sin x$$

(in the notation above, $a' = \sin a = \sin 0 = 0$, $b' = \sin b = \sin \frac{1}{2}\pi = 1$) and

$$\int_0^1 4w^3 \, dw = [w^4]_0^1 = 1$$

(in the notation above, $Q(w) = w^4$, $1 = Q(1) - Q(0)$).   □

When a definite integral has been evaluated in terms of a new variable w after substitution, it may be checked by converting the antiderivative $Q(w)$ to $P(x)$ in the original variable, and using $P(b) - P(a)$. Also then $P(x)$ can be checked by differentiating.

Example 10.22
Evaluate $\int_0^1 \sqrt{(2x+1)} \, dx$.

Substitute $w = \sqrt{(2x+1)}$. Then $w^2 = (2x+1)$ so $2w \, dw = 2 \, dx$.

$$\therefore \quad \int_0^1 \sqrt{(2x+1)} \, dx = \int_1^{\sqrt{3}} w(w \, dw) = [w^3/3]_1^{\sqrt{3}} = \sqrt{3} - (1/3)$$

Check: $[w^3/3]_1^{\sqrt{3}} = [(2x+1)^{3/2}/3]_0^1 = \sqrt{3} - (\frac{1}{3})$ and   differentiating $\frac{1}{3}(2x+1)^{3/2}$ gives $\frac{1}{2}(2)(2x+1)^{1/2}$, which is the given integrand.   □

The rule for making a change of variable from x to w is evidently to express both $f(x)$ and dx in terms of w and dw. The choice of substitution must always consider dw as well as w.

Example 10.23
(i) Although $\exp w$ is a standard form (SF3), it is not possible to change $\int \exp(x^2) \, dx$ to a standard form. Substituting $w = x^2$ gives $dw = 2x \, dx$ and so $dx = dw/2\sqrt{w}$:

$$\int \exp(x^2) \, dx = \int \frac{e^w}{2\sqrt{w}} \, dw,$$

which is not a standard form. In fact an antiderivative cannot be expressed in terms of the functions taken as known in this chapter.
(ii) However $\int x \exp(x^2) \, dx$ contains an extra x which fits nicely with $dw = 2x \, dx$ from $w = x^2$:

$$\int x \exp(x^2) \, dx = \frac{1}{2} \int (2x \, dx) \exp(x^2)$$

$$= \frac{1}{2} \int e^w \, dw = \frac{1}{2}e^w + C = \frac{1}{2} \exp(x^2) + C$$

Check:
$$d(\tfrac{1}{2}\exp x^2) = d(\tfrac{1}{2}\exp w) \quad (\text{with } w = x^2)$$
$$= \tfrac{1}{2}\exp w \, dw = x \exp(x^2) \, dx. \qquad \square$$

The check also demonstrates that integration by substitution is just the inverse of differentiating a composite function.

Because of the validity of substitution, the results in the standard table of integrals at the end of the chapter are written in terms of w rather than x, so that w can be replaced by any function of x (or any other variable). However if $w = g(x)$, the dw becomes $g'(x)\,dx$ when the standard result is written in terms of x. Conversely g must be chosen so that $g'(x)$ is a suitable factor in a given integrand if substitution is to give a direct reduction to a standard form (cf. the previous example).

For the particular substitution $w = ax + b$, $dw = a\,dx$, and the constant $1/a$ can always be taken out of the integrand (Exercise 10.1.1).

Example 10.24

$$\int \sin(3t+1)\,dt = \int \sin w \,(\tfrac{1}{3}dw) \quad (w = 3t+1)$$

$$= \tfrac{1}{3}\int \sin w \,dw = -\tfrac{1}{3}\cos w + C$$

$$= -\tfrac{1}{3}\cos(3t+1) + C. \quad \square$$

Example 10.25
(i) Example 6.15 on p. 109 showed that
$$d(\operatorname{Sin}^{-1} x) = dx/\sqrt{(1-x^2)}.$$

The inverse result is
$$\int \frac{dx}{\sqrt{(1-x^2)}} = \operatorname{Sin}^{-1} x + C. \tag{10.1}$$

Put $x = w/a$, where a is a constant. Then $dx = dw/a$, and
$$\int \frac{dx}{\sqrt{(1-x^2)}} = \int \frac{dw}{a\sqrt{(1-w^2/a^2)}} = \int \frac{dw}{\sqrt{(a^2-w^2)}}.$$

It is convenient to use this, rather than equation (10.1), to record a standard result (SF14 in the table on p. 253).
(ii) Similarly, the inverse to the result of Example 6.12(ii) on p. 107 is
$$\int \frac{dx}{\sqrt{(x^2-1)}} = \ln|x+\sqrt{(x^2-1)}| + C.$$

Substituting $x = w/a$, $dx = dw/a$ gives $\int dw/\sqrt{(w^2-a^2)}$, as above. Writing
$$\ln\left|\frac{w}{a}+\sqrt{\left(\frac{w^2}{a^2}-1\right)}\right| = \ln\left|\frac{w+\sqrt{(w^2-a^2)}}{a}\right|$$

$$= \ln|w+\sqrt{(w^2-a^2)}| - \ln|a|$$

gives SF15, since the constant $-\ln|a|$ can be absorbed into the arbitrary constant C. $\quad \square$

Note that the form of an antiderivative is not unique. From Example 6.12(i), one could equally well write $\int dx/\sqrt{(x^2-1)} = \text{Cosh}^{-1} x + C$, but this would not be so convenient as the log form, because the log function is tabulated, and is available on most computers. Similarly Example 6.15(ii) shows that

$$\int \frac{dx}{\sqrt{(1-x^2)}} = -\text{Cos}^{-1} x + C$$

is an alternative to equation (10.1). This means that an antiderivative should not be rejected as wrong if it differs from a result derived independently by somebody else, at least not without considering whether one form can be manipulated into the other. Reverse differentiation provides the unambiguous check of the answer.

Example 10.26
Evaluate $\int dx/\sin x$ (i) by substituting $u = \tan \frac{1}{2}x$, (ii) by substituting $v = \cos x$.

(i) If $u = \tan \frac{1}{2}x$, then $du = \frac{1}{2} \sec^2 \frac{1}{2}x \, dx = \frac{1}{2}(1 + u^2) \, dx$.
Also

$$\cos^2 \tfrac{1}{2}x = \frac{1}{\sec^2 \frac{1}{2}x} = \frac{1}{1 + u^2}$$

and

$$\sin^2 \tfrac{1}{2}x = 1 - \cos^2 \tfrac{1}{2}x = u^2/(1 + u^2).$$

so

$$\sin x = 2 \sin \tfrac{1}{2}x \cos \tfrac{1}{2}x = 2u/(1 + u^2),$$

and

$$\int \frac{dx}{\sin x} = \int \frac{du}{u} = \ln|u| + C = \ln|\tan \tfrac{1}{2}x| + C.$$

(ii) If $v = \cos x$, $dv = -\sin x \, dx$, and $dx/\sin x = -dv/\sin^2 x = dv/(v^2 - 1)$.
From (SF12),

$$\int \frac{dv}{v^2 - 1} = \tfrac{1}{2} \ln \left| \frac{v-1}{v+1} \right| + C$$

Hence

$$\int \frac{dx}{\sin x} = \tfrac{1}{2} \ln \left| \frac{1 - \cos x}{1 + \cos x} \right| + C.$$

The antiderivatives obtained in (i) and (ii) look rather different. However $\cos x = 2\cos^2 \frac{1}{2}x - 1 = 1 - 2\sin^2 \frac{1}{2}x$, so

$$\frac{1 - \cos x}{1 + \cos x} = \frac{2 \sin^2 \frac{1}{2}x}{2 \cos^2 \frac{1}{2}x} = \tan^2 \tfrac{1}{2}x,$$

and

$$\ln(\tan^2 \tfrac{1}{2}x) = 2 \ln|\tan \tfrac{1}{2}x|. \quad \square$$

Example 10.27

Find an antiderivative of $1/\cosh x$.

Let $w = e^x$; then $\cosh x = \frac{1}{2}w + \frac{1}{2}/w = (w^2 + 1)/2w$ and $dw = e^x\,dx = w\,dx$

$$\therefore \quad \int \frac{dx}{\cosh x} = \int \frac{2\,dw}{w^2 + 1}$$

$$= 2\,\mathrm{Tan}^{-1}\,w + C$$

$$= 2\,\mathrm{Tan}^{-1}(e^x) + C.$$

Check: $\quad d(2\,\mathrm{Tan}^{-1}(e^x) + C) = 2d(\mathrm{Tan}^{-1}\,w)$ with $w = e^x$

$$= \frac{2\,dw}{1 + w^2} = \frac{2e^x\,dx}{1 + (e^x)^2} = \frac{dx}{\frac{1}{2}(e^{-x} + e^x)}.$$

As in the previous example, different forms of the result may be obtained using other substitutions. Other possible formula were given in Exercise 3.23 on p. 71. □

Exercises (answers on p. 252)

10.2.1 (cf. Examples 10.21 and 10.26(ii)). Find antiderivatives of (i) $\cos^5 x \sin x$, (ii) $\cos x \sin^{-3} x$, (iii) $\cos^3 x \sin^2 x$, (iv) $\sin^3 x \cos^{-2} x$.

10.2.2 (cf. Example 10.22). Find antiderivatives of (i) $\sqrt{(3x-2)}$, (ii) $1/\sqrt{(2x-1)}$, (iii) $(2x+3)/\sqrt{(3x+2)}$.

10.2.3 (cf. Example 10.23). Find antiderivatives of (i) $x\exp(-x^2)$, (ii) $x\cos(x^2)$, (iii) $x\sin(x^2+2)$, (iv) $x\sqrt{(x^2+2)}$, (v) $x/\sqrt{(x^2+3)}$, (vi) $w/\sqrt{(w^2+1)}$, (vii) $v/(v^2+1)$.

10.2.4 (cf. Example 10.26(i)). Find antiderivatives of (i) $1/(1+\cos x)$, (ii) $1/(1-\cos x)$, (iii) $1/(-2+3\cos x)$, (iv) $1/(3+2\cos x)$.

10.2.5 (cf. Example 10.27). Find an antiderivative of $1/(5\cosh x + 3\sinh x + 4)$.

10.2.6 (cf. Exercise 10.2.1). Find antiderivatives of (i) $\cosh^3 x \sinh x$, (ii) $\sinh x \cosh^{-5} x$, (iii) $\cosh^4 x \sinh^3 x$.

10.2.7 Evaluate $\int_1^2 f(x)\,dx$ for the following integrands $f(x)$: (i) $1/\sqrt{(2x+1)}$, (ii) $2x/\sqrt{(9x^2-1)}$, (iii) $x\exp(-4x^2)$.

10.2.8 (cf. Example 10.26). Evaluate $\int dx/\cos x$.

10.3   Integration by Parts

The rule for differentiating a product,

$$d(uv) = u\,dv + v\,du$$

gives

$$\int d(uv) = \int u\,dv + \int v\,du$$

or

$$\int u\,dv = uv - \int v\,du. \tag{10.2}$$

Application of this formula is called **integration by parts**.

Putting $u = u(x)$ and $v = v(x)$, the formula becomes

$$\int u(x)v'(x)\,dx = u(x)v(x) - \int v(x)u'(x)\,dx. \qquad \textbf{(10.3)}$$

This can evidently be applied to the integration of a product uv' in which one of the factors v' has a known antiderivative. However the application gives another integral $\int v(x)u'(x)\,dx$, and so is only useful if this integral can be evaluated.

Example 10.30
Find antiderivatives for (i) $\ln x$, (ii) $\mathrm{Tan}^{-1}x$, (iii) $\mathrm{Sin}^{-1}x$.

(i) $\int \ln x\,dx$ is $\int u\,dv$ with $u = \ln x$, $dv = dx$, $v = x$. Then $\int v\,du = \int x\,d(\ln x) = \int x(dx/x) = \int dx = x + C$. So equation (10.2) gives $\int \ln x\,dx = x\ln x - x - C$.

Check: $d[x\ln x - x - C] = [\ln x + (x/x) - 1]\,dx = \ln x\,dx$. The check requires differentiation of uv using the product rule, and makes it obvious that integration by parts is just the inverse of differentiating a product.

(ii)
$$\int \mathrm{Tan}^{-1}x\,dx = \int u\,dv \quad \text{with } v = x,\ u = \mathrm{Tan}^{-1}x$$

$$= x\,\mathrm{Tan}^{-1}x - \int v\,du$$

and

$$\int v\,du = \int \frac{x\,dx}{x^2+1} = \int \frac{\frac{1}{2}dw}{w} \quad \text{where } w = x^2+1$$

$$= \tfrac{1}{2}\ln w + C = \tfrac{1}{2}\ln(x^2+1) + C$$

$$\therefore \quad \int \mathrm{Tan}^{-1}x\,dx = x\,\mathrm{Tan}^{-1}x - \tfrac{1}{2}\ln(x^2+1) - C$$

(iii) $\int \mathrm{Sin}^{-1}x\,dx = x\,\mathrm{Sin}^{-1}x - \int x\,d(\mathrm{Sin}^{-1}x)$, using equation (10.2) with $v = x$, and

$$-\int \frac{x\,dx}{\sqrt{(1-x^2)}} = \int \frac{w}{w}\,dw \quad \text{where } w^2 = 1 - x^2,\ 2w\,dw = -2x\,dx$$

$$= w + C = \sqrt{(1-x^2)} + C$$

$\therefore \quad \{x\,\mathrm{Sin}^{-1}x + \sqrt{(1-x^2)}\}$ is an antiderivative of $\mathrm{Sin}^{-1}x$.

Check: Differentiating gives

$$\mathrm{Sin}^{-1}x + \frac{x}{\sqrt{(1-x^2)}} + \tfrac{1}{2}v^{-1/2}\,dv,$$

where $v = 1 - x^2$, $dv = -2x\,dx$, so that the last two terms cancel. $\quad \square$

In each part of this example, equation (10.3) is applied with $v' = 1$, by which device any integrand could be considered as a product. Again this was only useful because the functions ln, Tan^{-1} and Sin^{-1} had derivatives u' which allowed the evaluation of $\int v(x)u'(x)\,dx$. This remains true when v' is any polynomial.

Example 10.31
Evaluate $\int 3x^2 \text{Tan}^{-1} x\,dx$

Integrate by parts, taking

$$u(x) = \text{Tan}^{-1} x, \qquad v'(x)\,dx = 3x^2\,dx$$

so that

$$u'(x) = 1/(1+x^2), \qquad v(x) = x^3.$$

Then

$$\int (3x^2\,dx)\,\text{Tan}^{-1} x = x^3\,\text{Tan}^{-1} x - \int x^3\,dx/(1+x^2)$$

and

$$-\int \frac{x^3\,dx}{1+x^2} = \int \left(-x + \frac{x}{1+x^2}\right)\,dx$$

$$= -\tfrac{1}{2}x^2 + \tfrac{1}{2}\ln(1+x^2) + C,$$

as in Example 10.23(ii).

$$\therefore \quad \int 3x^2 \text{Tan}^{-1} x\,dx = x^3\,\text{Tan}^{-1} x - \tfrac{1}{2}x^2 + \tfrac{1}{2}\ln(1+x^2) + C.$$

Again, in the check by differentiation, differentiating the product $x^3 \text{Tan}^{-1} x$ gives two terms: one is the given integrand, and the other must be exactly cancelled by the derivative of $-\tfrac{1}{2}x^2 + \tfrac{1}{2}\ln(1+x^2)$.   □

In another type of application of integration by parts, u is a polynomial, and v' is a function which can be integrated as many times as is necessary.

Example 10.32

$$\int x \sin x\,dx \text{ is } \int u\,dv \text{ with } u = x,\ dv = \sin x\,dx$$

so

$$du = dx, \qquad v = -\cos x$$

$$\therefore \quad \int x \sin x\,dx = -x \cos x + \int \cos x\,dx$$

$$= -x \cos x + \sin x + C.$$

Check: $d(-x \cos x + \sin x) = (-\cos x + x \sin x) + \cos x.$ □

Example 10.33

$$\int (x^2+3x) \sin x\,dx = \int (x^2+3x)\,d(-\cos x)$$

$$= \int u \, dv$$

$$= -(x^2+3x) \cos x + \int \cos x \, d(x^2+3x)$$

and $\int v \, du = \int -(\cos x)(2x+3) \, dx$ is like the previous example, and may evidently be evaluated by a further application of integration by parts:

$$\int (2x+3) \, d(\sin x) = (2x+3) \sin x - \int (\sin x) \, d(2x+3)$$

$$= (2x+3) \sin x + 2 \int (-\sin x) \, dx$$

$$\therefore \quad \int (x^2+3x) \sin x \, dx = -(x^2+3x) \cos x + (2x+3) \sin x + 2 \cos x + C.$$

Check:

$$\{-(x^2+3x) \cos x\}' = -(2x+3) \cos x + (x^2+3x) \sin x$$

$$\{(2x+3) \sin x\}' = 2 \sin x + (2x+3) \cos x$$

$$(2 \cos x + C)' = -2 \sin x.$$

Adding gives the integrand. □

The previous two examples indicate that n applications of integration of parts would be required if u was a polynomial of nth degree. For $n>2$ the formulas to be discussed in Section 10.5 may give a more convenient calculation.

When integration by parts is applied to a definite integral $\int_a^b u(x)v'(x) \, dx$, then $u(x)v(x)$ is part of the required primitive, and so $u(b)v(b) - u(a)v(a)$ has to be evaluated. This may be done before $\int v \, du$ is considered.

Example 10.34

Evaluate

$$I = \int_0^{\pi/4} x \sec^2 x \, dx.$$

$$I = \int_0^{\pi/4} x \, d(\tan x)$$

$$= x \tan x \big|_0^{\pi/4} - \int_0^{\pi/4} \tan x \, dx$$

$$= \tfrac{1}{4}\pi - J$$

From (SF7),

$$J = [-\ln |\cos x|]_0^{\pi/4} = -\ln(1/\sqrt{2}) + \ln 1 = \ln\sqrt{2} + 0$$

$$I = \tfrac{1}{4}\pi - \tfrac{1}{2} \ln 2.$$ □

Because the functions *sin* and *cos* reappear after integrating them twice, there are some examples where the original integrand reappears after two applications of integration by parts. Then it may be convenient to consider simultaneously two integrands differing only in the replacement of *sin* by *cos*.

Example 10.35
Evaluate

$$S = \int_0^\pi \sin ax \sin bx \, dx$$

and

$$C = \int_0^\pi \cos ax \cos bx \, dx$$

$$S = \int_0^\pi \sin ax \, d(\cos bx)(-1/b)$$

$$= (-\sin ax \cos bx)/b\big|_0^\pi + (a/b) \int_0^\pi \cos bx \cos ax \, dx.$$

Multiplying by *b*, and rearranging:

$$aC - bS = \sin a\pi \cos b\pi. \tag{10.4}$$

Similarly

$$C = \int_0^\pi \cos ax \, d(\sin bx)(1/b)$$

$$= (\cos ax \sin bx)/b\big|_0^\pi + (a/b)S$$

giving

$$bC - aS = \cos a\pi \sin b\pi. \tag{10.5}$$

Then (10.4) and (10.5) are two equations for the the two unknowns *C* and *S*, and can be solved for *C* and *S* provided $a \neq b$. In the important special case where *a* and *b* are unequal integers, $\sin a\pi = \sin b\pi = 0$, and the solution of equations (10.4) and (10.5) is $C = S = 0$.

If $a = b$, then $C + S = \int_0^\pi 1 \, dx = \pi$, and equation (10.4) or (10.5) reduces to $C - S = (\sin a\pi \cos a\pi)/a$. If also *a* is an integer, then $C = S = \frac{1}{2}\pi$.

Summarizing the special case:

if *a* and *b* are integers, then

$$\int_0^\pi \sin ax \sin bx \, dx = \int_0^\pi \cos ax \cos bx \, dx = 0 \quad \text{if } a \neq b$$

$$= \tfrac{1}{2}\pi \quad \text{if } a = b > 0. \quad \square$$

Exercises (answers on p. 252)
10.3.1   (cf. Examples 10.30 and 10.31). Find antiderivatives of (i) $x \ln x$, (ii) $\ln(x^2+1)$, (iii) $x \, \text{Tan}^{-1} x$.

10.3.2   (cf. Examples 10.32 and 10.33). Find antiderivatives of (i) $(x^2+1)\cos x$, (ii) $x^2 e^x$,
(iii) $x\cos 3x$, (iv) $(\pi-x)\sin mx$.

10.3.3   (cf. Example 10.35). If $C=\int e^{ax}\cos bx\,dx$ and $S=\int e^{ax}\sin bx\,dx$ use integration
by parts to obtain the equations

$$bC+aS=e^{ax}\sin bx, \qquad aC-bS=e^{ax}\cos bx.$$

Hence obtain expressions for C and S.

10.3.4   Evaluate $\int\sin(\ln x)\,dx$ and $\int\cos(\ln x)\,dx$.

10.4   Rational Functions

It is possible to obtain the indefinite integral of any rational function, say $f=N/D$,
where N and D are polynomials.

The complexity of the calculation increases with the degree of the denominator polynomial
D. If $D(x)=1$, then f is a polynomial, and its antiderivative can be written down at once.
To describe the method of treating any rational function, it is convenient to consider in
succession cases with D linear, quadratic and cubic.

Example 10.40
To evaluate $\int dx/(ax+b)$, substitute $w=ax+b$, $dw=a\,dx$, giving

$$\int\frac{1}{aw}\,dw=\frac{1}{a}\int\frac{dw}{w}=\frac{1}{a}\ln|w|+C \qquad\text{(from SF2)}$$

$$=\frac{1}{a}\ln|ax+b|+C. \quad\square$$

The same substitution $u=ax+b$ is sufficient whenever D is just a power of $ax+b$.

Example 10.41
To evaluate $\int 8x\,dx/(3+2x)^4$, substitute $u=3+2x$, $du=2\,dx$, giving

$$\int\frac{8}{u^4}\frac{(u-3)}{2}\frac{du}{2}=2\int\left(\frac{1}{u^3}-\frac{3}{u^4}\right)du$$

$$=2\int u^{-3}\,du-6\int u^{-4}\,du$$

$$=2\left(\frac{u^{-2}}{-2}\right)-6\left(\frac{u^{-3}}{-3}\right)+C \qquad\text{(SF1)}$$

$$=-\frac{1}{u^2}+\frac{2}{u^3}+C=\frac{-1}{(2x+3)^2}+\frac{2}{(2x+3)^3}+C$$

$$=-\frac{2x+1}{(2x+3)^3}+C.$$

Check: differentiate, using the quotient rule (Exercise 6.2.1 on p. 113). $\square$

Next suppose D is quadratic, and N a constant. Then after completing the square on
D, there is an obvious substitution.

Example 10.42

(i)
$$\int \frac{dx}{x^2-2x+5} = \int \frac{dx}{(x-1)^2+4}.$$

Substituting $w = x - 1$ gives (SF11):

$$\int \frac{dw}{w^2+2^2} = \tfrac{1}{2}\,\text{Tan}^{-1}\left(\frac{w}{2}\right) + C = \tfrac{1}{2}\,\text{Tan}^{-1}\left(\frac{x-1}{2}\right) + C.$$

(ii)
$$\int \frac{dx}{x^2-6x+5} = \int \frac{dx}{(x-3)^2-4} = \int \frac{dw}{w^2-2^2} \quad \text{if } w = x - 3.$$

Using (SF12) gives $C + \tfrac{1}{4}\ln|(w-2)/(w+2)| = C + \tfrac{1}{4}\ln|(x-5)/(x-1)|$. $\square$

Since an integrand $du/(u^2+b)$ is either SF11 or SF12, and $2u\,du/(u^2+b)$ is SF2 with $w = u^2 + b$ (e.g. $\int v\,du$ on p. 231), the integrand with quadratic denominator and linear numerator can be integrated after completing the square.

Example 10.43
For $\int (4x+9)/(x^2+9)\,dx$, completion of the square is not necessary.

$$\int \frac{4x+9}{x^2+9}\,dx = \int \frac{2dw}{w} + 9 \int \frac{dx}{x^2+9}, \quad \text{where } w = x^2 + 9.$$

$$= 2\ln|w| + 3\,\text{Tan}^{-1}(x/3) + C \qquad \text{(SF2 and SF11)}$$

$$= 2\ln(x^2+9) + 3\,\text{Tan}^{-1}(x/3) + C.   \square$$

Example 10.44
For

$$\int \frac{(5-x)\,dx}{x^2+4x+13} = \int \frac{(5-x)\,dx}{(x+2)^2+9},$$

put $u = x + 2$. This gives

$$\int \frac{(7-u)\,du}{u^2+9} = -\int \frac{u\,du}{u^2+9} + 7\int \frac{du}{u^2+9}$$

$$= -\tfrac{1}{2}\frac{dw}{w} + 7\int \frac{du}{u^2+9} \quad \text{with } w = u^2 + 9$$

$$= -\tfrac{1}{2}\ln|w| + \frac{7}{3}\,\text{Tan}^{-1}\left(\frac{u}{3}\right) + C \qquad \text{(SF2 and SF11)}$$

$$= -\tfrac{1}{2}\ln(x^2+4x+13) + \frac{7}{3}\,\text{Tan}^{-1}\left(\frac{x+2}{3}\right) + C.   \square$$

The procedure for $\int (ax+b)\,dx/Q(x)$, where $Q(x)$ is a quadratic, is summarized in Procedure B2 in Appendix B. It is then possible to integrate $N(x)\,dx/Q(x)$ for any polynomial N, because N/Q can be divided out to get a polynomial plus a quotient with linear numerator. This procedure has already been demonstrated for $\int x^3\,dx/(1+x^2)$ in Example 10.31 (p. 232).

If D is a cubic, and N has degree less than 3, then N/D can always be written as a sum of terms which have already been considered in the previous examples. This algebraic work is called expressing N/D in **partial fractions**. There are three possible forms for the partial fractions, corresponding to the number of distinct roots of D. In all cases the first step is to factorize $D(x)$ as $(x-t)Q(x)$, where t is a root of $D(x)$, and $Q(x)$ is a quadratic.

Example 10.45
Consider
$$\int \frac{5x^2-11x+8}{x^3-3x^2+2x}\,dx.$$
Then
$$D(x) = x(x^2-3x+2) \qquad (t=0)$$
$$= x(x-2)(x-1)$$
the case of 3 distinct roots.

Assume
$$\frac{5x^2-11x+8}{x(x-2)(x-1)} = \frac{A}{x} + \frac{B}{x-2} + \frac{C}{x-1} \quad \text{for some numbers } A, B, C$$
$$= \frac{A(x-2)(x-1) + Bx(x-1) + Cx(x-2)}{D(x)}.$$

The numerators must be equal for all x. Putting $x = 0, 1, 2$ gives $8 = 2A$, $2 = -C$, $6 = 2B$, so
$$\frac{5x^2-11x+8}{x^3-3x^2+2x} = \frac{4}{x} + \frac{3}{x-2} - \frac{2}{x-1}.$$

Check: $x = 3$ gives
$$\frac{45-33+8}{27-27+6} = \frac{4}{3} + 3 - 1 \quad \text{(correct)}.$$

$$\therefore \quad \int \frac{5x^2-11x+8}{x^3-3x^2+2x}\,dx = 4\ln|x| + 3\ln|x-2| - 2\ln|x-1| + C,$$

where C is an arbitrary constant.
Check: the derivative is
$$\frac{4}{x} + \frac{3}{x-2} - \frac{2}{x-1} = \frac{4(x^2-3x+2) + 3(x^2-x) - 2(x^2-2x)}{x(x-2)(x-1)}. \quad \square$$

Example 10.46
Consider
$$\int \frac{16\,dx}{x^3-2x^2-4x+8}.$$
Since $t = 2$ is a root of the cubic denominator, $(x-2)$ is a factor:
$$D(x) = (x^3-2x^2-4x+8) = (x-2)(x^2-4) = (x-2)^2(x+2),$$

the case of 2 distinct roots. Assume

$$\frac{16}{(x-2)^2(x+2)} = \frac{A}{(x-2)^2} + \frac{B}{(x-2)} + \frac{C}{(x+2)}$$

$$= \frac{A(x+2) + B(x+2)(x-2) + C(x-2)^2}{D(x)}.$$

Then, comparing the numerators,

$$x = -2 \text{ gives } 16 = 16C, C = 1;$$

$$x = 2 \text{ gives } 16 = 4A, A = 4;$$

$$x = 0 \text{ gives } 16 = 2A - 4B + 4C, B = -1, \text{ so}$$

$$\frac{16}{x^3 - 2x^2 - 4x + 8} = \frac{4}{(x-2)^2} - \frac{1}{x-2} + \frac{1}{x+2}.$$

Check: $x = 1$ gives $\frac{16}{3} = 4 + 1 + \frac{1}{3}$ (correct).

$$\therefore \quad \int \frac{16 \, dx}{x^3 - 2x^2 - 4x + 8} = -4(x-2)^{-1} - \ln|x-2| + \ln|x+2| + C.$$

Check: Differentiating gives

$$\frac{1}{x+2} - \frac{1}{x-2} + \frac{4}{(x-2)^2} = \frac{(x^2 - 4x + 4) - (x^2 - 4) + 4(x+2)}{(x+2)(x-2)^2}. \quad \square$$

Example 10.47
Consider

$$\int \frac{4x^2 - 9x + 10}{x^3 - 4x^2 + 5x} \, dx.$$

$D(x) = x(x^2 - 4x + 5)$ has only one root $(t = 0)$, so assume

$$\frac{4x^2 - 9x + 10}{x(x^2 - 4x + 5)} = \frac{A}{x} + \frac{Bx + C}{x^2 - 4x + 5} = \frac{A(x^2 - 4x + 5) + Bx^2 + Cx}{x(x^2 - 4x + 5)}$$

Then, comparing the numerators

$$x = 0 \text{ gives } 10 = 5A, A = 2;$$

$$\text{coefficients of } x^2 \text{ give } 4 = 2 + B, B = 2;$$

$$\text{coefficients of } x \text{ give } -9 = -8 + C, C = -1; \text{ so}$$

$$\frac{4x^2 - 9x + 10}{x^3 - 4x^2 + 5x} = \frac{2}{x} + \frac{2x - 1}{x^2 - 4x + 5}. \tag{*}$$

Check: $x = 1$ gives

$$\frac{4 - 9 + 10}{1 - 4 + 5} = \frac{2}{1} + \frac{1}{1 - 4 + 5} \quad \text{(correct)}.$$

$$\therefore \quad \int \frac{4x^2 - 9x + 10}{x^3 - 4x^2 + 5x} \, dx = 2 \ln|x| + I$$

where

$$I = \int \frac{(2x-1)\, dx}{(x-2)^2+1} = \int \frac{2u+3}{u^2+1}\, du$$

$$= \ln(u^2+1) + 3\, \mathrm{Tan}^{-1} u + C$$

$$= \ln(x^2-4x+5) + 3\, \mathrm{Tan}^{-1}(x-2) + C.$$

Check: differentiating gives

$$\frac{2}{x} + \frac{2x-4}{x^2-4x+5} + \frac{3}{(x-2)^2+1} = \frac{2}{x} + \frac{2x-4+3}{x^2-4x+5} \qquad (\mathrm{cf}\,(*)). \quad \square$$

If an invalid form is assumed for partial fractions, the equations for the unknown constants will be inconsistent.

Example 10.48

Let

$$\frac{16}{x^3-2x^2-4x+8} = \frac{A}{x-2} + \frac{Bx+C}{x^2-4} = \frac{A(x^2-4)+(Bx+C)(x-2)}{(x-2)(x^2-4)}.$$

In the numerator, equate coefficients of x^2, of x, and of x^0 (constants):

$$0 = A+B, \qquad 0 = C-2B, \qquad 16 = -4A-2C.$$

Apparently three equations are obtained for the three unknowns A, B, and C, but substituting $A=-B$ and $C=2B$ in the third equation gives $16=0$. This contradiction indicates that the assumed form for the partial fractions was invalid. $\square$

In principle the same method will produce an antiderivative of any given rational function N/D, as outlined in Procedure B3 in Appendix B.

Example 10.49

$$I = \int \frac{x^6+5x^5+17x^4+27x^3+20x^2-8x+2}{x^5+3x^4+6x^3+2x^2-7x-5}\, dx.$$

(i) $$\frac{N(x)}{D(x)} = x+2+\frac{5x^4+13x^3+23x^2+11x+12}{D(x)} = x+2+\frac{N_1(x)}{D(x)}.$$

(ii) $$D(x) = (x-1)(x+1)^2(x^2+2x+5).$$

(iii) $$\frac{N_1(x)}{D(x)} = \frac{2}{x-1} + \frac{1}{x+1} - \frac{2}{(x+1)^2} + \frac{2x+3}{x^2+2x+5}.$$

Since

$$\frac{2x+3}{x^2+2x+5} = \frac{2w+1}{w^2+2^2}, \qquad (x = w-1)$$

$$I = \tfrac{1}{2}x^2+2x+2\ln|x-1|+\ln|x+1|+\frac{2}{x+1}+\ln(x^2+2x+5)+\tfrac{1}{2}\mathrm{Tan}^{-1}\left(\frac{x+1}{2}\right)+C. \quad \square$$

Exercises (answers on p. 252)

10.4.1   Find antiderivatives of

(a) $\dfrac{x-2}{x+1}$, (b) $\dfrac{x^2-3x-2}{(2x-1)^3}$.

10.4.2   Evaluate

(a) $\displaystyle\int \dfrac{dx}{x^2+6x+34}$, (b) $\displaystyle\int \dfrac{dx}{x^2+6x}$, (c) $\displaystyle\int \dfrac{4x-7}{x^2+2x+3}\,dx$,

(d) $\displaystyle\int \dfrac{4x-7}{x^2-4x+3}\,dx$, (e) $\displaystyle\int \dfrac{x^3+1}{x^2+1}\,dx$.

10.4.3   Find antiderivatives of

(a) $\dfrac{5x^2-11x+8}{x^3-2x^2+2x}$, (b) $\dfrac{2x^3-x-4}{x^3-5x^2+2x+8}$.

10.4.4   Evaluate

$$\int \dfrac{4x^3+5}{(2x+3)(x^2+2)}\,dx.$$

10.5   Reduction Formulas

In Example 10.33, on p. 232, integration by parts reduced the evaluation of $\int x^2 \sin x\,dx$ to that of $\int 2x \cos x\,dx$, which in turn was reduced to the evaluation of $\int 2\sin x\,dx$. Each application of the integration by parts formula reduces the power of x by 1, so that n applications would be needed in order to evaluate $\int x^n \sin x\,dx$. In such cases it is convenient to apply the integration by parts formula to the general case, reducing n to $(n-1)$ or $(n-2)$, depending on the particular example. The resulting **reduction formula** can then be used for any value of n without specifically integrating by parts.

Example 10.50
Evaluate $\int x^5 \sin x\,dx$.

Let $I_n = \int x^n \sin x\,dx$. Integrating by parts,

$$I_n = \int x^n\,d(-\cos x) \qquad (u=x^n,\ v=-\cos x)$$

$$= uv - \int v\,du = -x^n \cos x + n\int x^{n-1} \cos x\,dx$$

$$I_n = -x^n \cos x + nJ_{n-1} \tag{10.6}$$

where

$$J_n = \int x^n \cos x\,dx = \int x^n\,d(\sin x)$$

$$= x^n \sin x - n\int x^{n-1} \sin x\,dx$$

$$J_n = x^n \sin x - nI_{n-1}. \tag{10.7}$$

By repeated application of equations (10.6) and (10.7), integrals of the types I_n or J_n can be reduced either to $I_0 = \int \sin x \, dx = C - \cos x$, or to $J_0 = \int \cos x \, dx = C + \sin x$. Having established the reduction formulas (10.6) and (10.7), the integration by parts formula need not be used again. For instance

$$I_5 = -x^5 \cos x + 5J_4, \quad \text{using equation (10.6) with } n = 5$$

$$5J_4 = 5x^4 \sin x - 20I_3, \quad \text{using equation (10.7) with } n = 4$$

$$-20I_3 = 20x^3 \cos x - 60J_2, \quad \text{using (10.6) with } n = 3$$

$$-60J_2 = -60x^2 \sin x + 120I_1, \quad \text{using (10.7) with } n = 2$$

$$120I_1 = -120x \cos x + 120 \sin x + C, \quad \text{using (10.6) and evaluating } J_0.$$

Adding,

$$I_5 = (-x^5 + 20x^3 - 120x)\cos x + (5x^4 - 60x^2 + 120)\sin x + C.$$

Check:

$$I_5' = (-5x^4 + 60x^2 - 120)\cos x + (x^5 - 20x^3 + 120x)\sin x$$

$$+ (5x^4 - 60x^2 + 120)\cos x + (20x^3 - 120x)\sin x$$

$$= x^5 \sin x. \quad \square$$

Example 10.51
Let $C_n = \int \cos^n x \, dx$. Then

$$C_n = \int \cos^{n-1} x \cos x \, dx = \int \cos^{n-1} x \, d(\sin x).$$

Integrate by parts with $v = \sin x$, $u = \cos^{n-1} x$,

$$du = (n-1) \cos^{n-2} x \, (-\sin x) \, dx$$

$$C_n = \sin x \cos^{n-1} x + (n-1) \int \sin^2 x \cos^{n-2} x \, dx$$

$$= \sin x \cos^{n-1} x + (n-1)(C_{n-2} - C_n),$$

since $\sin^2 x = 1 - \cos^2 x$.
So

$$nC_n = \sin x \cos^{n-1} x + (n-1)C_{n-2} \tag{10.8}$$

is a reduction formula for C_n, which can thereby be reduced either to C_1 or $C_0 = \int dx$. $\square$

Example 10.52
Let $T_{m,n} = \int \cos^m x \sin^n x \, dx$. Then

$$T_{m,n} = \int u \, dv \quad \text{with } u = \cos^m x \sin^{n-1} x, \qquad v = -\cos x$$

$$= -\cos^{m+1} x \; \sin^{n-1} x - \int v \, du.$$

From Example 6.19, with $a = n-1$ and $b = m$, (see p. 110)

$$du = \cos^{m-1} x \ [(1-m-n) \sin^n x + (n-1) \sin^{n-2} x],$$

so

$$-\int v \, du = (1-m-n) T_{m,n} + (n-1) T_{m,n-2}.$$

The resulting reduction formula

$$(m+n) T_{m,n} = -\cos^{m+1} x \ \sin^{n-1} x + (n-1) T_{m,n-2} \qquad (10.9)$$

will reduce $T_{m,n}$ either to

$$T_{m,1} = -\int \cos^m x \, d(\cos x)$$

$$= -\frac{1}{m+1} \cos^{m+1} x + C$$

or to $T_{m,0} = C_m$ in Example 10.51. □

For finding antiderivatives, the reduction formulas are usually used with m and/or n positive integers, since the final cases after reduction ($n=1$ or 0) are known results. However the formulas are valid for any values of m and n. Some further results can be obtained by considering negative integral values.

Example 10.53
In equation (10.8), change n to m, and then replace m by $2-n$:

$$(2-n) C_{2-n} = \sin x \cos^{1-n} x + (1-n) C_{-n}.$$

Since $C_{-n} = \int \sec^n x \, dx$ and $C_{2-n} = \int \sec^{n-2} x$, this can be rearranged to give the reduction formula:

$$(n-1) \int \sec^n x \, dx = \sin x \sec^{n-1} x + (n-2) \int \sec^{n-2} x \, dx. \qquad (10.10)$$

If n is even, $\int \sec^n x \, dx$ can be reduced to $\int dx$ ($n=0$). If n is odd, $\int \sec^n x \, dx$ can be reduced to $\int \sec x \, dx$ (see Exercise 10.2.8 on p. 230). □

Substitutions give further formulas.

Example 10.54
In equation (10.8), put $\sin x / \cos x = \tan x$, and replace n by $2n-2$:

$$(2n-2) \int \cos^{2n} x \cos^{-2} x \, dx = \tan x \cos^{2n-2} x + (2n-3) \int \cos^{2n-2} x \cos^{-2} x \, dx.$$

Now substitute $\tan x = u/a$, $du/a = \sec^2 x \, dx = \cos^{-2} x \, dx$, and (with $k = n$ or $n-1$) $\cos^{2k} x = (\sec^2 x)^{-k} = (1 + \tan^2 x)^{-k} = a^{2k}/(u^2 + a^2)^k$:

$$(2n-2) \int \frac{a^{2n}}{(a^2+u^2)^n} \frac{du}{a} = \frac{ua^{2n-3}}{(a^2+u^2)^{n-1}} + (2n-3) \int \frac{a^{2n-2}}{(a^2+u^2)^{n-1}} \frac{du}{a}.$$

Check: if a and u are lengths, each term is dimensionless.

Dividing by a^{2n-1} gives the reduction formula

$$(2n-2)P_n = \frac{u}{a^2(a^2+u^2)^{n-1}} + \frac{(2n-3)}{a^2} P_{n-1} \qquad (10.11)$$

where $P_n = \int du/(u^2+a^2)^n$.   □

The fact that P_n can be evaluated for any integer n is required to support the statement that an antiderivative of any rational function can be obtained, since integrals of this type can appear in the partial fractions. If n is a half-integer (i.e. half an odd integer), then equation (10.11) reduces P_n to $P_{3/2}$ or $P_{1/2}$, which is also a standard form (SF14 or SF15). The formula (10.11) can also be used with $+a^2$ replaced by $-a^2$.

Reduction formulas can also be given for definite integrals.

Example 10.55

Evaluate $K_n = \int_0^{\pi/2} \cos^n \theta \, d\theta$.

Applying equation (10.8), $nK_n = 0 + (n-1)K_{n-2}$, provided $n > 1$.

$$[\text{If } n = 1, \cos^{n-1} \cdot \theta = 1, \text{ and so } (\sin \tfrac{1}{2}\pi)(\cos^{n-1} \tfrac{1}{2}\pi) = 1].$$

So $K_n = [(n-1)/n]K_{n-2}$, and (replacing n by $n-2$)
$K_{n-2} = [(n-3)/(n-2)]K_{n-4}$, etc., reducing to K_0 if n even, K_1 if n odd.

$$K_0 = \int_0^{\pi/2} d\theta = \tfrac{1}{2}\pi, \; K_1 = \int_0^{\pi/2} \cos \theta \, d\theta = 1.$$

If n even,

$$K_n = \frac{(n-1)(n-3) \cdots 1}{n(n-2) \cdots 2} \frac{\pi}{2}$$

If n odd,

$$K_n = \frac{(n-1)(n-3) \cdots 2}{n(n-2) \cdots 3}.$$

Substituting $\theta = \tfrac{1}{2}\pi - \phi$ shows that also $\int_0^{\pi/2} \sin^n \phi \, d\phi = K_n$.   □

Exercises (answers on p. 252)

10.5.1   Use reduction formulas to obtain antiderivatives of (a) $\cos^4 x$, (b) $\sin^4 x \cos^2 x$, (c) $(x^2+4)^{-3}$.

10.5.2   Evaluate $\int_0^{\pi/2} \cos^8 x \, dx$.

10.5.3   Find an antiderivative of $\sin^6 x$.

10.5.4   Evaluate (i) $\int_0^{\pi/4} \sec^4 \theta \, d\theta$, (ii) $\int_0^a dx/(x^2+a^2)^2$.

10.5.5   By substituting in equation (10.8), obtain a reduction formula for $L_n = \int \cos^n k\theta \, d\theta$.

10.5.6   Use equation (10.11) to find antiderivatives of (i) $(x^2+a^2)^{-3/2}$, (ii) $(x^2+a^2)^{1/2}$.

10.5.7   Obtain a reduction formula for $E_n = \int x^n e^{ax} dx$.

10.6 Systematic Integration

The previous four sections have described the available methods for reducing an integral to a standard form. There is only one general result:

> an antiderivative can always be found for a rational function. The object of a substitution, or of integrating by parts, is therefore to change the integrand either to a standard form, or to a rational function.

A survey of the methods already discussed allows the formulation of a systematic method for deciding whether an antiderivative can be found in terms of known functions. One such procedure is shown by the flow chart in Fig. 10.1. Some further discussions of the different techniques will now be given, in the order that they are encountered in the flow chart.

The term **surd** refers to the square root of an expression. The substitution $w = \sqrt{(ax+b)}$ removes the **linear surd** $\sqrt{(ax+b)}$, as in Example 10.22 on p. 227. After completing the square, a **quadratic surd** $\sqrt{(cx^2+dx+e)}$ becomes one of the three cases:

$$\sqrt{(u^2+a^2)}: \quad \text{substitute } u = a \tan \theta \text{ or } u = a \sinh \theta$$

$$\sqrt{(u^2-a^2)}: \quad \text{substitute } u = a \sec \theta \text{ or } u = a \cosh \theta$$

$$\sqrt{(a^2-u^2)}: \quad \text{substitute } u = a \sin \theta.$$

Example 10.60

$$I = \int x \sqrt{\frac{a+x}{a-x}}\, dx.$$

Since

$$I = \int \frac{x(a+x)}{\sqrt{(a^2-x^2)}}\, dx,$$

the integrand involves the quadratic surd $\sqrt{(a^2-x^2)}$, and the suggested substitution is $x = a \sin \theta$, $dx = a \cos \theta\, d\theta$. Thus

$$I = a^2 \int (\sin \theta + \sin^2 \theta)\, d\theta = a^2 \left[-\cos \theta + \tfrac{1}{2} \int (1 - \cos 2\theta)\, d\theta \right]$$

$$= a^2 (\tfrac{1}{2}\theta - \cos \theta - \tfrac{1}{4} \sin 2\theta) + C$$

$$= \tfrac{1}{2}a^2 \operatorname{Sin}^{-1}(x/a) - (a + \tfrac{1}{2}x)\sqrt{(a^2-x^2)} + C. \quad \square$$

However the special integrand $(ax+b)/(cx^2+dx+e)^{\lambda}$ with $\lambda = \tfrac{1}{2}$ (or any other half-integer) may be treated in the same way as for $\lambda = 1$.

Example 10.61
(cf. Example 10.44 on p. 236)

$$\int \frac{(5-x)\, dx}{\sqrt{(x^2+4x+13)}} = -\tfrac{1}{2} \int w^{-1/2}\, dw + 7 \int \frac{du}{\sqrt{(u^2+9)}}, \qquad (u = x+2, \ w = u^2+9)$$

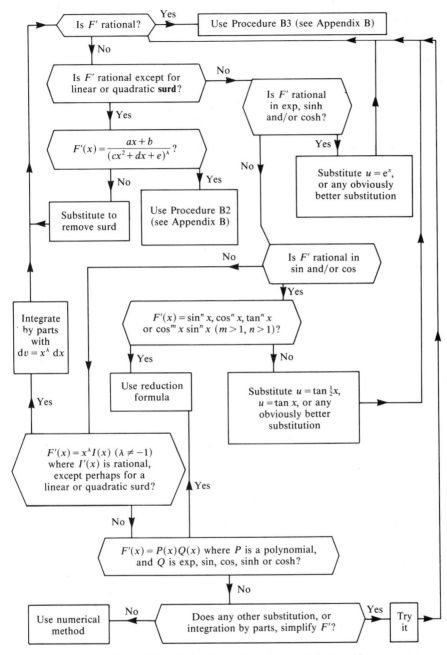

Figure 10.1 Systematic antiderivation: find F given F'

$$= -w^{1/2} + 7 \ln[u + \sqrt{(u^2 + 9)}] + C$$
$$= -\sqrt{(x^2 + 4x + 13)} + 7 \ln[x + 2 + \sqrt{(x^2 + 4x + 13)}] + C. \quad \square$$

Example 10.27 illustrated the treatment of an *integrand rational in* e^x, *cosh x and/or sinh x* (see p. 230).

Example 10.26(i) illustrates the use of the substitution $u = \tan \frac{1}{2}x$ when F' is *rational in sin and/or cos*. If all terms have even degree in *sin* and *cos*, then $u = \tan x$ is usually better.

Example 10.62

$$I = \int \frac{dx}{2 + 2 \sin x \cos x - \sin^2 x}$$

$$= \int \frac{\sec^2 x \, dx}{2(1 + \tan^2 x) + 2 \tan x - \tan^2 x}$$

$$= \int \frac{du}{u^2 + 2u + 2} \qquad (u = \tan x)$$

$$= \int \frac{du}{(u+1)^2 + 1} = \text{Tan}^{-1}(1 + u) + C$$

$$= \text{Tan}^{-1}(1 + \tan x) + C. \quad \square$$

Examples 10.21 and 10.26(ii) illustrate the use of 'obviously better substitutions' (see pp. 227 and 229).

The type $F'(x) = x^\lambda I(x)$ includes $\tan^{-1}$, $\ln$, $\sinh^{-1}$, $\cosh^{-1}$, $\sin^{-1}$ and $\cos^{-1}$ for I, as in Example 10.30 ($\lambda = 0$) and Example 10.31 ($\lambda = 2$). The method works if x^λ is replaced by a polynomial, as noted before Example 10.31 (see p. 232).

Example 10.63

$$I = \int (3x^2 + 2x - 1) \ln(1 + x) \, dx$$

$$= \int u \, dv \qquad \text{with } u = \ln(1 + x), \qquad v = x^3 + x^2 - x$$

$$= (x^3 + x^2 - x) \ln(1 + x) - \int v \, du$$

and

$$\int v \, du = \int \frac{x^3 + x^2 - x}{1 + x} \, dx = \int (w^2 - 2w + 1/w) \, dw \qquad (w = 1 + x)$$

$$= \frac{1}{3}(x + 1)^3 - (x + 1)^2 + \ln|x + 1| + C$$

$$I = (x^3 + x^2 - x - 1) \ln|x + 1| + (x + 1)^2 - \frac{1}{3}(x + 1)^3 + C. \quad \square$$

Examples 10.32 and 10.33 illustrate the type $F'(x) = P(x)Q(x)$ where P is a polynomial. Example 10.33 can now be integrated using the reduction formula R1 for

$I_n = \int x^n \sin ax\, dx$: (see p. 253 for R1).

(see p. 253 for R1)

$$\int (x^2+3x) \sin x\, dx = I_2 + 3I_1$$

$$= -x^2 \cos x + 2J_1 + 3I_1$$

$$= -x^2 \cos x + 2x \sin x - 2I_0 - 3x \cos x + 3J_0$$

and $I_0 = -\cos x$, $J_0 = \sin x$.

Exercises (see note on p. 252)

(see note on p. 252)

For each of the following expressions, state whether an antiderivative can be found in terms of known functions. If so, indicate a method of obtaining an antiderivative.

10.6.1 $(x^2+3) \operatorname{Tan}^{-1} x$
10.6.2 $(e^{2x}+1)/(e^{3x}+e^x-1)$
10.6.3 $(x^4+1)e^{2x^2}$
10.6.4 $x^3 e^{2x^2}$
10.6.5 $xe^x \sin x$
10.6.6 $\cos^2 2x \sin^6 2x$
10.6.7 $\cos^2 2x \sin^6 x$
10.6.8 $\sqrt{(x^3+x^2+1)}$
10.6.9 $1/\sqrt{(x^4+x^2-1)}$
10.6.10 $x/\sqrt{(x^4+x^2-1)}$.

10.7   Improper Integrals

In Chapter 9, the Riemann integral $R_a^b(f) = \int_a^b f(x)\, dx$ was defined as the limit of a sequence $\{R_n\}$, and it was then shown that for f continuous on $[a, b]$,

$$\int_a^b f(x)\, dx = P(b) - P(a) \tag{9.13}$$

where P is an antiderivative of f. A geometrical interpretation is that equation (9.13) is the area in $[a, b]$ between the curve $y = f(x)$ and the x-axis. If $f(x) \to 0$ as $x \to \infty$, then it is possible for this area to approach a limit as $b \to \infty$.

Example 10.70

$$\int_0^b e^{-x}\, dx = -e^{-x}\big|_0^b = -e^{-b}+1, \tag{*}$$

and $\operatorname{Lim}_{b\to\infty} \int_0^b e^{-x}\, dx = 1$, so it is sensible to say that the area between $y = e^{-x}$ and the positive axes is 1, meaning that the area (Fig. 10.2) in $[0, b]$ has the limit 1 as $b \to \infty$. The calculation (*) is usually written

$$\int_0^\infty e^{-x}\, dx = -e^{-x}\big|_0^\infty = -e^{-\infty} + e^0 = 1$$

again with the convention that a limit is implied whenever the symbol ∞ appears.   □

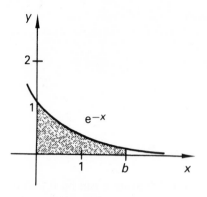

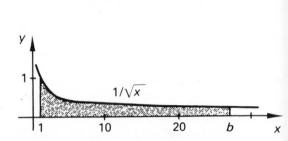

Figure 10.2   Shaded area is $\int_0^b e^{-x}\, dx$

Figure 10.3   Shaded area is $\int_1^b x^{-1/2}\, dx$

Example 10.71

$$\int_1^\infty dx/\sqrt{x} = \operatorname*{Lim}_{b\to\infty} \int_1^b dx/\sqrt{x}, \quad \text{if this exists.}$$

But $\int_1^b x^{-1/2}\, dx = 2x^{1/2}\big|_1^b = 2(\sqrt{b}-1) \to \infty$ as $b\to\infty$. Thus $\int_1^\infty dx/\sqrt{x}$ does not exist (the area in Fig. 10.3 can be made as large as desired by choosing b large enough).   □

Terminology borrowed from series is to say that $\int_0^\infty e^{-x}\, dx$ **converges** (to the limit 1), while $\int_1^\infty dx/\sqrt{x}$ **does not converge**.

Even in the convergent case, the definition of integral as the limit of a sequence $\{R_n\}$ no longer applies, so the integral is called **improper**.

Similarly the improper integral $\int_{-\infty}^b f(x)\, dx$ is $\operatorname{Lim}_{a\to-\infty} \int_a^b f(x)\, dx$ if this limit exists, and does not converge if there is no limit.

Example 10.72

$$\int_{-\infty}^\infty \frac{dx}{x^2+1} \quad\text{means}\quad \operatorname*{Lim}_{\substack{a\to-\infty \\ b\to\infty}} \int_a^b \frac{dx}{x^2+1}$$

$$\int_{-\infty}^\infty \frac{dx}{x^2+1} = \operatorname{Tan}^{-1} x\big|_{-\infty}^\infty = \tfrac{1}{2}\pi - (-\tfrac{1}{2}\pi) = \pi.$$ □

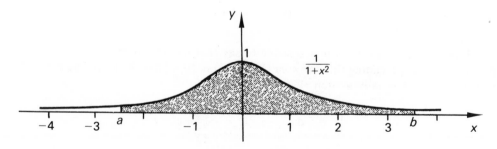

Figure 10.4   Shaded area is $\int_a^b (x^2+1)^{-1}\, dx$

Another situation in which the definition $R_a^b(f) = \text{Lim}_{n\to\infty} R_n$ breaks down (see, for example, Exercise 9.3.4) is when $f(x)$ is unbounded on $[a, b]$. Again it may be sensible to consider a suitable limit.

Example 10.73

$R_0^1(\ln) = \int_0^1 \ln x \, dx$ is not defined as $\text{Lim}\{R_n\}$ since $\ln x \to -\infty$ as $x \to 0$. Some of the sequences $\{R_n\}$ do not exist, and others have no limit. However

$$\underset{c\to 0}{\text{Lim}} \int_c^1 \ln x \, dx = \underset{c\to 0}{\text{Lim}}(-1 - c \ln c + c) = -1$$

so the improper integral $\int_0^1 \ln x \, dx$ converges to the value -1. □

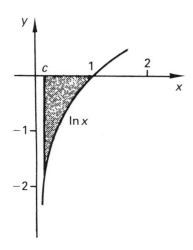

Figure 10.5   Shaded area is $\int_c^1 \ln x \, dx$

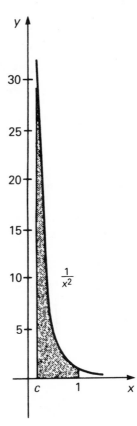

Figure 10.6   Shaded area is $\int_c^1 x^{-2} \, dx$

Example 10.74

$$\int_0^1 x^{-2} \, dx = \underset{c\to 0}{\text{Lim}} \int_c^1 x^{-2} \, dx \qquad \text{if this exists.}$$

But

$$\int_c^1 x^{-2} \, dx = -x^{-1}|_c^1 = 1 - c^{-1}$$

has no limit as $c \to 0$, so the improper integral $\int_0^1 x^{-2} \, dx$ does not exist. □

From the point of view of the area interpretation, there is no essential distinction between improper integrals arising by letting $a \to -\infty$ or $b \to \infty$ and those arising because $f(x) \to \infty$. For example, interchanging x and $-y$ shows that the area in Fig. 10.2 is the area in Fig. 10.5 (in the limit); and interchanging x and y in Fig. 10.3 gives Fig. 10.6, so the nonconvergence of both integrals is consistent.

If $f(x) \to \pm\infty$ as $x \to a+$, then the improper integral $\int_a^b f(x)\, dx = \text{Lim}_{c \to a+} \int_c^b f(x)\, dx$, if this exists. If $f(x) \to \pm\infty$ as $x \to b-$, then the improper integral $\int_a^b f(x)\, dx = \text{Lim}_{c \to b-} \int_a^c f(x)\, dx$, if this exists. If $f(x) \to \pm\infty$ as $x \to e$, where $a < e < b$, then the improper integral $\int_a^b f(x)\, dx$ can be considered as $\int_a^e f(x)\, dx + \int_e^b f(x)\, dx$, if both these exist. When taking the limits the table on p. 91 should be consulted as necessary.

Example 10.75

$$A_n = \int_0^\infty x^n e^{-x}\, dx = -\int_0^\infty x^n\, d(e^{-x})$$

$$= [-x^n e^{-x}]_0^\infty + nA_{n-1} = nA_{n-1} \quad \text{if } n > 0.$$

Successive applications of this reduction formula give

$$A_n = nA_{n-1} = n(n-1)A_{n-2} = n(n-1)(n-2)A_{n-3} = \cdots$$

$$\cdots = n!A_0, \quad \text{for integer } n$$

$$= n!,$$

since Example 10.70 on p. 247 gives $A_0 = 1$. $\square$

After the integration by parts in the previous example, $\text{Lim}_{x \to \infty} u(x)v(x)$ was taken, but it may be necessary to defer taking the limit until $\int v\, du$ has been evaluated.

Example 10.76

Consider $I = \int_0^1 (x-1) \ln x\, dx$, which is improper because $(x-1) \ln x \to \infty$ as $x \to 0$.

$$\int (x-1) \ln x\, dx = \tfrac{1}{2} \int \ln x\, d(x-1)^2 = \int u\, dv$$

$$= \tfrac{1}{2}(x-1)^2 \ln x - \tfrac{1}{2} \int (x-1)^2 \frac{dx}{x}. \tag{*}$$

In (*), $u(x)v(x) = \tfrac{1}{2}(x-1)^2 \ln x \to -\infty$ as $x \to 0$, but it cannot be concluded that I does not exist, because the remaining integral $\int_0^1 v\, du$ is still improper. Since

$$-\int v\, du = -\tfrac{1}{2} \int (x-2+x^{-1})\, dx = -\tfrac{1}{4}x^2 + x - \tfrac{1}{2} \ln x,$$

$$\int (x-1) \ln x\, dx = (\tfrac{1}{2}x^2 - x) \ln x - \tfrac{1}{4}x^2 + x.$$

Since $\text{Lim}_{x \to 0} (\tfrac{1}{2}x - 1)x \ln x = (-1)\, \text{Lim}_{x \to 0} x \ln x = 0$,

$$I = \int_0^1 (x-1) \ln x\, dx = -\tfrac{1}{4} + 1 = \tfrac{3}{4}. \quad \square$$

As with series, it is of some value to be able to decide whether an improper integral converges, even when an antiderivative cannot be found, since numerical approximations can be obtained for the value once it is known to exist.

Example 10.77
If $f(x) = \sin^2 x / x^2$, show that $\int_0^\infty f(x)\, dx$ exists.

Although the x^2 term in the denominator suggests an unbounded integrand as $x \to 0$, Example 4.32 on p. 83 gives $f(x) = (\sin x / x)^2 \to 1$ as $x \to 0$. Thus the only limit to be discussed is $\mathrm{Lim}_{b \to \infty} \int_0^b f(x)\, dx$.
  Since $f(x) \geq 0$, $\int_0^b f(x)\, dx$ is an increasing function of b.
  Also $f(x) \leq x^{-2}$, and (see Example 6.72, p. 131) $f(x) \leq 1$ for $0 \leq x \leq 1$, so

$$\int_0^b f(x)\, dx \leq \int_0^1 1\, dx + \int_1^b x^{-2}\, dx$$

$$= 1 + [-1/x]_1^b = 2 - 1/b < 2.$$

Thus $\int_0^b f(x)\, dx$ increases with b, but is bounded, and must therefore have a limit as $b \to \infty$. Note that this argument is the same as in Theorem 8.2 on the convergence of series, and the use of the inequality $f(x) \leq x^{-2}$ is the same as the use of the comparison test to show the convergence of a series. □

Example 10.78
Show that $\int_0^\infty \sin x / x\, dx$ converges.

$$\int_0^b \frac{\sin x}{x}\, dx = \int_0^b \frac{\sin t}{t}\, dt = \int_0^{b/2} \frac{\sin 2x}{x}\, dx \qquad (t = 2x)$$

$$= \int_0^{b/2} u\, dv \quad \text{with } u = x^{-1},\, dv = 2 \sin x \cos x\, dx,\, v = \sin^2 x$$

$$= \frac{\sin^2 x}{x} \Big|_0^{b/2} + \int_0^{b/2} \frac{\sin^2 x}{x^2}\, dx.$$

As $x \to 0$, $\sin^2 x / x = (\sin x / x) \sin x \to 0$ (Example 4.32), and as $b \to \infty$, $2 \sin^2 \frac{1}{2} b / b < 2 / b \to 0$. Thus $\int_0^\infty \sin x / x\, dx$ exists, having the same value as $\int_0^\infty \sin^2 x / x^2\, dx$, which was shown to exist in the previous example. □

Exercises
10.7.1 Determine whether each of the following improper integrals converges or not, and evaluate those which converge:
  (i) $\int_{-1}^1 x^{-2/3}\, dx$, (ii) $\int_1^\infty x^{-3/2}\, dx$, (iii) $\int_0^1 (1-x)^{-1/2}\, dx$ (iv) $\int_0^\infty dx/(1+e^x)$,
  (v) $\int_0^{\pi/2} \tan \theta\, d\theta$, (vi) $\int_0^\infty \cos \theta\, d\theta$.
10.7.2 Find the values of p for which the following exist:
  (i) $\int_0^1 x^p\, dx$, (ii) $\int_1^\infty x^p\, dx$.

Answers to Exercises 10.1.1–10.7.2

10.1.1 $\int c\,dv = c\int dv.$

10.1.2 (i) $\mathrm{Sin}^{-1}(\frac{1}{2}x) + C$, from SF14

(ii) $\frac{1}{3}\mathrm{Tan}^{-1}(x/3) + C$, from SF11

(iii) $\frac{1}{5}e^{-2t}(-2\cos t + \sin t) + C$, from SF17.

10.2.1 and **10.2.2** See Exercise 6.1.1 on pp. 111 and 152.

10.2.3 See Exercise 6.1.2 on pp. 112 and 152.

10.2.4 See Exercise 6.1.3 on pp. 112 and 152.

10.2.5 $-(4e^x + 2)^{-1} + C.$

10.2.6 (i) $\frac{1}{4}c^4$, (ii) $-\frac{1}{4}c^{-4}$, (iii) $\frac{1}{7}c^7 - \frac{1}{5}c^5$ where $c = \cosh x.$

10.2.7 (i) $\sqrt{5} - \sqrt{3}$, (ii) $2(\sqrt{35} - \sqrt{8})/9$, (iii) $(e^{-4} - e^{-16})/8.$

10.2.8 Use either of the substitutions of Example 10.26, on p. 229, or replace x by t in Example 10.26 and then substitute $t = \frac{1}{2}\pi - x.$

10.3.1 and **10.3.2** See Exercise 6.1.4 on pp. 112 and 152.

10.3.3 See SF16 and SF17.

10.3.4 See Exercise 6.1.5 on pp. 112 and 152.

10.4.1 and **10.4.2** See Exercise 6.1.6 on pp. 112 and 152.

10.4.3 See Exercise 6.1.7 on pp. 112 and 152.

10.4.4 $2x - \ln|2x+3| - \ln(x^2+2) - \sqrt{\frac{1}{2}}\,\mathrm{Tan}^{-1}(x\sqrt{\frac{1}{2}}) + C.$

10.5.1 See Exercises 6.1.8 and 6.2.2 (pp. 112, 113, 152–3).

10.5.2 $35\pi/256.$

10.5.3 Put $m = 0$, $n = 6$ in equation (10.9), etc., to get

$$-\cos x(\tfrac{1}{6}\sin^5 x + \tfrac{5}{24}\sin^3 x + \tfrac{5}{16}\sin x) + \tfrac{5}{16}x.$$

10.5.4 (i) $\frac{4}{3}$, (ii) $(1 + \frac{1}{2}\pi)/4a^3.$

10.5.5 $nL_n = k^{-1}\sin k\theta \cos^{n-1} k\theta + (n-1)L_{n-2}.$

10.5.6 (i) $P_{3/2} = x/a^2\sqrt{(a^2+x^2)}$, which can be checked by differentiation.

(ii) Putting $n = \frac{1}{2}$, $P_{-1/2} = \frac{1}{2}x(x^2+a^2)^{1/2} + \frac{1}{2}a^2\ln|x + \sqrt{(x^2+a^2)}|.$

10.5.7 See R2 in table of reduction formulas (p. 253).

10.6.1–10 Assume that an antiderivative can be found for any rational function, but note that this will usually require Newton's method (Chapter 7) to find the roots of the denominator.

10.7.1 (i) 6, (ii) 2, (iii) 2, (iv) $\ln 2$, (v) and (vi) do not exist.

10.7.2 (i) $p > -1$, (ii) $p < -1.$

Table of Antiderivatives

	$P'(w)$	$P(w)$	Reference †
SF1	$w^a (a \neq -1)$	$w^{a+1}/(a+1)$	
SF2	$1/w$	$\ln|w|$	Example 6.13
SF3	e^w	e^w	Example 6.11
SF4	$\cos w$	$\sin w$	
SF5	$\sin w$	$-\cos w$	
SF6	$\sec^2 w = 1/\cos^2 w$	$\tan w$	
SF7	$\tan w$	$-\ln|\cos w|$	(∗) below, with $g = \cos$
SF8	$\cot w = 1/\tan w$	$\ln|\sin w|$	(∗) below, with $g = \sin$
SF9	$\cosh w$	$\sinh w$	Equation (3.13)
SF10	$\sinh w$	$\cosh w$	Equation (3.14)
SF11	$\dfrac{1}{w^2 + a^2}$	$\dfrac{1}{a} \mathrm{Tan}^{-1}\left(\dfrac{w}{a}\right)$	
SF12	$\dfrac{1}{w^2 - a^2}$	$\dfrac{1}{2a} \ln\dfrac{|w-a|}{|w+a|}$	Example 6.13
SF13	$\dfrac{1}{(w^2 + a^2)^2}$	$\dfrac{1}{2a^3}\left[\mathrm{Tan}^{-1}\left(\dfrac{w}{a}\right) + \dfrac{aw}{w^2 + a^2}\right]$	Example 6.14
SF14	$\dfrac{1}{\sqrt{(a^2 - w^2)}}$	$\mathrm{Sin}^{-1}\left(\dfrac{w}{a}\right)$	Example 6.15(i)
SF15	$\dfrac{1}{\sqrt{(w^2 + b)}}$	$\ln|w + \sqrt{(w^2 + b)}|$	Example 6.12(ii)
SF16	$e^{aw} \sin bw$	$\dfrac{e^{aw}(a \sin bw - b \cos bw)}{(a^2 + b^2)}$	
SF17	$e^{aw} \cos bw$	$\dfrac{e^{aw}(a \cos bw + b \sin bw)}{(a^2 + b^2)}$	Exercise 10.3.3

These results may also be written $\int P'(w)\, dw = P(w) + C$.
The variable w can be any one-to-one function of x. In particular the second result can be written, putting $w = g(x)$,

SF2
$$\int \frac{g'(x)\, dx}{g(x)} = \ln|g(x)| + C \qquad (\ast)$$

† In general, the results here may be written down as inverse to results in the table of derivatives at the end of Chapter 6.

For more comprehensive tables of integrals, see the references in Appendix G.

Table of Reduction Formulas

R1 $I_n = \int x^n \sin ax \, dx, \ J_n = \int x^n \cos ax \, dx$

$aI_n = -x^n \cos ax + nJ_{n-1}, \qquad aJ_n = x^n \sin ax - nI_{n-1}$

R2 $E_n = \int x^n \, e^{ax} \, dx, \qquad aE_n = x^n \, e^{ax} - nE_{n-1}$

R3 $C_n = \int \cos^n ax \, dx$

$anC_n = \sin ax \cos^{n-1} ax + a(n-1)C_{n-2}$

R4 $S_n = \int \sin^n ax \, dx$

$anS_n = -\cos ax \sin^{n-1} ax + a(n-1)S_{n-2}$

R5 $T_{m,n} = \int \cos^m ax \sin^n ax \, dx$

$a(m+n)T_{m,n} = -\cos^{m+1} ax \quad \sin^{n-1} ax + a(n-1)T_{m,n-2}$

$\qquad\qquad\quad = \cos^{m-1} ax \quad \sin^{n+1} ax + a(m-1)T_{m-2,n}$

R6 $R_n = \int \sec^n ax \, dx$

$a(n-1)R_n = \sin ax \sec^{n-1} ax + a(n-2)R_{n-2}$

R7 $Q_n = \int \tan^n ax \, dx$

$(n-1)aQ_n = \tan^{n-1} ax - a(n-1)Q_{n-2}$

R8 $P_n = \int (a^2 + x^2)^{-n} \, dx$

$a^2(2n-2)P_n = x(a^2 + x^2)^{1-n} + (2n-3)P_{n-1}$

R9 $G_n = \int x^n \, e^{-ax^2} \, dx$

$2aG_n = -x^{n-1} \, e^{-ax^2} + (n-1)G_{n-2}$

Further Exercises on Chapter 10

10.1 Evaluate (i) $\int_{-1/2}^{1/2} (1 - x^2)^{-1/2} \, dx$, (ii) $\int_0^1 (1 + x^2)^{-1} \, dx$.

10.2 Evaluate (i) $\int_0^{a/2} (a^2 - x^2)^{-1/2} \, dx$, (ii) $\int_{-a}^a (a^2 + x^2)^{-1} \, dx$.

10.3 Find an antiderivative of $a^{bx}(a > 0)$.

10.4 Evaluate (i) $\int_0^{a\sqrt3} (x^2 + a^2)^{-1/2} \, dx$, (ii) $\int_{a\sqrt2}^{a\sqrt{10}} (x^2 - a^2)^{-1/2} \, dx$.

10.5 Find antiderivatives of

(i) $\dfrac{x+1}{\sqrt{(2x-x^2)}}$, (ii) $\dfrac{1-x}{\sqrt{(8+2x-x^2)}}$.

10.6 Evaluate

(i) $\displaystyle\int \dfrac{dx}{1+4e^{-x}+5e^{-2x}}$, (ii) $\displaystyle\int \dfrac{e^t(3+2e^t)\,dt}{4e^{2t}+4e^t+5}$.

10.7 Evaluate

(i) $\displaystyle\int \dfrac{(1+\sin\theta+\cos\theta)\,d\theta}{(1+\cos\theta)(2\sin\theta-3\cos\theta-2)}$ (ii) $\displaystyle\int \dfrac{(1+\cos x)\,dx}{2\sin x+\sin^2 x}$.

10.8 Find antiderivatives of the following:

(i) $(a+b\sqrt{x})^{-1}$, (ii) $(x+a)/(x+b)$, (iii) $(1+e^{2x})^{-1/2}$.

10.9 Evaluate

(i) $\displaystyle\int_0^1 x\ln(2x+1)\,dx$, (ii) $\displaystyle\int_0^4 \dfrac{2x^2+3x-1}{x^2-4x+8}\,dx$.

10.10 Find antiderivatives of (i) $\ln^2 x$, (ii) $(x^3+a^3)^{-1}$.

10.11 Obtain the reduction formula R4
   (i) directly, using $dv=\sin ax\,dx$
   (ii) by replacing x in equation (10.8) by $\frac{1}{2}\pi-x$ (see p. 241)
   (iii) by putting $m=0$ in equation (10.9) (see p. 242)

10.12 If $T_n = \int_0^1 (1-x^m)^n\,dx$, show that $(mn+1)T_n = mnT_{n-1}$ $(m>0,\,n>0)$.

In Exercises 10.13–10.20, state whether an antiderivative of the given expression can be found in terms of known functions. If so, indicate the method of obtaining the antiderivative.

10.13 $\tan^{12}(3x+2)$

10.14 $x^3+2x^2+3x\sqrt{(2x+1)}$

10.15 $(\tan^2 x+2)/(3\tan^2 x+2\tan x-1)$

10.16 2^{3x+4}

10.17 $(x^2+4x+5)^{-7}$

10.18 $(\cos 5x)/(\sin 3x)$

10.19 $(2x+1)^{1/2}\,\text{Tan}^{-1}x$

10.20 $(\sin x)/x$

10.21 Express $\int_0^\infty x^{2n+1}\exp(-x^2)\,dx$ in terms of n, where n is a positive integer.

10.22 Show that $\int_0^\infty e^{-x^2}\,dx$ exists, by comparing it with $\int_0^\infty e^{-x}\,dx$.

10.23 Evaluate the improper integral

$$\int_0^1 x^{-2}\{1+(x-1)e^x\}\,dx$$

by substituting $t=x^{-1}(e^x-1)$.

10.24 By comparing with a suitable convergent integral, show that

$$\int_0^\infty \frac{(x^2+3x+2)\,dx}{x^4+17x^3+12x^2+6x+2} \quad \text{exists.}$$

10.25 Show that $\int_0^{\pi/2} x^{-3/2}\sin x\,dx$ exists.

10.26 Use the substitution $u=\frac{1}{2}+\tan(\frac{1}{2}x)$ to evaluate

(i) $\displaystyle\int \frac{dx}{2+\sin x}$ \qquad (ii) $\displaystyle\int_0^{2\pi} \frac{dx}{2+\sin x}$.

10.27 Evaluate $\int x^b \log(ax)\,dx$ \qquad $(a>0)$.

10.28 Obtain reduction formulas for $\int e^{ax}\sin^n bx\,dx$ and $\int e^{ax}\cos^n bx\,dx$ (reducing n to $n-2$).

In Exercises 10.29–10.32, derive the given formula, and state the values of the constants for which the result is valid.

10.29 $\displaystyle\int_0^1 x^p \ln(ax)\,dx = \frac{\ln a}{p+1} - \frac{1}{(p+1)^2}$.

10.30 $\displaystyle\int \frac{dx}{(x-r)(x-s)} = \frac{1}{s-r}\ln\left|\frac{x-s}{x-r}\right| + C$.

10.31 $\displaystyle\int_a^b \frac{dx}{(x-r)(x-s)} = \frac{1}{s-r}\ln\left[\frac{(s-b)(a-r)}{(b-r)(a-s)}\right]$.

10.32 $\displaystyle\int_{-\infty}^\infty \frac{dx}{x^2+2px+q} = \frac{\pi}{\sqrt{(q-p^2)}}$.

10.33 Let $F_n = \int_{-\pi}^\pi x^n e^{imx}\,dx$, where m is a nonzero integer. Use the reduction formula R2 to show that

$$m^2 F_n = 2n\pi^{n-1}(-1)^m - \pi n(n-1)F_{n-2} \qquad \text{if } n \text{ is even;}$$

$$m^2 F_n = -2im\pi^n(-1)^m - \pi n(n-1)F_{n-2} \qquad \text{if } n \text{ is odd.}$$

10.34 Let $A_n = \int_{-\pi}^\pi x^n \cos mx\,dx$, $B_n = \int_{-\pi}^\pi x^n \sin mx\,dx$, where m is a nonzero integer. Use the reduction formulas R1 to show that

$$mB_n = -2\pi^n(-1)^m + nA_{n-1}, \; mA_n = -nB_{n-1}.$$

Use these formulas
(i) to evaluate A_0, B_1, A_2, B_3, and A_4 (see p. 416);
(ii) to obtain the results of Exercise 10.33.

10.35 By substituting $t=-x$ in $\int_{-a}^0 f(t)\,dt$, show that

$$\int_{-a}^0 f(x)\,dx = \int_0^a f(-x)\,dx.$$

Deduce that

if f is even, $\int_{-a}^a f(x)\,dx = 2\int_0^a f(x)\,dx$, while if f is odd, $\int_{-a}^a f(x)\,dx = 0$.

Explain these results in terms of areas.

10.36 If $u = \tan \frac{1}{2}x$, show that $\cos x = (1 - u^2)/(1 + u^2)$ (cf. Example 10.26). Assuming that a and b are positive and unequal,
   (i) evaluate $\int (a + b \cos x)^{-1} \, dx$;
   (ii) show that

$$\frac{d}{dx}\left(\frac{b \sin x}{a + b \cos x}\right) = \frac{a}{a + b \cos x} - \frac{a^2 - b^2}{(a + b \cos x)^2}$$

   (iii) evaluate $\int (a + b \cos x)^{-2} \, dx$.

10.37 Evaluate

$$\int \frac{x + 4}{x^3 + 2x^2 + 10x} \, dx.$$

On what intervals $[a, b]$ does

$$\int_a^b \frac{x + 4}{x^3 + 2x^2 + 10x} \, dx$$

exist?

10.38 Evaluate $\int_0^{\pi/4} \tan^7 t \, dt$.

10.39 Evaluate

(i) $\displaystyle\int \frac{2e^{2t} + 3e^t}{4e^{2t} + 4e^t + 5} \, dt$, (ii) $\displaystyle\int \frac{x + 3}{\sqrt{(2x - x^2)}} \, dx$, (iii) $\displaystyle\int y^2 \sin y \, dy$.

10.40 For each of the following, either obtain the value, or show that the improper integral does not exist:

(i) $\displaystyle\int_{-\infty}^0 e^x \, dx$ (ii) $\displaystyle\int_{-\infty}^\infty \frac{1}{x^2} \, dx$ (iii) $\displaystyle\int_0^4 (4 - x)^{-1/2} \, dx$.

10.41 Find an antiderivative of $(\cos ax \sin bx)$.

10.42 Suppose $v(x)$ is positive and decreasing for $x \geqslant 1$, and that $v(x) \to 0$ as $x \to \infty$. Consider the series with terms $v_k = v(k)$.
   (i) By considering areas in Fig. 10.7(b), show that

$$\sum_{k=1}^n v_k > \int_1^n v(x) \, dx.$$

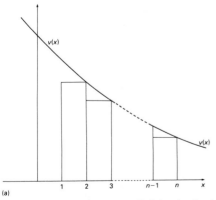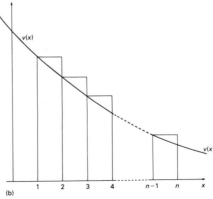

Figure 10.7   Height of strips is: $v_1, v_2, \ldots, v_{n-1}$ in (b); $v_2, v_3, \ldots, v_n$ in (a)

(ii) By considering areas in Fig. 10.7(a), show that

$$\sum_{k=2}^{n} v_k < \int_{1}^{n} v(x)\,dx.$$

(iii) Using (i), show that

if $\int_{1}^{\infty} v(x)\,dx$ does not exist, then the series $\sum_{k=1}^{\infty} v_k$ does not converge. $(v_k > 0)$

(iv) Using (ii), show that

if $\int_{1}^{\infty} v(x)\,dx$ does exist, then the series $\sum_{k=1}^{\infty} v_k$ does converge. $(v_k > 0)$

10.43 Use (iii) and (iv) of the previous exercise to determine the behaviour of the series $\sum_{k=1}^{\infty} 1/n^p$ for different values of p.

10.44 Consider Examples 10.70, 10.72, 10.75, 10.78, and Exercise 10.7.1(iv). What results on the convergence of series are obtained by using Exercise 10.42?

11

Line Integrals and Double Integrals

11.1 Length of a Space Curve given Parametrically

In Example 9.22 on p. 200 the length of the plane curve $y = f(x)$ in the interval $[a, b]$ was shown to be $\int_a^b g(x)\,dx$, where $g = \sqrt{(1 + f'^2)}$. If the curve equations are given parametrically by

$$x = x(t), \qquad y = y(t) \tag{11.1}$$

then the slope $y'(t)/x'(t)$ is naturally obtained in terms of t, as in Section 6.5. The integration required to get the length is often done most easily in terms of t also. This amounts to a change of variable from x to t using the substitution $x = x(t)$, $dx = x'(t)\,dt$; and with this substitution $f'(x)$ becomes $y'(t)/x'(t)$. Thus

$$\int g(x)\,dx = \int \left[1 + \left\{ \frac{y'(t)}{x'(t)} \right\}^2 \right]^{1/2} x'(t)\,dt$$

$$= \int \sqrt{(x'^2 + y'^2)}\,dt.$$

Usually, after obtaining the antiderivative as a function of t, it will be convenient to substitute the **parameter** values of the end-points, rather than change back to x in order to use $x = a$ and $x = b$. If A and B are the end-points, it is best to write

$$\text{Length of arc AB} = \int_A^B \sqrt{(1 + f'^2)}\,dx = \int_A^B \sqrt{(x'^2 + y'^2)}\,dt, \tag{11.2}$$

where A and B indicate that end-point values of the appropriate variable are to be used.

Example 11.10
Find the length of the curve (a **cycloid**) represented by

$$x(t) = a(t - \sin t), \qquad y(t) = a(1 - \cos t),$$

from $A(0, 0)$ to $B(a\pi, 2a)$.

Since $x'(t) = a(1 - \cos t)$ and $y'(t) = a \sin t$, the length is

$$\int_A^B dt \, \sqrt{\{a^2(1 - \cos t)^2 + a^2 \sin^2 t\}}$$

$$= a \int_A^B dt \, \sqrt{(2 - 2 \cos t)} = a \int_A^B dt \, \sqrt{(4 \sin^2 \tfrac{1}{2} t)}$$

$$= 2a \int_A^B \sin \tfrac{1}{2} t \, dt = -4a [\cos \tfrac{1}{2} t]_A^B. \tag{*}$$

At A(0, 0), $x = 0 \Rightarrow t - \sin t = 0 \Rightarrow t = 0$; *check*: $t = 0 \Rightarrow y = 0$. At B($a\pi, 2a$), $t - \sin t = \pi \Rightarrow t = \pi$; *check*: $t = \pi \Rightarrow y = 2a$. The length is $-4a[\cos \frac{1}{2} t]_0^\pi = -4a(0 - 1) = 4a$.

The slope of the cycloid is given by the derivative

$$\frac{dy}{dx} = \frac{y'(t)}{x'(t)} = \frac{\sin t}{1 - \cos t},$$

but the derivative does not exist when $y = 0$ as $\cos t = 1$ ($t = 0, \pm 2\pi, \pm 4\pi \ldots$). An arc length which includes interior points with $y = 0$ must be calculated by dividing it into pieces by these points. Then the derivative exists in each piece; the insertion of parameter values into (∗) must be done separately for each piece, and the results summed.

Also the step $\sqrt{(4 \sin^2 \frac{1}{2} t)} = 2 \sin \frac{1}{2} t$ is actually $\sqrt{(4 \sin^2 \frac{1}{2} t)} = 2|\sin \frac{1}{2} t|$. For example, an arc CD in $-2\pi \leqslant t \leqslant 0$ would have length $-2a \int_C^D \sin \frac{1}{2} t \, dt$, since $\sin \frac{1}{2} t \leqslant 0$. □

Suppose s denotes an arc length function, measuring the length of the curve $y = f(x)$ from some fixed point with $x = a$. Then

$$s(x) = \int_a^x g(u) \, du = \int_a^x \sqrt{\{1 + f'^2(u)\}} \, du.$$

From the fundamental theorem (in Section 9.4), $s' = g = \sqrt{(1 + f'^2)}$. The differential of this arc length function is

$$ds = s'(x) \, dx = dx \sqrt{\left\{ 1 + \left(\frac{dy}{dx} \right)^2 \right\}} = \sqrt{(dx^2 + dy^2)}. \tag{11.3}$$

This equation is also valid when the curve is represented by parametric equations, dx and dy being the differentials of the functions $x(t)$ and $y(t)$ in equations (11.1). From equation (11.2), if c is the parameter of the fixed point, then

$$s = \int_c^t \sqrt{[\{x'(u)\}^2 + \{y'(u)\}^2]} \, du$$

and the fundamental theorem gives

$$ds/dt = \sqrt{[\{x'(t)\}^2 + \{y'(t)\}^2]}.$$

Then

$$ds = dt \sqrt{\left[\left(\frac{dx}{dt} \right)^2 + \left(\frac{dy}{dt} \right)^2 \right]} = \sqrt{(dx^2 + dy^2)}.$$

In other words equation (11.3) holds irrespective of whether x or t (or y) is regarded as the independent variable.

The differential ds has a simple geometrical interpretation in Fig. 11.1. Evidently, as $ds^2 = dx^2 + dy^2$, ds is the length PS along the tangent at P.

If the curve is given by the vector parametric equation

$$r(t) = x(t) i + y(t) j$$

then $dr = dx \, i + dy \, j$, according to the discussion in Section 6.5 (see p. 124). Hence $ds = |dr|$.

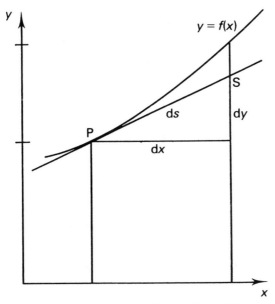

Figure 11.1 Interpretation of length differential ds

The extension of these results to a space curve in three dimensions can now be made. Suppose its equation is

$$r(t) = x(t)i + y(t)j + z(t)k \tag{2.12}$$

and $s(t)$ is the arc-length function measured from some fixed point. Then the arc length from A to B is $\int_A^B ds = \int_A^B s'(t)\,dt$, and d$s$ must be related to the functions in equation (2.12) as in the previous two-dimensional case:

$$ds = |dr| = \sqrt{(dx^2 + dy^2 + dz^2)}. \tag{11.4}$$

Again ds is interpreted geometrically as a length along the tangent to the space curve.

Example 11.11
Find the length of one turn $(0 \leqslant t \leqslant 2\pi)$ of the helix

$$r(t) = (\cos t)i + (\sin t)j + tk.$$

Since $x = \cos t$, $y = \sin t$, $z = t$,

$$dx = -\sin t\,dt, \qquad dy = \cos t\,dt, \qquad dz = dt,$$

and

$$ds^2 = \sin^2 t\,dt^2 + \cos^2 t\,dt^2 + dt^2 = 2\,dt^2.$$

The length is

$$\int_0^{2\pi} ds = \int_0^{2\pi} \sqrt{2}\,dt = t\sqrt{2}\,\Big|_0^{2\pi} = 2\pi\sqrt{2}.$$

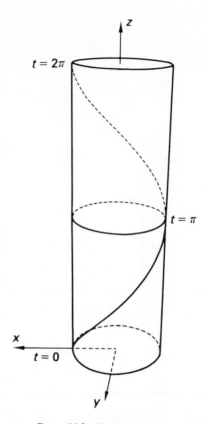

Figure 11.2   Helix on cylinder

Check: is this a reasonable value for the curve in Fig. 11.2? In this particular example, the calculation can be completely checked geometrically. Cut the cylinder of length 2π parallel to its axis, from $(1, 0, 0)$ ($t = 0$) to $(1, 0, 2\pi)$ ($t = 2\pi$), and roll out flat. This gives a square of side 2π, with the curve as a diagonal. □

As an alternative check, it is sometimes possible to re-evaluate the length using a different independent variable, for example x instead of t. This is the same as the check previously suggested in Section 10.2 for any definite integral evaluated by substitution. The use of alternative variables will be considered further in Section 11.3.

Exercises   (answers on p. 287)

11.1.1   Find the length of the curve

$$x = \ln t, \qquad y = (t^2 + 1)/2t$$

from $t = 1$ to $t = e^2$.

11.1.2   Calculate the length of the curve

$$r = (2\sqrt{3})t^3 i + 3t^2 j$$

from $(2\sqrt{3}, 3)$ to $(128\sqrt{3}, 48)$.

11.1.3   Find the length of the curve

$$x = (\cos t + 2 \sin t + 2t)/3$$
$$y = (2 \cos t - 2 \sin t + t)/3$$
$$z = (2 \cos t + \sin t - 2t)/3$$

from $\left(\dfrac{1}{3}, \dfrac{2}{3}, \dfrac{2}{3}\right)$ to $\left(\dfrac{2\pi - 1}{3}, \dfrac{\pi - 2}{3}, \dfrac{-2 - 2\pi}{3}\right)$.

11.1.4   Find the length of the cycloid

$$x = t - \sin t, \qquad y = 1 - \cos t,$$

from $(1 - \tfrac{1}{2}\pi, 1)$ to $(\tfrac{3}{2}\pi + 1, 1)$.

11.2   Work done during Motion along a Curve

In the previous section the result of Example 9.22 for the length of a plane curve was extended to a space curve. In this section

the work done by a force during motion along a curve

will be obtained, generalising the result of Example 9.20. This showed that $\int_a^b F(x)\,dx$ is the work done by a force $F(x)$ during motion along a straight line (the x-axis) from $x = a$ to $x = b$. For space motion the force will be a vector, and will have a value at every point (or at least throughout some three-dimensional region). The force function is therefore a vector field $F(x, y, z)$, which can be specified as a sum of three vector components, the projections of F in the directions of the axes. The work done by F can be obtained as the sum of the contributions by each component.

Example 11.20
Find the work done by the force

$$F(x, y) = (y + 2x)i - xyj$$

during motion along the parabola $y^2 = 4x$ from A(1, 2) to B(4, 4). (See Fig. 11.3).

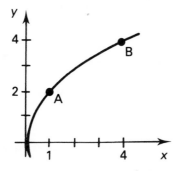

Figure 11.3   Parabola $y^2 = 4x$

Denoting the components by F_1 and F_2, the required work is $W_1 + W_2 = $ (Work done by $F_1 i$) + (Work done by $F_2 j$). The work depends only on values of F at points (x, y) of the curve, so that $x = y^2/4$ or $y = 2\sqrt{x}$. This means that the x-component F_1 can be expressed as a function of x only:

$$F_1 = y + 2x = 2\sqrt{x} + 2x. \qquad (11.5)$$

The work done by $F_1 i$ depends only on motion in the x-direction, and not on motion in the perpendicular y-direction. This work is therefore given by the previous result in Example 9.20. Motion from A to B changes x from 1 to 4, so

$$W_1 = \int_1^4 F_1 \, dx = \int_1^4 (2x^{1/2} + 2x) \, dx, \qquad \text{using equation (11.5)}$$

$$= [\tfrac{4}{3}x^{3/2} + x^2]_1^4 = \tfrac{73}{3}.$$

Similarly the work done by $F_2 j$ is $\int_2^4 F_2 \, dy$, since it depends only on the displacement from A to B in the y-direction. The y-component $F_2 = -xy$ may be written $F_2 = -y^3/4$ at points on the curve. Thus

$$W_2 = \int_2^4 (-y^3/4) \, dy = -y^4/16|_2^4 = -15$$

and the required work is $W_1 + W_2 = 28/3$. □

Example 11.21

Find the work done by the force

$$F(x, y, z) = (x^2 - z^2)i - j - xyk$$

in motion from A(1, 1, 0) to B(0, 0, 1) along the curve

$$x = y, \qquad z^2 = 1 - x^2.$$

$W = W_1 + W_2 + W_3$, adding the work done by each component.

$$W_1 = \int_{x=1}^0 (x^2 - z^2) \, dx$$

$$= \int_1^0 (2x^2 - 1) \, dx \quad \text{since } z^2 = 1 - x^2 \text{ on the curve}$$

$$= \tfrac{1}{3}$$

$$W_2 = \int_{y=1}^0 (-1) \, dy = 1$$

$$W_3 = \int_{z=0}^1 (-xy) \, dz$$

$$= \int_0^1 (z^2 - 1) \, dz, \quad \text{using the curve equations}$$

$$= -\tfrac{2}{3}. \qquad \text{Hence } W = \tfrac{2}{3}. □$$

For this calculation, the curve was not sketched as there would be no advantage in doing so. The curve is shown in Figs 11.4 and 11.5.

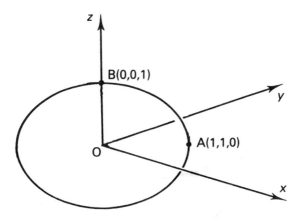

Figure 11.4   Path for integral in Example 11.21

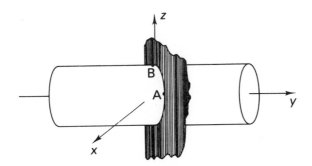

Figure 11.5 $y = x$ (shaded), and $z^2 = 1 - x^2$ (cylinder)

The general result can be written down on the basis of the above examples.

The work done by the force

$$F(x, y, z) = F_1(x, y, z)i + F_2(x, y, z)j + F_3(x, y, z)k$$

during motion from A(a, c, e) to B(b, d, f) along some curve with given equation, is

$$W = \int_{x=a}^{b} F_1 \, dx + \int_{y=c}^{d} F_2 \, dy + \int_{z=e}^{f} F_3 \, dz \qquad \textbf{(11.6)}$$

in which the given curve equations are used to express F_1 as a function of x only, F_2 as a function of y only, and F_3 as a function of z only.

If the curve is specified geometrically, then equations must be derived.

Example 11.22

Find the work done by the force

$$F(x, y, z) = (y + 2x)i + zj - xk$$

in motion along the straight line from A(1, 1, 1) to B(2, 3, 4).

$$W = \int_1^2 (y+2x)\, dx + \int_1^3 z\, dy + \int_1^4 (-x)\, dz.$$

The equations of the line, which are required to evaluate the integrals, were obtained in Example 2.31 (p. 28):

$$x + 1 = (y+3)/2 = (z+5)/3$$

So

$$W = \int_1^2 (4x - 1)\, dx + \int_1^3 (\tfrac{3}{2}y - \tfrac{1}{2})\, dy - \int_1^4 \tfrac{1}{3}(z+2)\, dz$$

$$= 5 + 5 - \tfrac{9}{2} = \tfrac{11}{2}. \quad \square$$

Exercises   (answers on p. 287)

11.2.1   Find the work done by the force $F = 3xy\mathbf{i} - y^2\mathbf{j}$ in motion along the plane curve $y = 2x^2$ from $(0, 0)$ to $(1, 2)$.

11.2.2   Find the work done by the force $F = (z^2 + y)\mathbf{i} + z\mathbf{j} + x\mathbf{k}$ in motion along the space curve represented by

$$y + 2z = 5, \qquad z^2 + y - x = 4$$

from $(1, 1, 2)$ to $(0, 3, 1)$.

11.2.3   Find the work done by the force

$$F(x, y, z) = z^2\mathbf{i} + (3x - 1)\mathbf{j} + yz\mathbf{k}$$

in motion along the straight line from $(0, 0, 0)$ to $(-1, 1, 2)$.

11.3   Further Techniques for Line Integrals

In the result (11.6), the work done by F_1 is calculated as $\int_a^b F_1\, dx$ after using the curve equations to express F_1 as a function of x. This integral can be transformed by any convenient substitution. Possible examples are the change of variable to y or z using the curve equations. In these cases the substitution can be made on $F_1(x, y, z)\, dx$ without first changing to x.

Example 11.30

In Example 11.22 $W_1 = \int (y+2x)\, dx$ and on the line $2x + 2 = y + 3$. A change of variable to y requires substituting for the differential dx after differentiating the path equation relating x and y: $2x + 2 = y + 3 \Rightarrow 2\, dx = dy$; the integration end-points become the y-coordinates of the path end-points:

$$W_1 = \int_1^3 (2y + 1)\tfrac{1}{2}\, dy = \tfrac{1}{2}(y^2 + y)|_1^3 = 6 - 1 = 5. \quad \square$$

Thus in evaluating (11.6), the essential point is to

use the curve equations to express each integral in terms of *one variable only.*

The alternative selections for this variable give a check on the calculations, for instance Example 11.30 checks part of Example 11.22.

When the path is given by parametric equations, it is usually convenient to express the integrals in terms of the parameter.

Example 11.20 (again)

The parabola $y^2 = 4x$ may be specified by parametric equations $x = t^2$, $y = 2t$. Then $t = 1$ and $t = 2$ are the parameters of the end-points A(1, 2) and B(4, 4). Since $dx = 2t\,dt$ and $dy = 2\,dt$,

$$W_1 = \int_A^B (y + 2x)\,dx = \int_1^2 (2t + 2t^2)(2t\,dt)$$

$$W_2 = \int_A^B (-xy)\,dy = \int_1^2 (-2t^3)2\,dt,$$

and

$$W = \int_1^2 4t^2\,dt = [4t^3/3]_1^2 = \tfrac{28}{3}. \quad \square$$

It is convenient to write $\int_A^B$ until the integration variable has been chosen, as in equation (11.2) on p. 259.

In general when the path is given by parametric equations

$$x = x(t), \qquad y = y(t), \qquad z = z(t),$$

equation (11.6) on p. 265 becomes

$$W = \int_\alpha^\beta \{F_1(t)x'(t) + F_2(t)y'(t) + F_3(t)z'(t)\}\,dt \tag{11.7}$$

where α and β are the parameters of the end-points A and B. Since the vector form of the parametric equation is

$$r = x(t)i + y(t)j + z(t)k,$$

giving

$$dr/dt = x'(t)i + y'(t)j + z'(t)k,$$

the curly bracket in equation (11.7) is the scalar product $F \cdot dr/dt$. Thus $W = \int_\alpha^\beta F(t) \cdot r'(t)\,dt$ is a vector form of (11.7). The result can also be written

$$W = \int_A^B F \cdot dr \tag{11.8}$$

This is equation (11.7) if expressed in terms of the parameter, and is equation (11.6) if expressed in terms of x, y, and z, because $dr = dx\,i + dy\,j + dz\,k$. The vectors $r(t)$ and $F(t)$ are shown in Fig. 11.6; dr and dr/dt are tangent to the curve.

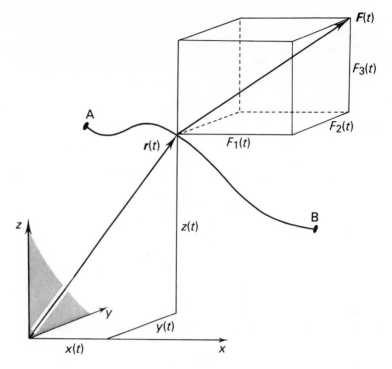

Figure 11.6   Components of vectors **r** and **F** at general point of path from A($t=\alpha$) to B($t=\beta$)

Example 11.31
Find the work done by the force

$$F(x, y, z) = (x^2 - z^2)i - j - xyk$$

in motion from A(1, 1, 0) to B(0, 0, 1) along the curve

$$r = (\cos t)i + (\cos t)j + (\sin t)k.$$

This is Example 11.21 again, with the path equation given in parametric form.

$$W = \int_A^B F \cdot dr = \int_A^B \{(x^2 - z^2)\, dx - dy - xy\, dz\} \tag{11.9}$$

Note that the given **F** is not used again once this is written down, and that this first step is the same however the path equation is given. The curve equations $x = \cos t = y$, $z = \sin t$, and the consequent relations

$$dx = -\sin t\, dt = dy, \qquad dz = \cos t\, dt$$

between differentials, express W in terms of t.
   The parameters α and β of A(1, 1, 0) and B(0, 0, 1) satisfy

$$\cos \alpha = 1, \qquad \sin \alpha = 0 \quad \text{and} \quad \cos \beta = 0, \qquad \sin \beta = 1,$$

so $\alpha = 0$ and $\beta = \frac{1}{2}\pi$. Thus equation (11.9) becomes

$$W = \int_0^{\pi/2} (-\cos^2 t \sin t + \sin^3 t + \sin t - \cos^3 t) \, dt$$

$$= \int_1^0 x^2 \, dx + \int_0^{\pi/2} \sin^3 t \, dt + [-\cos t]_0^{\pi/2} - \int_0^{\pi/2} \cos^3 t \, dt$$

$$= -\frac{1}{3} + \frac{2}{3} + 1 - \frac{2}{3}, \text{ using the result of Example 10.55 on p. 243.}$$

Again this alternative choice of integration variable checks Example 11.21. □

Example 11.22 (again)
Parametric equations of the line joining A(1, 1, 1) and B(2, 3, 4) were obtained in Example 2.30 (p. 27), for instance

$$r = i + j + k + u(-2i - 4j - 6k)$$

or

$$x = 1 - 2u, \qquad y = 1 - 4u, \qquad z = 1 - 6u.$$

The points A and B have parameters $u = 0$ and $u = -\frac{1}{2}$. Hence

$$W = \int_0^{-1/2} \{(3 - 8u)(-2 \, du) + (1 - 6u)(-4 \, du) - (1 - 2u)(-6 \, du)\}$$

$$= \int_0^{-1/2} (-4 + 28u) \, du = [-4u + 14u^2]_0^{-1/2} = \frac{11}{2},$$

checking the previous calculation. □

When the path is given by parametric equations, it is sufficient to know the vector field as a function of the parameter.

Example 11.32
Evaluate $\int_A^B F \cdot dr$ along the curve

$$r = (\cos \pi t)i + t^3 j - (3 \sin \pi t)k$$

from the point A where $t = -1$ to the point B where $t = 1$, with

$$F = (3 \sin \pi t)i + 2tj + (\cos \pi t)k.$$

Since $dr = \{(-\pi \sin \pi t)i + 3t^2 j - (3\pi \cos \pi t)k\} \, dt$,

$$\int_A^B F \cdot dr = \int_{-1}^1 (-3\pi + 6t^3) \, dt = -6\pi. □$$

Integrals of the type $\int F \cdot dr$ are called **line integrals**. An alternative notation writes $\int_C F \cdot dr$ where C stands for the arc along which the line integral is taken. For instance, Example 11.30 on p. 266 could be phrased: evaluate $\int_C F \cdot dr$ where C is the parabola $y^2 = 4x$ from (1, 2) to (4, 4).

Changes of variable are restricted to those in which the old and new variables are related by a one-to-one function (see p. 226 or Appendix E). Integration variables should be either increasing or decreasing along the path.

Example 11.33

Evaluate $\int_A^B (yi) \cdot d\mathbf{r}$ along the space curve $y + 2z = 5$, $z^2 + y - x = 4$ from $A(1, 1, 2)$ to $B(1, 5, 0)$.

In Cartesian coordinates the integral is $\int_A^B y \, dx$.

(i) Using x as the integration variable gives $\int_{x=1}^1 y \, dx$, which is apparently zero (for any y) because the integration end-points are the same.

(ii) Using z as the integration variable gives

$$ y = 5 - 2z, \qquad x = z^2 + 5 - 2z - 4, \qquad dx = (2z - 2) \, dz, $$

$$ \int_A^B y \, dx = \int_2^0 (5 - 2z)(2z - 2) \, dz = \tfrac{8}{3}. $$

It is the first calculation which is incorrect. The points $(\tfrac{1}{4}, 2, \tfrac{3}{2})$, $(0, 3, 1)$ and $(\tfrac{1}{4}, 4, \tfrac{1}{2})$ between A and B on the curve show that as y increases from 1 to 5, x decreases from 1 to 0 and then increases from 0 to 1. (The curve is a parabola in the plane $y + 2z = 5$.) Hence the relation between x and y is not one-to-one, and the substitution implicit in calculation (i) is invalid.   □

In this section $\int_C \mathbf{F} \cdot d\mathbf{r}$ has been defined as a sum of three definite integrals corresponding to the Cartesian components of $\mathbf{F}$. This decomposition is not essential to the definition of a line integral. An alternative approach is given in Section 11.4.

The method of evaluating a line integral is summarized in Procedure B5 in Appendix B.

Exercises   (answers on p. 287)

11.3.1   Express the line integral in Example 11.20 as an integral over y.

11.3.2   Find the work done by the force $\mathbf{F}(x, y) = (x - y)\mathbf{i} + xy\mathbf{j}$ in plane motion from $(0, 0)$ to $(1, 4)$ along the curve $\mathbf{r} = t\mathbf{i} + (3t^2 + t)\mathbf{j}$.

11.3.3   Suppose $\mathbf{A} = x\mathbf{i} + y^2\mathbf{j} - xz\mathbf{k}$ and $W = \int_C \mathbf{A} \cdot d\mathbf{r}$ where C is the straight line from $P(0, 0, 0)$ to $Q(1, 2, 3)$. Find the Cartesian equations of PQ. Evaluate W as an integral over x, and check the result using an integral over y.

11.4   Alternative Derivation of the Work Formula

In Section 11.1 the result of Example 9.22 on the length of a plane curve was extended to a space curve. The essential step was to obtain (see p. 261) the expression (11.4) for the differential ds of the length function, by a suitable generalization of the plane result (11.3). This method can also be applied to the result for the work done by a force, to generalize from motion along the x-axis to motion along a space curve. The required work function can be obtained by integrating a suitable differential dW. The differential for motion along a space curve will be obtained as a plausible generalization of the differential for linear motion.

The equation of the space curve will be assumed known in parametric form. Cartesian equations can always be converted to parametric form (at least in principle) by using one of the Cartesian coordinates as parameter; or the length along the curve from some fixed point is always a possible parameter.

In motion along the x-axis from a fixed point A with coordinate a, suppose $W(x)$ is the work done by a force F when the point with coordinate x has been reached. Then Example 9.20 on p. 199 gives $W(x) = \int_a^x F(u)\,du$, and the fundamental theorem gives

$$dW = W'(x)\,dx = F(x)\,dx. \tag{11.10}$$

For motion along a space curve given by parametric equations with parameter t, suppose $W(t)$ is the work done by a force when the point P with parameter t has been reached, from some fixed point with parameter $t = a$. Then

$$W(t) = \int_a^t dW \tag{11.11}$$

where dW is the generalization of $F(x)\,dx$ in equation (11.10). If $F(t)$ is the value of the force at P, only its component F_T in the direction of motion does work. Thus in equation (11.10) $F(x)$ is replaced by $F_T(t)$, the component of $F(t)$ in the direction of the tangent to the path curve. Also in (11.10) dx is the differential of length in the direction of motion, and is therefore replaced by ds, the differential of length along the curve. So the dW in equation (11.11) is $F_T(t)\,ds$.

To convert equation (11.11) to the previous result, note that $d\mathbf{r}$ is a tangent vector (cf. Section 6.4) and so (cf. Section 1.3)

$$F_T = \mathbf{F} \cdot d\mathbf{r}/|d\mathbf{r}| = \mathbf{F} \cdot d\mathbf{r}/ds, \qquad dW = \mathbf{F} \cdot d\mathbf{r}.$$

The final form of (11.11) is therefore

$$W(t) = \int_a^t \mathbf{F} \cdot d\mathbf{r}$$

as before.

This integral can be evaluated for any vector $\mathbf{F}$, and so may not necessarily represent work. Similarly in $\int F_T\,ds$, the force component F_T along the tangent to the curve gives just one example of a line integral. More generally one can write down (and evaluate) $\int f(x, y, z)\,ds$ for any scalar field f. The definition is given in equation (11.14).

11.5 Integrals of Functions of Two Variables

The Riemann integral for a function $f(x)$ of one variable was defined in Section 9.1. A given interval $[a, b]$ in the domain of f is divided into subintervals.

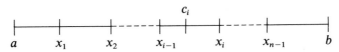

For each subinterval a value $f(c_i)$ is multiplied by the subinterval length $\delta = (b - a)/n = (x_i - x_{i-1})$. Then the integral is the limit of the sum $\sum_i \delta f(c_i)$, as the number of subintervals increases ($n \to \infty$) and the size of each subinterval tends to zero:

$$\int_a^b f(x)\,dx = \operatorname*{Lim}_{\delta \to 0} \delta \sum_i f(c_i) \tag{9.1}$$

This definition will now be extended to a function $g(x, y)$ of two variables. Suppose R is a given region in the domain of g. Divide R into subregions as in Fig. 11.7(i). In each subregion take a value $g(c_i, c_j)$ and multiply by the area of the subregion. Sum over all the subregions, and take the limit as the number of subregions increases and the size of every subregion tends to zero. As with equation (9.1), different choices for the point (c_i, c_j) in the subregion give the same value for the limit, if it exists. The shape of the subregions is also arbitrary provided all tend to zero size. The formulas presented below will therefore assume subdivision by a rectangular grid, as in Fig. 11.7(i).

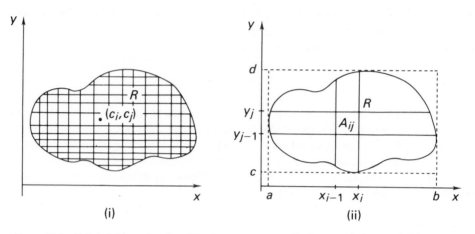

Figure 11.7 (i) Subdivision of region R by lines $x = x_i$, $y = y_j$ $(i = 1, \ldots, n; j = 1, \ldots, m)$. (ii) Area of rectangular subregion

Suppose a and b give the least and greatest values of x in R; and c and d give the extremum values of y (Fig. 11.7(ii)). Then a rectangular grid may be obtained by subdividing (a, b) into n equal subintervals of length $\delta = (b - a)/n$, and subdividing (c, d) into m equal subintervals of length $\varepsilon = (d - c)/m$. Each subregion then has area (Fig. 11.7(ii))

$$A_{ij} = (x_i - x_{i-1})(y_j - y_{j-1}) = \frac{(b - a)}{n} \frac{(d - c)}{m} = \delta\varepsilon \tag{11.12}$$

and the definition corresponding to equation (9.1) above can be written

$$\iint_R g(x, y)\, \mathrm{d}A = \operatorname*{Lim}_{\delta \to 0} \operatorname*{Lim}_{\varepsilon \to 0} \delta\varepsilon \sum_i \sum_j g(c_i, c_j) \tag{11.13}$$

A double sum (over i and j) is necessary, and the limiting process involves a double limit. Correspondingly, as will be shown in subsequent sections, evaluation using anti-derivatives requires two operations, and so two integration symbols $\int$ have been written on the left side of equation (11.13). (The defined integral is often called a **double integral**.) Summation limits on i and j in equation (11.13) must be chosen so that only subregions of R are included (not $i = 1, \ldots, n$ *and* $j = 1, \ldots, m$, which would give subdivisions of the whole rectangle enclosed by the dashed lines in Fig. 11.7(ii)). Subregions on the boundary of R are not actually rectangles, so equation (11.12) is incorrect for their area. However, this does not affect the values of the limit, because the total area of such boundary subregions tends to zero as the limit is taken.

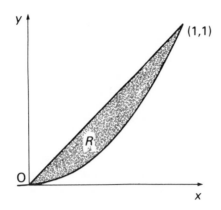

Figure 11.8   Region R enclosed by $y = x$ and $y = x^2$

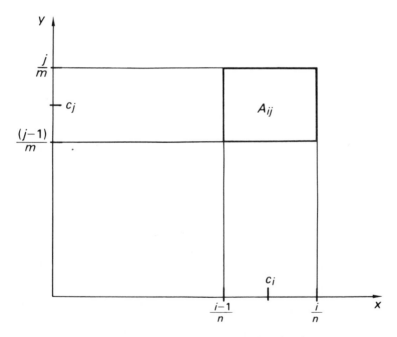

Figure 11.9 (c_i, c_j) centre of rectangular subregion

Example 11.50
Take $g(x, y) = 3x^2 + 2y$, and the region R enclosed by the line $y = x$ and the parabola $y = x^2$ (Fig. 11.8). Then $\delta = 1/n$ and $\varepsilon = 1/m$. Choosing the points (c_i, c_j) at the centre of each rectangle means that $c_i = (i - \tfrac{1}{2})/n$, $c_j = (j - \tfrac{1}{2})/m$ (Fig. 11.9). Computations show

a slow convergence, as in the following table:

		Number of points	
$m = 1/\varepsilon$	$n = 1/\delta$	(c_i, c_j)	$\delta\varepsilon \sum\sum g(c_i, c_j)$
50	50	412	0.2773
100	100	1 663	0.2807
200	200	6 662	0.2822
400	200	13 416	0.2851
200	400	13 333	0.2827
300	300	14 986	0.2825
400	400	26 662	0.28283
500	500	41 652	0.28288

The number of evaluations of g, given in the third column, is much larger than in comparable calculations with a function of one variable (cf. Example 9.12 on p. 198). The double sum is $\sum_{i=1}^{n} \sum_{j=k+1}^{l}$, where k is the integer part of mc_i^2 and l is the integer part of mc_i. $\square$

In Chapter 9 $\int_a^b f(x)\,dx$ was interpreted as the area bounded by the curve $y = f(x)$, the x-axis, and the lines $x = a$, $x = b$. Each term in the sum $\sum \delta f(c_i)$ is the area of a rectangle of height $f(c_i)$ and width δ.

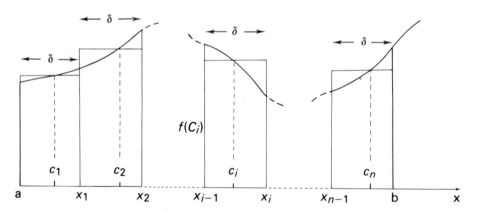

Figure 11.10   Area under $y = f(x)$ between $x = a$ and $x = b$

The extension of this interpretation to $\iint g(x, y)\,dA$ in equation (11.13) involves the surface which is represented by $z = g(x, y)$. Each term in the double sum $\sum\sum \delta\varepsilon g(c_i, c_j)$ is the volume of a rectangular column of height $g(c_i, c_j)$ and widths δ and ε in the x- and y-directions (Fig. 11.11(a)). The double sum adds the volumes of similar rectangular columns covering the region R. Suppose vertical lines (parallel to the z-axis) are drawn at all points of the boundary of R. These lines intersect the surface in a curve bounding a region R_g on the surface (Fig. 11.11(b)).

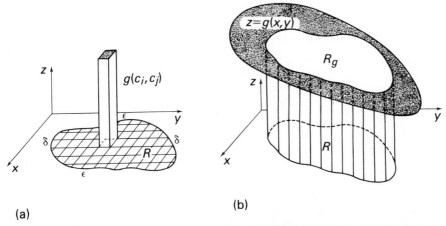

Figure 11.11 (a) Column with rectangular cross-section $\delta\varepsilon$. (b) Cylindrical volume on base R

Then the limit in equation (11.13) gives the volume of the cylindrical object enclosed by R (flat base), R_g (top), and the vertical lines.

As with the area interpretation of $\int_a^b f(x)\,\mathrm{d}x$, the volume interpretation of $\int\int g(x, y)\,\mathrm{d}A$ requires volumes below the $z = 0$ plane to be assigned negative values, since then $g(c_i, c_j) < 0$.

Example 11.51
If $g(x, y) = 1 + (1 - x^2 - y^2)^{1/2}$, then $z = g(x, y)$ represents the curved surface of the hemisphere which is the upper half of the sphere $x^2 + y^2 + (z - 1)^2 = 1$ (Fig. 11.12). If the region R is the disc $x^2 + y^2 \leqslant 1$, then R_g is the whole hemisphere, and $\int\int_R g(x, y)\,\mathrm{d}A$ is the volume of a cylinder with hemispherical cap (Fig. 11.12), i.e. $(\pi + \frac{2}{3}\pi)$. □

If $g(x, y) = 1$, the value of $\int\int_R g(x, y)\,\mathrm{d}A$ is just the area of the region R, since the volume is a lamina of unit thickness.

Example 11.52
The computations in Example 11.50 also display a sequence with limit the area of the region R in Fig. 11.8. If $g(x, y) = 1$, the double sum $\sum\sum g(c_i, c_j)$ is just the number of points (c_i, c_j). Multiplying by the corresponding values of $\delta\varepsilon = 1/mn$ gives the sequence ($m = n$ is evidently sufficient)

$$\frac{412}{2500} = 0.1648, \qquad \frac{1662}{10\,000} = 0.1662, \qquad \frac{6662}{40\,000} = 0.16655,\ 0.16651,\ 0.16663,\ 0.1661,\ldots$$

The value of the limit is $\int_0^1 x\,\mathrm{d}x - \int_0^1 x^2\,\mathrm{d}x = \frac{1}{6}$. □

The above method of defining the integral over a region R of a function defined on R can be used in a variety of other situations. For example suppose C is a plane curve with end-points A and B, and that C is contained in the domain of g. The C can be subdivided by points $A = P_0,\ P_1, \ldots, P_{n-1},\ P_n = B$, and in each subdivision a value $g(C_i)$ chosen at a point C_i of the curve (Fig. 11.13).

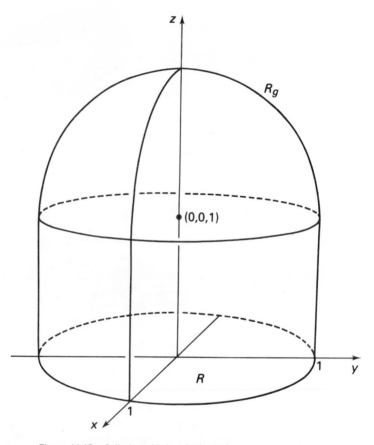

Figure 11.12   Cylinder with hemispherical cap

The line integral of g along C is defined as

$$\int_C g \, ds = \lim_{n \to \infty} \sum_{i=1}^{n} g(C_i)(P_{i-1}P_i) \qquad \textbf{(11.14)}$$

where $P_{i-1}P_i$ is the length of the curve segment,

and all these segment lengths tend to zero as the limit is taken. This definition is unchanged when g is a function of three variables and C is a space curve. If g is the component along the curve of a vector field, the integral obtained is just the line integral considered in the previous sections.

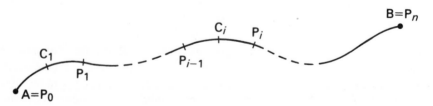

Figure 11.13   Subdivision of curve AB

Similarly,

the integral over a surface S of a function g defined on S is defined as

$$\iint_S g \, \mathrm{d}S = \mathrm{Lim} \sum g(C_{ij})(\delta S_{ij})$$

where the sum is obtained by subdividing the surface S into elements, C_{ij} is a point on the surface in the element with area δS_{ij}, and the area of all elements tends to zero as the limit is taken.

Exercises (answers on p. 288)

11.5.1 Formulate a definition for the integral over a volume V of a function $g(x, y, z)$.

11.5.2 Consider the tetrahedron with corners at $A(-1, 0, 0)$, $B(1, 1, 1)$, $C(0, 1, 0)$ and $D(\frac{1}{2}, \frac{1}{2}, 1)$.

   (i) Find the equations of the planes ABD and ACD, and write them in the form
$$z = g_i(x, y) \; (i = 1, 2).$$

   (ii) Show in a diagram the regions R, S of the $x - y$ plane such that (volume of tetrahedron) $= \iint_R g_1(x, y) \, \mathrm{d}A + \iint_S g_2(x, y) \, \mathrm{d}A$.

11.6 Specification of Regions

The integral of a function $g(x, y)$ over a region R in the $x - y$ plane was defined in the previous section. In general

the boundary of R may be specified in two alternative ways.

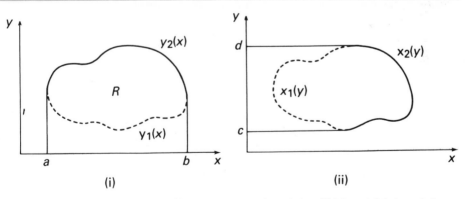

Figure 11.14   Specification of region by (i) lower and upper boundaries, (ii) left and right boundaries

In Fig. 11.14(i), the least and greatest values of x in R are denoted by a and b, and the equations $y = y_1(x)$ and $y = y_2(x)$ represent the curves giving lower and upper sections of the boundary. In Fig. 11.14(ii), c and d denote the least and greatest values of y for the same region R, and $x = x_1(y)$, $x = x_2(y)$ represent the curves giving the left and right sections of the boundary.

Example 11.60

Suppose R is the upper half of the disc $x^2 + y^2 \leqslant 1$. Then its boundary can be specified either by (Fig. 11.15(a))

$$a = -1 < x < 1 = b, \quad y_1(x) = 0 < y < \sqrt{(1-x^2)} = y_2(x),$$

or by (Fig. 11.15(b))

$$c = 0 < y < 1 = d, \quad x_1(y) = -\sqrt{(1-y^2)} < x < \sqrt{(1-y^2)} = x_2(y).$$

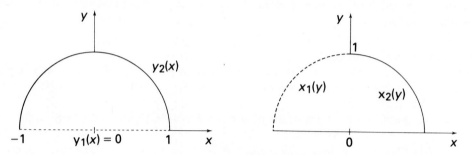

Figure 11.15   Alternative specifications of semi-circle: (a) upper boundary $y = (1-x^2)^{1/2}$ (b) left, right boundaries $x = \pm (1-y^2)^{1/2}$

One notation for these results is to write for R

$$\text{either} \quad \{(x, y): -1 < x < 1, \quad 0 < y < \sqrt{(1-x^2)}\}$$

$$\text{or} \quad \{(x, y): \ 0 < y < 1, -\sqrt{(1-y^2)} < x < \sqrt{(1-y^2)}\}. \quad \square$$

Since the definition of $\iint g(x, y) \, dA$ is independent of whether or not R includes its boundary, the specification need not include the boundary.

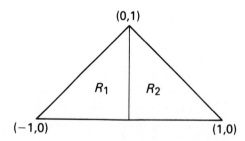

Figure 11.16   Upper boundaries of R_1 and R_2 are $y = 1 \pm x$ respectively

Example 11.61

Suppose R is the triangle with corners $(-1, 0)$, $(1, 0)$ and $(0, 1)$. Then the extreme values of x are $a = -1$ and $b = 1$ and the lower boundary is $y = y_1(x) = 0$. Because the upper boundary consists of two lines with different equations, it is necessary to consider the region R in two parts, R_1 and R_2, where (Fig. 11.16)

$$R_1 \text{ is } \{(x, y): -1 < x < 0, 0 < y < 1 + x\}$$

and

$$R_2 \text{ is } \{(x, y): \quad 0 < x < 1, 0 < y < 1 - x\}.$$

The alternative specification

$$c = 0 < y < 1 = d, \ x_1(y) = y - 1 < x < 1 - y = x_2(y)$$

does not need consideration of two parts separately. $\square$

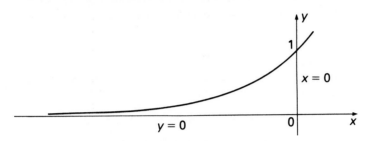

Figure 11.17   Upper (or left) boundary is $y = e^x$ (or $x = \ln y$)

Example 11.62
($a \to -\infty$; see Fig. 11.17)

$$\{(x, y): x < 0 = b, \ y_1(x) = 0 < y < e^x = y_2(x)\},$$
$$\{(x, y): 0 < y < 1, \ x_1(y) = \ln y < x < 0 = x_2(y)\}. \quad \square$$

Example 11.63
Suppose R is the triangle with corners $(-2, -1)$, $(-1, 2)$ and $(1, 1)$. Its sides are the lines $y - 3x = 5$, $2y + x = 3$, and $3y - 2x = 1$ (Fig. 11.18(a)). Then R can be specified by dividing it into two regions R_1 and R_2 by the line $x = -1$ (Fig. 11.18(b)), where

$$R_1 = \{(x, y): -2 < x < -1, \tfrac{1}{3}(2x + 1) < y < 3x + 5\},$$
$$R_2 = \{(x, y): -1 < x < 1, \tfrac{1}{3}(2x + 1) < y < \tfrac{1}{2}(-x + 3)\}.$$

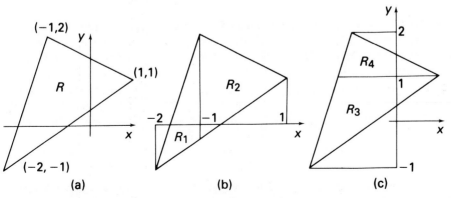

Figure 11.18   Boundaries: (b) lower $y = (2x + 1)/3$; upper $y = 3x + 5 (R_1)$, $y = \tfrac{1}{2}(-x + 3)(R_2)$; (c) left $x = (y - 5)/3$; right $x = \tfrac{1}{2}(3y - 1)(R_3)$, $x = -2y + 3 (R_4)$

Alternatively R can be divided into regions R_3 and R_4 by the line $y = 1$ (Fig. 11.18(c)). Then

$$R_3 = \{(x, y): -1 < y < 1, \tfrac{1}{3}(y-5) < x < \tfrac{1}{2}(3y-1)\},$$
$$R_4 = \{(x, y): \quad 1 < y < 2, \tfrac{1}{3}(y-5) < x < -2y+3\}. \quad \square$$

Some regions may be more simply specified using coordinates other than Cartesian. For instance, in polar coordinates $(r = \sqrt{(x^2+y^2)}, \theta = \tan^{-1}(y/x))$ the region in Fig. 11.15 is $\{(r, \theta): 0 < r < 1, 0 < \theta < \pi\}$. In such cases the evaluation of a double integral *may* be simplified by changing to the new coordinates, but these transformations will not be treated here.

Exercises (answers on p. 288)

11.6.1 Draw diagrams showing each of the following regions. In each case find a, b, $y_1(x)$ and $y_2(x)$ so that the region is

$$\{(x, y): a < x < b, y_1(x) < y < y_2(x)\} \tag{11.15}$$

and also c, d, $x_1(y)$ and $x_2(y)$ so that the region is

$$\{(x, y): c < y < d, x_1(y) < x < x_2(y)\} \tag{11.16}$$

   (a) the smaller segment of a disc of unit radius, centre $(0, 0)$, cut off by the chord joining $(-1, 0)$ and $(0, 1)$;
   (b) the triangle with corners $(0, 0)$, $(2, 0)$ and $(0, 3)$;
   (c) the rectangle with corners at $(2, \pm 1)$ and $(-2, \pm 1)$;
   (d) the region enclosed by the axes and the parabola $y = -(x-1)^2$.

11.6.2 Repeat Exercise 11.6.1 for the following regions, splitting them into suitable parts when necessary:
   (a) the triangle with corners at $(0, -2)$, $(0, 1)$ and $(1, 0)$;
   (b) the region enclosed by the parabola $y = 2 - x^2$ and the chord joining $(-3, -7)$ and $(1, 1)$.

11.7 Evaluation of Double Integrals

First consider a region R specified by

$$\{(x, y): c < y < d; x_1(y) < x < x_2(y)\}. \tag{11.16}$$

Divide the interval $c < y < d$ into m equal parts, and so divide R into strips, parallel to the x-axis, of width $(d-c)/m$. The jth strip goes from $x = a_j$ to $x = b_j$, where $a_j = x_1(y_j)$ and $b_j = x_2(y_j)$ (Fig. 11.19). The subdivision of R can then be completed by dividing each strip into n parts (cf. Fig. 11.7 on p. 272).

Along the jth strip, the n points (c_i, c_j) at which $g(c_i, c_j)$ is evaluated can all be chosen with $c_j = y_j$. Then the values $g(c_i, c_j) = g(c_i, y_j)$ are values of a function $h(x) = g(x, y_j)$ of x only. Hence summing over the n parts of the strip, and letting $n \to \infty$, just gives

$$\int_{a_j}^{b_j} h(x)\, dx \tag{11.17}$$

Since $h(x) = g(x, y_j)$, $a_j = x_1(y_j)$ and $b_j = x_2(y_j)$, the value of (11.17) depends only on y_j, and can be written $f(y_j)$. Then when the double sum is completed by summing over m and letting $m \to \infty$, the result is $\int_c^d f(y)\, dy$.

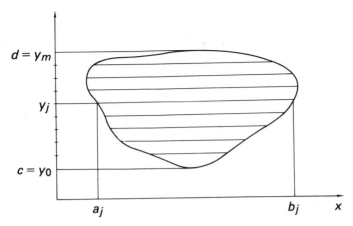

Figure 11.19   Subdivision of $c < y < d$ gives strips in x-direction

This argument shows how to evaluate $\iint_R g(x, y)\, dA$ by dividing R into strips parallel to the x-axis, first integrating along each strip (i.e. with respect to x) and then integrating over the strips (i.e. with respect to y). In summary,

this procedure for evaluating $\iint_R g(x, y)\, dA$ is:
(i) Evaluate $f(y) = \int_{x_1(y)}^{x_2(y)} g(x, y)\, dx$, regarding y as a constant;

(ii)
$$\iint_R g(x, y)\, dA = \int_c^d f(y)\, dy.$$

The integration limits $x_1(y)$, $x_2(y)$, c and d are obtained (in practice, using a sketch) from the specification of the boundary of R as in (11.16) and/or Fig. 11.14(ii).

Since $\iint_R g(x, y)\, dA$ is thus evaluated in the form $\int \left(\int g(x, y)\, dx \right) dy$, it is usual to write dA as $dx\, dy$.

Example 11.70
Evaluate $\iint_R (3x^2 - y^2)\, dx\, dy$, where R is the interior of the triangle with corners at $(-1, 0)$, $(0, 1)$ and $(1, 0)$.

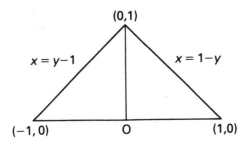

Figure 11.20   Left and right boundaries give ends of strips in x-direction

The functions $x = x_1(y) = y - 1$ and $x = x_2(y) = 1 - y$ give the boundary of R. So

$$\iint_R (3x^2 - y^2)\, dx\, dy = \int_{y=0}^{1} dy \int_{x=y-1}^{1-y} (3x^2 - y^2)\, dx = \int_0^1 dy [x^3 - y^2 x]_{x=y-1}^{x=1-y}$$

$$= \int_0^1 dy \, \{(1-y)^3 - y^2(1-y) - (y-1)^3 + y^2(y-1)\}$$

$$= \int_0^1 dy \, \{2 - 6y + 4y^2\} = \tfrac{1}{3}. \quad \square$$

Similarly a region specified by

$$\{(x, y): a < x < b;\ y_1(x) < y < y_2(x)\} \tag{11.15}$$

is divided into strips parallel to the y-axis. Then $g(x, y)$ is first integrated along each strip by integrating with respect to y, keeping x constant, using $y_1(x)$ and $y_2(x)$ as the integration limits (Fig. 11.21).

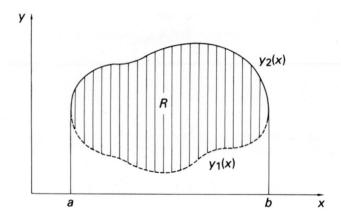

Figure 11.21   Subdivision of $a < x < b$ gives strips in y-direction

This gives a function of x, which is integrated from $x = a$ to $x = b$, i.e.

$$\iint_R g(x, y)\, dy\, dx = \int_a^b dx \int_{y=y_1(x)}^{y=y_2(x)} g(x, y)\, dy.$$

Example 11.71

Evaluate $\iint_R (2x^2 y + 4y^3)\, dA$, where R is the half-disc

$$\{(x, y): -1 < x < 1;\ 0 < y < \sqrt{(1 - x^2)}\}.$$

The above description of R was given in Example 11.60 and is shown in Fig. 11.22(a).

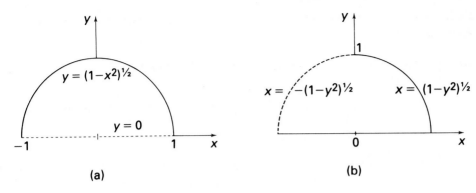

Figure 11.22   (a) Lower and upper boundaries give integration limits on y (b) Left and right boundaries give integration limits on x

Then

$$\iint_R (2x^2y+4y^3)\,dx\,dy = \int_{-1}^{1} dx \int_0^{y=\sqrt{(1-x^2)}} (2x^2y+4y^3)\,dy$$

$$= \int_{-1}^{1} [x^2y^2+y^4]_{y=0}^{y=\sqrt{(1-x^2)}}$$

$$= \int_{-1}^{1} dx\,(x^2-x^4+1-2x^2+x^4) = \tfrac{4}{3}. \quad \Box$$

Since in many examples it is possible to evaluate $\iint_R g(x, y)\,dA$ either as $\int_a^b dx \int_{y_1(x)}^{y_2(x)} g(x, y)\,dy$ or as $\int_c^d dy \int_{x_1(y)}^{x_2(y)} g(x, y)\,dx$, the alternative procedure can be used as a check.

Example 11.71   (Again)
From Fig. 11.22(b), the integral is also

$$\int_0^1 dy \int_{-\sqrt{(1-y^2)}}^{\sqrt{(1-y^2)}} dx(2x^2y+4y^3) = \int_0^1 \{\tfrac{4}{3}y(1-y^2)^{3/2}+8y^3(1-y^2)^{1/2}\}\,dy$$

Substituting $t=(1-y^2)^{1/2}$, $y^2=1-t^2$, $y\,dy=-t\,dt$ gives

$$\int_{t=0}^{t=1} \{\tfrac{4}{3}t^3+8(1-t^2)t\}t\,dt = \tfrac{4}{15}+\tfrac{8}{3}-\tfrac{8}{5}=\tfrac{20}{15}. \quad \Box$$

Example 11.72
Evaluate the (improper) integral $\iint_R xy^{-1/2}\,dA$, where R is the region enclosed by the curve $y=e^x$ and the axes.

The region R was shown in Fig. 11.17; the two specifications of the boundary were given in Example 11.62.

(i) $\displaystyle\int_{-\infty}^{0} dx \int_{0}^{e^x} xy^{-1/2}\, dy = \int_{-\infty}^{0} dx [2xy^{1/2}]_{y=0}^{y=e^x} = \int_{-\infty}^{0} 2x\, e^{x/2}$

$\displaystyle\qquad\qquad = [4x\, e^{x/2}]_{-\infty}^{0} - \int_{-\infty}^{0} 4e^{x/2}\, dx \quad \text{(integrating by parts)}$

$\displaystyle\qquad\qquad = 0 - [8e^{x/2}]_{-\infty}^{0} = -8.$

(ii) $\displaystyle\int_{0}^{1} dy \int_{\ln y}^{0} xy^{-1/2}\, dx = \int_{0}^{1} dy [\tfrac{1}{2}x^2 y^{-1/2}]_{x=\ln y}^{x=0} = -\int_{0}^{1} (\ln y)^2 \tfrac{1}{2} y^{-1/2}\, dy.$

Substituting $t = y^{1/2}$, $dt = \tfrac{1}{2} y^{-1/2}\, dy$, $\ln y = 2 \ln t$ gives

$\displaystyle -4\int_{0}^{1} (\ln t)^2\, dt = -4[(\ln t)(t \ln t - t)]_{0}^{1} + 4\int_{0}^{1} \frac{1}{t}(t \ln t - t)\, dt \quad \text{(integrating by parts)}$

$\displaystyle\qquad\qquad = 4[t \ln t - t - t]_{0}^{1} = -8. \quad \square$

The two previous examples indicate that one of the two methods of evaluating $\iint_{R} g(x, y)\, dA$ may be easier or more obvious than the other. In fact in some examples only one of the two methods allows an integration using known functions. Should the integral be given in the other form, then it is necessary to 'change the order of integration'. This involves changing the specification of R from (11.15) to (11.16), or vice-versa.

Example 11.73
Evaluate $\int_{y=-2}^{0} dy \int_{x=-y/2}^{x=1} e^{-x^2}\, dx.$

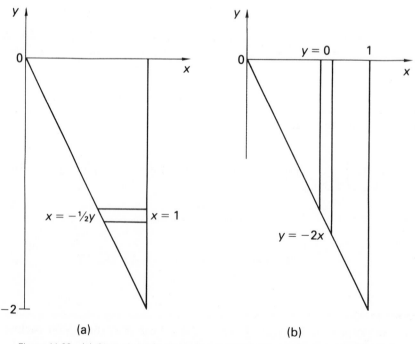

(a)   (b)

Figure 11.23   (a) Given order (x-integration first), (b) Other order (y-integration first)

Since $\int e^{-x^2} dx$ cannot be given in terms of elementary functions, the effect of changing the order is considered. After sketching the region of integration (Fig. 11.23), the alternative order of integration is seen to give

$$\int_{x=0}^{1} dx \int_{y=-2x}^{y=0} e^{-x^2} dy = \int_{0}^{1} dx[y \, e^{-x^2}]_{y=-2x}^{y=0} = \int_{0}^{1} 2x \, e^{-x^2} dx$$

$$= [-e^{-x^2}]_{0}^{1} = 1 - \frac{1}{e}. \quad \square$$

Changing the order of integration may require dividing the region into two parts.

Example 11.74
Evaluate $\int\int_R e^{x+y} \, dA$, where R is the interior of the triangle with corners at $(-1, 0)$, $(0, 1)$ and $(1, 0)$, and check the result by changing the order of integration.

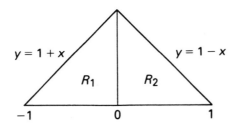

Figure 11.24   Alternative evaluation corresponds to vertical strips

The region R is shown in Fig. 11.24, and the alternative specifications of the region were given in Example 11.61. The simpler evaluation is

$$\int_{y=0}^{1} dy \int_{x=y-1}^{1-y} e^x \, e^y \, dx = \int_{0}^{1} e^y \, dy[e^x]_{y-1}^{1-y}$$

$$= \int_{0}^{1} (e - e^{2y-1}) \, dy = [ey - \tfrac{1}{2} e^{2y-1}]_{0}^{1}$$

$$= \tfrac{1}{2} e + \tfrac{1}{2} e^{-1} = \cosh 1.$$

The alternative evaluation requires (Fig. 11.24)

$$\int\int_{R_1} e^{x+y} \, dA = \int_{-1}^{0} e^x \, dx \int_{0}^{1+x} e^y \, dy = \int_{-1}^{0} e^x (e^{1+x} - 1) \, dx$$

$$= [\tfrac{1}{2} e^{2x+1} - e^x]_{-1}^{0} = \tfrac{1}{2} e - 1 + \tfrac{1}{2} e^{-1},$$

$$\int\int_{R_2} e^{x+y} \, dA = \int_{0}^{1} e^x \, dx \int_{0}^{1-x} e^y \, dy = \int_{0}^{1} e^x (e^{1-x} - 1) \, dx$$

$$= [ex - e^x]_{0}^{1} = 1. \quad \square$$

Example 11.75
Find the volume of an ellipsoid (Fig. 11.25).

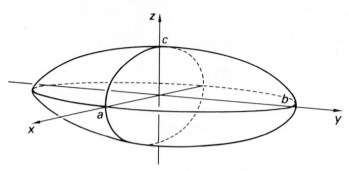

Figure 11.25   Ellipsoid with axes of length $2a$, $2b$, $2c$

The ellipsoid is the generalization to solid geometry of the ellipse. Its surface can be represented by the equation $(a > 0, b > 0, c > 0)$

$$\frac{x^2}{a^2} + \frac{y^2}{b^2} + \frac{z^2}{c^2} = 1$$ **(11.18)**

The symmetry with respect to the coordinate axes and planes means it is sufficient to calculate the volume in the positive quadrant, and then multiply by 8. The equation of the upper half of the surface is

$$z = g(x, y) = c\left(1 - \frac{x^2}{a^2} - \frac{y^2}{b^2}\right)^{1/2}.$$ (11.19)

Putting $z = 0$ in equation (11.18) shows that the surface cuts the $x - y$ plane in the ellipse $x^2/a^2 + y^2/b^2 = 1$. The required volume in the positive quadrant is obtained by integrating equation (11.19) over the region R enclosed by the ellipse and the positive Ox and Oy axes (Fig. 11.26), i.e.

$$\left\{(x, y): 0 < x < a; 0 < y < b\left(1 - \frac{x^2}{a^2}\right)^{1/2}\right\}.$$

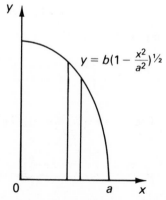

Figure 11.26   Integration region R: section of ellipsoid in $z=0$ plane

Thus the volume of the ellipsoid is

$$8c \int_0^a dx \int_0^{b\sqrt{(1-x^2/a^2)}} dy \left(1 - \frac{x^2}{a^2} - \frac{y^2}{b^2}\right)^{1/2}.$$

For the integration with respect to y, substitute (note x is constant)

$$\frac{y}{b} = \left(1 - \frac{x^2}{a^2}\right)^{1/2} \sin t, \qquad dy = b\left(1 - \frac{x^2}{a^2}\right)^{1/2} \cos t \, dt$$

giving

$$b\left(1 - \frac{x^2}{a^2}\right) \int_{t=0}^{\pi/2} (1 - \sin^2 t)^{1/2} \cos t \, dt = \tfrac{1}{4}\pi b\left(1 - \frac{x^2}{a^2}\right).$$

Then

$$\text{Volume} = 2\pi bc \int_0^a \left(1 - \frac{x^2}{a^2}\right) dx = 2\pi bc \left[x - \frac{x^3}{3a^2}\right]_0^a$$

$$\boxed{\text{Volume of ellipsoid (11.18)} = \tfrac{4}{3}\pi abc \quad \square}$$

Simple checks based on dimension may be used as for integrals of functions of one variable (cf. Example 10.10).

Example 11.76
Consider $\int_{y=-2a}^0 dy \int_{x=-y/2}^a \exp(-x^2/a^2) \, dx$. Assuming x and y are lengths, so are ds, dy and a. The dimension of sums and limit is $(\text{length})^2$, and so a^2 must be an overall factor in the correct result.
    Modifying Example 11.73 gives $a^2(1 - 1/e)$. $\square$

Exercises
11.7.1   Evaluate the integral considered in Example 11.50.
11.7.2   Check Example 11.70 by changing the order of integration (cf. Example 11.74).
11.7.3   Evaluate $\int\int xy^3 \, dA$ over each of the regions in Exercise 11.6.1, checking the results by reversing the order of integration.
11.7.4   Evaluate $\int\int xy \, dA$ over each of the regions in Exercise 11.6.2, checking the results by interchanging the order of integration.
11.7.5   Evaluate $\int\int_R y \cos x^5 \, dA$, where R is the region enclosed by the parabola $y = x^2$, the x-axis, and the line $y = 1$.
11.7.6   Evaluate $\int\int_R e^{y^2} \, dA$, where R is the interior of the triangle with corners at $(-1, 1)$, $(0, 0)$ and $(1, 1)$.

Answers to Exercises 11.1.1–11.7.6

11.1.1 $\sinh 2$ **11.1.2** $670/3$ **11.1.3** $\pi\sqrt{2}$
11.1.4   8 (see the last two paragraphs in Example 11.10 on p. 260). Alternatively a sketch of the curve shows that the required length is twice that found in Example 11.10.
11.2.1 $-\tfrac{7}{6}$ **11.2.2** $-\tfrac{11}{6}$ **11.2.3** $-\tfrac{5}{2}$ (Line is $-x = y = \tfrac{1}{2}z$)
11.3.1 $\int_2^4 \{(y + \tfrac{1}{2}y^2)(\tfrac{1}{2}y \, dy) - \tfrac{1}{4}y^3 \, dy\}$ **11.3.2** $311/60$

11.3.3   Line is $x = y/2 = z/3$.

$$W = \int_0^1 (x - x^2)\, dx = \tfrac{1}{8} \int_0^2 (2y - y^2)\, dy = \tfrac{1}{6}.$$

11.5.1   Suppose (a, b), (c, d) and (e, f) give the extremum values of x, y and z in the volume. Divide the volume into elements by subdividing (a, b) into n equal intervals, (c, d) into m equal intervals and (e, f) into k equal intervals. Then, as in equation (11.13)

$$\iiint_V g(x, y, z)\, dV = \operatorname*{Lim}_{n \to \infty} \operatorname*{Lim}_{m \to \infty} \operatorname*{Lim}_{k \to \infty} \frac{(b - a)(d - c)(f - e)}{nmk} \Sigma \Sigma \Sigma\, g(c_i, c_j, c_k)$$

with the triple sum over all elements in V, and the (c_i, c_j, c_k) selected points, one in each element.

11.5.2   (i) $g_1(x,y) = 2y,\ g_2(x,y) = x - y + 1$

(ii)

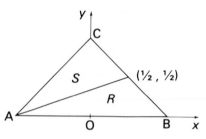

Figure 11.5.2

11.6.1

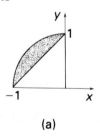
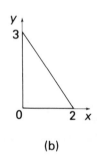
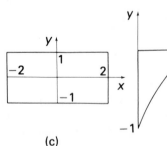

(a)   (b)   (c)   (d)

Figure 11.6.1

	a	b	$y_1(x)$	$y_2(x)$	c	d	$x_1(y)$	$x_2(y)$
(a)	-1	0	$x + 1$	$\sqrt{(1 - x^2)}$	0	1	$-\sqrt{(1 - y^2)}$	$y - 1$
(b)	0	2	0	$3 - (3x/2)$	0	3	0	$2 - (2y/3)$
(c)	-2	2	-1	1	-1	1	-2	2
(d)	0	1	$-(x - 1)^2$	0	-1	0	0	$1 - \sqrt{y}$

11.6.2

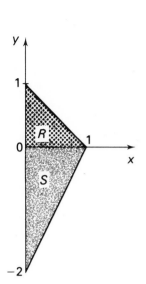

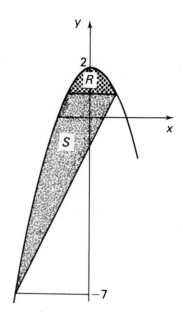

Figure 11.6.2

	a	b	$y_1(x)$	$y_2(x)$	c	d	$x_1(y)$	$x_2(y)$	
(a)	0	1	$2x-2$	$1-x$	-2	0	0	$1+\frac{1}{2}y$	(R_1)
					0	1	0	$1-y$	(R_2)
(b)	-3	1	$2x-1$	$2-x^2$	-7	1	$-\sqrt{(2-y)}$	$\frac{1}{2}(y+1)$	(R_1)
					1	2	$-\sqrt{(2-y)}$	$\sqrt{(2-y)}$	(R_2)

11.7.1 Limit of sequence in Example 11.50
11.7.3 Use above answer to 11.6.1   **11.7.4** Use above answer to 11.6.2
11.7.5 $\frac{1}{10}\sin 1 = 0.084147$ **11.7.6** $e-1$

Further Exercises on Chapter 11

11.1 Find the lengths of the following:
   (i) $r = b(i \ln t + \frac{1}{2}tj + \frac{1}{2}t^{-1}j)$, from $t=1$ to $t=e^2$ $(b>0)$
   (ii) $r = a(2\sqrt{3}t^6 i + 3t^4 j)$, from $t=0$ to $t=1$. $(a>0)$
   (iii) $r = a(\cos^3\theta\, i + \sin^3\theta\, j)$, from $(0, a)$ to $(a, 0)$ $(a>0)$
11.2 The average value of a function $f(x, y)$ along a plane curve C is defined to be $(1/l)\int_C f(x, y)\, ds$, where l is the length of C (cf. Example 9.21 on p. 200).
   Find the average value of the function $f(x, y) = y\, e^x$ along the curve in Exercise 11.1.1 (p. 262).
11.3 Evaluate $\int_C F \cdot dr$, where

$$F(x, y, z) = (1+\tfrac{1}{3}z)i + (1+\tfrac{1}{9}xz)^{-1/2}j + (\tfrac{1}{3}x)^{1/2}k$$

and C is the curve $r = 3t^2 i + t^3 j + 3tk$ from $(0, 0, 0)$ to $(3, 1, 3)$.

11.4   For $F(x, y) = (e^y + y^2 e^x)i + (x e^y + 2y e^x)j$, evaluate $\int_A^B F \cdot dr$ from A(1, 1) to B(3, 4)
   (i) along the straight line AB
   (ii) along the curve $2x^2 = 2y + 5x - 5$.

11.5   For $F(x, y, z) = (x^2 + xy)i + xyzj + (xz + 3)k$, evaluate $\int_A^B F \cdot dr$ from A(0, 1, 0) to
   B(1, 2, 3)
   (i) along the straight line AB
   (ii) along the curve $y = x + 1$, $z = y^2 - 1$.

11.6   If $F(x, y, z) = yi + zj + xk$, evaluate $\int_C F \cdot dr$, where C is the curve

$$r = t^2 i + (2t + 3)j + (1 - t)k \text{ from } (1, 1, 2) \text{ to } (1, 5, 0).$$

11.7   If $F(x, y, z) = f(x)i + g(y)j + h(z)k$, show that $\int_A^B F \cdot dr$ has the same value for any
   path from A to B.

11.8   (i) Find the length of the curve $x = \tfrac{1}{3}t^3$, $y = t^2$ from $(0, 0)$ to $(\tfrac{1}{3}t^3, t^2)$.
   (ii) Find the length of the parabola $y = x^2$ from $(1, 1)$ to $(4, 4)$.

11.9   Suppose the plane curve C has parametric equations

$$x = x(s), y = y(s)$$

   where the parameter s is the length along the curve measured from some fixed
   point Q. If C (with end-points A and B) is subdivided as in Fig. 11.27, suppose s_i
   are the parameters of the points P_i, and c_i are the parameters of the points C_i.
   Show that equation (11.14) is the Riemann integral $\int_a^b h(s) \, ds$, where a and b are
   the parameters of A and B, and $h(s) = g(x(s), y(s))$.

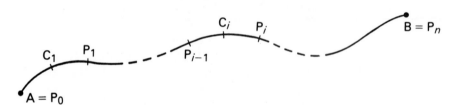

Figure 11.27 C_i is any point on the arc $P_{i-1}P_i$ $(i = 1, \ldots, n)$

11.10 Evaluate $\iint_R (x + y) \, dA$, where R is the interior of the triangle with corners at
   $(-2, -1)$, $(-1, 2)$ and $(1, 1)$ (see Fig. 11.18). Check the result by interchanging the
   order of integration.

11.11 Evaluate $\iint_R e^{y^2} \, dA$, where R is the interior of the triangle with corners at $(-1, 1)$,
   $(0, 0)$ and $(1, 1)$.

11.12 Consider $I = \int_0^b dy \int_{x=y-b}^{b-y} e^{a(x+y)} \, dx$. If x and y are lengths, what are the dimensions
   of a, b, and I? What can immediately be said about the form of I as a function
   of a and b? Deduce the function by inspection of Example 11.74.

11.13 Evaluate $\iint_R e^{y^2} \, dA$, where R is the interior of the quadrilateral with corners at
   $(1, 2)$, $(3, 6)$, $(4, 2)$ and $(12, 6)$.

11.14 Find the volume of the tetrahedron in Exercise 11.5.2
   (i) using (volume) $= \tfrac{1}{3}$(base area) $\times$ (height) with the regions R_1 and R_2 as base;
   (ii) by computing the $\iint_{R_i} g_i(x, y) \, dA$.

11.15 Write down the results for double integrals corresponding to equations (9.6), (9.7),
   (9.8) and (9.10) in Section 9.3.

11.16 Let $F(x, y, z) = yzi + zxj + xyk$. Evaluate $\int_A^B F \cdot dr$ along the curve

$$x = t + 1, \qquad y = t^2 + 1, \qquad z = 1/t,$$

from $A(2, 2, 1)$ to $B(3, 5, \frac{1}{2})$. Obtain a definite integral which gives the length of the curve.

11.17 If $F = yi + zj + xk$, evaluate $\int_A^B F \cdot dr$ along the curve

$$x = y + 1, \qquad z = 1 - x^2$$

from $A(1, 0, 0)$ to $B(2, 1, -3)$.

11.18 Let $A = (2x - 3y)i + 5xzj + (y^2 - 2z)k$. Evaluate $\int_P^Q A \cdot dr$ along the straight line from $P(0, 1, 0)$ to $Q(1, 2, 1)$.

11.19 Let $F(x, y) = (x - y)i + xyj$.
(i) Evaluate $\int_C F \cdot dr$, where the path of integration C is along the curve $x = 2t - 1$, $y = 3t^2$ from the point A with $t = 0$ to the point B with $t = 1$.
(ii) Evaluate $\int_A^B F \cdot dr$ along the straight line from A to B, the end-points of C in part (i).

11.20 Denote by C the portion of the curve

$$r = \tfrac{1}{4} t^4 i + \tfrac{2}{3} t^3 j + t^2 k$$

between the points $(\frac{1}{4}, \frac{2}{3}, 1)$ and $(4, \frac{16}{3}, 4)$. Show that
(a) the length of C is $27/4$;
(b) $\int_C ((1/z)i + j + xk) \cdot dr = 137/12$.

11.21 If R is the rectangle bounded by the lines $x = \pm \frac{1}{2}\pi$, $y = 0$ and $y = \frac{1}{2}\pi$, show that $\iint_R \sin(x + y) \, dx \, dy = 2$.

11.22 Find the volume of the prism bounded by the planes $y = 1$, $y = x$, $x = 1$, $z = 0$ and $z = 3 - x - y$.

11.23 Evaluate $\int_{y=0}^1 dy \int_{x=y}^1 (\sin x/x) \, dx$ by changing the order of integration.

11.24 Evaluate $\iint_R (x^2 + y^2) \, dx \, dy$ where R is the interior of the square with corners at $(0, 0)$, $(1, -1)$, $(2, 0)$ and $(1, 1)$.

12
Complex Algebra and Functions

12.1 De Moivre's Theorem

The product of two complex numbers of unit modulus also has unit modulus, and the argument of the product is the sum of the arguments of the factors:

$$(\cos \phi + i \sin \phi)(\cos \theta + i \sin \theta) = \{\cos(\phi + \theta) + i \sin(\phi + \theta)\} \qquad (12.1)$$

(see Section A.6 in Appendix A). Taking $\phi = \theta$ gives

$$(\cos \theta + i \sin \theta)^2 = \cos 2\theta + i \sin 2\theta. \qquad (12.2)$$

Put $z = \cos \theta + i \sin \theta$, so that (12.2) is z^2. Then $z^3 = z^2 z$ is given by equation (12.1) on taking $\phi = 2\theta$:

$$(\cos \theta + i \sin \theta)^3 = z^3 = \cos 3\theta + i \sin 3\theta. \qquad (12.3)$$

Similarly $z^4 = z^3 z$ is given by equation (12.1) with $\phi = 3\theta$, since equation (12.3) gives z^3:

$$(\cos \theta + i \sin \theta)^4 = z^4 = \cos 4\theta + i \sin 4\theta. \qquad (12.4)$$

Continuing, z^5 is obtained from $\phi = 4\theta$ in equation (12.1). Similarly $\phi = n\theta$ leads to a proof by induction of the result for an arbitrary integer n:

$$(\cos \theta + i \sin \theta)^n = \cos n\theta + i \sin n\theta. \qquad \textbf{(12.5)}$$

This is **de Moivre's theorem**.

Example 12.10

$$z = (1+i)/\sqrt{2} \text{ has modulus 1 and argument } \pi/4 \text{ (Fig. 12.1),}$$

$$\text{i.e.} \quad z = \cos(\pi/4) + i \sin(\pi/4).$$

Then $z^{30} = \cos(30\pi/4) + i \sin(30\pi/4)$

$$= \cos(8\pi - \tfrac{1}{2}\pi) + i \sin(8\pi - \tfrac{1}{2}\pi) = -i. \quad \square$$

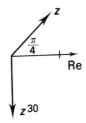

Figure 12.1 $\arg z = \pi/4$; $\arg(z^{30}) = 30\pi/4$

Figure 12.2   Powers of z when $|z|=1$

Equation (12.5) can also be obtained by considering the geometric interpretation in the complex plane (see Section A.6 of Appendix A). Since z has modulus 1 and argument θ, multiplication of a number by z rotates through θ the vector represented by the number. Thus, in the vector representation (see Fig. 12.2):

$z = z1$ is 1 rotated through θ, and so has argument θ;

$z^2 = zz$ is z rotated through θ, and so has argument 2θ;

$z^3 = zz^2$ is z^2 rotated through θ, and so has argument 3θ;
$$\vdots$$

$z^n = zz^{n-1}$ is z^{n-1} rotated through θ, and so has argument $n\theta$.

Since $|z| = 1$, there is no change in length. Thus z^n has modulus 1, and equation (12.5) just shows its polar form.

Defining z^0 to be 1 makes De Moivre's theorem (12.5) valid for $n = 0$. Also it is easy to check that it is true for $n = -1$:

$$\cos(-\theta) + i \sin(-\theta) = \cos\theta - i\sin\theta$$

and $(\cos\theta + i \sin\theta)(\cos\theta - i\sin\theta) = 1$, so $\cos(-\theta) + i\sin(-\theta)$ is $(\cos\theta + i\sin\theta)^{-1}$. Similarly the definition of z^{-n} as the reciprocal of z^n leads to a direct check of the validity of equation (12.5) when n is any negative integer.

Example 12.11

$$\frac{2^{24}}{(\sqrt{3}-i)^{24}} = \frac{1}{\{\frac{1}{2}(\sqrt{3}-i)\}^{24}} = \{\tfrac{1}{2}(\sqrt{3}-i)\}^{-24}$$

$$= \{\cos(-\pi/6) + i\sin(-\pi/6)\}^{-24} \text{ (see Fig. 12.3)}$$

$$= \cos 4\pi + i\sin 4\pi = 1. \quad \square$$

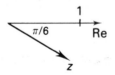

Figure 12.3 $z = \tfrac{1}{2}(\sqrt{3}-i)$; arg $z = -\pi/6$

Example 12.12

$$\cos 3\theta + i\sin 3\theta = (\cos\theta + i\sin\theta)^3$$

$$= \cos^3\theta + 3\cos^2\theta(i\sin\theta)$$

$$+ 3\cos\theta(i^2\sin^2\theta) + i^3\sin^3\theta.$$

Equating real parts:

$$\cos 3\theta = \cos^3\theta - 3\cos\theta\sin^2\theta$$

$$= 4\cos^3\theta - 3\cos\theta.$$

Equating imaginary parts:

$$\sin 3\theta = \sin\theta(3\cos^2\theta - \sin^2\theta)$$

$$= \sin\theta(4\cos^2\theta - 1). \quad \square$$

In general, by equating the real or imaginary parts of each side of equation (12.5), $\cos n\theta$ or $\sin n\theta$ is expressed in terms of $\cos\theta$ and $\sin\theta$. In the binomial expansion

$$(\cos\theta + i\sin\theta)^n = \sum_{k=0}^{n} \binom{n}{k} \cos^{n-k}\theta\, i^k \sin^k\theta,$$

even values of k give real terms and odd values of k give pure imaginary terms. Thus $\cos n\theta$ involves only even powers of $\sin\theta$, i.e. powers of $\sin^2\theta = 1 - \cos^2\theta$, showing that $\cos n\theta$ is a polynomial in $\cos\theta$. Similarly $\sin n\theta$ involves only odd powers of $\sin\theta$, and can be written in terms of $\cos\theta$ after taking out a factor $\sin\theta$.

Equation (12.5) says that to get the nth power of a complex number of modulus 1 it is only necessary to multiply the argument by n. Conversely, an nth root can be obtained by dividing the argument by n. Define $\sqrt[n]{z}$ or $z^{1/n}$ to be a number satisfying $(z^{1/n})^n = z$. Provided $|z| = 1$, so that $z = \cos\theta + i\sin\theta$ with $\theta = \arg z$, a value for $z^{1/n}$ is $\cos(\theta/n) + i\sin(\theta/n)$. Finally, defining $z^{m/n}$ as $(z^{1/n})^m$, equation (12.5) gives

$$\cos\left(\frac{m\theta}{n}\right) + i\sin\left(\frac{m\theta}{n}\right)$$

as one value of $z^{m/n}$, and

de Moivre's theorem

$$(\cos\theta + i\sin\theta)^b = \cos b\theta + i\sin b\theta \qquad (12.6)$$

is true for any (real) rational value of b.

Example 12.13
Find a cube root of i.

Since $i = \cos\frac{1}{2}\pi + i\sin\frac{1}{2}\pi$,

$$i^{1/3} = \sqrt[3]{i} = \cos(\pi/6) + i\sin(\pi/6) = \tfrac{1}{2}(\sqrt{3} + i).$$

Check:

$$\{\tfrac{1}{2}(\sqrt{3}+i)\}^3 = \tfrac{1}{8}(3\sqrt{3} + 9i + 3\sqrt{3}i^2 + i^3) = i, \quad \text{since } i^3 = -i. \quad \square$$

Example 12.14
Find a complex value of $(-1)^{2/3}$.

Since $-1 = \cos\pi + i\sin\pi$,

$$(-1)^{2/3} = \cos(2\pi/3) + i\sin(2\pi/3) = -\tfrac{1}{2} + \tfrac{1}{2}i\sqrt{3}. \quad \square$$

In Section 6.11 e^{it} was defined as $\cos t + i\sin t$.

De Moivre's theorem (12.6) can therefore be written

$$(e^{i\theta})^b = e^{ib\theta}. \qquad (12.7)$$

Exercises (answers on p. 308)

12.1.1   Evaluate z^{10}, z^{-8} and $z^{8/3}$ for $z = \sqrt{\tfrac{1}{2}}(1-i)$.

12.1.2   Use values of sin and cos to evaluate $\{\tfrac{1}{3}(2i+\sqrt{5})\}^7$.

12.1.3   Express $\cos 4\theta$ as a polynomial in $\cos \theta$.

12.1.4   Express $\sin 5t$ as a polynomial in $\sin t$.

12.1.5   Find a solution of the equation $z^6 + 1 = 0$. Verify that the complex conjugate of your solution is another solution.

12.2   Powers of Complex Numbers

For any complex number z with polar form $z = r(\cos\theta + i\sin\theta)$,

$$z^n = r^n(\cos\theta + i\sin\theta)^n = r^n(\cos n\theta + i\sin n\theta),$$

which is a polar form of z^n, so $\arg(z^n) = n\arg z$ is true for any non-zero complex number, and $|z^n| = r^n = |z|^n$.

Example 12.20

$$4 - 4i = 4\sqrt{2}\{\cos(-\pi/4) + i\sin(-\pi/4)\},$$

so

$$(4 - 4i)^4 = 1024\{\cos(-\pi) + i\sin(-\pi)\} = -1024.$$

The polar forms can also be written using the exponential function:

$$[4\sqrt{2}\exp(-i\pi/4)]^4 = 1024\exp(-i\pi). \quad \square$$

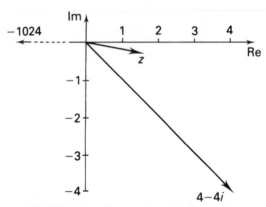

Figure 12.4 $z = \sqrt[5]{(4-4i)}$; $\arg z = -\pi/20$, $|z| = \sqrt{2}$

The nth power of a complex number is obtained by taking the nth power of the modulus, and multiplying the argument by n. Conversely, **an nth root can be obtained by dividing the argument by n, and taking the nth root of the modulus.**

Example 12.21

$$(4 - 4i)^{1/5} = [4\sqrt{2}\exp(-i\pi/4)]^{1/5} \quad \text{(see Fig. 12.4)}$$

$$= \sqrt{2}\exp(-i\pi/20)$$

$$= \sqrt{2}\{\cos(-\pi/20) + i\sin(-\pi/20)\}$$

$$= 1.4 - 0.22\,i. \quad \square$$

Taking the unique positive value of the nth root of the modulus ensures that $r^{1/n}\{\cos(\theta/n)+i\sin(\theta/n)\}$ is in polar form.

Various examples already given indicate that $z^{1/n}$ does not have a unique value. In the simplest case of square roots, there are always two values differing in sign, because $z^2=(-z)^2$. Example 12.13 obtained $\frac{1}{2}(\sqrt{3}+i)$ for $\sqrt[3]{i}$, but since $(-i)^3=i^2(-i)=i$, $-i$ is also a value for $\sqrt[3]{i}$. Example 12.14 obtained $-\frac{1}{2}+\frac{1}{2}i\sqrt{3}$ as a value for $(-1)^{2/3}$; but taking $\sqrt[3]{(-1)}=-1$ gives $(-1)^2=1$ as an alternative. Since $(-1)^4=i^4=(-i)^4=1$, there are always at least four values for $z^{1/4}$, since $z^{1/4}=(z1)^{1/4}=z^{1/4}1^{1/4}$, and there are four values ±1, $\pm i$ for $1^{1/4}$.

Example 12.22
From $\sqrt[4]{16}=2$, three alternative values $2i$, -2, and $-2i$ can be written down.   □

The problems that have to be considered are: how many distinct values are there of $z^{1/n}$, and how can they all be calculated?

Example 12.23
The computation of $\frac{1}{2}(\sqrt{3}+i)$ for $\sqrt[3]{i}$ in Example 12.13 was the reverse of the cubing operation (given in the check), which in polar form is $[\exp(i\pi/6)]^3=\exp(i\pi/2)=i$. In Fig. 12.5, the cubing is illustrated by a point rotating round the unit circle. Applying the same check to the alternative cube root $-i$ gives

$$(-i)^3=[\exp(-i\pi/2)]^3=\exp(-3i\pi/2)$$
$$=\cos(-3\pi/2)+i\sin(-3\pi/2)=i.$$

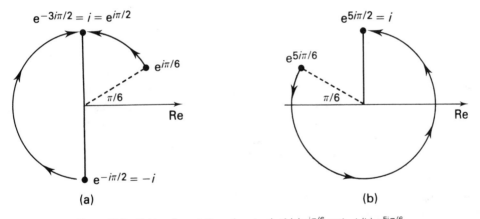

Figure 12.5 Cubing (by rotation of vectors) of (a) $e^{i\pi/6}$ and $-i$ (b) $e^{5i\pi/6}$

The reverse operation shows that $-i$ would be obtained for $\sqrt[3]{i}$ if the polar form of i used $-3\pi/2$ for arg i. This indicates that the multi-valued nature of the cube root results from the multi-valuedness of the argument. A third value for $\sqrt[3]{i}$ may be obtained by taking $\arg i=\frac{1}{2}\pi+2\pi=5\pi/2$:

$$\sqrt[3]{i}=[\exp(5i\pi/2)]^{1/3}=\exp(5i\pi/6)=\cos(5\pi/6)+i\sin(5\pi/6)=\tfrac{1}{2}(-\sqrt{3}+i).$$

The cubing check is illustrated in Fig. 12.5(b). However, no further distinct values are obtained. For instance:

$$[\exp(9i\pi/2)]^{1/3}=\exp(3i\pi/2)=\exp(-i\pi/2)=-i \quad \text{(again)}. \quad □$$

In fact three and only three distinct values for $\sqrt[3]{z}$ are obtained by taking different values of arg z. If 2π or 4π is added to arg z, then $2\pi/3$ or $4\pi/3$ is added to the argument of the resulting cube root, giving distinct values. However, if arg z is changed by 6π, the argument of $\sqrt[3]{z}$ changes by 2π, giving a value already obtained. The same thing happens if arg z is changed by any other multiple of 2π (-2π can replace 4π, as in Example 12.23).

Similarly, in calculating $\sqrt[n]{z}$, distinct values are obtained by changing arg z by multiples of 2π which are less than $2n\pi$.

> So there are n distinct values of $\sqrt[n]{z} = z^{1/n}$.

Example 12.22 (again)
Find the values of $16^{1/4}$.

$$|16| = 16, \quad \arg 16 = 0, 2\pi, 4\pi, 6\pi$$

$$|16^{1/4}| = 2, \quad \text{(taking the unique positive value of } \sqrt[4]{16})$$

$$\arg 16^{1/4} = 0, \tfrac{1}{2}\pi, \pi, 3\pi/2 \quad \text{(dividing by 4 the arguments of 16).}$$

The values are $2e^{i0} = 2$, $2e^{i\pi/2} = 2i$, $2e^{i\pi} = -2$, $2e^{3i\pi/2} = -2i$.

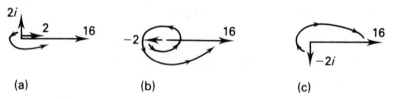

| (a) | (b) | (c) |

Figure 12.6   Fourth powers (by rotation) of (a) 2i (arg $2i = \tfrac{1}{2}\pi \to 2\pi$); (b) -2 (arg $-2 = \pi \to 4\pi$);
(c) $-2i$ (arg $-2i = -\tfrac{1}{2}\pi \to -2\pi$)

Here it is easy to check the four results by computing their 4th powers. In some examples it may be easier to use a geometrical check on the vectors represented by the solutions. Consider the 4th powers of the solutions by changing the length of the vectors by taking the 4th power ($2 \to 16$ here), and rotating each vector so as to multiply the argument by 4. Note that the argument of $-2i$ is taken as $-\tfrac{1}{2}\pi$ and so becomes -2π by clockwise rotation (Fig. 12.6).   □

Example 12.24
Calculate the 5th roots of $4 + 4i$.

$|4 + 4i| = \sqrt{32} = 2^{5/2}$, so the 5th roots have modulus $2^{1/2} = \sqrt{2}$.

$$\arg(4 + 4i) = \frac{\pi}{4}, \frac{9\pi}{4}, \frac{17\pi}{4}, \frac{-7\pi}{4}, \frac{-15\pi}{4}$$

$$\arg(4 + 4i)^{1/5} = \frac{\pi}{20}, \frac{9\pi}{20}, \frac{17\pi}{20}, \frac{-7\pi}{20}, \frac{-15\pi}{20}.$$

The 5 values are (Fig. 12.7) $\sqrt{2}\exp(i\pi/20) = \sqrt{2}(\cos 9° + i\sin 9°)$, $\sqrt{2}\exp(i9\pi/20)$, $\sqrt{2}\exp(17i\pi/20)$, $\sqrt{2}\exp(-7i\pi/20)$, $\sqrt{2}\exp(-15i\pi/20)$.   □

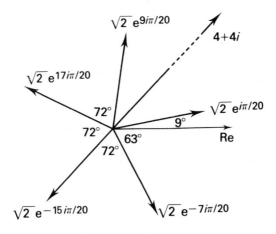

Figure 12.7 5th roots of $4+4i$

Since

all values of $\sqrt[n]{z}$ have the same modulus, and their arguments differ by $2\pi/n$,

it is sufficient to find one root, draw the corresponding vector in the Argand diagram, and apply successive rotations of $2\pi/n$ to get the other distinct roots.

Exercises (answers on p. 309)
12.2.1 Evaluate (i) $(1+i)^{12}$ (ii) $(\sqrt{3}-i)^8$.
12.2.2 Evaluate the cube roots of (i) -8 (ii) $2-2i$.
12.2.3 Calculate the values of $(-\sqrt{3}-i)^{1/5}$.
12.2.4 Calculate the values of $(-1-i)^{3/5}$.

12.3 Solution of Polynomial Equations

The work in the previous section, showing how to calculate the n distinct nth roots of a complex number, allows the solution of a polynomial equation of the special form $az^n + b = 0$. A more general polynomial equation is algebraically soluble if it can be reduced to the calculation of nth roots. For example, the formula for the roots of a quadratic reduces the problem of solving any quadratic equation to the calculation of square roots (see Example 18A at the end of Section A.5). More complicated manipulations, which may be found in older textbooks on algebra, reduce the solution of any cubic equation to the calculation of cube roots, and reduce the solution of any quartic equation to the calculation of square roots. Complex numbers were in fact invented in order to obtain the solution of a cubic equation. However it can be proved that the solution of a *general* polynomial equation of degree higher than 4 cannot be reduced to the calculation of nth roots.

One special case that is algebraically soluble has the form

$$az^{2n} + bz^n + c = 0,$$

which is a quadratic in $w = z^n$.

Example 12.30

Solve $z^4 + (3 - 2i)z^2 + 8 + 6i = 0$.

Putting $w = z^2$ gives a quadratic equation for w, with solutions

$$w = \tfrac{1}{2}[-3 + 2i \pm \sqrt{\{(3 - 2i)^2 - 32 - 24i\}}]$$
$$= \tfrac{1}{2}[-3 + 2i \pm \sqrt{(-27 - 36i)}] = \tfrac{1}{2}[-3 + 2i \pm 3i\sqrt{(3 + 4i)}]$$

and $u + iv = \sqrt{(3 + 4i)}$ if $u^2 - v^2 = 3$ and $uv = 2$, giving $u^4 - 3u^2 - 4 = 0$, $u^2 = 4$ or -1, $u = \pm 2$, $v = \pm 1$.

$$w = \tfrac{1}{2}[-3 + 2i \pm 6i \mp 3] = -3 + 4i \text{ or } -2i.$$

Similarly $z = x + iy = \sqrt{(-3 + 4i)}$ if $x^2 - y^2 = -3$ and $xy = 2$ giving $x = \pm 1$, $y = \pm 2$, and $x + iy = \sqrt{(-2i)}$ if $x^2 = y^2$ and $xy = -1$ giving $x = \pm 1$, $y = \mp 1$.

The solutions are therefore,

$$z = 1 + 2i, \ -1 - 2i, \ 1 - i, \text{ and } -1 + i.$$

These solutions are easily checked by substitution.   □

Each root r of a polynomial corresponds to a linear factor $(z - r)$.

Example 12.31

From Example 12.30,

$$z^4 + (3 - 2i)z^2 + 8 + 6i = (z - 1 - 2i)(z + 1 + 2i)(z - 1 + i)(z + 1 - i). \quad □$$

> The fundamental theorem of complex algebra states that every nth degree polynomial can be factored in this way into n linear factors.

As the same factor can be repeated, there may not be n distinct roots, but there are at most n distinct roots.

In the factored form, the coefficient of z^k is the sum of the $\binom{n}{k}$ possible products of $(n - k)$ roots, which is therefore equal to the coefficient of z^k in the polynomial.

Example 12.32

The 5th roots of 1 are 1,

$$w = \exp(2i\pi/5), \ w^2, \ w^3, \text{ and } w^4 \quad \text{(Fig. 12.8)}.$$

These are the roots of the polynomial $z^5 - 1$. As there is no z^4 term, the sum of the roots is zero.

$$1 + w + w^2 + w^3 + w^4 = 0.$$

Let $\lambda = w + w^4$ and $\mu = w^2 + w^3$, so that $\lambda + \mu = -1$. From Fig. 12.8,

$$\lambda = 2 \cos 72° > 0, \qquad \mu = -2 \cos 36° < 0.$$

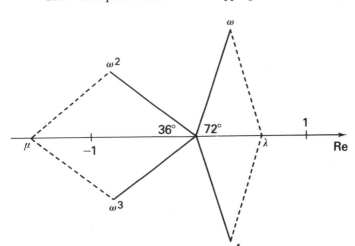

Figure 12.8   5th roots of 1 shown by solid lines

Also

$$\lambda\mu = w^3 + w^4 + w^6 + w^7 = w^3 + w^4 + w + w^2, \quad \text{since } w^5 = 1$$

$$= -1.$$

So $(\lambda - \mu)^2 = (\lambda + \mu)^2 - 4\lambda\mu = 5$, $\lambda - \mu = \sqrt{5}$, since $\lambda - \mu > 0$.

$$\lambda + \mu = -1, \qquad \lambda - \mu = \sqrt{5} \quad \Rightarrow \quad \lambda = \tfrac{1}{2}(-1+\sqrt{5}), \qquad \mu = -\tfrac{1}{2}(1+\sqrt{5}),$$

i.e. $\cos 72° = \tfrac{1}{4}(-1+\sqrt{5})$, $\cos 36° = \tfrac{1}{4}(1+\sqrt{5})$. $\square$

Exercises (answers on p. 309)
12.3.1   Solve the equation $z^4 - 6z^2 + 25 = 0$.
12.3.2   Factorize $z^6 + 8z^3 + iz^3 + 8i$ into 6 linear factors.
12.3.3   Solve the equation $z^6 + (1 - 8i)z^3 = 8i$.

12.4   Complex Functions as Mappings between Complex Planes

A real function, which establishes a pairing (x, y) associating a real number y with each real number x in the domain of the function, is illustrated by plotting the points (x, y) in a plane. A complex function establishes a pairing (z, w) associating a complex number w with each complex number z in the domain of the function. The sets of numbers z and w forming the domain and range of the function can be illustrated as sets of points in the complex plane. To obtain a useful illustration

> it is usually necessary to use two planes, the z-plane showing the domain, and the w-plane showing the range.

The function $z \to w$ then represents a mapping $P \to P'$ of a set of points $\{P\}$ in the z-plane onto a set of points $\{P'\}$ in the w-plane. The set $\{P'\}$ is called the **image** of $\{P\}$.

If the domain of a function is not stated, it is assumed to be the natural domain consisting of all numbers z for which the given rule is defined.

Example 12.40

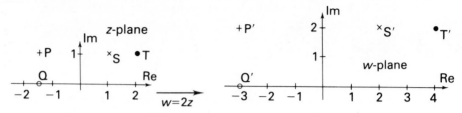

Figure 12.9   Mapping (by $w=2z$) of {P, Q, S, T} to {P′, Q′, S′, T′}

Example 12.41

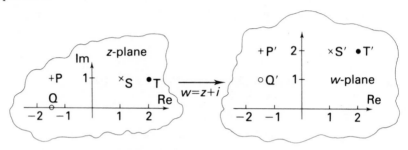

Figure 12.10   Mapping by $w=z+i$

A curve in the z-plane will generally map onto a curve in the w-plane, and a better picture of the mapping is given by showing suitable curves.

Example 12.42

The mapping $z \rightarrow w = 2z$ doubles the modulus, but leaves the argument unchanged. A circle centre O becomes a circle of twice the radius, while a radial line from O maps onto the same radial line (in the w-plane, see Fig. 12.11).

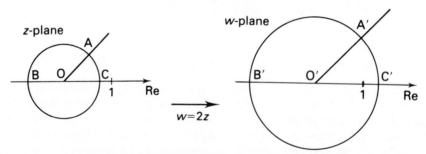

Figure 12.11   Mapping of circle CAB and radial line OA

Example 12.43

The mapping $z \rightarrow w = z+i$ displaces any point one unit in the imaginary direction. The image of a horizontal line is a parallel line one unit higher, and a vertical line maps into the same line. Consider, for example, the lines PT and PQ in Fig. 12.10.   □

Just as with real functions (see, for example, Fig. 6.16 on p. 134, the illustration of a mapping may be facilitated by considering a complex function as a composite of simpler functions with obvious or known mappings.

Example 12.44
The function $w = 2z + i$ is a composite of the functions considered in the previous two examples, so the mapping can be considered in the two stages $z \to 2z \to 2z + i$. Figure 12.12 shows the mapping of a line L and a circle C, with the intermediate step given as a dashed curve.

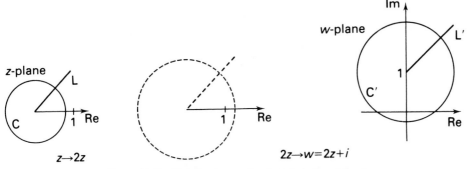

Figure 12.12 Mapping by $w = 2z + i$ of circle C and line L □

Similarly a region of the z-plane will generally map onto a region in the w-plane. The easiest way to locate corresponding regions is usually to consider curves forming the boundaries.

Example 12.45

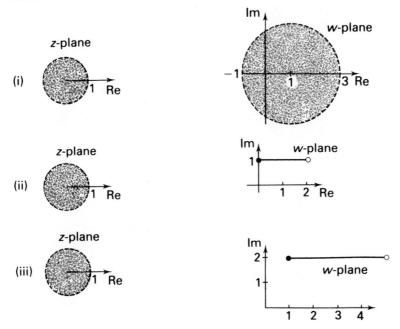

Figure 12.13 Mapping of the disc $|z| < 1$ by (i) $w = 2z + 1$ (ii) $w = 2|z| + i$ (iii) $w = 4|z| + 1 + 2i$

These three mappings can be obtained in stages:
  (i) $z \to 2z \to 2z + 1$
  (ii) $z \to |z| \to 2|z| \to 2|z| + i$
  (iii) $z \to |z| \to 4|z| \to 4|z| + 1 \to 4|z| + 1 + 2i.$ □

Example 12.46

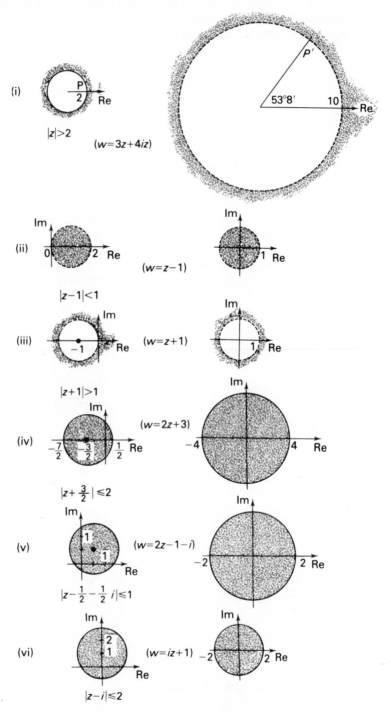

Figure 12.14   Regions in *z*-plane, on left. Images (in *w*-planes, on right) are the regions   (i) $|w|>10$
(ii) $|w|<1$ (iii) $|w|>1$ (iv) $|w|\leq4$ (v) $|w|\leq2$ (vi) $|w|\leq2$ □

In general, if the rule of a function is simplest in terms of the Cartesian representation $z = x + iy$, then the images of lines parallel to the axes should be considered. If the rule is simpler in terms of the polar form, the mapping of radial lines and circles centred on the origin should give a simpler picture. This is the case for powers of z.

Example 12.47
If $w = z^2$, the vector represented by z is rotated through an angle arg z, and its length is changed to $|z|^2$. The vectors to points of a radial line all have the same direction, and so the rotated vectors also all have a common direction. Thus a radial line transforms into a radial line. Similarly the vectors to points of a circle with centre O all have the same length, and the transformed vectors also all have a common length, so the circle maps into a circle. Any region bounded by radial lines and segments of circles centred on the origin maps onto a region with boundaries of the same type (Fig. 12.15).

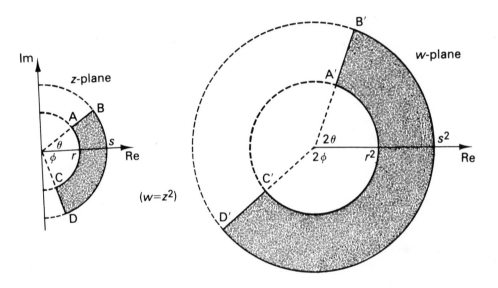

Figure 12.15   Mapping by $w = z^2$ of the region $\{z : r \leqslant |z| \leqslant s, -\phi \leqslant \arg z \leqslant \theta\}$

As arguments are doubled, the image of a semi-circle centred on O will be a circle. The image of a circle is evidently a circle taken twice: in Fig. 12.16 both the points A_1 and A_2 in the z-plane are mapped onto A' in the w-plane, etc.

To obtain a one-to-one function with an inverse, the domain would have to be restricted. □

Similarly $w = z^n$ maps a circle centred on O onto a circle, each point of which is the image of n different points of the circle in the z-plane.

Example 12.22 (yet again)
Under the mapping $z \to w = z^4$, the point $w = 16$ is the image of the four points $z = \pm 2, \pm 2i$. □

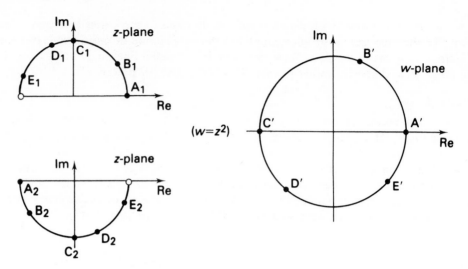

Figure 12.16   Both A_1 and A_2 map into A' (etc.); (z-plane split for clarity)

Exercises (answers on p. 309)

12.4.1   Illustrate the function $w = 3z - 2i$ by Argand diagrams showing the following sets of points in the z-plane, and their images in the w-plane.

   (i) the point $A(\frac{1}{2}, \frac{1}{2})$ (ii) the lines Re $z = \pm 2$ and Im $z = \pm 1$
   (iii) the circle $|z| = 3$.

12.4.2   The function $w = f(z)$ has rule $w = 3z - 2i$ and domain the interior of the rectangle enclosed by Re $z = \pm 2$ and Im $z = \pm 1$. Give Argand diagrams showing the domain and range of f.

12.4.3   Illustrate the function $w = 2iz - 3i$ by Argand diagrams showing the mapping of
   (i) a single point (consider $z \to iz \to 2iz \to 2iz - 3i$);
   (ii) radial lines and circles centred on the origin ($z = 0$).

12.4.4   How are the modulus and argument of z^3 related to those of z?
      Show in Argand diagrams the domain and range of the function $w = f(z) = z^3$ with domain $\{z : |z| \leq 2, \text{Re } z \geq 0\}$.
      Does this function have an inverse?

12.4.5   Illustrate the function $w = 1/z (z \neq 0)$ by Argand diagrams showing the mapping of radial lines and circles centred on the origin.

12.5   The Complex Exponential Function

The object of this section is to define exp z for any complex number z, if possible in a way that will retain familiar properties such as

$$(\exp z)(\exp w) = \exp(z + w). \qquad \textbf{(12.8)}$$

If z is real, then exp $z = \exp x$ is already defined. In Section 6.11 the definition

$$\exp(it) = \cos t + i \sin t \qquad (6.16)$$

was introduced, for any real t, so exp z is also already defined when z is purely imaginary.

Then the special case of equation (12.8),

$$(\exp x)(\exp iy) = \exp(x+iy),$$

can serve to complete the definition of $\exp(x+iy)$. Thus

the complex exponential function exp z, or e^z, is defined by

$$\exp z = \exp(x+iy) = (\exp x)(\cos y + i \sin y). \qquad \textbf{(12.9)}$$

or

$$e^z = e^x(\cos y + i \sin y).$$

The domain is the whole complex plane.

It is then straightforward to show that equation (12.8) is true for any two complex numbers z and w.

Since the real functions cos and sin are periodic, so also is the function exp z. The value (12.9) is the same if y is changed by an integer multiple of 2π, i.e. if z is changed by an integer multiple of $2i\pi$:

$$\exp(z+2in\pi) = \exp(x+i\{y+2n\pi\}) = \exp(x+iy), \qquad \textbf{(12.10)}$$

since $\cos(y+2n\pi) = \cos y$, $\sin(y+2n\pi) = \sin y$. **The complex exponential function has period $2i\pi$.**

The effect of this periodicity on the mapping $z \to e^z = w$ is that each point P' in the w-plane is the image of an infinity of points P_k in the z-plane, on a line parallel to the imaginary axis (Fig. 12.17).

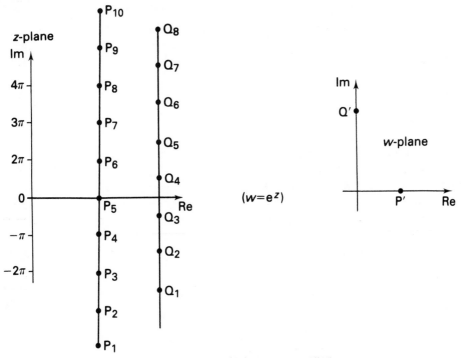

Figure 12.17   Points $P_k(Q_k)$ all map into $P'(Q')$

The value $\exp z = e^x(\cos y + i \sin y)$ is a polar form of $\exp z$, since $e^x > 0$. An alternative statement of the definition is therefore

$$|\exp z| = e^x = \exp(\text{Re } z), \qquad \arg(\exp z) = \text{Im } z = y. \qquad \textbf{(12.11)}$$

The easiest way to illustrate the mapping is therefore to use Cartesian coordinates in the z-plane and polar coordinates in the w-plane (Fig. 12.18).

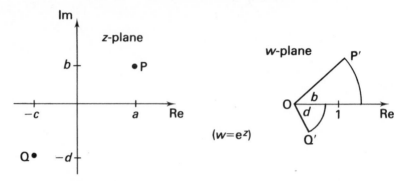

Figure 12.18   Mapping of $P(a + ib)$ and $Q(-c - id)$; $OP' = e^a$, $OQ' = e^{-c}$

Since e^x takes all positive values (Fig. 3.2), the range of $w = \exp z$ is all complex numbers except zero. To obtain all these values of w only requires y in equation (12.9) to vary through 2π.

So any horizontal strip of the z-plane, of vertical width 2π, maps onto the whole of the w-plane (except for $w = 0$).

To illustrate the mapping only one of these strips need be considered, say $-\pi < y \leqslant \pi$ so that $y = \text{Arg } w$. The domain can be restricted to this strip if a one-to-one function is required.

Exercises (answers on p. 311)

12.5.1   Find numerical values of the real and imaginary parts of e^z for the following values of z:

(i) 1   (ii) -1 (iii) i (iv) $-i$ (v) $2+i$
(vi) $1-2i$ (vii) $1+4i$ (viii) $-1-3i$
Verify from the results that $e^{1-2i} = e^1 e^{-i} e^{-i}$.

12.5.2   Give Argand diagrams showing the square with corners at the points represented by $\pm\frac{1}{2}i\pi$, $\pi \pm \frac{1}{2}i\pi$, and the image of this square under the mapping $w = e^z$.

12.5.3   For each of the following functions, express $|w|$ and $\arg w$ in terms of x and y $(z = x + iy)$:
(i) $w = e^{2z}$ (ii) $w = e^{-z}(= 1/e^z)$ (iii) $w = e^{iz}$
What are the periods of these functions?

Answers to Exercises 12.1.1–12.5.3

12.1.1 $i, 1, -\frac{1}{2} - \frac{1}{2}i\sqrt{3}$ **12.1.2** $0.385 - 0.923i$
12.1.3 $8c^4 - 8c^2 + 1$, $c = \cos\theta$

12.1.4 $16s^5 - 20s^3 + 5s$ ($t = \pi/6$ is a good check), $s = \sin t$

12.1.5 Solutions are $\pm i, \frac{1}{2}\sqrt{3} \pm \frac{1}{2}i, -\frac{1}{2}\sqrt{3} \pm \frac{1}{2}i$

12.2.1 (i) -64 (ii) $128(1 + i\sqrt{3})$

12.2.2 (i) $-2, 1 \pm i\sqrt{3}$ (ii) $-1 - i, 1.37 - 0.37i, -0.37 + 1.37i$

12.2.3 $\sqrt[5]{2}\exp(-i\pi/6) = 0.995 - 0.574i$
$\sqrt[5]{2}\exp(7i\pi/30) = 0.854 + 0.769i$
$\sqrt[5]{2}\exp(19i\pi/30) = -0.467 + 1.049i$
$\sqrt[5]{2}\exp(-29i\pi/30) = -1.142 - 0.111i$
$\sqrt[5]{2}\exp(-17i\pi/30) = -0.239 - 1.124i$

12.2.4 The values all have modulus $2^{3/10}$, and their arguments are $7\pi/20, 3\pi/4, -\pi/20$, $-9\pi/20$, $-17\pi/20$,   i.e. $0.559 + 1.097i$, $-0.870 + 0.870i$, $1.216 - 0.193i$, $0.193 - 1.216i, -1.097 - 0.559i$.

12.3.1 $2 \pm i, -2 \pm i$

12.3.2 $(z^3 + i)(z^3 + 8)$
$= (z - i)(z - \frac{1}{2}\sqrt{3} + \frac{1}{2}i)(z + \frac{1}{2}\sqrt{3} + \frac{1}{2}i)(z + 2)(z - 1 - i\sqrt{3})(z - 1 + i\sqrt{3})$

12.3.3 $z^3 = 8i$ or -1,
$z = \pm\sqrt{3} + i, -2i, -1, \frac{1}{2} \pm \frac{1}{2}i\sqrt{3}$

12.4.1

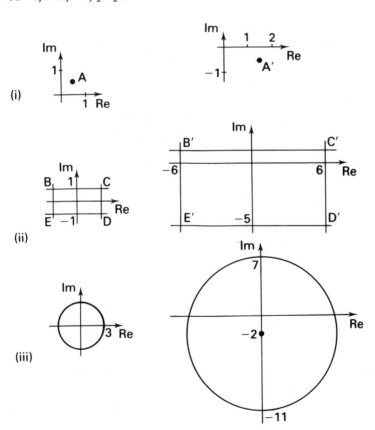

Figure 12.4.1   *z*-planes on left; *w*-planes on right

12.4.2 Domain and range are the interiors of the rectangles BCDE and B′C′D′E′ in 12.4.1(ii)

12.4.3

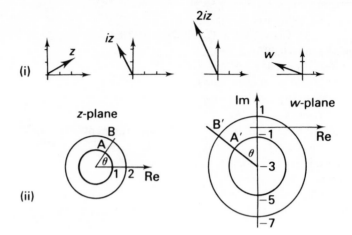

Figure 12.4.3

12.4.4 $|z^3| = |z|^3$, arg $z^3 = 3$ arg z

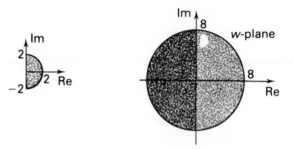

Figure 12.4.4

No inverse because each point of the left half of the range (darker shade) is obtained from two points of the domain

12.4.5

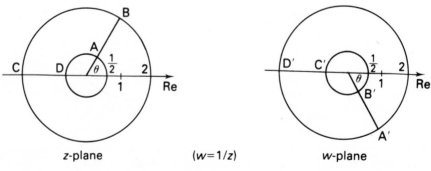

Figure 12.4.5

12.5.1   (i) $2.72+0i$ (ii) $0.368+0i$ (iii) $0.540+0.841i$
(iv) $0.540-0.841i$ (v) $3.99+6.22i$ (vi) $-1.131-2.47i$
(vii) $-1.78-2.06i$ (viii) $-0.364-0.0519i$

12.5.2

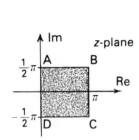

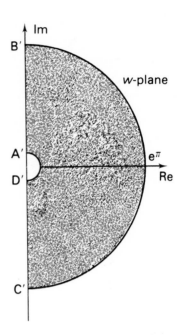

$(w=e^z)$

Figure 12.5.2

12.5.3   (i) $|w|=e^{2x}$, arg $w=2y$, period $i\pi$
(ii) $|w|=e^{-x}$, arg $w=-y$, period $2i\pi$
(iii) $|w|=e^{-y}$, arg $w=x$, period 2π

Further Exercises on Chapter 12

12.1   Suppose the points P_1, P_2, P_3 in the complex plane are represented by the complex numbers z_1, z_2 and z_3. Find, in terms of z_1, z_2 and z_3, complex numbers representing the following points:
(i) The midpoints Q_1, Q_2, Q_3 of P_2P_3, P_3P_1 and P_1P_2 respectively.
(ii) The trisection points G_k of P_kQ_k

$$(P_kG_k=2G_kQ_k; \ k=1, 2, 3).$$

What geometrical property of a triangle is demonstrated by the results of (ii)?

12.2   Suppose $z_k=x_k+iy_k$ $(k=1, 2, \ldots, n)$ are n complex numbers. If $a+ib=\sqrt{(z_1^2+z_2^2+\cdots+z_n^2)}$ show that

$$ab=(x_1y_1+x_2y_2+\cdots+x_ny_n)$$
$$a^2-b^2=(x_1^2+x_2^2+\cdots+x_n^2)-(y_1^2+y_2^2+\cdots+y_n^2).$$

12.3   Express z^3+27i as a product of three linear factors.

12.4   Find the cube roots of $-i/8$.

12.5 Express $z^6 - 7z^3 + 8$ as a product of six linear factors.

12.6 Solve the equation

$$z^4 - 5iz^2 + 36 = 0.$$

12.7 Show in an Argand diagram the range of the function $f(z) = z^3 + 1$ with domain

$$\{z = x + iy: x \geqslant 0, y \leqslant 0\}.$$

What is the solution of the equation $f(z) = 0$?

12.8 Give Argand diagrams showing the set

$$\{z: |z| \leqslant 2\} \cap \{z: \operatorname{Re} z > 0\}$$

and the image of this region under the mapping $w = z^2 + 1$.

12.9 (i) Find the region of the z-plane which is mapped onto the disc $|w - 1 - i| \leqslant 6$ by the transformation $w = 3z - 2i$.

(ii) Solve the inequality $|3z - 1 - 3i| \leqslant 6$.

12.10 Solve the equation

$$e^{2z} + (2 - 4i) e^z - 6 = 0$$

by substituting $w = e^z$.

12.11 (i) Give Argand diagrams showing the set

$$\{z = x + iy: 0 \leqslant x \leqslant 1, -\tfrac{1}{2}\pi \leqslant y \leqslant \pi\}$$

and its image under the mapping $z \to w = \exp(2z)$.

(ii) Under this mapping, what region of the z-plane would map onto that part of the w-plane which is both outside the circle $|w| = e$ and in the upper half of the w-plane?

12.12 Show in an Argand diagram the set

$$\{w: \tfrac{1}{2}\pi \leqslant \arg w \leqslant \pi, e^{-1} \leqslant |w| \leqslant e\}.$$

Find a region of the z-plane, with $-\pi \leqslant \operatorname{Im} z \leqslant \pi$, which is mapped onto the above set by the function $w = e^z$.

12.13 From the definition

$$\exp(x + iy) = e^x(\cos y + i \sin y)$$

show that $(\exp z)(\exp w) = \exp(z + w)$ for any two complex numbers z and w.

12.14 Find the image of the region $\{z: 2 \leqslant |z| \leqslant 3, \pi/3 \leqslant \arg z \leqslant \pi/2\}$ under the mapping $w = z^2$.

12.15 Evaluate e^z for the following values of z:

(i) $\ln 2 + i\pi$ (ii) $-\ln 3 - \tfrac{1}{2}i\pi$ (iii) $2 \ln 2 + \tfrac{1}{3}i\pi$.

12.16 Find the image under the mapping $w = e^z$ of the rectangle in the z-plane with corners at $-\tfrac{1}{4}i\pi, 2 - \tfrac{1}{4}i\pi, 2 + \tfrac{1}{3}i\pi, \tfrac{1}{3}i\pi$.

12.17 Find the cube roots of $2i - 2$.

12.18 Find the 4th roots of $-8\sqrt{3} + 8i$ in the form $x + iy$.

12.19 Find the real and imaginary parts of (i) $(1 + i)^{10}$ (ii) $(\sqrt{3} + i)^{10}$.

12.20 For each of mappings (i) $w = iz$ (ii) $w = 1/z$, describe the image of the region R defined by

$$\{z: 1 \leqslant |z| \leqslant 3, -\pi/3 < \arg z < \pi/6\}.$$

What region of the ζ-plane is mapped onto R by $e^\zeta = z$?

12.21 Solve the following equations:

(i) $z^2 - 3iz = 2$ (ii) $z^2 - 4iz = 4$ (iii) $z^3 = 27i$ (iv) $e^{2z} = -e$.

12.22 Let

$$P = \begin{bmatrix} 1 & 1 & 1 \\ 1 & \omega & \omega^2 \\ 1 & \omega^2 & \omega^4 \end{bmatrix}$$

where ω is a complex cube root of 1.

If $\bar{P}$ is the matrix obtained from P by taking the complex conjugate of every element, show that $\bar{P}P$ is a multiple of the unit matrix.

13

Differential Equations

13.1 Separable First-Order Equations

Given the equation representing a curve, the slope of the curve at any point is found by differentiating the equation. For example, the slope of the parabola

$$y = x^2 + 1 \tag{13.1}$$

is $dy/dx = 2x$.

The equation may also be given in parametric form or in implicit form. For example

$$x = \sin t, \qquad y = \sin 2t$$
$$\Rightarrow \quad dy/dx = 2\cos 2t / \cos t = \pm 2\sqrt{(1-y^2)}/\sqrt{(1-x^2)} \tag{13.2}$$

and

$$x^2 + xy + y^2 = 7$$
$$\Rightarrow \quad 2x + \left(x\frac{dy}{dx} + 1y\right) + 2y\frac{dy}{dx} = 0, \qquad \frac{dy}{dx} = -\frac{2x+y}{x+2y}. \tag{13.3}$$

The inverse problem is finding the equation of a curve, given its slope at any point. If dy/dx is given as a function of x, the antiderivative of this function is required. For example, given $dy/dx = 2x$, an antiderivative is $y = x^2$. Comparing with equation (13.1) shows that a curve cannot be determined uniquely from its slope only, and that the indefinite integral is required, i.e. $dy/dx = 2x \Rightarrow y = x^2 + C$. To obtain equation (13.1), one point of the curve must also be known. For instance, given $(0, 1)$,

$$y = x^2 + C \Rightarrow 1 = 0 + C, \qquad C = 1, \qquad y = x^2 + 1.$$

Equations (13.2) and (13.3) contain y (a function of x) as well as x, so the curve cannot be found immediately by finding an antiderivative. In general the slope may be given as a relation between x, y, dx and dy, called **a differential equation**. These differential equations are **first-order** because they contain no differentials (or derivatives) of higher order. **Solving** the equation means finding the curve equation, i.e. the corresponding relation between x and y. As with the general antiderivative problem [which is solving a differential equation of the special form $dy = f(x)\,dx$], the **general solution** will involve an arbitrary constant.

Example 13.10
The general solution of

$$\frac{dy}{dx} = -\frac{2x+y}{x+2y} \tag{13.3}$$

is $x^2 + xy + y^2 = C$, since replacing 7 by C does not affect the calculation of the derivative in (13.3). This general solution represents a family of curves (Fig. 13.1), one for each

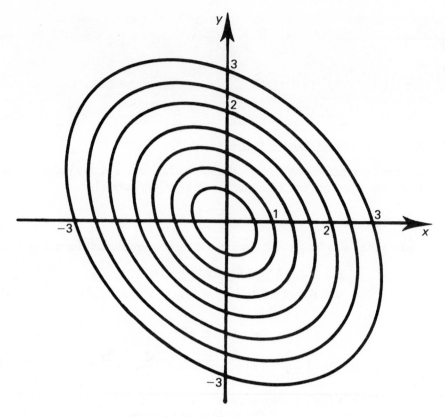

Figure 13.1 $x^2 + xy + y^2 = C$ for $C = 0.36$, 1, 1.7, 2, 4, 6, 9

positive value assigned to C. As with the parabola (13.1), one given point will determine C. For example, if $(-1, 3)$ is on the curve, then $C = 7$; $x^2 + xy + y^2 = 7$ is called a **particular solution** of equation (13.3).   □

If a curve equation contains a constant, a family of curves may be obtained by assigning all possible values to the constant. After differentiating, the constant can be eliminated between the curve equation and the derivative equation, leaving a single differential equation satisfied by every member of the family.

Example 13.11

If

$$y^2 = (1 + B/x) \tag{13.4}$$

then

$$\frac{dy}{dx} = \frac{-By}{2x(x + B)} \quad \text{(cf. Example 6.21 on p. 113).}$$

From the curve equation, $B = xy^2 - x$; substituting into dy/dx gives

$$dy/dx = (1 - y^2)/2xy. \tag{13.5}$$

Then equation (13.4) is a solution of the differential equation (13.5) for any value of the arbitrary constant B (which does not appear in the differential equation). The solutions of (13.5) represent the family of curves obtained by varying B in equation (13.4). (Figure 13.2; cf. Exercise 6.8.2.) □

In general, a process which obtains y from dy/dx will involve one (indefinite) integration at some stage, introducing an arbitrary constant. (Capital letters are conventionally used for these constants, as in the previous examples.) Unless conditions on the solution are given,

> solving a differential equation means finding the general solution containing the arbitrary constant.

In most examples the general solution can be given in a form such that all particular solutions are obtained from the general solution by assigning particular values to the arbitrary constant. Even if only a particular solution is required, the general solution is usually obtained first, and then the value for the arbitrary constant found.

Differentiating an implicit function of the form $G(y) = F(x) + C$ gives $G'(y)\,dy/dx = F'(x)$. This is conveniently written

$$G'(y)\,dy = F'(x)\,dx \qquad\qquad \textbf{(13.6)}$$

so that integrating each side gives the solution. Rearranging an equation to the form (13.6) is called **separating the variables** (y and dy from x and dx). A first-order differential equation is called **separable** if this rearrangement is possible.

This can be ascertained by solving for dy/dx, and attempting to write dy/dx as a quotient (or equivalently, a product) of functions of x and y. The differential equations (13.2) and (13.5) are separable, but (13.3) is not separable. (The substitution $y = xv$ does change (13.3) to a separable equation, as in Exercise 13.3.)

Example 13.12
Solve the equation

$$dy/dx = (1+y^2)/\sqrt{(1-x^2)} \qquad\qquad (13.7)$$

and find the particular solution passing through $(0, 0)$.

Separating the variables gives

$$dy/(1+y^2) = dx/\sqrt{(1-x^2)} \qquad\qquad (\text{cf. }(13.6))$$

or

$$d(\text{Tan}^{-1}\,y) = d(\text{Sin}^{-1}\,x).$$

This last step involves knowing, or determining by the methods of Chapter 10, antiderivatives of the expressions in x and y. Then integrating gives

$$(\text{Tan}^{-1}\,y) + A = (\text{Sin}^{-1}\,x) + B$$

where A and B are arbitrary constants. Since $B - A$ is equivalent to a single arbitrary constant C, it is only necessary to include a constant on one side of the equation. Thus

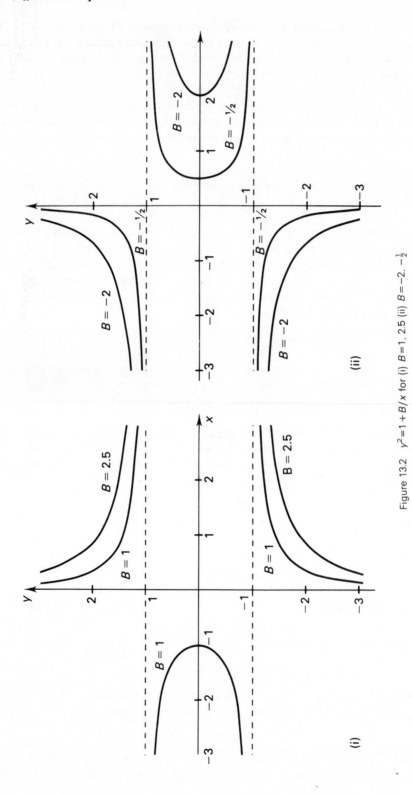

Figure 13.2 $y^2 = 1 + B/x$ for (i) $B = 1, 2.5$ (ii) $B = -2, -\frac{1}{2}$

the general solution of equation (13.7) is given (implicitly) by

$$\mathrm{Tan}^{-1} y = (\mathrm{Sin}^{-1} x) + C. \tag{13.8}$$

To get the required particular solution, substitute the given condition $y = 0$ when $x = 0$ into equation (13.8), to obtain $0 = C$. The particular solution is $y = \tan(\mathrm{Sin}^{-1} x)$.

In Chapter 10 it was observed that different methods of treating an indefinite integral might produce correct antiderivatives that looked different (see, for instance, Example 10.26). This is also true regarding solutions of differential equations. The particular solution here is $y = \tan z$ with $z = \mathrm{Sin}^{-1} x$. Then $\sin z = x$ and $\cos z = \sqrt{(1 - x^2)}$, and so the particular solution can be written $y = x/\sqrt{(1 - x^2)}$. Similarly the general solution (13.8) is

$$y = \tan(z + C) = \sin(z + C)/\cos(z + C)$$

$$= (\sin z + \cos z \tan C)/(\cos z - \sin z \tan C)$$

or

$$y = \frac{x + A\sqrt{(1 - x^2)}}{-Ax + \sqrt{(1 - x^2)}} \tag{13.9}$$

on using the equivalent arbitrary constant $A = \tan C$. $\square$

> The method of checking a solution is to differentiate it and substitute into the given equation, and verify that this produces an identity in x. For a general solution, this substitution must also give an identity in the arbitrary constant; for a particular solution, the condition defining the particular solution should also be checked.

The correctness of equation (13.9) as the general solution of (13.7) was shown in Example 6.110 on p. 111. The graphs at the bottom of p. 138 show the general form of the solution curves.

Example 13.13
Solve the differential equation

$$\frac{dy}{dx} = \frac{1 - y^2}{2xy} \tag{13.5}.$$

Separating the variables gives $2y\, dy/(1 - y^2) = dx/x$, or

$$-2y\, dy/(y^2 - 1) = dx/x.$$

Integrating:

$$-\ln|y^2 - 1| + C = \ln|x|.$$

For any value of C, the function defined (implicitly) by this equation is a particular solution. The following manipulation gives the solutions explicitly:

$$C = \ln|y^2 - 1| + \ln|x| = \ln(|y^2 - 1||x|) = \ln|xy^2 - x|,$$

$$e^C = |xy^2 - x|, \qquad xy^2 - x = \pm e^C.$$

Now $\pm e^C$, with C arbitrary, is just an alternative arbitrary constant, say B:

$$x(y^2 - 1) = B, \qquad y^2 = 1 + B/x, \qquad y = \pm\sqrt{(1 + B/x)}. \tag{13.10}$$

This is the general solution.

Although the derivation of the solution is invalid for $B = 0$, since $e^C \neq 0$, equation (13.10) does give solutions on putting $B = 0$. These lines $y = \pm 1$ have $dy/dx = 0$, and obviously satisfy the equation.

A complete check requires differentiating (13.10) (Examples 6.17 or 6.21). The form of the curves represented by these solutions was shown in Fig. 13.2. From equation (13.10), the natural domain of a solution is determined by the condition $1 + B/x \geq 0$; all solutions are symmetric about Ox; and since changing the sign of both B and x leaves equation (13.10) unaltered, two solutions with B having opposite sign are reflections in Oy. The trivial solutions $y = \pm 1$, shown by dashed lines, are asymptotes to all the other solutions. The y-axis ($x = 0$) is also an asymptote to every solution except $y = \pm 1$, and this asymptote $x = 0 = dx$ evidently satisfies $2xy\, dy = (1 - y^2)\, dx$, which is a rearrangement of equation (13.5).

The symmetry properties of the solutions also serve as partial checks. Since the operations of changing the sign of x, or of y, convert a solution into a solution, the differential equation (13.5) should be unchanged by either operation. (Note that dx or dy also change sign.) $\square$

Exercises (answers on p. 347)

13.1.1   Which of the following differential equations are first-order and separable? Find the general solution of those that are
   (i) $dy/dx = x^2 + y^2$ (ii) $dy/dx = x^2 \exp(x + y)$
   (iii) $d^2y/dx^2 = x^3 y^4$ (iv) $(\sin x)(dy/dx) + y \cos x = 0$.

13.1.2   Verify that equation (13.10) is obtained if, when integrating, modulus signs are not used, and the arbitrary constant is introduced in the form $\ln B$.

13.1.3   Solve the equation $dy/dx = \cot y$.

13.2 First-order Linear Equations

A first-order differential equation is **linear** if the expression for dy/dx is first degree in y (i.e. linear in y). Any such equation can be written

$$dy/dx + Q(x)y = R(x). \tag{13.11}$$

For arbitrary Q and R, this can be solved in the sense that the solution can be reduced to evaluating certain indefinite integrals.

Example 13.20
Solve

$$dy/dx + (\cot x)y = 2 \cos x. \tag{13.12}$$

This is equation (13.11) with $Q(x) = \cot x$, $R(x) = 2 \cos x$. Multiplying by $\sin x\, dx$, the left side becomes $dy \sin x + y \cos x\, dx$. From the rule for differentiating a product (rule II in Section 6.1, with $v = \sin x$ and $u = y$), this is $d(y \sin x)$, and the equation becomes

$$d(y \sin x) = 2 \sin x \cos x\, dx.$$

Integrating:

$$y \sin x = \sin^2 x + C.$$

The general solution is

$$y = \sin x + (C/\sin x). \tag{13.13}$$

Check: (13.13) gives $dy/dx = \cos x - (C \cos x / \sin^2 x)$

and

$$(\cot x)y = \cos x + C \cos x / \sin^2 x.$$

Adding these two equations shows that (13.13) satisfies equation (13.12) for any value of C.

(See Answer 6.39 in Appendix F for some graphs of particular solutions.)   □

This example could be solved because multiplying by $\sin x \, dx$ made the left side the differential of the product $y \sin x$. Because of this, $\sin x$ is called an **integrating factor** for equation (13.12). An integrating factor exists for any first-order linear equation.

Suppose $I(x)$ is an integrating factor for equation (13.11), i.e. when the equation is multiplied by $I(x) \, dx$, the left side

$$dy \, I(x) + yQ(x)I(x) \, dx$$

is the differential of a product. Comparing with

$$d(yI) = dy \, I + y \, dI$$

shows that I is an integrating factor if $dI = QI \, dx$, or

$$dI/I = Q(x) \, dx.$$

Integrating this gives

$$\boxed{\ln I = \int Q(x) \, dx.} \tag{13.14}$$

In Example 13.20, $Q(x) = \cot x = \cos x / \sin x$, so

$$\int Q(x) \, dx = \int d(\sin x)/\sin x = \ln(\sin x)$$

and equation (13.14) gives $I = \sin x$.

When using equation (13.14) it is not necessary to consider the arbitrary constant of integration, because any solution of $dI = QI \, dx$ gives an integrating factor.

Example 13.21
Solve

$$(1 - x^2)(dy/dx) + xy = (1 - x^2)^{3/2}. \tag{13.15}$$

First change to the standard form (13.11) of the linear equation (otherwise equation (13.14) will not give an integrating factor):

$$(dy/dx) + xy/(1 - x^2) = (1 - x^2)^{1/2}. \tag{13.16}$$

The integrating factor I is now given by (13.14):

$$\ln I = \int x\, dx/(1-x^2) = -\tfrac{1}{2}\ln(1-x^2)$$

$$= \ln(1-x^2)^{-1/2}.$$

Hence $I = (1-x^2)^{-1/2}$, and equation (13.16) is multiplied through by $(1-x^2)^{-1/2}\, dx$:

$$dy(1-x^2)^{-1/2} + yx(1-x^2)^{-3/2}\, dx = dx.$$

The left side should now be the differential of yI.

Check:

$$d(yI) = dy\, I + y\, dI,$$

and

$$dI = d(w^{-1/2}) \qquad (\text{with } w = 1 - x^2)$$

$$= -\tfrac{1}{2}w^{-3/2}\, dw = x(1-x^2)^{-3/2}\, dx.$$

So the equation is now

$$d[y(1-x^2)^{-1/2}] = dx$$

and integrating gives

$$y(1-x^2)^{-1/2} = x + A.$$

The general solution of equation (13.15) is therefore

$$y = (x+A)\sqrt{(1-x^2)}. \qquad (13.17)$$

This can be checked by differentiating and substituting into (13.15)

$$dy = dx\sqrt{(1-x^2)} + (x+A)\, d\sqrt{(1-x^2)} \qquad (\text{product rule})$$

and

$$d\sqrt{(1-x^2)} = dw^{1/2} = \tfrac{1}{2}w^{-1/2}\, dw = -x\, dx/\sqrt{(1-x^2)}$$

$$\therefore \quad (1-x^2)(dy/dx) = (1-x^2)^{3/2} - x(x+A)\sqrt{(1-x^2)}.$$

From equation (13.17)

$$xy = x(x+A)\sqrt{(1-x^2)}.$$

Addition gives equation (13.15) as required. □

Multiplying equation (13.11) by $I\, dx$ gives $d(yI) = IR\, dx$, and so $yI = P + A$, where P is an antiderivative of IR, and A is the arbitrary constant. Putting $P/I = s$ and $1/I = u$ shows that the general solution of (13.11) has the form

$$y = s(x) + Au(x). \qquad (13.18)$$

This structure is clear in the previous examples: in equation (13.17), $s(x) = x\sqrt{(1-x^2)}$ and $u(x) = \sqrt{(1-x^2)}$; in equation (13.13), $s(x) = \sin x$ and $u(x) = 1/\sin x$.

In equation (13.18) s is evidently a particular solution (taking $A = 0$). The significance of u may be seen by considering the process of checking (13.18) by substituting into $y' + Qy = R$:

$$s' + Au' + Q(s + Au) = R.$$

If this is true for all A, the terms containing A must give zero (as in the checks of the previous examples). Thus $u' + Qu = 0$.

These results can be restated as a theorem concerning the first-order linear equation.

Call $y' + Qy = 0$ the **reduced equation** of $y' + Qy = R$. Then the general solution of $y' + Qy = R$ has the form $y = s + Au$ where
  (i) A is the arbitrary constant
  (ii) s is a particular solution
  (iii) u satisfies the reduced equation.

For instance, the explicit general solution (13.13) shows that $u(x) = 1/\sin x$ in Example 13.20. The reduced equation of (13.12) is $dy/dx + (\cot x)y = 0$, and $1/\sin x$ is a solution of this equation (cf. Exercise 13.1.1 (iv)).

Procedure B6 in Appendix B summarizes the technique suggested here for the integration of first-order linear differential equations.

Exercises (answers on p. 347)
13.2.1 Which of the following differential equations are first-order and linear? Find the general solutions of those that are.
  (i) $dy/dx = x^2 + y^2$ (ii) $dy/dx = x + y$
  (iii) $(x + y)(dy/dx) = 1$ (iv) $d^2y/dx^2 = (x + y)^2$.
13.2.2 Find the particular solution of $x(dy/dx) = y + x^2$ which passes through $(3, 12)$.
13.2.3 Show that
  (i) If y_1 and y_2 are two solutions of a linear equation, then $(y_1 - y_2)$ satisfies the corresponding reduced equation.
  (ii) If y_1 is a solution of a linear equation, and u is a solution of the corresponding reduced equation, then $y_1 + u$ is another solution of the linear equation.

13.3 Second-order Linear Equations

Writing y'' for d^2y/dx^2 and y' for dy/dx, a differential equation of the form

$$y'' + P(x)y' + Q(x)y = R(x) \qquad \text{(13.19)}$$

is **second-order** because it contains the second derivative of y, but no higher derivative. It is **linear** because there are no terms higher than first degree in y, y' and y''

(which may be regarded as the unknowns when solving the equation). Although equation (13.19) is an obvious generalization of

$$y' + Q(x)y = R(x) \qquad \text{(13.11)}$$

there is now no general method of solution. However the theorem on the **structure** of the solution of equation (13.11) does generalize.

A process which obtains y from the second-order equation (13.19) will usually require two integrations $(y'' \to y' \to y)$, so the general solution of a second-order equation is expected to contain *two* arbitrary constants. For example if $y'' = 6x + 2$, then $y' = 3x^2 + 2x + A$, and $y = x^3 + x^2 + Ax + B$, where A and B are arbitrary.

To consider the theorem on the structure of the solution of equation (13.19), call $y'' + Py' + Qy = 0$ the **reduced equation** of (13.19). If s is a particular solution of (13.19), and u and v are particular solutions of the reduced equation, then $y = s + Au + Bv$ satisfies equation (13.19) for any values of the constants A and B. This is easily verified by direct substitution into (13.19). The required theorem is then:

the general solution of the second-order linear equation $y'' + Py' + Qy = R$ has the form $y = s + Au + Bv$, where
  (i) A and B are the **arbitrary constants**
  (ii) s is a **particular solution**
  (iii) u and v are **different solutions of the reduced equation** $y'' + Py' + Qy = 0$, different meaning that one is not a constant multiple of the other.

For example, the general solution of $y'' = 6x + 2$ may be obtained from the particular solution $s(x) = x^3 + x^2$, and the solutions $u(x) = x$ and $v(x) = 1$ of the reduced equation $y'' = 0$.

The reason why v must not be a multiple of u is that if $u = kv$, then $Au + Bv = (Ak + B)v$, and $Ak + B$ can be replaced by a single arbitrary constant C. The general solution cannot be $y = s + Cv$, since the general solution contains **two independent** arbitrary constants.

When $y = s + Au + Bv$ is shown (by substitution) to be a solution of equation (13.19), the work shows also that $Au + Bv$ satisfies the reduced equation. Since $Au + Bv$ contains two arbitrary constants, it gives the general solution of the reduced equation. So another way of stating the above theorem is to say that

the general solution of equation (13.19) is obtained from any particular solution by adding the general solution of the reduced equation. This part $Au + Bv$ is called the **complementary function**.

The reduced equation may also be called the **associated homogeneous equation**.

Exercises (answers on p. 347)
13.3.1 In Example 6.32 it was shown that

$$y = A\,e^{-x} \cos 3x + B\,e^{-x} \sin 3x + (\cos 3x + 6 \sin 3x)/37$$

satisfied the differential equation $\mathrm{d}^2y/\mathrm{d}x^2 + 2\,\mathrm{d}y/\mathrm{d}x + 10y = \cos 3x$. In this example of a solution of a second-order linear equation, identify the functions P, Q, R, s, u, and v. What is the complementary function?

13.3.2 (i) Verify (by substitution) that $y = s + Au + Bv$ satisfies equation (13.19) if s is a particular solution and if both u and v satisfy the reduced equation.
(ii) Show that the results in Exercise 13.2.3 hold for the second-order linear equation.

13.4   Linear Equations with Constant Coefficients

If the functions $P(x)$ and $Q(x)$ in equation (13.19) are constants, the equation is said to have **constant coefficients**. An example was shown in Exercise 13.3.1. In this section simple rules will be obtained for *writing down* the complementary function of a constant coefficient linear equation. For particular cases of $R(x)$, rules for finding a particular solution s will also be given.

Applications of the constant coefficient linear equation include:

(i) if the coordinate y gives the position at time t of a particle moving in one dimension, and the forces on the particle are an attraction $-Sy$ towards the equilibrium position $y = 0$, a resistance proportional to the velocity dy/dt, and other time-dependent forces F, then the Newtonian equation of motion is

$$-Sy - C\frac{dy}{dt} + F(t) = m\frac{d^2y}{dt^2}.$$

(In practice x would be used instead of y, but in this section x is reserved to denote an independent variable.)

(ii) if an electrical circuit contains a time-dependent applied voltage $e(t)$, a condenser of constant capacity C, a constant inductance L, and a constant resistance R, all connected in series, the current $i(t)$ satisfies the equation

$$L\frac{d^2i}{dt^2} + R\frac{di}{dt} + \frac{1}{C}i = \frac{de}{dt}.$$

To discuss the equation with constant coefficients, it is convenient to write $P(x) = 2a$ and $Q(x) = b$ in equation (13.19). The reduced equation is then

$$y'' + 2ay' + by = 0. \tag{13.20}$$

For the complementary function, two different solutions u and v of the reduced equation are required. If $u'' + 2au' + bu$ is to be zero, then u, u' and u'' must depend on x in the same way, otherwise the required cancellation could not occur. This suggests an exponential function, whose derivatives are multiples of the same function. Try $u(x) = e^{\sigma x}$, where σ is a constant to be found. Then $u'(x) = \sigma e^{\sigma x}$, $u''(x) = \sigma^2 e^{\sigma x}$, and

$$u'' + 2au' + bu = (\sigma^2 + 2a\sigma + b)\, e^{\sigma x}. \tag{13.21}$$

This is zero if σ is a root of the quadratic $\sigma^2 + 2a\sigma + b$. If the quadratic has two real roots, these give two values of σ, and hence two solutions u and v as required.

Example 13.40
Find two independent solutions of $y'' - 3y' - 4y = 0$.

The roots of $\sigma^2 - 3\sigma - 4 = 0$ are $\sigma = [3 \pm \sqrt{(9 + 16)}]/2$, i.e. $\sigma = 4$ or -1. Hence two solutions are $u(x) = e^{4x}$ and $v(x) = e^{-x}$.

Check:

$$u = e^{4x}, \quad u' = 4\,e^{4x}, \quad u'' = 16\,e^{4x}, \quad u'' - 3u' - 4u = e^{4x}(16 - 12 - 4) = 0$$

$$v = e^{-x}, \quad v' = -e^{-x}, \quad v'' = e^{-x}, \quad v'' - 3v' - 4v = e^{-x}(1 + 3 - 4) = 0.$$

Note that the general solution of $y'' - 3y' - 4y = 0$ is $y = A\,e^{4x} + B\,e^{-x}$ (see the last paragraph of the previous section), and that $A\,e^{4x} + B\,e^{-x}$ is the complementary function for any equation $y'' - 3y' - 4y = R(x)$. □

If $a^2 = b$, then $\sigma^2 + 2a\sigma + b$ has only one root $\sigma = -a$, and only one solution $u(x) = e^{-ax}$ appears. Suppose the general solution of

$$y'' + 2ay' + a^2 y = 0 \qquad (13.22)$$

has e^{-ax} as a factor, i.e. $y = h(x)\,e^{-ax}$. Then

$$y' = h'\,e^{-ax} - ah\,e^{-ax}$$

and $y'' = h''\,e^{-ax} - 2ah'\,e^{-ax} + a^2 h\,e^{-ax}$.

Substituting into equation (13.22) gives

$$(h'' - 2ah' + a^2 h + 2ah' - 2a^2 h + a^2 h)\,e^{-ax} = 0,$$

which reduces to $h''(x) = 0$.

Integrating:

$$h'(x) = B, \qquad h(x) = A + Bx.$$

Thus $y = (A + Bx)\,e^{-ax} = A\,e^{-ax} + Bx\,e^{-ax}$; this contains $u(x) = e^{-ax}$, as expected, and $v(x) = x\,e^{-ax}$. The rule is simply: when the quadratic is a perfect square, multiply the first solution u by x to get the second solution v. (For a check, see Exercise 6.3.2.)

Example 13.41

What is the general solution of $y'' - 10y' + 25y = 0$?

Since $\sigma^2 - 10\sigma + 25 = 0$ if $\sigma = 5$, $u(x) = e^{5x}$ is a solution.

(*Check*: $u' = 5u$, $u'' = 5u' = 25u$, $u'' - 10u' + 25u = 25u - 50u + 25u = 0$.)

As $\sigma^2 - 10\sigma + 25 = (\sigma - 5)^2$ has only one root, the second solution is $v(x) = x\,e^{5x}$, and the general solution $y = (A + Bx)\,e^{5x}$. □

If $a^2 < b$, then the quadratic $\sigma^2 + 2a\sigma + b$ has no real roots. However the complex roots $-a \pm i\sqrt{(b - a^2)}$ both have the same real part $-a$, suggesting that e^{-ax} may again appear in the solutions, and that the substitution $y = h\,e^{-ax}$ should be tried again. It leads to

$$(h'' + c^2 h)\,e^{-ax} = 0, \quad \text{where } c^2 = b - a^2.$$

As $h''(x) = -c^2 h(x)$ is satisfied by both $\cos cx$ and $\sin cx$, $u(x) = e^{-ax}\cos cx$ and $v(x) = e^{-ax}\sin cx$ are solutions of equation (13.20). The rule is simply: when the quadratic $\sigma^2 + 2a\sigma + b$ has complex roots $-a \pm ic$, then $u(x) = e^{-ax}\cos cx$ and $v(x) = e^{-ax}\sin cx$.

Example 13.42

What is the general solution of $y'' + 2y' + 10y = 0$?

The quadratic $\sigma^2 + 2\sigma + 10 = 0$ has roots $-1 \pm \sqrt{(1 - 10)} = -1 \pm 3i$. So the general solution is $y = A\,e^{-x}\cos 3x + B\,e^{-x}\sin 3x$. □

The work so far in this section has shown that the complementary function for $y'' + 2ay' + by = R(x)$ can be written down after solving the quadratic equation

$\sigma^2 + 2a\sigma + b = 0$. It remains to find a particular solution s (unless $R(x) = 0$, in which case $s = 0$ is a particular solution, and the complementary function is the general solution).

As in equation (13.21), if y is an exponential function then $y'' + 2ay' + by$ is a multiple of the same exponential function. Conversely, if $R(x)$ is an exponential function, then some multiple of this function should be a particular solution.

Example 13.43
Find a particular solution of $y'' - 3y' - 4y = 2\,e^{2x}$, and hence the general solution.

For $R(x) = 2\,e^{2x}$ (an exponential function) try $s(x) = k\,e^{2x}$ (a multiple of $R(x)$), where k is to be determined by substituting into the given equation:

$$s' = 2s, \ s'' = 2s' = 4s, \qquad s'' - 3s' - 4s = -6s = -6k\,e^{2x}.$$

This is $2\,e^{2x}$ if $k = -1/3$. Thus $s(x) = (-1/3)\,e^{2x}$ is a particular solution.

Check:

$$s'(x) = (-2/3)\,e^{2x}, \qquad s''(x) = (-4/3)\,e^{2x},$$
$$s'' - 3s' - 4s = e^{2x}(-4/3 + 2 + 4/3) = 2\,e^{2x}.$$

The general solution is obtained by adding the complementary function, which was found in Example 13.40. Thus the general solution of $y'' - 3y' - 4y = 2\,e^{2x}$ is

$$y = (-1/3)\,e^{2x} + A\,e^{4x} + B\,e^{-x},$$

where A and B are arbitrary constants.   □

Similarly, if y has the form $\lambda \sin \omega x + \mu \cos \omega x$, which is called a **linear combination** of $\sin \omega x$ and $\cos \omega x$, then $y'' + 2ay' + by$ is (another) linear combination of $\sin \omega x$ and $\cos \omega x$. Conversely, if $R(x)$ has this form, some other linear combination of $\sin \omega x$ and $\cos \omega x$ would be a particular solution.

Example 13.44
Find a particular solution of $y'' + 2y' + 10y = \cos 3x$, and hence the general solution.

Given $R(x) = \cos 3x$, try $s(x) = \lambda \sin 3x + \mu \cos 3x$, where λ and μ are to be determined by substituting into the given equation:

$$s'(x) = 3\lambda \cos 3x - 3\mu \sin 3x$$
$$s''(x) = -9\lambda \sin 3x - 9\mu \cos 3x$$
$$2s'(x) = -6\mu \sin 3x + 6\lambda \cos 3x$$
$$10s(x) = 10\lambda \sin 3x + 10\mu \cos 3x.$$

Adding the last three lines shows that $s'' + 2s' + 10s$ is $\cos 3x$ if $\lambda - 6\mu = 0$ and $\mu + 6\lambda = 1$. Solving these simultaneous equations for λ and μ gives $\mu = 1/37$, $\lambda = 6/37$. Thus

$$s(x) = (6 \sin 3x + \cos 3x)/37$$

is a particular solution.

The general solution is now obtained by adding the complementary function, which was obtained in Example 13.42 to get

$$y = A e^{-x} \cos 3x + B e^{-x} \sin 3x + (\cos 3x + 6 \sin 3x)/37. \quad \square$$

The complete check of this solution was given in Example 6.32 on p. 114. However, s, u, and v can be checked separately. As the general form of u and v is known, the check need only be on the constants appearing in the exponential and trigonometric functions; when the quadratic has complex roots it is therefore sufficient to check only one of u and v.

If y is a polynomial, then $y'' + 2ay' + by$ is a polynomial of the same degree. Conversely if $R(x)$ is a polynomial, there should be a polynomial of the same degree which is a particular solution of $y'' + 2ay' + by = R(x)$.

Example 13.45

Find the general solution of

$$y'' - 2y' + 6y = x.$$

Since $\sigma^2 - 2\sigma + 6 = 0$ gives $\sigma = 1 \pm \sqrt{(-5)} = 1 \pm i\sqrt{5}$, the complementary function is $y = e^x[A \cos(x\sqrt{5}) + B \sin(x\sqrt{5})]$. Since $R(x) = x$ is a polynomial of degree 1, try $s(x) = \lambda x + \mu$, where λ and μ are to be chosen to give a particular solution. Since $s'(x) = \lambda$ and $s''(x) = 0$, substituting into the given equation yields $-2\lambda + 6(\lambda x + \mu) = x$, which is true if

$$-2\lambda + 6\mu = 0 \quad \text{and} \quad 6\lambda = 1.$$

Solving these two equations for λ and μ: $\lambda = \frac{1}{6}$, $\mu = \frac{1}{18}$.

Check: $s = (3x + 1)/18$, $s' = \frac{1}{6}$, $s'' = 0$, $s'' - 2s' + 6s = (-\frac{1}{3}) + x + (\frac{1}{3})$. The complementary function is checked as in Exercise 6.3.3 on p. 118. Hence the general solution is

$$y = (3x + 1)/18 + e^x[A \cos(x\sqrt{5}) + B \sin(x\sqrt{5})]. \quad \square$$

Examples 13.43–13.45 illustrate how to find a particular solution s of $y'' + 2ay' + by = R(x)$ when R is an exponential function, $\sin mx$ or $\cos mx$, or a polynomial. The method is to determine constants in a suitable trial function, by substituting into the given equation. If R is a sum or product of the same types of function, then a sum or product of the appropriate trial functions may be tried. This is shown in the following table, in which the first three rows are from Examples 13.43–13.45.

$R(x)$	Trial function for s
$2 e^{2x}$	$k e^{2x}$
$\cos 3x$	$\lambda \sin 3x + \mu \cos 3x$
x	$\lambda x + \mu$
$x + \cos 3x$	$\lambda \sin 3x + \mu \cos 3x + \lambda' x + \mu'$
$2x e^{2x}$	$(\lambda x + \mu) e^{2x}$
$2x \cos 3x$	$(x + \mu')(\lambda \sin 3x + \mu \cos 3x)$
x^n	$\lambda_1 x^n + \lambda_2 x^{n-1} + \cdots + \lambda_n x + \lambda_{n+1}$

When R is a product, one of the undetermined constants in the trial function may be set equal to 1. For example,

$$(\lambda x + \mu)k e^{2x} = [(\lambda k)x + \mu k] e^{2x} = (\lambda' x + \mu') e^{2x},$$

so k is clearly superfluous.

The suggested trial functions have to be modified if the usual rule gives a function already included in the complementary function. It is then sufficient to multiply the usual function by x, as many times as is necessary.

Example 13.46

Solve $y'' - 3y' - 4y = 2\,e^{4x}$.

Previous work suggests the trial function $s(x) = k\,e^{4x}$, but this is included in the complementary function (see Example 13.40 on p. 325). As s is a solution of the reduced equation, $s'' - 3s' - 4s = 0$ for any k, and k cannot be chosen to give a solution.

Then try $s(x) = kx\,e^{4x}$. Substituting $s'(x) = (k + 4kx)\,e^{4x}$ and $s''(x) = (8k + 16kx)\,e^{4x}$ into the equation yields

$$e^{4x}(8k + 16kx - 3k - 12kx - 4kx) = 2\,e^{4x} \tag{13.23}$$

which requires $5k = 2$, $k = 2/5$. The general solution is

$$y = (2x/5)\,e^{4x} + A\,e^{4x} + B\,e^{-x}. \quad \square$$

Example 13.47

Solve $y'' - 10y' + 25y = 3\,e^{5x}$.

The complementary function $A\,e^{5x} + Bx\,e^{5x}$ was obtained in Example 13.41. Here $R(x) = 3\,e^{5x}$, suggesting $k\,e^{5x}$ as the trial solution, but this is included in the complementary function. So is $kx\,e^{5x}$, so a further multiplication by x is required. Substituting $s(x) = kx^2\,e^{5x}$, $s'(x) = k(2x + 5x^2)\,e^{5x}$, $s''(x) = k(2 + 10x + 10x + 25x^2)\,e^{5x}$ into the equation yields

$$k(2 + 20x + 25x^2 - 20x - 50x^2 + 25x^2)\,e^{5x} = 3\,e^{5x} \tag{13.24}$$

which is true if $k = 3/2$. The general solution is

$$y = (A + Bx + 3x^2/2)\,e^{5x}.$$

The correctness of the three parts of this result ($u = e^{5x}$, $v = x\,e^{5x}$, $s = \frac{3}{2}x^2\,e^{5x}$) is checked as in the three parts of Exercise 6.3.2. $\square$

Note that on the left sides of equations (13.23) and (13.24), there are some terms which are multiples of $R(x)$ and which determine k, and others which must cancel. If the others do not cancel, either a mistake has been made in differentiating and substituting, or the form of the assumed trial solution is incorrect.

The methods that have been described in this section for obtaining particular solutions are summarized in Procedure B7 in Appendix B.

Since there are two arbitrary constants in the general solution of a second-order equation, two conditions are required to specify a particular solution.

Example 13.48

Find the four particular solutions of $y'' + 2y' - 3y = 6$ determined by the following pairs of conditions:

(i) $y(0) = 0$, $y'(0) = 1$, i.e. $y = 0$ and $dy/dx = 1$ at $x = 0$;

(ii) $y(0) = 0 = y(1)$;

(iii) $y(0) = 0$ and $y(x)$ has a finite limit as $x \to \infty$;

(iv) $y(0) = 0$ and $y(x)$ has a finite limit as $x \to -\infty$.

The method is to determine the general solution, and then to use the given conditions to fix values for the arbitrary constants.

The complementary function is determined after solving $\sigma^2 + 2\sigma - 3 = 0$. This gives $\sigma = -3$ or 1, so e^{-3x} and e^x are solutions of the reduced equation.

Check: $(e^{-3x})'' + 2(e^{-3x})' - 3 e^{-3x} = (9 - 6 - 3) e^{-3x} (e^x$ obvious). The complementary function is therefore $A e^{-3x} + B e^x$. As $R(x) = 6$ is a polynomial of degree zero (a constant), there is a constant particular solution $s(x) = k$ for some k. (This has not already appeared in the complementary function.) Substituting gives $k = -2$; as then $s(0) = -2$, this solution is not one of those specified by conditions (i)-(iv). However the general solution is

$$y = A e^{-3x} + B e^x - 2,$$

with derivative

$$y' = -3A e^{-3x} + B e^x.$$

(i) $y(0) = 0$ requires $0 = A + B - 2$; $y'(0) = 1$ requires $1 = -3A + B$. Solving the two equations for A and B gives $A = 1/4$, $B = 7/4$. The required particular solution is

$$y = s_1(x) = -2 + (e^{-3x} + 7 e^x)/4.$$

Check: $s_1(0) = -2 + 2$, $s_1'(x) = (-3 e^{-3x} + 7 e^x)/4$, $s_1'(0) = 1$.

(ii) $y(0) = 0 = y(1)$ requires $A + B - 2 = 0 = A/e^3 + B e - 2$. Solving these equations for A and B, and putting the values obtained into the general solution, gives the required particular solution:

$$y = s_2(x) = -2 + \frac{2 e^{3-3x} + 2(e^2 + e + 1) e^x}{e^3 + e^2 + e + 1}.$$

(iii) $y(0) = 0$ requires $A + B = 2$; and $y(x) \to \pm\infty$ as $x \to \infty$ unless $B = 0$. So $A = 2$, $B = 0$ and $y = s_3(x) = 2(-1 + e^{-3x})$.

(iv) $y(x) \to \pm\infty$ as $x \to -\infty$ unless $A = 0$; then $y(0) = 0$ if $B = 2$. So $y = s_4(x) = 2(-1 + e^x.)$ □

In constructing the general solution, any particular solution can be added to the complementary function. For example it would be quite correct to give

$$y = A e^{-3x} + B' e^x + s_4(x)$$

as the general solution to $y'' + 2y' - 3y = 6$. (The previous form of the general solution is obtained by writing the arbitrary constant B' in the equivalent form $B - 2$.)

The general solution of $d^2y/dx^2 + 2a \, dy/dx + by = R(x)$ is separated into a complementary function $h(x) = A e^{\sigma_1 x} + B e^{\sigma_2 x}$, which contains the arbitrary constants and does not depend on $R(x)$, and a particular solution $s(x)$ which does depend on $R(x)$. If σ_1 and σ_2 are negative (or have negative real part), then the asymptotic form (as $x \to \infty$) of any solution is $y(x) \sim s(x)$, because $h(x) \to 0$. This has special physical significance when the independent variable is the time. Then h is called the **transient solution**, and s the **steady-state solution**. After a sufficient time for the transient solution to be negligible, the steady-state solution is the solution for any given conditions at time zero (because these only determine the arbitrary constants).

Exercises (answers on p. 347)

13.4.1   Solve $y'' - 2y' = 0$

13.4.2   Solve $y'' + 4y' + 5y = 0$

13.4.3   Solve $y'' - 6y' + 5y = 145 \sin 2x$

13.4.4   Solve $y'' + 2y' + 5y = 2x + 1$

13.4.5   Solve $y'' + 4y = 2 \cos 2x$

13.4.6   By substituting the (incorrect) trial function $s(x) = kx\, e^{2x}$ into $y'' - 3y' - 4y = 2\, e^{2x}$, show that there is no solution of this form.

13.4.7   What trial function should be used to find a particular solution of $d^2 i/dt^2 + (R/L)\, di/dt + (1/CL)i = A \cos(\omega t + \phi)$, where A, ω and ϕ are constants?

13.4.8   Using the result of Exercise 6.3.2(iii), write down the solution of

$$\frac{d^2 y}{dx^2} + 2a \frac{dy}{dx} + a^2 y = \lambda\, e^{-ax}.$$

13.5   Reduction of Order

The following result applies to the general second-order linear equation (13.19). Suppose $u(x)$ is a known solution of the reduced equation. Then

> if $y = hu$ is substituted into equation (13.19), so that $h(x)$ becomes the unknown function, the terms containing h cancel. This leaves h' and h'' the unknown functions; putting $h' = g$ and $h'' = g'$, the equation becomes a first-order equation in g.

Thus the substitution reduces the order. Moreover, the equation for g is also linear, so the method of Section 13.2 may be used.

One example of this procedure appeared in solving equation (13.22), on p. 326. The reduced equation is the same equation. The substitution led to $h'' = 0$, i.e. $g' = 0$ which is first-order in g.

Example 13.50

Consider again $y'' - 3y' - 4y = 2\, e^{2x}$, which has already been solved in Example 13.43. From the complementary function found in Example 13.40 $u(x) = e^{4x}$ satisfies the reduced equation. So substitute

$$y = h\, e^{4x}, \qquad y' = (h' + 4h)\, e^{4x}, \qquad y'' = (h'' + 8h' + 16h)\, e^{4x}.$$

The given equation becomes

$$(h'' + 8h' + 16h - 3h' - 12h - 4h)\, e^{4x} = 2\, e^{2x}.$$

(The cancellation of the terms in h is exactly the same as in the check in Example 13.40 that u satisfies $y'' - 3y' - 4y = 0$.) Setting $h' = g$ and $h'' = g'$ gives

$$(g' + 5g)\, e^{4x} = 2\, e^{2x}$$

or

$$g' + 5g = 2\, e^{-2x}.$$

This is a first-order linear equation for g; from equation (13.14), on p. 321, an integrating factor is given by $\ln I = \int 5 \, dx = 5x$. $I = e^{5x}$, so

$$dg \ e^{5x} + g(5 \ e^{5x} \ dx) = 2 \ e^{-2x} \ e^{5x} \ dx$$

$$d(g \ e^{5x}) = 2 \ e^{3x} \ dx.$$

Integrating:

$$g \ e^{5x} = (2/3) \ e^{3x} + C \qquad (13.25)$$

$$h' = g = (2/3) \ e^{-2x} + C \ e^{-5x}.$$

Integrating again:

$$h = (-1/3) \ e^{-2x} + (-C/5) \ e^{-5x} + A \qquad (13.26)$$

$$y = h \ e^{4x} = (-1/3) \ e^{2x} + (-C/5) \ e^{-x} + A \ e^{4x}.$$

This is the general solution since it contains two arbitrary constants C and A. Writing $(-C/5)$ as an equivalent arbitrary constant B gives exactly the result of Example 13.43.   □

For the constant coefficient equation, a solution of the reduced equation can always be found, so reduction to a first-order linear equation is possible whatever the form of $R(x)$. This can be solved provided the form of $R(x)$ makes it possible to effect the integrations at the stages corresponding to equations (13.25) and (13.26) in the previous example.

For the general case of equation (13.19) where P and/or Q depend on x, there is no general method of finding a solution u of the reduced equation. If u is known, an integrating factor for the first-order equation can be found if $\int P(x) \, dx$ can be evaluated (see Exercise 13.21(i)). In the next example, u is obvious by inspection.

Example 13.51
Solve $x^2 y'' - (x^2 + 2x)y' + (x + 2)y = x^4$.

The reduced equation $x^2 y'' - (x^2 + 2x)y' + (x + 2)y = 0$ is obviously satisfied by $y = u(x) = x$. So substitute into the given equation $y = hx$, $y' = h + h'x$, $y'' = 2h' + h''x$:

$$2x^2 h' + x^3 h'' - x^2 h - x^3 h' - 2xh - 2x^2 h' + x^2 h + 2xh = x^4.$$

Putting

$$g = h' \quad \text{gives} \quad g' - g = x. \qquad (13.27)$$

The integrating factor is given by $\ln I = \int (-1) \, dx = -x$, so $I = e^{-x}$.

$$d(g \ e^{-x}) = x \ e^{-x} \ dx$$

$$g \ e^{-x} = -x \ e^{-x} + \int e^{-x} \ dx \quad \text{(by parts)}$$

$$= -(x + 1) \ e^{-x} + A$$

$$h'(x) = g(x) = -x - 1 + A \ e^{x} \qquad (13.28)$$

$$h(x) = -\tfrac{1}{2}x^2 - x + A \ e^{x} + B$$

$$y = xh = -\tfrac{1}{2}x^3 - x^2 + Bx + Ax \ e^{x}.$$

Check:

$$y' = -\tfrac{3}{2}x^2 - 2x + B + A\,e^x + Ax\,e^x$$

$$y'' = -3x - 2 + A\,e^x + A\,e^x + Ax\,e^x$$

$$-xy' + y = x^3 + x^2 - Ax^2\,e^x$$

$$(x+2)(-xy'+y) = x^4 + x^3 + 2x^3 + 2x^2 - Ax^2(x+2)\,e^x$$

$$x^2 y'' = -3x^3 - 2x^2 + Ax^2(x+2)\,e^x.$$

Adding the last two lines shows that the given differential equation is satisfied. □

Exercise (answer on p. 348)
13.5.1 Solve Exercise 13.4.5 by reducing the order.

13.6 Change of Variable

In the previous section the order of the differential equation was reduced by changing the dependent variable from y to a new unknown h. Alternatively, it may be possible to put a differential equation into a soluble form by changing the independent variable. This is like integration by substitution (certainly insofar as intuition is usually required to guess a suitable substitution); the only new feature, for second-order equations, is the transformation of the second derivative d^2y/dx^2.

One standard application is to change an equation of the form

$$x^2 y'' + pxy' + qy = R(x), \tag{13.29}$$

where p and q are constants, to a constant coefficient equation. This is effected by the substitution $x = e^t$.

Then $dx = e^t\,dt = x\,dt$. For any variable z, $dz/dx = (dz/dt)(dt/dx)$

$$\therefore \quad \frac{dz}{dx} = e^{-t}\frac{dz}{dt} \quad \text{or} \quad \frac{dz}{dt} = x\frac{dz}{dx}.$$

Since the function z is arbitrary, these equations may be written

$$d/dx = e^{-t}(d/dt) \quad \text{or} \quad d/dt = x(d/dx)$$

and considered as relating the **operations** of differentiating with respect to x and differentiating with respect to t. In using these relations, d/dx should only be applied to functions which have been expressed entirely in terms of x, and d/dt should only be applied to expressions containing t and not x.

To transform the second derivative of the differential equation, one can either start from d^2y/dx^2 or from d^2y/dt^2.

(i) $$\frac{d^2y}{dx^2} = \frac{d}{dx}\left(\frac{dy}{dx}\right) = e^{-t}\frac{d}{dt}\left(\frac{dy}{dx}\right)$$

$$= e^{-t}\frac{d}{dt}\left(e^{-t}\frac{dy}{dt}\right)$$

$$= e^{-t}\left(-e^{-t}\frac{dy}{dt} + e^{-t}\frac{d^2y}{dt^2}\right), \quad \text{using the product rule.}$$

$$\therefore \quad x^2\frac{d^2y}{dx^2} = -\frac{dy}{dt} + \frac{d^2y}{dt^2}, \quad \text{since } x = e^t.$$

Also

$$x\frac{dy}{dx} = x\,e^{-t}\frac{dy}{dt} = \frac{dy}{dt},$$

so equation (13.29) becomes

$$\frac{d^2y}{dt^2} - \frac{dy}{dt} + p\frac{dy}{dt} + qy = R(e^t)$$

which is a constant coefficient equation.

Or (ii) $\dfrac{d^2y}{dt^2} = \dfrac{d}{dt}\left(\dfrac{dy}{dt}\right) = x\dfrac{d}{dx}\left(x\dfrac{dy}{dx}\right)$

$$= x\left(\frac{dy}{dx} + x\frac{d^2y}{dx^2}\right), \quad \text{using the product rule.}$$

$$\therefore \quad x^2\frac{d^2y}{dx^2} = \frac{d^2y}{dt^2} - x\frac{dy}{dx} \quad \text{and} \quad x\frac{dy}{dx} = \frac{dy}{dt}.$$

The complementary function for equation (13.29) can be written down from the roots of the quadratic $\sigma^2 + (p-1)\sigma + q = 0$.

Exercises (answers on p. 348)
13.6.1   Solve $x^2y'' + 2xy' - 2y = 2\log x$
13.6.2   Solve the equation (given in Exercise 6.3.5 on p. 118)

$$(\cos x)\frac{d^2y}{dx^2} + (\sin x)\frac{dy}{dx} + (4\cos^3 x)y = 8\cos^5 x$$

by making the change of variable $t = \sin x$.

13.7   The Use of Complex Functions

In Section 6.11 it was shown that the derivative of a complex function $z(t)$ of type $R \to C$ is obtained by differentiating the two real functions defined by the real and imaginary parts of $z(t)$. Defining e^{it} as $\cos t + i\sin t$ then gave $(d/dt)\,e^{it} = ie^{it}$. In Section 12.5, the exponential function was defined for an arbitrary complex number, so the function $z(t) = e^{\sigma t}$ can now be considered for any complex constant σ.
   If $\sigma = a + ic$, then

$$z(t) = e^{(a+ic)t} = e^{at}\cos ct + ie^{at}\sin ct,$$

from equation (12.9) on p. 307.
   Then

$$z'(t) = \frac{d}{dt}(e^{at}\cos ct) + i\frac{d}{dt}(e^{at}\sin ct)$$

$$= a\,e^{at}\cos ct - c\,e^{at}\sin ct + ia\,e^{at}\sin ct + ic\,e^{at}\cos ct$$

$$= (a+ic)\,e^{at}(\cos ct + i\sin ct)$$

$$\text{i.e.} \quad \frac{d}{dt}e^{\sigma t} = \sigma\,e^{\sigma t}. \tag{13.30}$$

Because the form of this equation is the same for complex σ as for real σ, most of the work in Sections 13.3–13.6 can be formally extended to differential equations of the form

$$\frac{d^2z}{dt^2} + P(t)\frac{dz}{dt} + Q(t)z = R(t) \tag{13.31}$$

where the required unknown solution $z(t)$ is a complex function of type $R \to C$. The given coefficient functions $P(t)$, $Q(t)$ and $R(t)$ may also be complex.

Example 13.70
Solve the differential equation

$$\frac{d^2z}{dt^2} + 2\frac{dz}{dt} + 10z = 0.$$

As with polynomial equations, the notation z for the unknown function usually means that complex solutions are required. This does not affect the structure of the general solution, which is

$$z(t) = \alpha u(t) + \beta v(t)$$

where u and v are any independent particular solutions, and α and β are **complex** arbitrary constants. Moreover u and v can still be written down from the roots $-1 \pm 3i$ of the quadratic

$$\sigma^2 + 2\sigma + 10 = 0.$$

However for a complex solution it is irrelevant whether the roots are complex or not. Thus

$$u(t) = e^{(-1+3i)t} \quad \text{and} \quad v(t) = e^{(-1-3i)t}$$

are independent solutions, and the general solution is

$$z(t) = \alpha\, e^{(-1+3i)t} + \beta\, e^{(-1-3i)t}$$
$$= e^{-t}(\alpha\, e^{3it} + \beta\, e^{-3it}).$$

Note that choosing $\alpha = \beta = \frac{1}{2}$ gives the real solution $e^{-t}\cos 3t$, and choosing $\alpha = 1/2i = -\beta$ gives the real solution $e^{-t}\sin 3t$. (cf. Example 13.42). $\square$

> Any complex differential equation is equivalent to two real differential equations by separating it into real and imaginary parts.

If the given functions P and Q in equation (13.31) are real, then putting $z(t) = x(t) + iy(t)$ and taking real and imaginary parts shows that x and y satisfy the equations:

$$\ddot{x} + P\dot{x} + Qx = \text{Re } R$$

$$\ddot{y} + P\dot{y} + Qy = \text{Im } R$$

(using dots for derivatives with respect to t). Thus if $z(t)$ is a complex solution of equation (13.31), with P and Q real, then the real and imaginary parts of $z(t)$ are solutions of related differential equations. In particular, if $R = 0$, then the real and imaginary parts of $z(t)$ are both solutions of the same equation (13.31).

Example 13.71

Find two independent real solutions of $\ddot{z}+2\dot{z}+5=0$.

The complex solution $e^{(-1+3i)t}=e^{-t}(\cos 3t+i\sin 3t)$ is obtained as in Example 13.70. Its real and imaginary parts $e^{-t}\cos 3t$ and $e^{-t}\sin 3t$ are two real solutions (cf. Example 13.42).   □

Example 13.72

Find a particular solution of $d^2y/dx^2+2\,dy/dx+10y=\cos 3x$.

Since $\cos 3x$ is the real part of e^{3ix}, and the coefficients 2 and 10 are real, a particular solution can be obtained by taking the real part of a complex solution of

$$\frac{d^2z}{dx^2}+2\frac{dz}{dx}+10z=e^{3ix}.$$

Try $z=k\,e^{3ix}$, where k is to be determined by substituting:

$$(3i)^2k\,e^{3ix}+2(3i)k\,e^{3ix}+10k\,e^{3ix}=e^{3ix},$$

using equation (13.30) for the derivatives.

$$\therefore\quad k=\frac{1}{1+6i}=\frac{1-6i}{37}$$

$$z(t)=(\tfrac{1}{37}-\tfrac{6}{37}i)(\cos 3x+i\sin 3x).$$

The real part is $(\cos 3x+6\sin 3x)/37$ (cf. Example 13.44 on p. 327).   □

Example 13.73

Find the particular solution of

$$\frac{d^2z}{dt^2}+(4+2i)\frac{dz}{dt}+(3+2i)z=6\,e^{it} \tag{13.32}$$

satisfying

$$z=1 \quad\text{and}\quad dz/dt=2-3i \quad\text{at } t=0. \tag{13.33}$$

Give the equivalent real differential equations and initial conditions.

The complementary function is written down from the roots of

$$\sigma^2+(4+2i)\sigma+(3+2i)=0,$$

i.e. $\sigma=-1$ or $-3-2i$ (Exercise A2.6 in Appendix A). Thus

$$\alpha\,e^{-t}+\beta\,e^{(-3-2i)t}$$

is the general solution of the reduced equation. For a particular solution try $z=k\,e^{it}$. Substituting, and cancelling e^{it}, gives

$$i^2k+(4+2i)ik+(3+2i)k=6.$$

Thus $6ik=6$, $k=-i$, and $-i\,e^{it}$ is a solution. The general solution is

$$z=\alpha\,e^{-t}+\beta\,e^{(-3-2i)t}-i\,e^{it}$$

giving

$$\frac{dz}{dt} = -\alpha\,e^{-t} - (3+2i)\beta\,e^{(-3-2i)t} + e^{it}.$$

The given initial conditions require

$$\alpha + \beta = i + 1 \quad \text{and} \quad -\alpha - (3+2i)\beta = 1 - 3i.$$

Adding,

$$-(2+2i)\beta = 2 - 2i, \qquad \beta = \frac{i-1}{1+i} = \frac{(i-1)(1-i)}{2} = i.$$

Then $\alpha = 1$, and

$$z = e^{-t} + i\,e^{(-3-2i)t} - i\,e^{it}.$$

Writing $z = e^{-t} + i\,e^{-3t}(\cos 2t - i \sin 2t) - i(\cos t + i \sin t)$ shows that the real and imaginary parts of this solution are

$$x = e^{-t} + e^{-3t}\sin 2t + \sin t \tag{13.34}$$

$$y = e^{-3t}\cos 2t - \cos t. \tag{13.35}$$

Writing equation (13.32) as (dots denoting derivatives)

$$(\ddot{x} + i\ddot{y}) + (4+2i)(\dot{x} + i\dot{y}) + (3+2i)(x + iy) = 6(\cos t + i \sin t)$$

enables its real and imaginary parts to be read off. Thus equations (13.34) and (13.35) are the solution of the simultaneous differential equations

$$\frac{d^2x}{dt^2} + 4\frac{dx}{dt} - 2\frac{dy}{dt} + 3x - 2y = 6\cos t$$

$$\frac{d^2y}{dt^2} + 2\frac{dx}{dt} + 4\frac{dy}{dt} + 2x + 3y = 6\sin t$$

determined by the initial conditions (from equation (13.33))

$$x = 1, \qquad y = 0, \qquad \frac{dx}{dt} = 2, \qquad \frac{dy}{dt} = -3, \quad \text{at } t = 0. \quad \square$$

Exercises (answers on p. 348)

13.7.1   Find the solution of (cf. Example 13.70)

$$\frac{d^2z}{dt^2} + 2\frac{dz}{dt} + 10z = 0$$

satisfying $z = i$ and $dz/dt = -i$ at $t = 0$.

13.7.2   Find the general solution of

$$\frac{d^2z}{dt^2} - 3\frac{dz}{dt} - 4z = i\,e^{2it}.$$

Deduce the general solutions of the real equations

$$\frac{d^2y}{dt^2} - 3\frac{dy}{dt} - 4y = \cos 2t$$

and

$$\frac{d^2x}{dt^2} - 3\frac{dx}{dt} - 4x = -\sin 2t.$$

13.7.3   Solve the equation

$$\frac{d^2z}{dt^2} - 6\frac{dz}{dt} + 5z = 145\,e^{2it}.$$

Deduce the solution of Exercise 13.4.3.

13.7.4   Find a particular solution of

$$\frac{d^2z}{dt^2} - 4\frac{dz}{dt} + 8z = e^{(2+2i)t}$$

and hence find a particular solution of

$$\frac{d^2x}{dt^2} - 4\frac{dx}{dt} + 8x = e^{2t}\cos 2t.$$

13.8   Some Applications of Differential Equations

Example 13.80

Liquid flows into the top of a cylindrical tank at a volumetric flow rate $B\,e^{-t/\tau_1}$ at time t, where B and τ_1 are constants. Liquid flows out of a valve at the bottom of the tank at a volumetric flow rate $h(t)/R$ proportional to the height $h(t)$ of liquid in the tank, R being a constant determined by the design of the valve. Find the function $h(t)$, given $h(0) = h_0$.

If A is the cross-sectional area of the tank, the volume of liquid in the tank at time t is $Ah(t)$. The rate of change of this volume is the difference between the inflow rate and the outflow rate:

$$\frac{d}{dt}(Ah) = B\,e^{-t/\tau_1} - h/R.$$

This is a first-order linear equation for $h(t)$

$$AR\frac{dh}{dt} + h = BR\,e^{-t/\tau_1}. \tag{13.36}$$

The required particular solution will be determined by the initial condition $h = h_0$ at $t = 0$. Three methods of finding the solution will now be given.

(i) Using an integrating factor (cf. Section 13.2). Comparing with equation (13.11) on p. 320, $Q(t)$ is the constant $1/AR$, and $\ln I = \int Q\,dt = t/AR$ gives the integrating factor. Thus equation (13.36) becomes

$$e^{t/AR}\frac{dh}{dt} + \frac{1}{AR}\,e^{t/AR}h = \frac{B}{A}\,e^{pt}$$

where $p = 1/AR - 1/\tau_1$. Integrating:

$$h\, e^{t/AR} = \frac{B}{Ap}\, e^{pt} + C$$

where the arbitrary constant C is now determined by the initial condition:

$$h_0 = \frac{B}{Ap} + C.$$

Thus

$$h\, e^{t/AR} = h_0 + \frac{B}{Ap}\, (e^{pt} - 1)$$

and

$$h(t) = h_0\, e^{-t/AR} + \frac{B}{Ap}\, (e^{-t/\tau_1} - e^{-t/AR}).$$

Check: The constants B, A, p have dimensions $(\text{length})^3/\text{time}$, $(\text{length})^2$, and $(\text{time})^{-1}$, so (B/Ap) is a length.

(ii) Using rules for finding a complementary function and particular integral (cf. Section 13.4).
    Since equation (13.36) has constant coefficients, $u(t) = e^{\sigma t}$ is a solution of the reduced equation if $AR\sigma + 1 = 0$. Thus the complementary function is

$$h_c(t) = C\, e^{-t/AR}.$$

For a particular solution try $h_p = k\, e^{-t/\tau_1}$ where k is to be found by substituting into (13.36):

$$ARk\left(-\frac{1}{\tau_1}\right) e^{-t/\tau_1} + k\, e^{-t/\tau_1} = BR\, e^{-t/\tau_1}.$$

Thus $k = B/Ap$, and the general solution of equation (13.36) is

$$h(t) = h_c(t) + h_p(t) = C\, e^{-t/AR} + \frac{B}{Ap}\, e^{-t/\tau_1}.$$

The arbitrary constant C is found from the initial condition, as in (i).

(iii) Using a solution u of the reduced equation in a substitution $h = gu$ (cf. Section 13.5).
    A solution of the reduced equation, $u(t) = e^{-t/AR}$, was found in (ii). Substituting $h = g\, e^{-t/AR}$ into equation (13.36) gives

$$AR\frac{dg}{dt} e^{-t/AR} = BR\, e^{-t/\tau_1}$$

$$\frac{dg}{dt} = \frac{B}{A}\, e^{pt}, \qquad g(t) = \frac{B}{Ap}\, e^{pt} + C.$$

At $t = 0$, $g = h = h_0$, giving the same value of C. The required solution also agrees with that given in (i).

This substitution approach to the first-order linear equation is further discussed in Exercise 13.28 at the end of the chapter. □

Example 13.81

A sugar solution of concentration C_0 g/litre flows through a tank of volume V litre at a constant flow rate $\dot V$ litre/s. If the inlet concentration is increased to C_i g/litre, find the subsequent outlet concentration $C(t)$. Assume that stirring keeps a uniform concentration $C(t)$ throughout the tank.

$$\text{Rate of increase of sugar in tank} = \mathrm{d}(VC)/\mathrm{d}t = VC'(t)$$

$$= (\text{mass in per unit time}) - (\text{mass out per unit time})$$

$$= \dot V C_i - \dot V C(t).$$

Putting $\tau = V/\dot V$ gives the variables separable equation

$$\tau C'(t) = C_i - C(t).$$

The required particular solution will be determined by the initial condition $C(0) = C_0$, i.e. $C(t) = C_0$ at $t = 0$.

Separating the variables:

$$\frac{\mathrm{d}C}{C_i - C} = \frac{1}{\tau}\,\mathrm{d}t.$$

Integrating:

$$-\ln|C_i - C| = \frac{t}{\tau} + A.$$

Since the inlet concentration is increased, $C_i > C_0$, and $C(t)$ is expected to increase from C_0 at $t = 0$, and approach C_i. Thus $C(t) < C_i$ and $|C_i - C| = (C_i - C)$.

The initial condition $C = C_0$ at $t = 0$ determines the arbitrary constant A:

$$-\ln(C_i - C_0) = 0 + A.$$

Hence

$$-t/\tau = \ln(C_i - C) - \ln(C_i - C_0) = \ln\left[\frac{C_i - C}{C_i - C_0}\right]$$

$$e^{-t/\tau} = (C_i - C)/(C_i - C_0)$$

$$C(t) = C_i - (C_i - C_0)\,e^{-t/\tau}.$$

The result verifies that $C(t) < C_i$ if $C_0 < C_i$, since the exponential function is positive; and $C(t) \to C_i$ as $t \to \infty$. □

Example 13.82

Solve the equation

$$L\frac{\mathrm{d}i}{\mathrm{d}t} + Ri = V\cos\omega t \tag{13.37}$$

for the current $i(t)$ in a circuit containing a resistance R, an inductance L, and a time-dependent (a.c.) input voltage $V \cos \omega t$.

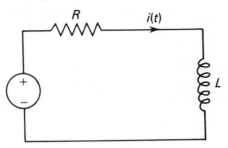

Figure 13.3   Circuit with input voltage $V \cos \omega t$

Since the equation is a first-order linear equation for $i(t)$, any of the three methods used in Example 13.80 could be used to solve the equation. However, method (ii) is always used, since the complementary function need not be considered in practice. A particular solution has the form $(\lambda \cos \omega t + \mu \sin \omega t)$ for some λ and μ which can be found by substitution. The complementary function is obtained by solving

$$L\frac{du}{dt} + Ru = 0, \qquad \frac{du}{u} = \frac{-R}{L}\,dt, \qquad u = C\,e^{-Rt/L}$$

and the general solution has the form

$$i(t) = C\,e^{-Rt/L} + \lambda \cos \omega t + \mu \sin \omega t.$$

As t increases, the first term (complementary function) tends to zero, and

$$i(t) \sim \lambda \cos \omega t + \mu \sin \omega t \quad \text{as } t \to \infty.$$

In practice this asymptotic form, which is the standard particular solution given by the rules stated in Section 13.4, is achieved in a short enough time for it to be the only solution of interest. It is called **the steady-state solution**.

Substituting $i = \lambda \cos \omega t + \mu \sin \omega t$ into the equation:

$$L\omega(-\lambda \sin \omega t + \mu \cos \omega t) + R(\lambda \cos \omega t + \mu \sin \omega t) = V \cos \omega t$$

requiring $-L\omega\lambda + R\mu = 0$, $L\omega\mu + R\lambda = V$. These are two equations for λ and μ which give

$$\lambda = VR/(R^2 + L^2\omega^2), \qquad \mu = L\omega V/(R^2 + L^2\omega^2).$$

The steady-state solution is therefore

$$i(t) = \frac{V}{R^2 + L^2\omega^2}\{R \cos \omega t + L\omega \sin \omega t\}.$$

To display the physical significance of this solution, a different form of it must be obtained. Since

$$\left[\frac{R}{\sqrt{(R^2 + L^2\omega^2)}}\right]^2 + \left[\frac{L\omega}{\sqrt{(R^2 + L^2\omega^2)}}\right]^2 = 1$$

there is an angle γ such that

$$\cos \gamma = R/\sqrt{(R^2 + L^2\omega^2)}, \qquad \sin \gamma = L\omega/\sqrt{(R^2 + L^2\omega^2)}.$$

Then the steady-state solution can be written

$$i(t) = \frac{V}{\sqrt{(R^2 + L^2\omega^2)}} \{\cos \gamma \cos \omega t + \sin \gamma \sin \omega t\}$$

$$= I_m \cos(\omega t - \gamma) \quad \text{where } I_m = V/\sqrt{(R^2 + L^2\omega^2)}.$$

Since the range of the function cos is $[-1, 1]$, the greatest value of $|i(t)|$ is I_m, which is called the amplitude or peak value. Since $\cos n\pi = \pm 1$ (more precisely, $\cos n\pi = (-1)^n$), $|i(t)|$ is greatest at times given by $\omega t - \gamma = 0, \pi, 2\pi, \ldots$, that is

$$t = (n\pi + \gamma)/\omega \qquad (n = 0, 1, 2, \ldots).$$

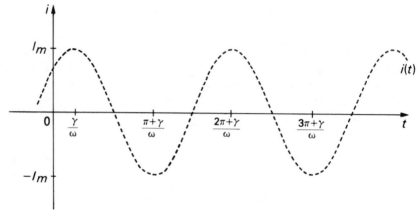

Figure 13.4   Steady-state current

The peak values $\pm V$ of the input voltage $V \cos \omega t$ occur at $t = 0, \pi/\omega, 2\pi/\omega, \ldots,$ $n\pi/\omega, \ldots$. Thus the peak values of the current are attained at times γ/ω later than the voltage peaks.

Changing the form of $i(t)$ to display I_m and γ reveals the important physical characteristics of the solution. This information can also be obtained by solving a complex equation, the real part of which is the actual circuit equation (13.37). The method was given (for a second-order equation) in Example 13.72 on p. 336. Rewrite equation (13.37) with the input voltage replaced by the complex function $V e^{j\omega t}(j^2 = -1)$. For a particular solution of

$$L\frac{dz}{dt} + Rz = V e^{j\omega t}$$

substitute the trial function $z = k e^{j\omega t}$ where k is a complex constant to be determined:

$$Lkj\omega e^{j\omega t} + Rk e^{j\omega t} = V e^{j\omega t}.$$

This gives

$$k = V/(R + jL\omega).$$

Since $|R + jL\omega| = \sqrt{(R^2 + L^2\omega^2)}$, the polar form of $R + jL\omega$ is

$$R + jL\omega = \sqrt{(R + L^2\omega^2)}(\cos \gamma + j \sin \gamma)$$

and so

$$k = \frac{V}{\sqrt{(R + L^2\omega^2)}\, e^{j\gamma}} = I_m\, e^{-j\gamma}.$$

The complex solution is therefore

$$z(t) = I_m\, e^{j(\omega t - \gamma)}.$$

This is in polar form, showing that $|z(t)|$ is the peak current I_m, and $\arg z(t) = \omega t - \gamma$ contains the constant γ which gives the phase lag of the current behind that of the applied voltage. In fact if $W(t) = V e^{j\omega t}$ is the complex applied voltage,

$$\gamma = \arg W - \arg z = \arg Z,$$

$$I_m = |k| = |z| = |W|/|Z|,$$

where $Z = R + jL\omega$ is the **complex impedance**.   □

Example 13.83
The primary circuit of an ignition system is shown in Fig. 13.5. Find the current $i(t)$ if $i = 0$ at $t = 0$ and the contact breaker switch is opened at time $t = t_0$.

From $t = 0$ to $t = t_0$ the condenser is short-circuited and the circuit, shown in Fig. 13.6, is the same as in the previous example except that the applied (d.c.) voltage V is constant. At $t = t_0$ the condenser with capacity C is brought into the circuit, giving the circuit diagram shown in Fig. 13.7.

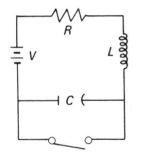

Figure 13.5   Switch (contact breaker)

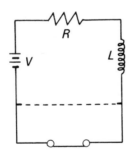

Figure 13.6   Switch closed

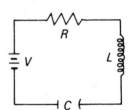

Figure 13.7   Switch open

From $t = 0$ to $t = t_0$ the differential equation for the current is (cf. equation (13.37)):

$$L\frac{di}{dt} + Ri = V. \qquad (13.38)$$

When the condenser is introduced, the equation contains an extra term $q(t)/C$ where $q(t)$ is the charge on the condenser. Since the current $i(t)$ is dq/dt, the charge $q(t)$ satisfies

$$L\frac{d^2q}{dt^2} + R\frac{dq}{dt} + \frac{1}{C}q = V. \qquad (13.39)$$

Both (13.38) and (13.39) are linear equations with constant coefficients. Since V is constant, each equation has a constant particular solution. (In terms of the rules in Section

13.4, V is a polynomial in t of degree zero). Thus $i_p = V/R$ satisfies equation (13.38), and $q_p = VC$ satisfies equation (13.39). However in this application, the main interest is in the part of the solution that comes from the complementary function.

For equation (13.38) the complementary function is $A\,e^{-Rt/L}$ as in the previous example, so the general solution of (13.38) is

$$i(t) = A\,e^{-Rt/L} + V/R.$$

The required particular solution has the value of A determined by the initial condition $i = 0$ at $t = 0$:

$$0 = A + V/R.$$

Thus

$$i(t) = \frac{V}{R}(1 - e^{-Rt/L}) \qquad (0 \leqslant t \leqslant t_0) \tag{13.40}$$

gives the current until the contact breaker switch opens (Fig. 13.8). The constant (steady-state) solution $i_p = V/R$ (Ohm's law) is just the limiting current which would be obtained if the switch remained closed.

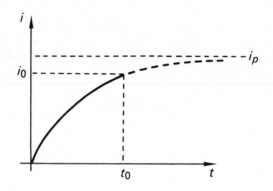

Figure 13.8   Current while switch closed

In this application, the constants L, R, C in equation (13.39) have values for which $R^2 < 4L/C$ so that

$$L\sigma^2 + R\sigma + 1/C = 0$$

has complex roots, say

$$\sigma = -\frac{R}{2L} \pm i\omega \quad \text{with} \quad \omega^2 = \frac{1}{LC} - \frac{R^2}{4L^2}. \tag{13.41}$$

The general solution of (13.39) can therefore be written

$$q(t) = e^{-Rt/2L}\{B \cos \omega t + D \sin \omega t\} + VC. \tag{13.42}$$

At $t = t_0$ it is known that $q = 0$ and, using equation (13.40),

$$\left.\frac{dq}{dt}\right|_{t=t_0} = i(t_0) = \frac{V}{R}(1 - e^{-Rt_0/L}) = i_0 \quad \text{(say)}.$$

These two equations determine the arbitrary constants B and D in the general solution (13.42). Some simplification of the algebra is now obtained by taking t_0 to be the zero of time for the second stage of the system. This does not alter (13.39) or (13.42), but allows the initial conditions $q = 0$ and $dq/dt = i_0$ to be applied at $t = 0$. From (13.42),

$$\frac{dq}{dt} = e^{-Rt/2L}\left\{\left(-\frac{BR}{2L} + D\omega\right)\cos\omega t + \left(-B\omega - \frac{DR}{2L}\right)\sin\omega t\right\} \tag{13.43}$$

so the initial conditions give

$$0 = B + VC, \qquad i_0 = -\frac{BR}{2L} + D\omega.$$

Then $B = -VC$, $D\omega = i_0 - VRC/2L$ and in equation (13.43)

$$-B\omega - \frac{DR}{2L} = \frac{1}{\omega}\left(VC\omega^2 - \frac{i_0 R}{2L} + \frac{VR^2 C}{4L^2}\right) = \frac{1}{\omega L}(V - \tfrac{1}{2}i_0 R), \quad \text{using equation (13.41)}.$$

Finally, replacing the arbitrary constants in equation (13.43) by their values, the required current is obtained:

$$i(t) = i_0\, e^{-Rt/2L}\left[\cos\omega t + \frac{1}{\omega L}\left(\frac{V}{i_0} - \tfrac{1}{2}R\right)\sin\omega t\right].$$

In this result time t is measured from when the contact breaker switch opens. The current is oscillatory, with amplitude decreasing exponentially from $i = i_0$ (Fig. 13.9).

To display the current function throughout one period of the system it is only necessary to fit together the graphs in Figs 13.8 and 13.9, giving Fig. 13.10.

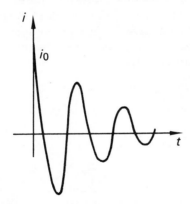

Figure 13.9   Current after switch opens (at $t=0$)

This example is taken from Chapter 5 of *Applications of Undergraduate Mathematics in Engineering* by B. Noble (Macmillan, 1967), and is reproduced here by permission of the Mathematical Association of America. Noble also discusses the secondary circuit which produces the spark.   □

Example 13.84
A solution of a substance S flows along a tube with constant speed v. A chemical reaction converts S into another substance S'. Find the function $C(x)$ giving the concentration of S in the solution at a distance x along the tube.

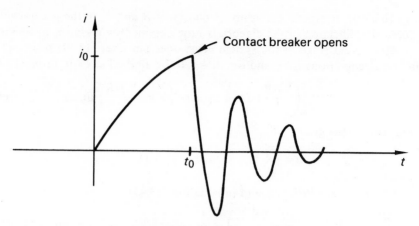

Figure 13.10   Current over one period

The differential equation satisfied by $C(x)$ is derived by considering the flux of S through an element of the tube in $[x, x + \delta x]$.

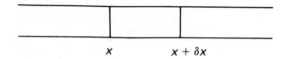

Figure 13.11   Element (of length δx) of tube

This flux is affected by the following three factors: the overall flow of the solution gives a flux $vC(x)$; the diffusion of S in the solution moves S from regions of high concentration to regions of low concentration, giving a flux proportional to $-C'(x)$; and, within the element considered, the reaction to form S' reduces the concentration by an amount proportional to the concentration. Thus

$$F_{in} = \text{Flux into section (at } x) = vC(x) - EC'(x) \tag{13.44}$$

$$F_{out} = \text{Flux out of section (at } x + \delta x) = vC(x + \delta x) - EC'(x + \delta x)$$

$$L = \text{rate of loss of S due to reaction} = k\delta x C(x). \tag{$*$}$$

Then $F_{in} = L + F_{out}$ gives

$$kC(x) + v\frac{C(x + \delta x) - C(x)}{\delta x} - E\frac{C'(x + \delta x) - C'(x)}{\delta x} = 0.$$

Taking the limit as $\delta x \to 0$ yields the differential equation

$$kC + v\frac{dC}{dx} - E\frac{dC'}{dx} = 0. \tag{13.45}$$

Since $dC'/dx = d^2C/dx^2$, this is a linear second-order equation with constant coefficients (the coefficients k and E will depend on the temperature, but at a given temperature are independent of x).

[In order to make this derivation quite precise, equation $(*)$ should really read $L = k\delta x C(X)$, where $C(X)$ is a suitable average value of $C(x)$ in the element considered. Since $X \to x$ as $\delta x \to 0$, the result (13.45) is not changed.]

The general solution of equation (13.45) has the form

$$C(x) = A\, e^{\sigma_1 x} + B\, e^{\sigma_2 x} \qquad (13.46)$$

where σ_1 and σ_2 are the (real) roots of $E\sigma^2 - v\sigma - k = 0$. The arbitrary constants A and B are determined by conditions from the ends of the tube, say $x = 0$ and $x = L$.

If C_1 is the concentration of the solution sent into the tube, the flux across the entrance $(x = 0)$ is vC_1. From equation (13.44) the required condition on $C(x)$ at $x = 0$ is

$$vC(0) - EC'(0) = vC_1.$$

Assuming that the tube is long enough for chemical equilibrium to be reached in the reaction $S \rightarrow S'$, at the other end of the tube the concentration is constant, so that the second condition is $C'(L) = 0$.

The equations to determine A and B are therefore

$$v(A + B) - E(A\sigma_1 + B\sigma_2) = 0 \qquad (13.47)$$

and

$$A\sigma_1\, e^{\sigma_1 L} + B\sigma_2\, e^{\sigma_2 L} = 0. \qquad (13.48)$$

The question of finding a particular solution of a second-order differential equation is called a **boundary value problem** if the given conditions are at different points. ☐

Hints and/or Answers to Exercises 13.1.1–13.7.4

13.1.1   (i) first-order but not separable
   (ii) separable because $e^{x+y} = e^x e^y$; using Exercise 10.3.2(ii) gives
      $-\exp(-y) = (x^2 - 2x + 2)\exp x + C$
   (iii) not first-order
   (iv) $y = C/\sin x.$

13.1.3 $e^x \cos y = C.$

13.2.1   (i) first-order; but not linear, since it contains y^2
   (ii) see the work from (13.27) to (13.28) in Example 13.51 (change g to y)
   (iii) first-order; but not linear, since it contains $y(dy/dx)$
   (iv) not first-order.

13.2.2 $Q(x) = -1/x,\ I(x) = 1/x;\ y = x^2 + x.$

13.2.3   (i) subtract the equations $y_i' + Qy_i = R\,(i = 1, 2)$
   (ii) use $y_1' + Qy_1 = R,\ u' + Qu = 0.$

13.3.1 $P(x) = 2,\quad Q(x) = 10,\quad R(x) = \cos 3x,\quad s(x) = (\cos 3x + 6\sin 3x)/37.$ The complementary function is $A\, e^{-x}\cos 3x + B\, e^{-x}\sin 3x = Au(x) + Bv(x).$

13.3.2   Use $s'' + Ps' + Qs = R,\ u'' + Pu' + Qu = 0,\ v'' + Pv' + Qv = 0,$ which hold because s is a solution, while $u,\ v$ satisfy the reduced equation.

13.4.1   Since $e^{0x} = 1,\ y = A + B\, e^{2x}.$

13.4.2 $y = e^{-2x}(A\sin x + B\cos x),$ since $\sigma^2 + 4\sigma + 5 = 0 \Rightarrow \sigma = -2 \pm i.$

13.4.3 $y = A\, e^x + B\, e^{5x} + \sin 2x + 12\cos 2x.$

13.4.4 $y = e^{-x}(A\sin 2x + B\cos 2x) + (10x + 1)/25.$

13.4.5   Trial function is $s(x) = \lambda x\cos 2x + \mu x\sin 2x;\ y = A\sin 2x + B\cos 2x + \tfrac{1}{2}x\sin 2x$ (cf. Exercise 6.3.4).

13.4.6 k cannot satisfy two required conditions $(4k - 3k = 2,\ 4k - 6k - 4k = 0).$

13.4.7 $s = \lambda\cos(\omega t + \phi) + \mu\sin(\omega t + \phi).$

13.4.8 $y = A e^{-ax} + Bx e^{-ax} + \frac{1}{2}\lambda x^2 e^{-ax}$.

13.5.1   Substituting $y = h \sin 2x$ leads to $h' \sin^2 2x = \frac{1}{2} \sin^2 2x + C$; or substituting $y = h \cos 2x$ leads to $h' \cos^2 2x = \int (1 + \cos 4x) \, dx$, and h may be obtained evaluating $\int x \sec^2 2x \, dx$ by parts.

13.6.1 $x = e^t$ leads to $y = A e^t + B e^{-2t} - t - \frac{1}{2}$
$$= Ax + (B/x^2) - \log x - \frac{1}{2}.$$

13.6.2   See Exercise 6.3.5 on p. 118
$$\left(\text{use } \frac{d^2 y}{dt^2} = \frac{\sin x}{\cos^3 x} \frac{dy}{dx} + \frac{1}{\cos^2 x} \frac{d^2 y}{dx^2} \right).$$

13.7.1 $z = \frac{1}{2}i e^{-t}(e^{3it} + e^{-3it}) = i e^{-t} \cos 3t$.

13.7.2 $z = \alpha e^{-4t} + \beta e^t - \frac{1}{50}(3 + 4i) e^{2it}$.
$y = A e^{-4t} + B e^t - \frac{1}{50}(4 \cos 2t + 3 \sin 2t)$
$x = C e^{-4t} + D e^t - \frac{1}{50}(3 \cos 2t - 4 \sin 2t)$.

13.7.3 $z = \alpha e^t + \beta e^{5t} + (1 + 12i) e^{2it}$.
The imaginary part is the solution to Exercise 13.4.3 (if t is changed to x).

13.7.4 $z = -\frac{1}{4}it e^{(2+2i)t}$, $x = \frac{1}{4}t e^{2t} \sin 2t$.

Further Exercises on Chapter 13

13.1   Use the result of Exercise 10.4.4 to find the general solution of
$$\frac{dy}{dx} = \frac{(y^2 - 1)(4x^3 + 5)}{y(2x + 3)(x^2 + 2)}.$$

13.2   Solve the differential equation
$$dy/dx = 2\sqrt{(1 - y^2)}/\sqrt{(1 - x^2)}. \tag{13.2}$$

Obtain the particular solution through $(0, 0)$; by substituting $t = \text{Sin}^{-1} x$, obtain a parametric form of this solution.
What is the difference between this solution and the particular solution through $(0, 0)$ of $(dy/dx)^2 = 4(1 - y^2)/(1 - x^2)$?
Express the general solution of (13.2) in a parametric form.

13.3   Show that the substitution $y = xv$ converts the equation
$$2xy\frac{dy}{dx} + (x^2 + y^2) = 0$$

into a variable separable equation in x and v, and hence solve the equation.

13.4   Rearrange the equation
$$(2xy + 1)\frac{dy}{dx} + y^2 + 1 = 0$$

to show that it is linear in x and dx/dy, and hence solve it.

13.5   Show that the substitution $y = 1/v$ converts the equation
$$x\frac{dy}{dx} + y = x^2 y^2 \ln x$$

into an equation linear in x and v, and hence solve it.

13.6 Solve the equation

$$\frac{dy}{dx} = ay + b\,e^{cx}$$

where a, b, c are constants, distinguishing special cases as necessary.

13.7 Find the particular solution of $y'' + 2y' + 2y = 5\cos x$ determined by the conditions $y = 2$ and $y' = 1$ when $x = 0$. Show that every solution of the equation has the same asymptotic form as $x \to \infty$.

13.8 If every solution of the constant coefficient differential equation $y'' + 2ay' + by = b$ satisfies the condition $y \to 1$ as $x \to \infty$, what can be deduced about the coefficients a and b? Repeat the exercise for the conditions $y \to 1$ as $x \to -\infty$.

13.9 Solve $y'' - y = x^2\,e^{2x}$.

13.10 Solve Exercise 13.4.3 by reducing the order.

13.11 Find a particular solution of

$$y'' + 2ay' + by = \lambda\,e^{cx}$$

distinguishing special cases as necessary.

13.12 Solve the equation $(1 - x^2)y'' - 2xy' + 2y = 1 - 2x^2$ by reducing the order.

13.13 Find a value of σ such that $e^{\sigma x}$ is a solution of the reduced equation of

$$(3x^2 + x - 1)y'' - (9x^2 + 9x - 2)y' + (18x + 3)y = 36x + 6. \qquad (*)$$

Find the particular solution $y = f(x)$ of $(*)$ satisfying $f(0) = 1$ and $\{f(-1) - 2\}\{f(1) - 6\} = 1$.

13.14 The inverse of equation (13.30) is

$$\int e^{\sigma t}\,dt = \frac{1}{\sigma}e^{\sigma t} + \alpha,$$

where α is an arbitrary complex constant. Obtain the two real indefinite integrals from the real and imaginary parts.

13.15 What is the condition (on the complex arbitrary constants α and β) for the complementary function

$$\alpha\,e^{-at - ict} + \beta\,e^{-at + ict}$$

to be real? (a and c are real).
Show that if this complementary function has the form $A\cos(ct + \phi)$, where A and ϕ are real, then

$$A = 2|\alpha|, \qquad \phi = \arg\alpha.$$

13.16 Find the general solution of the following differential equations:

(i) $y'' + 6y' + 9y = 9x^2$

(ii) $y'' + 5y' + 6y = 15\,e^{3x} + 6x$

(iii) $y'' - 6y' + 10y = (26x + 3)\,e^{-2x}$

(iv) $\dfrac{d^2z}{dt^2} - 2\dfrac{dz}{dt} + 4z = 4\,e^{it}$

(v) $\dfrac{d^2y}{dx^2} - 2\dfrac{dy}{dx} + 4y = 4\cos x.$

13.17 Find particular solutions of the following equations:

(i) $\dfrac{d^2z}{dt^2}+5\dfrac{dz}{dt}+6z=2\,e^{(3+2i)t}$

(ii) $\dfrac{d^2x}{dt^2}+5\dfrac{dx}{dt}+6x=2\,e^{3t}\sin 2t.$

13.18 Find the solution of

$$\dfrac{d^2y}{dx^2}-2\dfrac{dy}{dx}+y=x+e^x$$

satisfying $y=1$ and $dy/dx=0$ when $x=0$.

13.19 Find the general solution of each of the following differential equations:

(a) $\dfrac{dy}{dx}+\dfrac{4y}{x}=x^2+x+\dfrac{\cos x}{x^4}$

(b) $\dfrac{d^2y}{dx^2}=4y+e^{-2x}$

(c) $\dfrac{d^2y}{dx^2}-2\dfrac{dy}{dx}+3y=x+1.$

13.20 Find the solution of

$$\dfrac{d^2y}{dx^2}-2\dfrac{dy}{dx}+y=\cos x+e^{-x}$$

satisfying $y=dy/dx=0$ at $x=0$.

13.21 (i) Suppose u is a solution of the reduced equation of

$$y''+P(x)y'+Q(x)y=R(x).$$

Show that the substitutions $y=uh$, $h'=g$ give a first-order linear equation for g, with integrating factor given by $\ln I=2\ln u+\int P(x)\,dx$.
(ii) If $P(x)=a$ and $Q(x)=b$ (constants), and $u=e^{\lambda x}$, show that
$g(x)=e^{-(a+2\lambda)x}\int e^{(a+\lambda)x}R(x)\,dx$
(iii) Find the general solution of $y''+4y'+4y=6+25\sin x$.

13.22 Find the solution of

$$x^2\dfrac{d^2y}{dx^2}-2x\dfrac{dy}{dx}+2y=x^3+8$$

satisfying $y=dy/dx=\tfrac{27}{2}$ when $x=1$.

13.23 Find the solution of

$$\dfrac{d^2y}{dx^2}-5\dfrac{dy}{dx}-6y=14\,e^{-x}$$

satisfying $y=3$ and $dy/dx=9$ at $x=0$.

13.24 Consider the differential equation $x\,dy/dx=2y$. Show that

(i) there is no solution through $(0,b)$ unless $b=0$;

(ii) the condition $y=0$ when $x=0$ does not determine a particular solution.

13.25 Solve the equation

$$\frac{d^2y}{dx^2} - 2(1+\tan x)\frac{dy}{dx} + (1+2\tan x)y = 2\,e^x\sec x.$$

13.26 Find solutions of each of the following differential equations:

(i) $\dfrac{d^2y}{dt^2} + 5\dfrac{dy}{dt} + 6y = 2\,e^{3t}\cos 2t$

(ii) $\dfrac{d^2y}{dt^2} + 5\dfrac{dy}{dt} + 6y = 2\,e^{3t}\sin 2t$

satisfying $y = dy/dt = 0$ when $t = 0$.

13.27 Find the differential equation satisfied by the family of lines $y = Cx - \ln C$. Verify that $y = 1 + \log x$ also satisfies this equation (often called a singular solution since it is not given by any value of C in the general solution).

13.28 (i) Solve the equation $x(dy/dx) = y + x^2$ by finding a solution $u(x)$ of the reduced equation, then substituting $y = hu$ and finding $h(x)$.

(ii) Show that method (i) applied to any first-order linear equation only requires solving two variables-separable equations.

(iii) Use method (i) to solve Exercise 13.5 (with a suitable interpretation of 'reduced equation').

(iv) Show that the method solves the Bernoulli equation

$$\frac{dy}{dx} + Q(x)y = y^c R(x).$$

13.29 Find the particular solution of the differential equation

$$x\frac{dy}{dx} = y + x^2 + k^2$$

which passes through the point (a, a^2).

If a solution passes through $(0, 0)$, what must be the value of k?

13.30 Find a value of b so that the differential equation

$$\frac{dy}{dx} = \frac{b^2 + y^2}{b\sqrt{(b^2 - x^2)}}$$

has a solution passing through both $(0, 0)$ and $(4, 5)$.

13.31 Find the general solution of the equation

$$\frac{d^2y}{dx^2} - (p+q)\frac{dy}{dx} + pqy = ax + b$$

where p, q, a, b are constants such that $p > q > 0$.

13.32 Find the general solutions of the equations

(i) $\dfrac{d^2y}{dx^2} - 2p\dfrac{dy}{dx} + p^2 y = ax + b$

(ii) $\dfrac{d^2y}{dx^2} - p\dfrac{dy}{dx} = ax + b$

where $p \neq 0$, a and b are constants.

13.33 Find the general solution of the differential equation

$$\frac{dy}{dx}\cos x + 2y \sin x = \cos^4 x,$$

and the particular solution satisfying $y = 1$ when $x = 0$.

13.34 Find the particular solution of

$$\frac{d^2y}{dx^2} + 3\frac{dy}{dx} + 2y = 3 e^x$$

satisfying $y = 1$ and $dy/dx = -2$ when $x = 0$.

13.35 Solve the equation

$$x^2\frac{d^2y}{dx^2} - 2x\frac{dy}{dx} + 2y = x^3 + 8$$

given that $y = x$ is a solution of its reduced equation. Also solve

$$x^2\frac{d^2y}{dx^2} - 2x\frac{dy}{dx} + 2y = 2.$$

13.36 Find the general solution of $y \, dy/dx = e^{x+y}$.

13.37 Find the particular solution of

$$\frac{dy}{dx} = y \tan x + \sin x$$

satisfying $y = 7/4$ when $x = \pi/3$.

13.38 Find the particular solution of

$$\frac{d^2x}{dt^2} + 9x = e^{-t}$$

satisfying $x = 0$ and $dx/dt = 1$ at $t = 0$.
Also find the particular solution $x(t)$ for which

$$x \sim 2 \sin 3t \quad \text{as } t \to \infty.$$

What initial values of x and dx/dt at $t = 0$ should be specified in order to give this solution?

13.39 Use the change of variable $u = \cos x$ to solve

$$\sin x\frac{d^2y}{dx^2} - \cos x\frac{dy}{dx} = y \sin^3 x.$$

Obtain the particular solution satisfying $y = 2$, $dy/dx = 0$ when $x = \frac{1}{2}\pi$.

13.40 Obtain the general solution of the following differential equations:

(i) $y(x^2 + 1)\dfrac{dy}{dx} = y^2 + 1$

(ii) $\dfrac{d^2y}{dx^2} + \dfrac{dy}{dx} - 6y = -6x$

(iii) $\dfrac{dy}{dx} - 6y = -6x.$

13.41 Find the particular solution of the differential equation

$$x\frac{dy}{dx} = x - y$$

which passes through $(1, 2)$. Show also that only one particular solution is continuous for all x, and that all other solutions approach the continuous solution asymptotically.

Show that a solution which has turning points does not intersect the x-axis, and vice versa.

13.42 Use the change of variable $u = \sin x$ to solve

$$\cos x\frac{d^2y}{dx^2} + \sin x\frac{dy}{dx} = y\cos^3 x.$$

Consider the following conditions, and either find a particular solution satisfying the conditions, or state why such a solution does not exist.

(i) $y = \dfrac{dy}{dx} = 1$ at $x = 0$;

(ii) $y = 0$ at $x = 0$, $y = 1$ at $x = 2\pi$;

(iii) $y = 1$ at $x = 0$, $y \to 0$ as $x \to \infty$.

13.43 Find an explicit equation (of the form $y = s(x)$) for the particular solution of

$$(x-1)\frac{dy}{dx} + y^2 + 1 = 0$$

which passes through $(2, 0)$, and has domain $x > 1$.

13.44 Find the particular solution of

$$\frac{d^2y}{dx^2} - 7\frac{dy}{dx} + 10y = 10$$

which satisfies $y = -2$ and $dy/dx = 0$ at $x = 0$.

13.45 Use the change of variable $x = \tan t$ to solve

$$(1+x^2)\frac{d^2y}{dx^2} + 2x\frac{dy}{dx} = \frac{y}{1+x^2}.$$

13.46 Find the particular solution of

$$\frac{dy}{dx} = x\,e^{x+y}$$

which satisfies $y = \ln 2$ when $x = 1$.

13.47 Find the general solution of $x\,dy/dx + 2y = x^n$.

For what values of n does this equation have a particular solution with a limit as $x \to 0$?

13.48 Find the general solution of

(i) $\dfrac{d^2y}{dx^2} + 3\dfrac{dy}{dx} + 2y = x + e^{-x}$ (ii) $\dfrac{d^2y}{dx^2} - \dfrac{dy}{dx} - 2y = 10\cos x.$

13.49 Solve $x^2 \dfrac{d^2y}{dx^2} - 2x\dfrac{dy}{dx} + 2y = x^3 \cos x$.

13.50 Find the particular solution of

$$\frac{d^2z}{dt^2} + 2\frac{dz}{dt} + 5z = 0$$

satisfying $z = 3$ and $dz/dt = -3 - 2i$ at $t = 0$.
Find the two real solutions of $d^2x/dt^2 + 2\,dx/dt + 5x = 0$ satisfying

(i) $x = 3 = -\dfrac{dx}{dt}$ at $t = 0$

(ii) $x = 0, \dfrac{dx}{dt} = -2$ at $t = 0$.

13.51 (i) If y_{1p} and y_{2p} are two solutions of

$$\frac{d^2y}{dx^2} + f(x)\frac{dy}{dx} + g(x)y = r(x) \tag{1}$$

show that $y_1 = y_{1p} - y_{2p}$ satisfies

$$\frac{d^2y}{dx^2} + f(x)\frac{dy}{dx} + g(x)y = 0.$$

(ii) Give the form of the general solution of equation (1) in terms of three independent particular solutions y_{1p}, y_{2p} and y_{3p}. Give a condition showing the meaning of 'independent'.

13.52 Show that, if y_p is a particular solution of the Riccati equation

$$\frac{dy}{dx} = a(x)y^2 + b(x)y + c(x)$$

then the substitution $y = y_p + 1/h$ gives a linear equation for $h(x)$.

13.53 (i) Suppose $y_1(x)$ satisfies

$$\frac{d^2y}{dx^2} + P(x)\frac{dy}{dx} + Q(x)y = R(x)$$

when the nonhomogeneous term is $R(x) = f_1(x)$, and $y_2(x)$ is a solution when the nonhomogeneous term is changed to $f_2(x)$. Show that

(a) if $R(x) = c_1 f_1(x)$, then $c_1 y_1$ is a solution;

(b) if $R(x) = f_1(x) + f_2(x)$, then $y_1 + y_2$ is a solution;

(c) if $R(x) = c_1 f_1(x) + c_2 f_2(x)$, then $c_1 y_1 + c_2 y_2$ is a solution.

(ii) Extend (i)(c) to the case when

$$R = c_1 f_1 + c_2 f_2 + \cdots + c_n f_n.$$

13.54 In Exercise 13.53, suppose that $P(x)$ and $Q(x)$ are constants such that the complementary function tends to zero as $x \to \infty$, so that a steady-state solution exists (see p. 330). If the f_i in R are periodic trigonometric functions, for example $f_i(x) = \cos \omega_i x$, deduce from Exercise 13.53 that the steady-state solution is a combination of functions y_i which have the same periods as the f_i.

14

Functions of Two Variables, Solid Geometry and Surfaces

14.1 Geometric Interpretation of Partial Derivatives

If f is a function of one variable, its derivative

$$f'(x) = \underset{h \to 0}{\text{Lim}}\{f(x+h) - f(x)\}/h \qquad (6.1)$$

may be interpreted geometrically in terms of the curve represented by $z = f(x)$. (The dependent variable is denoted here by z because y will be used to denote a second independent variable.) Suppose P is the point (a, c), where $c = f(a)$. If $f'(a)$ exists, the curve is smooth at P and possesses a tangent at P. The slope of this tangent is $f'(a)$.

If f is a function of two variables, then $z = f(x, y)$ represents a surface consisting of points such as $P(a, b, c)$ where $c = f(a, b)$. Since the partial derivative

$$f_x(a, b) = \underset{h \to 0}{\text{Lim}}\{f(a+h, b) - f(a, b)\}/h \qquad (6.7)$$

involves only values of f with $y = b$, its geometrical interpretation involves only those points on the surface having $y = b$. As $y = b$ is a plane, these points lie on a plane curve, the intersection of the surface and the plane $y = b$.

Example 14.10
Figure 14.1(a) shows the surface $z = f(x, y) = 4 - x^2 - 2y^2$. The intersection of this surface with the plane $y = 1$ is the plane curve CDE shown in Fig. 14.1(b). (This curve is a parabola: $z = 2 - x^2$, $y = 1$.) The quotient $\{f(a+h, 1) - f(a, 1)\}/h$ is the slope (relative to the x-direction) of the chord PQ in Fig. 14.1(c). The limit as $h \to 0$ is the slope of the tangent at P, i.e. $\tan \psi$ where the angle ψ is shown in Fig. 14.1(d). $\square$

In general the geometric interpretation of $f_x(a, b)$ in the plane $y = b$ is essentially the same as that of $f'(a)$:

the limit $f_x(a, b)$ is the slope of the tangent at $(a, b, f(a, b))$ to the plane curve which is the intersection of the plane $y = b$ and the surface $z = f(x, y)$.

Similarly the partial derivative

$$f_y(a, b) = \underset{h \to 0}{\text{Lim}}\{f(a, b+h) - f(a, b)\}/h \qquad (6.8)$$

involves only values of f with $x = a$, corresponding to points on the intersection of the surface $z = f(x, y)$ and the plane $x = a$. This intersection is a plane curve. For any h, the quotient in equation (6.8) is the slope (relative to the y-direction) of a chord joining two points of this curve. The limit is the slope of the tangent to this curve at $(a, b, f(a, b))$.

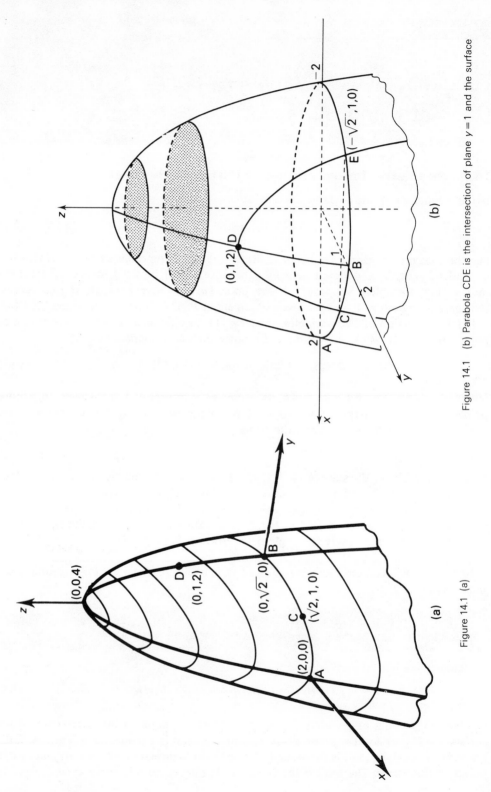

Figure 14.1   (b) Parabola CDE is the intersection of plane $y = 1$ and the surface

Figure 14.1 (a)

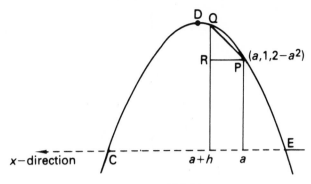

Figure 14.1 (c)

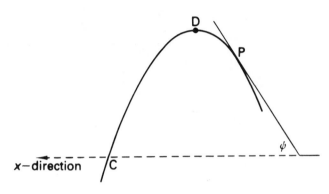

Figure 14.1 (d)

Example 14.11
Figure 14.2 shows the intersection (a parabola) of the surface $z = f(x, y) = 4 - x^2 - 2y^2$ and a plane $x = a$. The value $f_y(a, b)$ is the slope $\tan \phi$ of the tangent to this parabola at $P(a, b, 4 - a^2 - 2b^2)$. □

A tangent to a curve on a surface is also a tangent to the surface, in the same sense of double contact. So the tangent with slope given by f_x (or $\partial z/\partial x$) can be described as the tangent to the surface in the x-direction (Fig. 14.1). Similarly the tangent to the surface in the y-direction (illustrated, for example, in Fig. 14.2) has slope given by f_y (or $\partial z/\partial y$). If the intersection of a tangent line and a surface is found algebraically, the equation to be solved has a multiple root (normally a double root).

Example 14.12
The line $x = 3 - t$, $y = 1$, $z = -3 + 2t$ meets the surface $z = 4 - x^2 - 2y^2$ in points with parameters given by $-3 + 2t = 4 - (3 - t)^2 - 2$. This reduces to $(t - 2)^2 = 0$, so the line is a tangent at $(1, 1, 1)$. Since y is constant on the line, it is the tangent in the x-direction. □

Exercises (answers on p. 374)
14.1.1 Consider the surface $z = x^3 + 3x^2y^2 + 2y^2$. At the point $(-1, -1, 4)$, find the slopes of the tangents in the x-direction and the y-direction.

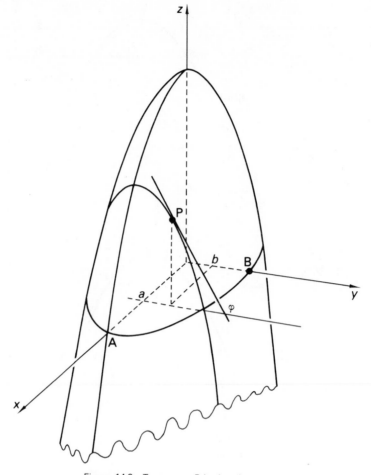

Figure 14.2   Tangent at P in the plane $x = a$

14.1.2   Consider the surface $z = x^4 y^2 + x^3 - y^2$.

(i) Find the angle between the y-direction and the tangent in the y-direction at the point $(0, -\frac{1}{2}, -\frac{1}{4})$.

(ii) Show that at the point $(-1, \frac{1}{2}\sqrt{3}, -1)$ the tangents in the x-direction and y-direction are both horizontal.

14.2   Tangent Planes

At a point $P(a, b, f(a, b))$ of the surface $z = f(x, y)$, there is a tangent in the x-direction with slope $f_x(a, b)$ and another in the y-direction with slope $f_y(a, b)$, provided the partial derivatives (i.e. the limits) exist. These lines are also tangents to the curves which are the intersections of the surface with the vertical planes $y = b$ and $x = a$.

A smooth surface is expected to have a tangent in any other direction also.

Example 14.20

The line $x = 1 + t$, $y = 1 + t$, $z = 1 - 6t$ is a tangent to the surface $z = 4 - x^2 - 2y^2$, because substituting the line equations into the surface equation gives a quadratic equation ($t^2 = 0$)

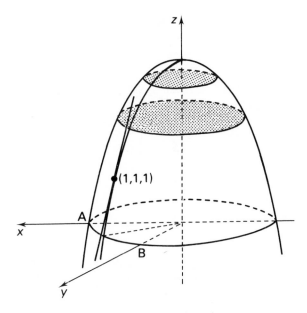

Figure 14.3   Tangent at $(1, 1, 1)$ in the plane $x = y$

with a double root. This is the tangent at $(1, 1, 1)$ in the direction $x = y$ (Fig. 14.3). It is also the tangent to the curve in which the vertical plane $x = y$ intersects the surface. ☐

The surface will be called **smooth** at P if there is a tangent line corresponding to every (horizontal) direction at P, and all these lines lie in a plane. This plane then touches the surface at P, and is called a **tangent plane**.

The equation of the tangent plane at a given point P can be written down after the normal direction has been found (see Example 2.20, p. 25). The normal direction is perpendicular to every tangent, and in particular to the tangents in the x-direction and the y-direction. Since the tangent in the x-direction has slope $f_x(P)$, the vector $\boldsymbol{i} + f_x(P)\boldsymbol{k}$ is along this tangent. Similarly $\boldsymbol{j} + f_y(P)\boldsymbol{k}$ is along the tangent in the y-direction. Taking the vector product of these gives

a vector $\boldsymbol{N}$ normal to the tangent plane (Fig. 14.4):

$$\boldsymbol{N} = \{\boldsymbol{i} + f_x(P)\boldsymbol{k}\} \times \{\boldsymbol{j} + f_y(P)\boldsymbol{k}\} = -f_x(P)\boldsymbol{i} - f_y(P)\boldsymbol{j} + \boldsymbol{k}. \qquad (14.1)$$

This vector is also said to be normal to the surface at P.

Example 14.21
Consider the point $P(1, 1, 1)$ on the surface $z = 4 - x^2 - 2y^2$. The partial derivatives have the values

$$\left. \frac{\partial z}{\partial x} \right|_P = (-2x)|_P = -2 \quad \text{and} \quad \left. \frac{\partial z}{\partial y} \right|_P = (-4y)|_P = -4.$$

So $2\boldsymbol{i} + 4\boldsymbol{j} + \boldsymbol{k}$ is normal to the surface; the equation of the tangent plane at P is $2x + 4y + z = D$, where D is determined by the fact that the plane passes through P: $2 + 4 + 1 = D$. ☐

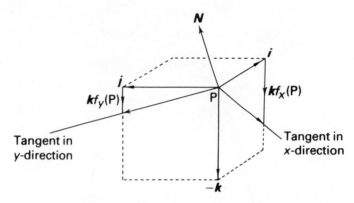

Figure 14.4   Negative values of the partial derivatives are illustrated

The calculation in the previous example assumes the existence of a tangent plane. Conditions (on the partial derivatives) to ensure this will not be given here, but the existence of f_x and f_y is not sufficient, since this does not necessarily mean there is a tangent in *every* direction. If the surface $z = f(x, y)$ does have a tangent plane at $P(a, b, f(a, b))$ then the function f is said to be **differentiable** at (a, b).

Example 14.22

Find the equations of the line through $P(1, 2, 3)$ which is normal to the surface $z = x^3 - xy + y^2$.

$$\frac{\partial z}{\partial x}\bigg|_P = (3x^2 - y)_P = 1, \qquad \frac{\partial z}{\partial y}\bigg|_P = (-x + 2y)_P = 3,$$

so $-i - 3j + k$ is normal to the surface at P, and is a vector along the required line. Since $\overrightarrow{OP} = i + 2j + 3k$, a vector equation for the line is (from equation (2.5), p. 27)

$$r = i + 2j + 3k + t(-i - 3j + k). \quad \square$$

In general the line through P perpendicular to the tangent plane at P is called the **normal** at P.

When equation (14.1) is computed, a possible check on the result comes from the fact that any perpendicular line should be a tangent.

Example 14.23 (cf. Example 14.22)

Check that $-i - 3j + k$ is normal at $(1, 2, 3)$ to the surface $z = x^3 - xy + y^2$.

$(3i - j)$ is an example of a vector perpendicular to $(-i - 3j + k)$, so the line

$$r = i + 2j + 3k + t(3i - j)$$

should touch the surface at $t = 0$. Since the line is

$$x = 1 + 3t, \qquad y = 2 - t, \qquad z = 3$$

its intersections with the surface are given by

$$3 = (1 + 3t)^3 - (1 + 3t)(2 - t) + (2 - t)^2$$

which reduces to

$$0 = 27t^3 + 31t^2.$$

Since $t = 0$ is a repeated root, the line is a tangent. □

To show that a surface $z = f(x, y)$ is smooth, i.e. to show that f is differentiable, requires showing that *every* line perpendicular to the normal is a tangent.

Exercises (answers on p. 374)

14.2.1 Find the equation of the tangent plane to the surface $z = x^2 + xy + y^2$ at the point $(-1, 3, 7)$.

14.2.2 Find a normal vector to the surface $z = x^2 + 3xy + y^2$ at the point $(1, 1, 5)$ and give equations for the normal.

14.2.3 The vector $N = -7i - 6j + k$ is perpendicular to the surface $z = x^2 + x + 4xy + y^2$ at $P(1, 1, 7)$. Write down a horizontal vector perpendicular to N, and hence obtain equations for the horizontal tangent at P. Verify that the line is a tangent by finding its intersection(s) with the surface.

14.3 Differentials

In the discussion, at the beginning of Chapter 6, of differentials for a function of one independent variable, a geometric definition was given: f is differentiable at $x = a$ if the curve $z = f(x)$ has a tangent (line) at $P(a, f(a))$, and dx and dz are differentials at $x = a$ if $S(a + dx, f(a) + dz)$ is on this tangent (Fig. 14.5). This extends to a function f of two variables, which represents a surface instead of a curve:

dx, dy, and dz are differentials for f at (a, b) if $S(a + dx, b + dy, f(a, b) + dz)$ is on a tangent at $P(a, b, f(a, b))$.

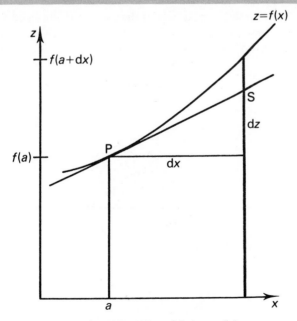

Figure 14.5   Differentials for $z = f(x)$

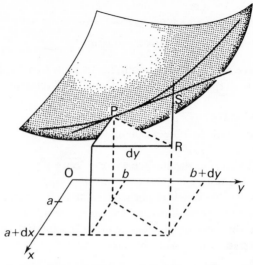

Figure 14.6   Curve is intersection of surface and plane PRS

(Figure 14.6). However there are now many tangent lines at P (Fig. 14.7); when these tangents form a tangent plane at P, f is differentiable at P, and differentials can be defined and used. There is a tangent line corresponding to every horizontal direction, so the differentials dx and dy are arbitrary.

The definition of differentials can also be expressed by saying that

$$\text{the vector } dx\, \boldsymbol{i} + dy\, \boldsymbol{j} + dz\, \boldsymbol{k} \qquad (=\overrightarrow{\text{PS}}) \tag{14.2}$$

is in the tangent plane at P.

A relation between differentials and partial derivatives is obtained from the fact that $\overrightarrow{\text{PS}}$ is perpendicular to the normal vector $\boldsymbol{N} = -f_x(\text{P})\boldsymbol{i} - f_y(\text{P})\boldsymbol{j} + \boldsymbol{k}$. Expressing $\boldsymbol{N} \cdot \overrightarrow{\text{PS}} = 0$ in components (cf. equation (14.2)) shows that dx, dy and dz are differentials at P if

$$dz = f_x(\text{P})\, dx + f_y(\text{P})\, dy. \tag{14.3}$$

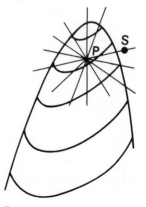

Figure 14.7   Tangents at P to surface all lie in a plane

This equation is the extension of $dz = f'(x)\,dx$ to a function of two variables. Note that although $f'(x)$ is a quotient of differentials, $f_x(P)$ and $f_y(P)$ are not. Thus although equation (14.3) is often written in the alternative notation

$$dz = \frac{\partial z}{\partial x}\,dx + \frac{\partial z}{\partial y}\,dy, \qquad (14.4)$$

the symbols $\partial z/\partial x$ and $\partial z/\partial y$ do not represent quotients.

Example 14.30

For $f(x, y) = x^3 - xy + y^2$, the relation (14.3) or (14.4) between differentials is

$$dz = (3x^2 - y)\,dx + (-x + 2y)\,dy. \qquad (14.5)$$

Thus, for example, differentials at the point $(1, 2)$ satisfy

$$dz = dx + 3\,dy.$$

If $dx = 3$ and $dy = -1$, then $dz = 0$, and the tangent PS, from $P(1, 2, 3)$ to $S(4, 1, 3)$, is horizontal. This tangent was used in the previous example.

If $dx = 1$ and $dy = 3$ then $dz = 10$, showing that the point $(1+1, 2+3, 3+10) = (2, 5, 13)$ is in the tangent plane at P. $\square$

In equations (14.3) and (14.4), z can be replaced by f. The symbol d represents the operation of taking the differential, for which the familiar laws of differentiation are valid.

Example 14.31

For $f(x, y) = x^3 - xy + y^2$,

$$df = d(x^3 - xy + y^2) = d(x^3) - d(xy) + d(y^2)$$

$$= 3x^2\,dx - \underbrace{(dx)y - x\,dy}_{\text{product rule}} + 2y\,dy \quad \text{(cf. equation (14.5)).} \quad \square$$

An important application of differentials is based on the idea that for small differentials the point S on the tangent plane is close to the corresponding point Q on the surface (see Fig. 14.10 on p. 366). The coordinates of Q are $(a+dx,\ y+dy,\ f(a+dx, b+dy))$, and the z-coordinate of S is

$$f(a, b) + dz = f(a, b) + f_x(a, b)\,dx + f_y(a, b)\,dy.$$

For any small increments dx and dy in the independent variables x and y, the change in f (actually RQ) is approximately

$$RS = dz = f_x(a, b)\,dx + f_y(a, b)\,dy = \frac{\partial z}{\partial x}\bigg|_P dx + \frac{\partial z}{\partial y}\bigg|_P dy. \qquad (14.6)$$

A common example of the use of this approximation is to estimate the error in a calculated value of f due to errors dx and dy in the values used for x and y.

Example 14.32

The height of a tower is calculated after observing that the elevation of the top is 42°12′ from ground level at a point 30 m from the base of the tower. If this elevation and the distance were measured to within 1 minute and 1 cm, respectively, find (to first order) the maximum resulting error in the calculated height.

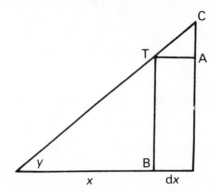

Figure 14.8   Tower TB: error d*x* in *x* causes error AC in calculated height

If *y* is the elevation measured at a distance *x* from the tower, its height *h* is (Fig. 14.8)

$$h(x, y) = x \tan y.$$

Then

$$dh = dx \tan y + x \, d(\tan y) = \tan y \, dx + x \sec^2 y \, dy. \qquad (14.7)$$

For this to be dimensionally correct, d*y* must be dimensionless, and so any value substituted for d*y* must be in **radians**.

The height calculated from $x = 30$ m and $y = 42°12′$ is $h = 27.201$ m. If *x* is changed by $dx = 1$ cm $= 0.01$ m, and *y* is changed by $dy = \pi/10800$ radians, then equation (14.7) gives

$$dh = 0.9067 \, dx + 54.66 \, dy = 0.009 \text{ m} + 0.015 \text{ m} = 2.4 \text{ cm}.$$

The values used for d*x* and d*y* are the maximum possible errors in *x* and *y*, and 2.4 cm is the maximum resulting error in the height. Thus $h = 27.20 \pm 0.02$ m (2D).

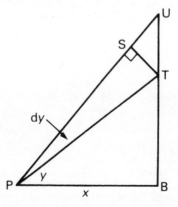

Figure 14.9   Error d*y* in *y* causes error TU in calculated height

The expansion (14.7) displays this approximation to the error as a sum of terms proportional to the independent errors in each of the measured quantities. In this example these two terms could be derived geometrically. In Fig. 14.8, AC is the error in h due to dx, and $AC/dx = AC/AT = \tan y$. The error in h due to dy is shown in Fig. 14.9, where $\angle STU = y + dy$, $ST = PT \sin dy$, and $TU = ST \sec(y + dy)$. Thus

$$TU/dy = x(\sec y)\left(\frac{\sin dy}{dy}\right) \sec(y + dy) \to x \sec^2 y \quad \text{as } dy \to 0,$$

i.e. $TU \sim (x \sec^2 y) \, dy$ as $dy \to 0$. $\square$

More generally equation (14.6) gives the first-order change in z as the sum of two terms, one resulting from a change in x with y kept constant, and the second resulting from a change in y with x kept constant. These terms are sometimes called **partial differentials**, while their sum dz is the **total differential**.

Exercises (answers on p. 374)

14.3.1 If $z = f(x, y) = x^4 y^2 + x^3 - y^2$, find the relation between differentials dx, dy and dz
(i) at the point $(1, 2)$, (ii) at the point $(2, 1)$.

14.3.2 If V is the volume of a cylinder of radius r and height h, express dV in terms of r, h, dr and dh. If the height and radius are subject to errors of 1 mm, compare the first-order errors in the volumes of cylinders of height 10 mm, radius 20 mm and height 40 mm, radius 10 mm.

14.4 Tangent Lines

This chapter began by interpreting the values of the partial derivatives f_x and f_y as the slopes of the surface $z = f(x, y)$ in the x-direction and y-direction respectively. In any other direction the slope of the surface is also the slope of the tangent plane. For any given horizontal displacement $(dx\mathbf{i} + dy\mathbf{j}) = \overline{PR}$, the vertical displacement to the tangent plane is $RS = dz = f_x \, dx + f_y \, dy$ (see Fig. 14.10). Then $dx\mathbf{i} + dy\mathbf{j} + dz\mathbf{k}$ is along the tangent in this direction, and equations for the tangent line can be written down. Its slope $dz/|dx\mathbf{i} + dy\mathbf{j}|$ (SR/PR in Fig. 14.10) can also be computed.

Example 14.40
Find the equation of the tangent line at $P(-1, -1, 4)$ to the surface $z = 3x^2 y^2 + x^3 + 2y^2$ in the direction $3\mathbf{i} + 4\mathbf{j}$. What is the slope of the surface at P in this direction?

$$dz = (6xy^2 + 3x^2) \, dx + (6x^2 y + 4y) \, dy = -3dx - 10dy \quad \text{at P.}$$

For the given horizontal direction, take $dx = 3$ and $dy = 4$. Then $dz = -49$, so $3\mathbf{i} + 4\mathbf{j} - 49\mathbf{k}$ is in the tangent plane and along the tangent line. The equation of the tangent line is

$$\mathbf{r} = -\mathbf{i} - \mathbf{j} + 4\mathbf{k} + t(3\mathbf{i} + 4\mathbf{j} - 49\mathbf{k}).$$

Check: Substituting these line equations

$$x = -1 + 3t, \, y = -1 + 4t, \, z = 4 - 49t$$

into the surface equation gives an equation with t^2 as a factor (no constant term or term

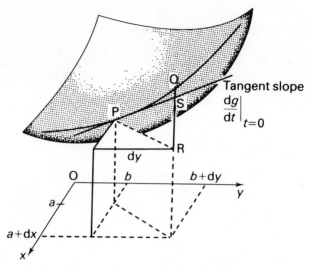

Figure 14.10   Tangent line PS is in tangent plane at P

in t), and hence a double root.

$$\text{The slope is } \frac{dz}{\sqrt{(dx^2 + dy^2)}} = -\frac{49}{5}. \quad \square$$

Example 14.41
The function $f(x, y)$ is differentiable at (a, b). At $P(a, b, f(a, b))$, the surface $z = f(x, y)$ has slope 1 in the direction $3i + 4j$, and slope 2 in the direction $4i + 3j$. Calculate $f_x(a, b)$ and $f_y(a, b)$.

The statement that f is differentiable means that

$$dz = f_x(P)\, dx + f_y(P)\, dy \tag{14.3}$$

is valid in any direction.
Since $|3i + 4j| = 5$, the given slope 1 implies $dz = 5$ when $dx = 3$ and $dy = 4$. Substituting into equation (14.3):

$$3f_x + 4f_y = 5. \tag{14.8}$$

Similarly $|4i + 3j| = 5$, so $dz = 10$ if the slope is 2. Substituting $dx = 4$, $dy = 3$, $dz = 10$ into equation (14.3):

$$4f_x + 3f_y = 10. \tag{14.9}$$

Solving equations (14.8) and (14.9) for f_x and f_y gives

$$f_x(a, b) = 25/7, \qquad f_y(a, b) = -10/7. \quad \square$$

Exercise (answer on p. 374)
14.4.1   Find the equations of tangent lines to the surface

$$z = x^2 + xy + y^2$$

at the point $P(1, -2, 3)$, (a) in the x-direction, (b) in the y-direction, (c) in the direction $9i + j$.

14.5 Composite Functions

If $z = f(x)$ where x is a function of t, then $dz = f'(x)\,dx$, and simply dividing by dt gives the correct formula for the rate of change of z with respect to t (differentiation rule IV on p. 106). This same process gives the derivative of a composite function of one variable when f is a function of two variables.

Example 14.50

$$z = x^2 y^3 \quad \text{where } x = t^3, \, y = t^2.$$

$$dz = 2xy^3\,dx + 3x^2 y^2\,dy \, .$$

$$\frac{dz}{dt} = 2xy^3 \frac{dx}{dt} + 3x^2 y^2 \frac{dy}{dt} = (2xy^3)(3t^2) + (3x^2 y^2)(2t) = 12t^{11}.$$

The result can be checked by first expressing z in terms of t and then differentiating. □

The procedure in the previous example (which is clearly more complicated than the check) is useful when $f(x, y)$ is not given explicitly.

Example 14.51

If $z = f(x, y)$ with $x = bt, \, y = ct^2$, then

$$dz = f_x\,dx + f_y\,dy = f_x b\,dt + f_y 2ct\,dt,$$

$$\frac{dz}{dt} = bf_x(bt, \, ct^2) + 2ctf_y(bt, \, ct^2).$$

In this result, f is any (differentiable) function of two variables. □

In the previous section, differentials were used to obtain the slope of a tangent line to a surface in an arbitrary horizontal direction. Another approach to this uses the idea of a composite function. In Fig. 14.10 the curve PQ is the intersection of the surface $z = f(x, y)$ and the vertical plane PRS. This is a plane curve, and can therefore be represented by a function of one variable. To get this representation, suppose PR makes an angle β with the x-direction. Then, with t the horizontal distance from P,

$$x = a + t \cos \beta, \qquad y = b + t \sin \beta \tag{14.10}$$

gives a point in the plane for any t (or z), and

$$\boxed{z = g(t) = f(a + t \cos \beta, \, b + t \sin \beta) = f(x, y)} \tag{14.11}$$

gives the points of the curve. Thus equation (14.11), a (composite) function of one variable t, represents the curve.

The slope of a tangent to this curve can therefore be obtained from

$$\boxed{\frac{dz}{dt} = f_x \frac{dx}{dt} + f_y \frac{dy}{dt} = f_x \cos \beta + f_y \sin \beta,} \tag{14.12}$$

since equation (14.10) gives $dx/dt = \cos \beta$, $dy/dt = \sin \beta$.

Example 14.52 (cf. Example 14.40)

What is the slope of the surface $z = 3x^2y^2 + x^3 + 2y^2$ at $P(-1, -1, 4)$ in the direction $3i + 4j$?

$$\frac{\partial z}{\partial x}\bigg|_P = -3, \qquad \frac{\partial z}{\partial y}\bigg|_P = -10 \quad \text{(as before)}.$$

For the direction $3i + 4j$, $\cos\beta = \frac{3}{5}$, $\sin\beta = \frac{4}{5}$. Hence the slope $(f_x \cos\beta + f_y \sin\beta)$ is $-49/5$. ☐

The result (14.12) for $dz/dt = g'(t)$ can be written

$$\frac{d}{dt} f(a + t\cos\beta, b + t\sin\beta) = f_x \cos\beta + f_y \sin\beta \tag{14.13}$$

where $f_x = f_x(a + t\cos\beta, b + t\sin\beta)$, and similarly f_y, are functions of t, and f is any differentiable function of two variables. Then f can be replaced by f_x or by f_y, giving

$$\frac{d}{dt} f_x(a + t\cos\beta, b + t\sin\beta) = f_{xx} \cos\beta + f_{xy} \sin\beta$$

$$\frac{d}{dt} f_y(a + t\cos\beta, b + t\sin\beta) = f_{yx} \cos\beta + f_{yy} \sin\beta.$$

Hence differentiating (14.13) again with respect to t gives

$$\frac{d^2}{dt^2} f(a + t\cos\beta, b + t\sin\beta) = f_{xx} \cos^2\beta + 2f_{xy} \sin\beta \cos\beta + f_{yy} \sin^2\beta \tag{14.14}$$

for the second derivative $g''(t)$ of the composite function.

Exercises

14.5.1   If $z = x^2y^2 + x^3 + y^3$, $x = bt$, $y = ct^2$, express z in terms of t and hence obtain dz/dt. Check by using the result of Example 14.51.

14.5.2   Evaluate equations (14.12) and (14.14) for $f(x, y) = xy^2$, and then use equation (14.10) to obtain dz/dt and d^2z/dt^2 in terms of t. Check by using equation (14.10) to express z in terms of t and then differentiating.

14.5.3   Use equations (14.10) and (14.11) to derive parametric equations for the ellipse in which the plane $y = x$ cuts the cylinder $z = \sqrt{(1 - x^2)}$.

14.6   Maxima and Minima

For a differentiable function g of one independent variable, sufficient conditions for a local minimum at $x = a$ are

$$g'(a) = 0, \qquad g''(a) > 0 \tag{14.15}$$

while sufficient conditions for a local maximum at $x = a$ are

$$g'(a) = 0, \qquad g''(a) < 0. \tag{14.16}$$

Geometrically, the condition $g'(a) = 0$ means that the tangent at $x = a$ is horizontal, i.e.

has zero slope. The condition on $g''(a)$ shows whether the tangent slope changes from negative to positive or vice-versa as x increases through a.

These results will now be extended to give the equivalent conditions for differentiable functions $f(x, y)$ of two independent variables.

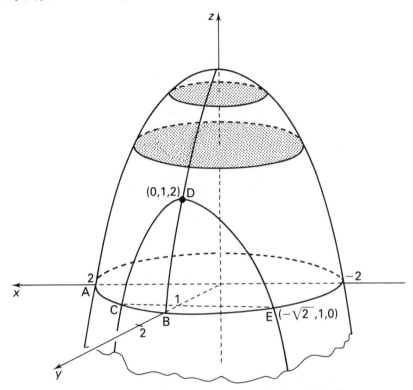

Figure 14.11 Plane curve ADE has a maximum at D $(x=0)$

In Section 14.1, $f_x(a, b)$ was interpreted geometrically (Fig. 14.11) as the slope of the tangent at $x = a$ to the plane curve which is the intersection of the plane $y = b$ and the surface $z = f(x, y)$. This curve corresponds to the function $g(x) = f(x, b)$, of one variable x only, and $g'(x) = f_x(x, b)$, $g''(x) = f_{xx}(x, b)$. If $f(x, y)$ has a minimum at (a, b), the plane curve will have a minimum at $x = a$. Conditions (14.15) give

$$f_x(a, b) = 0, \qquad f_{xx}(a, b) > 0. \tag{14.17}$$

Similarly, the intersection with the plane $x = a$ gives a curve (Fig. 14.12) which corresponds to the function $h(y) = f(a, y)$ of one variable y only. If f has a minimum at (a, b), h will have a minimum at $y = b$, and conditions (14.15) give

$$f_y(a, b) = 0, \qquad f_{yy}(a, b) > 0. \tag{14.18}$$

The conditions

$$f_x(a, b) = f_y(a, b) = 0 \tag{14.19}$$

are sufficient for the tangent plane to the surface $z = f(x, y)$ to be horizontal, so that $dz = 0$ at (a, b) in any direction. Then (a, b) is called a **stationary point** of f.

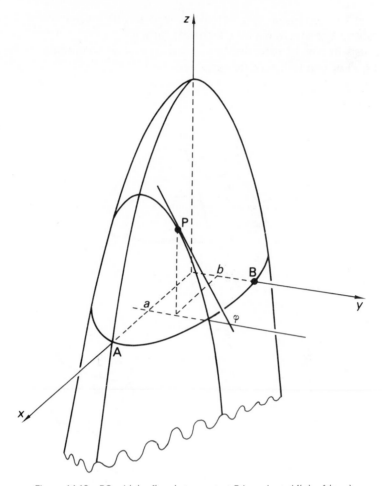

Figure 14.12 $PQ = h(c) = f(a, c)$; tangent at P has slope $h'(c) = f_y(a, c)$

However the conditions (14.17) and (14.18) are not sufficient for a maximum of f, because they only restrict the variation of $f(x, y)$ from (a, b) in the directions of the axes.

Example 14.60
Let $f(x, y) = x^2 - 2xy + y^2 - x^2y$. Then

$$f_x(0, 0) = f_y(0, 0) = 0, \qquad f_{xx}(0, 0) = f_{yy}(0, 0) = 2 > 0.$$

But in the direction $y = x$, the values of $f(x, y)$ are those of $k(x) = -x^3$, and so $f(x, y)$ decreases if one proceeds from $(0, 0)$ in the direction $y = x > 0$ (Fig. 14.13). Although conditions (14.17) and (14.18) are satisfied, $(0, 0)$ is not a minimum.   □

A minimum for f at (a, b) means that $f(x, y)$ increases on proceeding from (a, b) in *any* direction. Take a fixed direction making an angle β with the x-direction. Then the values of $f(x, y)$ which are obtained by moving from (a, b) in this direction are $f(a + t \cos \beta, b + t \sin \beta)$, where t is the horizontal distance. In Fig. 14.14, $t = MN = PR$, and as t varies the values of f are on the curve PQ in which the vertical plane PRNM

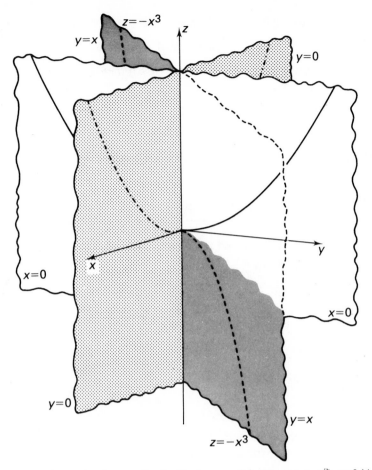

Figure 14.13 Intersections of surface $z = f(x, y)$ with planes $x = 0$ (solid curve $z = y^2$), $y = 0$ (dot-dash curve $z = x^2$), and $y = x$ ($z = -x^3$)

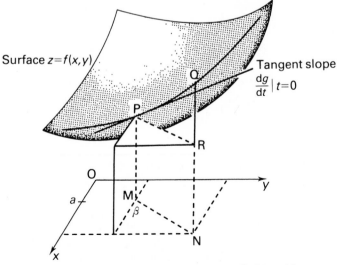

Figure 14.14 N is $(a + t \cos \beta, b + t \sin \beta, 0)$; $QN = g(t)$

intersects the surface. This curve corresponds to the function

$$z = g(t) = f(a + t \cos \beta, b + t \sin \beta) \tag{14.20}$$

of one variable t only. If f has a minimum at (a, b), then g must have a minimum at $t = 0$, and the two conditions (14.15) are

$$\left.\frac{dg}{dt}\right|_{t=0} = 0, \qquad \left.\frac{d^2g}{dt^2}\right|_{t=0} > 0.$$

From equations (14.13) and (14.14) in the previous section, this is

$$f_x(a, b) \cos \beta + f_y(a, b) \sin \beta = 0$$

$$f_{xx}(a, b) \cos^2 \beta + 2f_{xy}(a, b) \sin \beta \cos \beta + f_{yy}(a, b) \sin^2 \beta > 0.$$

These conditions must hold for any direction, i.e. for arbitrary β. So the first gives $f_x(a, b) = f_y(a, b) = 0$, already obtained in equation (14.19). The second can be written

$$f_{yy}(a, b) \lambda^2 + 2f_{xy}(a, b) \lambda + f_{xx}(a, b) > 0. \qquad (\lambda = \tan \beta) \tag{14.21}$$

As $f_{yy}(a, b) > 0$ (from equation (14.18)) this quadratic expression in λ is positive if the quadratic has no real zeros. This requires a negative value for the discriminant $(2f_{xy})^2 - 4f_{yy}f_{xx}$. The extension of (14.15) can now be given.

Sufficient conditions for $f(x, y)$ to have a local minimum at (a, b) are that partial derivatives at (a, b) satisfy

$$f_x = f_y = 0, \qquad f_{yy} > 0, \qquad f_{xx} > 0, \qquad f_{xx}f_{yy} > f_{xy}^2. \tag{14.22}$$

If a maximum is considered, the only change is that $f_{xx}(a, b)$ and $f_{yy}(a, b)$ are negative. If $f_{yy}(a, b) < 0$, the quadratic expression (14.21) is negative for all λ if it has no real zeros. The extension of (14.16) is therefore:

sufficient conditions for $f(x, y)$ to have a local maximum at (a, b) are that the partial derivatives at (a, b) satisfy

$$f_x = f_y = 0, \qquad f_{xx} < 0, \qquad f_{yy} < 0, \qquad f_{xx}f_{yy} > f_{xy}^2. \tag{14.23}$$

Note that conditions (14.22) and (14.23) are **sufficient**, but not necessary to the extent that f *may* have an extremum point if any of the inequalities gives equality, e.g. $f_{xx}f_{yy} = f_{xy}^2$. See also Exercise 14.14 at the end of the chapter.

Example 14.61

Find any maximum or minimum points of the function

$$f(x, y) = x^3 + y^3 - 6x^2 - 6y^2 + 9xy.$$

Stationary points must satisfy the equations

$$f_x = 3x^2 - 12x + 9y = 0, \quad \text{or } x^2 - 4x + 3y = 0 \tag{14.24}$$

$$f_y = 3y^2 - 12y + 9x = 0, \quad \text{or } y^2 - 4y + 3x = 0. \tag{14.25}$$

Subtracting the two equations gives $x^2 - y^2 = 7(x - y)$, so either $x = y$ or $x + y = 7$. Substituting $y = 7 - x$ into equation (14.24) gives $x^2 - 7x + 21 = 0$ with no solutions. Substituting $y = x$ gives $x^2 = x$, so $y = x = 0$ or 1. The stationary points are therefore $(0, 0)$ and $(1, 1)$.

The second partial derivatives are now evaluated at these points in order to test the conditions in (14.22) or (14.23):

$$f_{xx} = 6x - 12, \qquad f_{xy} = 9 = f_{yx}, \qquad f_{yy} = 6y - 12.$$

At $(0, 0)$, $f_{xx} = -12 < 0, f_{yy} = -12 < 0, f_{xx}f_{yy} = 144 > 81 = f_{xy}^2$. Conditions (14.23) show that $(0, 0)$ is a maximum point. At $(1, 1)$, $f_{xx} = -6 < 0, f_{yy} = -6 < 0$, but $f_{xx}f_{yy} = 36 < f_{xy}^2$ shows that this stationary point is neither a maximum nor a minimum. $\square$

In Example 14.60, $f_{xx}f_{yy} = f_{xy}^2$ at the stationary point $(0, 0)$, so the conditions (14.22) are inconclusive. In such cases one method is to return to principles used to derive (14.22).

Example 14.62
Show that, if b is nonzero, the function $f(x, y) = (x + y)^2 + bx^2 y$ has no maximum or minimum points.

$$f_x = 2x + 2y + 2bxy, \qquad f_y = 2x + 2y + bx^2,$$

so for stationary points $2xy = x^2$, $x = 0$ or $x = 2y$. Substituting $x = 2y$ in $f_x = 0$ gives $6y + 4by^2 = 0$, $y = 0$ or $-3/2b$. The stationary points are $O(0, 0)$ and $P(-3/b, -3/2b)$.

$$f_{xx} = 2 + 2by, \qquad f_{xy} = 2 + 2bx = f_{yx}, \qquad f_{yy} = 2.$$

At P, $f_{xx}f_{yy} = -2 < f_{xy}^2$, so P is not a maximum or minimum. At O, $f_{xx}f_{yy} = 4 = f_{xy}^2$, so consider the values

$$f(t, \lambda t) = (1 + \lambda)^2 t^2 + b\lambda t^3 \tag{14.26}$$

which are obtained on moving away from O in a direction given by $x = t$, $y = \lambda t$. Since $f(t, \lambda t) \to (1 + \lambda)^2 t^2$ as $t \to 0$, the values are positive (i.e. greater than $f(0, 0)$) except in the single direction with $\lambda = -1$. As $f(t, -t) = -bt^3$ changes sign on passing through $t = 0$, the stationary point $(0, 0)$ is not a minimum (or maximum). $\square$

A stationary point at which $f_{xx}f_{yy} < f_{xy}^2$ (neither a maximum nor a minimum) is called a saddle-point. The slope will be positive in some directions and negative in others.

Exercises
14.6.1 If $f(x, y) = x^3 + y^3 + 9x^2 + 9y^2 + 12xy$, show that

$$\frac{\partial f}{\partial x} - \frac{\partial f}{\partial y} = 3(x - y)(x + y + 2).$$

Deduce that the stationary points are a minimum at $(0, 0)$, a maximum at $(-10, -10)$, and saddle points at $(-4, 2)$ and $(2, -4)$.

14.6.2 Show that the stationary points of

$$f(x, y) = 2x - y - \tfrac{1}{2}x^2 + x^3 y^{-1}$$

are a minimum at $(-1, -1)$ and a saddle point at $(-4, -8)$.

Answers to Exercises 14.1.1–14.4.1

14.1.1 -3; -10.

14.1.2   (i) $\pi/4$.

14.2.1 $x + 5y - z = 7$.

14.2.2   Any scalar multiple of $-5i - 5j + k$

$$x = 1 - 5t, \qquad y = 1 - 5t, \qquad z = 5 + t \text{ (or equivalent)}$$

14.2.3   Any scalar multiple of $6i - 7j$

$$x = 1 + 6t, \qquad y = 1 - 7t, \qquad z = 7 \text{ (or equivalent)}$$

14.3.1   (i) $dz = 19\,dx$, (ii) $dz = 44\,dx + 30\,dy$.

14.3.2 $dV = \pi r(2h\,dr + r\,dh)$
800π mm^3 and 900π mm^3.

14.4.1   (a) $r = (1 + t)i - 2j + 3k$
(b) $r = i - 2j + 3k + t(j - 3k)$ $\left.\right\}$ (or equivalent)
(c) $r = i - 2j + 3k + t(9i + j - 3k)$

Further Exercises on Chapter 14

14.1   Use differentials to find an approximate value of a function $f(x, y)$ at the point $(1.1, 2.2)$, given that $f(1, 2) = 9$, $f_x(1, 2) = 7$, and $f_y(1, 2) = 3$.

14.2   Find the equation of the tangent plane to the surface

$$z = x^2 + 3xy + y^2$$

at the point P$(1, 1, 5)$. What is the slope of the surface at P in the direction of the vector $3i + 4j$?

14.3   Find the equation of the tangent plane to the surface

$$z = x^3 - xy + 3y^2$$

at the point P$(2, 1, 9)$. What is the slope of the surface at P in the direction of the vector $-11i - 4j$?

14.4   Find the equation of the tangent line to the surface

$$z = \sqrt{(1 - x^2)}$$

at the point $(\frac{1}{2}, \frac{1}{2}, \frac{1}{2}\sqrt{3})$ in the direction $-i - j$.

14.5   The thickness of a metal plating is measured by grinding through with a wheel of radius r and then measuring the width w of the resulting cavity (see Fig. 14.15). Find the thickness (with first order error) calculated from $r = (1 \pm 0.001)$ cm, $w = 0.038 \pm 0.004$ cm. (Note: Example 7.23 on p. 170 is relevant to this calculation.)

14.6   (i) Show that the area A of a triangle with base b and base angles θ and ϕ is $A = \frac{1}{2}b^2 st/(s + t)$ where $s = \tan\theta$ and $t = \tan\phi$ (see Fig. 14.16).
(ii) Assuming that b is constant, express dA in terms of ds and dt, and express ds and dt in terms of $d\theta$ and $d\phi$.
(iii) Use the results of (ii) to find (approximately) the area of a triangle with base 60 m and base angles $54°$ and $89°8'$, using only the values $\tan 53°8' = 4/3$ and $1° = 0.0175$ radian.

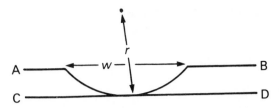

Figure 14.15   AB surface of plate; CD base metal

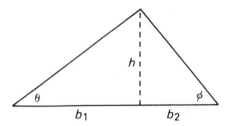

Figure 14.16 $s = h/b_1$, $t = h/b_2$

14.7   Find the equations of the tangent planes to the surface

$$x^2 + 2yz = 2$$

which are parallel to the plane $4x + y - 4z = 0$.

14.8   Assume that the earth is a sphere of radius r. Any point P on the surface can be specified by giving a longitude angle θ and a latitude angle ϕ (Fig. 14.17). Find, in terms of r, θ, and ϕ, the coordinates of P relative to origin O at the centre, axis Oz through the north pole, axis Ox through the point in the equatorial plane with zero longitude.

Find a normal vector at P by differentiating the equation of the spherical surface, and show that this vector is along the radius OP.

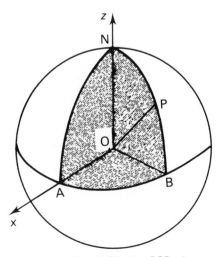

Figure 14.17 $\angle AOB = \theta$, $\angle BOP = \phi$

14.9 Find the coordinates of the points in which the normal at P(1, 1, 1) to the surface $3x + 2y^2 + z^3 = 6$ again cuts the surface.

14.10 Consider the surface $z = x^4 + 2xy + y^2$.

At the point P(1, 2, 1) find (horizontal) unit vectors in each of the following directions:

(a) the direction giving the maximum slope;

(b) the direction giving zero slope;

(c) the direction in which the slope is 8.

Find the equation of the tangent plane to the surface at P.

14.11 Use differentials to find an approximate value of a function $f(x, y)$ at the point $(-0.9, 1.9)$, given that $f(-1, 2) = 3$, $f_x(-1, 2) = 2$ and $f_y(-1, 2) = -1$.

14.12 The area of a triangle with base b and base angles θ and ϕ is given by

$$A = \tfrac{1}{2}b^2 st/(s+t)$$

where $s = \tan \theta$ and $t = \tan \phi$.

Express dA in terms of θ, ϕ, $d\theta$ and $d\phi$, assuming that b is a constant.

14.13 Show that

$$f(x, y) = (x + 2y + 2)/(x^2 + y^2 + 1)$$

has a minimum at $(-1, -2)$ and a maximum at $(\tfrac{1}{5}, \tfrac{2}{5})$.

14.14 Let $f(x, y) = x^2 - 2xy^2 + y^4 - y^5$.

(i) Show that $(0, 0)$ is a stationary point.

(ii) Use Equation (14.20) to show that g has a minimum at $t = 0$ for any β.

(iii) Show that $f(x, x^2) < 0$ for any $x \neq 0$, so that the stationary point $(0, 0)$ is not a minimum.

Note: this example shows that the derivation of conditions (14.22) and (14.23) does not actually show that the obtained conditions are sufficient. This can be shown by a more complicated proof.

15
Numerical Integration

15.1 The Trapezoidal Rule

If an antiderivative of f cannot be found, then the Riemann integral $R_a^b(f) = \int_a^b f(x)\,dx$ can still be evaluated using elementary numerical procedures based on the idea of approximating f by a function for which an antiderivative is known.

The simplest approximation replaces the curve $y = f(x)$ by a straight line. The resulting formula which approximates $\int_c^d f(x)\,dx$ may be obtained geometrically from Fig. 15.1. The dashed chord PQ is the approximation to $y = f(x)$, and the approximation to the integral is the area under this chord;

$$T_1 = (d - c)\tfrac{1}{2}\{f(c) + f(d)\}. \tag{15.1}$$

This is the area of a trapezium, so the formula (15.1) is called the **trapezoidal rule**.

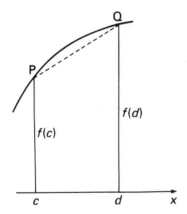

Figure 15.1   Trapezium under curve $y = f(x)$

Example 15.10
For $K_0 = \int_0^1 \exp(-x^2)\,dx$, the approximation given by equation (15.1) is

$$T_1 = \tfrac{1}{2}(e^0 + e^{-1}) = 0.684. \quad \square$$

As in Section 7.2, the error in equation (15.1) is defined as

$$(\text{approximate value}) - (\text{true value}).$$

In Fig. 15.1, this error is evidently negative, and its magnitude is the area between the chord and the curve. Also in Fig. 15.1 the curve is concave down, so $f''(x) < 0$ in $[c, d]$.

Thus **the error has the same sign as** f''. This can also be verified (by sketches) in the other 3 geometrical cases ($f''(x)>0$, $f(x)>0$; $f''(x)<0$, $f(x)<0$; and $f''(x)>0$, $f(x)<0$).

Equation (15.1) gives the exact area if $y=f(x)$ represents a straight line. If not the actual magnitude of the error is expected to be proportional to the magnitude of the second derivative, since the smaller $f''(x)$ is, the more closely $y=f(x)$ is approximately a straight line. In fact quantitative bounds on the error can be obtained in terms of the size of the second derivative. This important feature of the trapezoidal rule formula will be considered in detail in Section 15.3. The result is

$$\tfrac{1}{12}m(d-c)^3 \leqslant T_1 - \int_c^d f(x)\,dx \leqslant \tfrac{1}{12}M(d-c)^3 \qquad \textbf{(15.2)}$$

where m and M are lower and upper bounds for $f''(x)$ on $[c, d]$.

Example 15.11
In Example 15.10 $f(x)=\exp(-x^2)$; $[c, d]=[0, 1]$.

Then $f''(x)=(4x^2-2)\,e^{-x^2}$, $f^{(3)}(x)=4x(3-2x^2)\,e^{-x^2}$. Since $f^{(3)}(x)>0$ on $[0, 1]$, f'' is increasing. The minimum value of f'' on $[0, 1]$ is therefore $f''(0)=-2$, and the maximum value is $f''(1)=2/e$. In (15.2) one can take $m=-2$ and $M=2/e$, giving

$$-0.167 \leqslant 0.684 - K_0 \leqslant 0.062,$$

putting in for T_1 the value calculated in Example 15.10. So

$$-0.062 \leqslant K_0 - 0.684 \leqslant 0.167$$

$$0.622 \leqslant \int_0^1 \exp(-x^2)\,dx \leqslant 0.851.$$

The dismal conclusion is that T_1 may not have even one significant figure correct.   □

However this calculation has two good features. Firstly equation (15.2) gives definite bounds on the error. Secondly these bounds are better than would be obtained from a comparable calculation using the defining sequences $\{R_n\}$. Since equation (15.1) requires only two evaluations of the integrand $f(x)$, the comparison calculation is R_2. From Example 9.12 on p. 198, the bounds obtained from the sequences with $n=2$ are

$$L_2 = 0.57 \leqslant K_0 \leqslant U_2 = 0.89.$$

Equation (15.2) also shows that the error is proportional to $(d-c)^3$, and is therefore small if $(d-c)$ is much less than 1. Geometrically one also expects the approximation of a curve by a chord to be better the smaller the interval. This suggests improving the approximation by subdividing the interval, and applying equation (15.1) in each sub-interval.

Figure 15.2 shows $[a, b]$ divided into n subintervals of equal length $h=(b-a)/n$. Since

$$\int_a^b f(x)\,dx = \int_a^{x_1} f(x)\,dx + \cdots + \int_{x_{n-1}}^b f(x)\,dx,$$

equation (15.1) can be applied in each subinterval, and the results added. This gives the

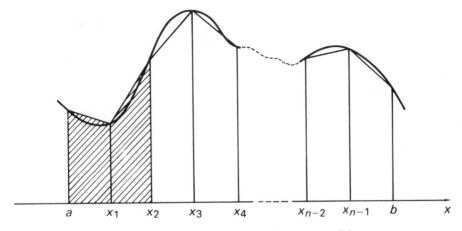

Figure 15.2   Trapezia of width *h* under curve *y* = *f*(*x*)

approximation

$$T_n = h\tfrac{1}{2}\{f(a)+f(x_1)\} + h\tfrac{1}{2}\{f(x_1)+f(x_2)\} + h\tfrac{1}{2}\{f(x_2)+f(x_3)\} + \cdots$$

$$+ h\tfrac{1}{2}\{f(x_{n-2})+f(x_{n-1})\} + h\tfrac{1}{2}\{f(x_{n-1})+f(b)\}$$

$$= h\{\tfrac{1}{2}f(a)+f(x_1)+f(x_2)+\cdots+f(x_{n-1})+\tfrac{1}{2}f(b)\}. \tag{15.3}$$

This formula is usually called the **trapezoidal rule**;

sometimes it is referred to as the **extended trapezoidal rule**, being an extension of equation (15.1).

Example 15.12

Taking $n = 10$ in equation (15.3) for an evaluation of $K_0 = \int_0^1 \exp(-x^2)\,dx$ gives

$$T_{10} = 0.1\{\tfrac{1}{2}e^0 + e^{-0.01} + e^{-0.04} + e^{-0.09} + e^{-0.16} + e^{-0.25}$$

$$+ e^{-0.36} + e^{-0.49} + e^{-0.64} + e^{-0.81} + \tfrac{1}{2}e^{-1.00}\} = 0.74621. \quad \square$$

For (15.3), the extension of equation (15.2) is

$$\tfrac{1}{12}m\frac{(b-a)^3}{n^2} \leqslant T_n - \int_a^b f(x)\,dx \leqslant \tfrac{1}{12}M\frac{(b-a)^3}{n^2} \tag{15.4}$$

where *m* and *M* are lower and upper bounds for $f''(x)$ on $[a, b]$.

Example 15.13

For K_0, bounds on $f''(x)$ have already been found in Example 15.11. There is no need to take the exact minimum and/or maximum for these bounds. Thus $m = -2$ and $M = 1$ can be used. Putting $n = 10$ in equation (15.4):

$$-0.00167 \leqslant T_{10} - K_0 \leqslant 0.00083$$

$$-0.00083 \leqslant K_0 - T_{10} \leqslant 0.00167$$

$$0.74538 \leqslant K_0 \leqslant 0.74788.$$

This shows that T_{10} is correct to 2 figures; and there is some information on the third figure, since $0.745 < K_0 < 0.748$. This result is considerably better than the comparable bounds $(0.71 < K_0 < 0.78)$ obtained from the defining sequences in Example 9.12 on p. 198. □

Letting $n \to \infty$ in equation (15.4) shows that $T_n \to \int_a^b f(x)\,dx$ as $n \to \infty$. The required integral is the limit of the sequence $\{T_n\}$. If a programmable calculator is available, the convergence of this sequence can be investigated numerically. Computer programs C2 for the evaluation of equation (15.3) are given in Appendix C, based on Procedure B9 in Appendix B.

Example 15.14
For $\int_0^2 \exp(-x^2)\,dx$, computation gives

n	2	4	8	16	32	64	128	256
T_n	0.877	0.8806	0.88170	0.88199	0.882058	0.882075	0.882080	0.882081

These values of T_n display a satisfactory convergence, and it is fairly safe to conclude that $\int_0^2 \exp(-x^2)\,dx = 0.88208$ (5S). However for a *certain* result, the error bounds in equation (15.4) should be evaluated. □

Numerical errors were previously discussed in Section 7.2. The general remarks made there apply equally well to the computations in this chapter. Equation (15.4) gives bounds on the **truncation error**

$$T_n - \int_a^b f(x)\,dx,$$

which may be reduced by increasing n. The other source of error is **rounding error** due to rounding off numbers during computations. If the sequence appears to converge up to some value N, after which there are (small) random fluctuations in the values T_n, this apparent lack of convergence is due to rounding errors building up and becoming larger than the truncation error.

Some computational effort is saved if T_n is calculated with n successive powers of 2, as in Example 15.14, because then $(n+1)$ of the subdivision points x_i for T_{2n} have already been used in T_n. So $(n+1)$ of the required values of f have already been calculated.

Exercise (answer on p. 391)
15.1.1   Use the following table of reciprocals

x	1	9/8	5/4	11/8	3/2	13/8	7/4	15/8	2
x^{-1}	1.000	0.889	0.800	0.727	0.667	0.615	0.571	0.533	0.500

to obtain the approximations T_2, T_4 and T_8 to $\int_1^2 dx/x$. Bound the errors.

15.2 Simpson's Rule

A better approximation to an integrand $f(x)$ is obtained using a quadratic $Q(x) = Ax^2 + Bx + C$ rather than a straight line. Since Q contains three constants A, B and C to be chosen, $Q(x)$ can be fitted to $f(x)$ at three points. To approximate $\int_c^d f(x)\,dx$ it is simplest to take $x = c$, d and $x = e = \frac{1}{2}(c+d)$ for these three points (Fig. 15.3). Then

$$S_2 = \int_c^d Q(x)\,dx \tag{15.5}$$

is the approximation to $\int_c^d f(x)\,dx$.

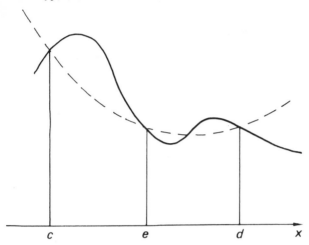

Figure 15.3   Quadratic approximation $Q(x)$ (dashed) to $f(x)$ (solid)

An explicit formula for S_2 may be obtained without actually finding the approximating quadratic Q. To derive this it is easiest to work with the variable $t = x - e$, and put $d - c = 2h$ (see Fig. 15.4). The dotted curves in Figs 15.3 and 15.4 are identical, both being the parabola represented by Q. So, if $Q(t) = At^2 + Bt + C$

$$t = -h \text{ gives } Ah^2 - Bh + C = f(c) \tag{15.6}$$

$$t = 0 \text{ gives } \qquad\qquad C = f(e) \tag{15.7}$$

$$t = h \text{ gives } \quad Ah^2 + Bh + C = f(d). \tag{15.8}$$

Figure 15.4 $Q(t)$ where $t = x - e$

Then

$$S_2 = \int_{-h}^{h} Q(t)\, dt = \int_{-h}^{h} (At^2 + Bt + C)\, dt$$

$$= \tfrac{2}{3}Ah^3 + 2Ch = h\{\tfrac{1}{3}f(c) + \tfrac{4}{3}f(d) + \tfrac{4}{3}f(e)\}, \quad \text{from equations (15.6-8).}$$

Thus an approximation for $\int_c^d f(x)\, dx$ is

$$S_2 = \tfrac{1}{6}(d-c)\{f(c) + 4f(e) + f(d)\}. \tag{15.9}$$

Example 15.20
For $K_0 = \int_0^1 \exp(-x^2)\, dx$, the approximation is

$$S_2 = \tfrac{1}{6}(e^0 + 4\, e^{-0.25} + e^{-1}) = 0.747. \quad \square$$

Again the approximation may be improved by subdividing the interval. Since Figs. 15.3 and 15.4 display two intervals, $[a, b]$ is divided into an even number of subintervals (Fig. 15.5). Then

$$\int_a^b f(x)\, dx = \int_a^{x_2} f(x)\, dx + \int_{x_2}^{x_4} f(x)\, dx + \cdots + \int_{x_{n-2}}^{b} f(x)\, dx$$

and equation (15.9) is applied to each of these integrals. This is equivalent to approximating f with a different quadratic Q_i in each pair of subintervals (Fig. 15.5). It gives the approximation

$$S_n = \tfrac{1}{3}h\{f(a) + 4f(x_1) + f(x_2)\} + \tfrac{1}{3}h\{f(x_2) + 4f(x_3) + f(x_4)\} + \cdots$$

$$+ \tfrac{1}{3}h\{f(x_{n-2}) + 4f(x_{n-1}) + f(b)\}$$

$$= \tfrac{1}{3}h\{f(a) + 4f(x_1) + 2f(x_2) + 4f(x_3) + 2f(x_4) + \cdots$$

$$+ 2f(x_{n-2}) + 4f(x_{n-1}) + f(b)\}. \tag{15.10}$$

This is **Simpson's rule**.

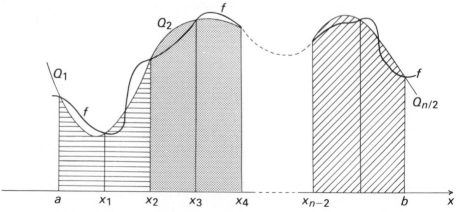

Figure 15.5 $Q_1(x)$ approximates $f(x)$ in $(a, x_2) = (a, a+2h)$, etc. Sum of shaded areas is equation (15.10)

Sometimes equation (15.9) is called Simpson's rule and equation (15.10) the **extended Simpson's rule**.

Example 15.21
Taking $n = 10$ in equation (15.10) for an evaluation of $K_0 = \int_0^1 e^{-x^2}\,dx$ gives

$$S_{10} = \tfrac{1}{3}(0.1)\{e^0 + 4e^{-0.01} + 2e^{-0.04} + 4e^{-0.09} + 2e^{-0.16} + 4e^{-0.25}$$

$$+ 2e^{-0.36} + 4e^{-0.49} + 2e^{-0.64} + 4e^{-0.81} + e^{-1.00}\} = 0.74682. \quad \square$$

This is expected to be more accurate than the corresponding trapezoidal rule result in Example 15.12.

The formula giving bounds on the truncation error for Simpson's rule (15.10) is

$$\tfrac{1}{180}m'\frac{(b-a)^5}{n^4} \le S_n - \int_a^b f(x)\,dx \le \tfrac{1}{180}M'\frac{(b-a)^5}{n^4} \qquad \textbf{(15.11)}$$

where m' and M' are lower and upper bounds for the 4th derivative $f^{(4)}(x)$ on $[a, b]$.

Example 15.22
For $f(x) = \exp(-x^2)$, $f^{(4)}(x) = (16x^4 - 48x^2 + 12)\exp(-x^2)$, and

$$f^{(5)}(x) = (-32x^5 + 160x^3 - 120x)\exp(-x^2)$$

$$= -32x(x^2 - 2.5 + \tfrac{1}{2}\sqrt{10})(x^2 - 2.5 - \tfrac{1}{2}\sqrt{10})\exp(-x^2)$$

$$= -32x(x^2 - 0.919)(x^2 - 4.081)\exp(-x^2).$$

Thus $f^{(5)}(x)$ changes sign at $x = \sqrt{0.919} = 0.959$. On $[0, 1]$, the integration interval for K_0 in Example 15.21, $f^{(5)}(x) < 0$ on $(0, 0.959)$, and $f^{(5)}(x) > 0$ on $(0.959, 1)$. Hence $f^{(4)}$ is decreasing on $(0, 0.959)$ and increasing on $(0.959, 1)$. Computing

$$f^{(4)}(0) = 12, \qquad f^{(4)}(0.959) = -7.4 \quad \text{and} \quad f^{(4)}(1) = -7.36,$$

one can evidently take $m' = -7.5$ and $M' = 12$ as bounds on $f^{(4)}(x)$ on $[0, 1]$ (Fig. 15.6). Substituting into equation (15.11) with $n = 10$

$$-\tfrac{1}{24}10^{-4} \le S_{10} - K_0 \le \tfrac{1}{15}10^{-4}$$

$$S_{10} - 7(10^{-6}) \le K_0 \le S_{10} + 4(10^{-6}) \qquad \textbf{(15.12)}$$

$-7(10^{-6})$ and $4(10^{-6})$ are corrections to the 6th decimal place, so it is worth evaluating S_{10} to 6D. Repeating the work in Example 15.21 to 6D gives $S_{10} = 0.746825$, and (15.12) is $0.746818 \le K_0 \le 0.746829$. Four figures are correct, and the 5th is either 2 or 3. $\quad \square$

Letting $n \to \infty$ in equation (15.11) shows that $\int_a^b f(x)\,dx$ is the limit of the sequence $\{S_n\}$.

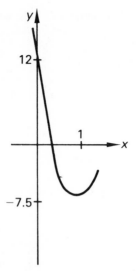

Figure 15.6   Minimum of $f^{(4)}(x)$ at $x=0.959$

Example 15.23

For $\int_0^2 \exp(-x^2)\,dx$, computation gives

n	2	4	8	16	32	64, 128, 256
S_n	0.830	0.8818	0.882066	0.882080	0.88208132	0.88208139
T_n	0.877	0.8806	0.88170	0.88199	0.882058	

Values of T_n from Example 15.14 are included for comparison. The value T_2 is unexpectedly better than S_2, because the curvature (i.e. f'') changes sign at $x=\sqrt{\tfrac{1}{2}}$ so that the errors in each trapezium have opposite sign.   □

Numerical integration formulas are usually called **quadrature formulas**, and the process called **quadrature**. This term originally meant a geometrical process for finding the area enclosed by a given curve.

Exercise (answer on p. 391)

15.2.1   For $f(x)=x^{-1}$, find bounds for $f^{(4)}(x)$ on $[1,2]$. Use these bounds in equation (15.11) with $n=2$, 4 and 8. From the results, decide to what number of decimal places it is worth evaluating S_2, S_4 and S_8 in approximating $\int_1^2 dx/x$. Compute these approximations, and compare with the results of Exercise 15.1.1 on p. 380.

15.3   Derivation of Bounds on the Trapezoidal Rule Error

Suppose $E(h)$ is the error when $\int_0^h f(t)\,dt$ is approximated using

$$T_1 = (d-c)\tfrac{1}{2}\{f(c)+f(d)\} \tag{15.1}$$

by putting $d=h$ and $c=0$ (this is still completely general, since a linear substitution changes $c \leqslant x \leqslant d$ to $0 \leqslant t \leqslant h$). Then

$$E(h) = (\text{approximation}) - (\text{true value}) = \tfrac{1}{2}hf(0) + \tfrac{1}{2}hf(h) - \int_0^h f(t)\, dt. \quad (15.13)$$

Differentiate with respect to h:

$$E'(h) = \tfrac{1}{2}f(0)$$

$$+\tfrac{1}{2}f(h) + \tfrac{1}{2}hf'(h) \qquad \text{(from the product rule)}$$

$$-f(h) \qquad \text{(from the fundamental theorem—see p. 212)}$$

$$= \tfrac{1}{2}f(0) - \tfrac{1}{2}f(h) + \tfrac{1}{2}hf'(h). \qquad (15.14)$$

Differentiate again with respect to h:

$$E''(h) = -\tfrac{1}{2}f'(h) + \tfrac{1}{2}f'(h) + \tfrac{1}{2}hf''(h) = \tfrac{1}{2}hf''(h).$$

Now suppose m and M are bounds on the second derivative, i.e.

$$m \leqslant f''(h) \leqslant M.$$

Then multiplying by $\tfrac{1}{2}h$ gives (assuming $h \geqslant 0$)

$$\tfrac{1}{2}mh \leqslant E''(h) \leqslant \tfrac{1}{2}Mh. \qquad (15.15)$$

Bounds on $E(h)$ are now obtained using

$$g(x) \leqslant f(x) \quad \text{on } (a, b) \quad \Rightarrow \quad \int_a^b g(x)\, dx \leqslant \int_a^b f(x)\, dx. \qquad (9.8)$$

Integrating (15.15) from $h = 0$ to $h = z$:

$$\tfrac{1}{2}m \int_0^z h\, dh \leqslant \int_0^z E''(h)\, dh \leqslant \tfrac{1}{2}M \int_0^z h\, dh$$

$$\tfrac{1}{4}mz^2 \leqslant E'(z) - E'(0) \leqslant \tfrac{1}{4}Mz^2.$$

From equation (15.14) $E'(0) = 0$.
  Integrate again, from $z = 0$ to $z = h$:

$$\tfrac{1}{4}m \int_0^h z^2\, dz \leqslant \int_0^h E'(z)\, dz \leqslant \tfrac{1}{4}M \int_0^h z^2\, dz$$

$$\tfrac{1}{12}mh^3 \leqslant E(h) - E(0) \leqslant \tfrac{1}{12}Mh^3.$$

From equation (15.13), $E(0) = 0$. Hence

$$\tfrac{1}{12}mh^3 \leqslant T_1 - \int_0^h f(t)\, dt \leqslant \tfrac{1}{12}Mh^3 \qquad (15.16)$$

where m and M are bounds on $f''(t)$ in $[0, h]$. In equation (15.16), h is the length of the integration interval, so is replaced by $(d - c)$ when T_1 is given by equation (15.1) and approximates $\int_c^d f(x)\, dx$:

$$\boxed{\tfrac{1}{12}m(d-c)^3 \leqslant T_1 - \int_c^d f(x)\, dx \leqslant \tfrac{1}{12}M(d-c)^3.} \qquad \mathbf{(15.17)}$$

To apply this to the extended formula (15.3) on p. 379, it is written down for each of the n subintervals, and the results summed. Since m and M can be any bounds of $f''(x)$, the bounds of $f''(x)$ over the whole interval $[a, b]$ can be used as the bounds for each subinterval. The subintervals all have the same length h. Thus the n results $(i = 1, 2, \ldots, n)$:

$$\tfrac{1}{12} mh^3 \leqslant \tfrac{1}{2} h\{f(x_{i-1}) + f(x_i)\} - \int_{x_{i-1}}^{x_i} f(x)\, dx \leqslant \tfrac{1}{12} Mh^3$$

all have the same bounds, and summing gives

$$\boxed{\tfrac{1}{12} mh^3 n \leqslant T_n - \int_a^b f(x)\, dx \leqslant \tfrac{1}{12} Mh^3 n.}$$

Putting $h = (b-a)/n$ gives equation (15.4) on p. 379.

Example 15.30

How many subdivisions should be used to ensure that the trapezoidal rule evaluates $K_0 = \int_0^1 \exp(-x^2)\, dx$ with error less than 0.0005?

From Example 15.11 on p. 378, $m = -2$ and $M = 2$ are bounds on the second derivative of $\exp(-x^2)$ on $[0, 1]$. Substituting into equation (15.4) on p. 379 gives

$$-\frac{1}{6n^2} \leqslant T_n - K_0 \leqslant \frac{1}{6n^2}, \quad \text{i.e. } |T_n - K_0| \leqslant \frac{1}{6n^2}. \tag{15.18}$$

The given requirement is achieved if n is chosen so that

$$\frac{1}{6n^2} < 0.0005 = \frac{1}{2000},$$

$$n^2 > \frac{2000}{6} = 333.3.$$

Thus $n = 19$ is the smallest number of subdivisions to ensure the required accuracy. (To simplify the computation one could take $n = 20$.)

To be certain of the accuracy, rounding error must also be considered. On computing T_n (see p. 379), the maximum rounding error is $\tfrac{1}{2}$ in the last figure for each evaluation of $f(x_i)$, giving a possible $\tfrac{1}{2} n$ error in the last figure when summed. The final division by n divides this rounding error by n, so the total rounding error is at most 1 in the last figure.

In the present example, this shows that working to 4D (for example using 4-figure tables for evaluating the $\exp(-x_i^2)$) will ensure that the rounding error in T_{20} will not affect the third figure.   □

The effects of rounding error depend on the way in which the arithmetic is done, which in turn may depend on the nature of any mechanical or electronic device used. Electronic calculators use binary numbers, so the rounding error statements will concern the last binary place rather than the last decimal place. If the rounding error in calculating T_n or S_n increases with n, it will eventually exceed the truncation error.

An example of **numerical instability**, where the rounding error reaches the same magnitude as the values being calculated, was given in Section 7.2, p. 170. This can also happen if reduction formulas are used in conjunction with approximate numerical values of definite integrals.

Example 15.31
Suppose it is required to calculate $I_m = \int_0^1 x^{m/3} e^x \, dx$ for $m = 1(1)30$.

A reduction formula, reducing the power of x, exists for this integral (see R2 on p. 253, or integrate by parts):

$$\int_0^1 x^n e^x \, dx = e - n \int_0^1 x^{n-1} e^x \, dx. \tag{15.19}$$

This allows I_m to be calculated from I_{m-3}, and appears to give a way of obtaining the required I_m after determining numerical values for I_0, I_1 and I_2. However initial errors are magnified by the use of equation (15.19), so the method is useless. Thus $I_4 = e - \frac{4}{3} I_1$, $I_7 = e - \frac{7}{3} I_4, \ldots, I_{28} = e - \frac{28}{3} I_{25}$ so an error of magnitude δ in I_1 becomes approximately $4\delta/3$ in I_4, $\frac{7}{3}(\frac{4}{3}\delta)$ in $I_7, \ldots$ The final error in I_{28} is approximately $(\frac{28}{3})(\frac{25}{3}) \cdots (\frac{4}{3})\delta > 9!\delta > (2\delta)\text{E5}$. For instance 6D accuracy for I_1 may only give 1D accuracy for I_{28}.

The reduction formula (or recurrence relation) is certainly useful for integer n, because $I_3 = 1.00$, with no error and I_6, $I_9, \ldots, I_{30}$ can be expressed in terms of e. For the non-integral values of n the only way to use equation (15.19) would be to calculate I_{28} and I_{29}, and then use (15.19) in reverse:

$$I_{25} = \tfrac{3}{28}(e - I_{28}), \qquad I_{22} = \tfrac{3}{25}(e - I_{25}), \ldots; \qquad I_{26} = \tfrac{3}{29}(e - I_{29}), \ldots. \quad \square$$

Exercise (answer on p. 391)
15.3.1 How many subdivisions should be used to ensure that the trapezoidal rule evaluates $\int_1^2 dx/x$ with error less than 0.00005?

15.4 General Integration Procedures

Two methods have now been given for the evaluation of $\int_a^b f(x) \, dx$. If f is continuous, and an antiderivative P can be found ($P' = f$) then

$$\int_a^b f(x) \, dx = P(b) - P(a). \tag{9.13}$$

Alternatively, numerical integration formulas such as the trapezoidal rule (p. 379) or Simpson's rule (p. 382) will evaluate $\int_a^b f(x) \, dx$ to a prescribed accuracy. Such formulas result from approximating f by a polynomial. For example, a first degree (linear) approximation gives the trapezoidal rule, and a second degree (quadratic) approximation gives Simpson's rule. The success of such approximations is dependent on f being like a polynomial on $[a, b]$, so the formulas cannot give satisfactory results if f is discontinuous, or if its low-order derivatives do not exist. The formulas giving bounds on the error also require certain derivatives to exist, for example $f^{(4)}$ with Simpson's rule.

The numerical integration formulas may still give the most efficient way of evaluating $\int_a^b f(x) \, dx$ even in cases where an antiderivative of f can be found.

Example 15.40

Evaluate $\displaystyle\int_{-1}^{0} \frac{dx}{x^5 - 5x + 2}$.

Since the integrand is a rational function, Procedure B3 may be used to obtain an antiderivative. However the factorization of $D(x) = x^5 - 5x + 2$ and the determination of the partial fraction expansion of $1/D(x)$ require a numerical determination (Example 7.11 on p. 162) of the roots s, r and t of $D(x)$. Even when the antiderivative is obtained, it will contain terms like $\ln(x - s)$, giving $\ln(x - s)|_{-1}^{0} = \ln(s/s + 1)$. These final logarithm (or Tan^{-1}) values may have to be computed, depending on available tables or calculators and what accuracy is required.

The alternative method of evaluating Simpson's rule (15.10) with $a = -1$, $b = 0$, $f(x) = (x^5 - 5x + 2)^{-1}$ and suitable values of n appears to involve less work.

Note that it is still desirable to get some information on the roots of $D(x)$, as in Example 6.71 on p. 129, to ensure that there is no root in $[-1, 0]$. (There is no merit in attempting a numerical evaluation of an (improper) integral which does not exist.)   □

Example 15.41

Evaluate $\displaystyle\int_{2}^{3} \frac{N(x)}{D(x)} \, dx$,

where

$$N(x) = x^6 + 5x^5 + 17x^4 + 27x^3 + 20x^2 - 8x + 2 \quad \text{and} \quad D(x) = x^5 - 3x^4 + 6x^3 + 2x^2 - 7x - 5.$$

The roots of $D(x)$ are integers, so an antiderivative can be obtained without any numerical computation. The algebraic work was outlined in Example 10.49 on p. 239. To decide how to evaluate the integral, this work must be compared with the labour of evaluating $N(x)$ and $D(x)$ at the 10 or more points required for Simpson's rule.   □

In general the choice between the antiderivative method and a numerical method is partly a matter of individual preference for algebraic or numerical work, but will also depend on the accuracy required and the computational aids which are available. If $\int_a^b f(x) \, dx$ is required for many different values of a and/or b, the antiderivative method is evidently advantageous.

Numerical integration formulas can also be used to tabulate an antiderivative when this cannot be obtained analytically. Given the integrand $f(x)$, with f continuous, the fundamental theorem states that $A(x) = \int_a^x f(u) \, du$ is an antiderivative of f. After choosing a numerical value of a, values $A(x)$ can be calculated using the trapezoidal rule or Simpson's rule. Giving a numerical value to a is equivalent to choosing a value for the arbitrary constant in the indefinite integral. This choice is often made to satisfy a condition

$y = b$ when $x = a$. Evidently

$$A(x) = b + \int_{a}^{x} f(t) \, dt \tag{15.20}$$

is the antiderivative which satisfies this condition.

This result gives a formal solution of the differential equation $dy/dx = f(x)$ with the condition $y = b$ when $x = a$, in a form allowing direct numerical computation of values of y using approximation formulas for the integral. Because of the existence of these methods for evaluating an integral, it is customary to regard a differential equation as solved once the solution is reduced to the evaluation of indefinite integrals. Particular solutions are obtained after incorporating given conditions as in equation (15.20).

Example 15.42

If $y = s(x)$ is the particular solution of

$$dy/dx = (y^2 - 1)(2x^3 + 7)/y(2x + 1)(x^2 + 2)$$

satisfying $y = \frac{1}{2}\sqrt{3}$ when $x = 0$, calculate $s(1)$.

Separating the variables gives

$$\frac{y \, dy}{y^2 - 1} = \frac{(2x^3 + 7) \, dx}{(2x + 1)(x^2 + 2)}.$$

Since the integrands are rational functions, it is possible to get the general solution by finding antiderivatives. However the algebra required to obtain partial fractions can be avoided, as only a particular solution is required. Integrating the left side shows that the general solution has the form (C is the arbitrary constant)

$$\frac{1}{2}\ln|y^2 - 1| + C = \int_a^x (2t^3 + 7) \, dt/(2t + 1)(t^2 + 2). \tag{15.21}$$

This is true for any value of a; to apply the condition $y = \frac{1}{2}\sqrt{3}$ at $x = 0$, it is convenient to take $a = 0$ so that $x = 0$ makes the integral zero. Hence

$$C = -\tfrac{1}{2}\ln|\tfrac{3}{4} - 1| = -\tfrac{1}{2}\ln\tfrac{1}{4} = \tfrac{1}{2}\ln 4$$

and the particular solution $y = s(x)$ is given implicitly by

$$\tfrac{1}{2}\ln(4|y^2 - 1|) = \int_0^x (2t^3 + 7) \, dt/(2t + 1)(t^2 + 2).$$

The required value of y is now obtained by putting $x = 1$ and evaluating the integral numerically. Simpson's rule with $n = 32$ or 50 gives

$$\int_0^1 (2t^3 + 7) \, dt/(2t + 1)(t^2 + 2) = 1.8072$$

so

$$\ln(4|y^2 - 1|) = 3.6144, \qquad |y^2 - 1| = 9.28.$$

If $y^2 > 1$ then $y^2 - 1 = 9.28$, $y^2 = 10.28$, $y = \pm 3.21$; if $y^2 < 1$ then $1 - y^2 = 9.28 \Rightarrow y^2 = -8.28$, which is impossible. Two values of y of opposite sign are expected because equation (15.21) depends on y only through y^2, which means that the graphs of the solutions are symmetric about Ox. If the required particular solution is understood to be a function, then the positive value $y = 3.21$ should be taken for $s(1)$, since $s(0)$ is positive, and an explicit solution for y would take the positive square root. □

In general if separation of variables gives

$$h(y)\, dy = f(x)\, dx$$

then the solution passing through (a, b) is given by

$$\int_b^y h(t)\, dt = \int_a^x f(s)\, ds.$$

If one of these integrals can be solved with an antiderivative, points (x, y) of the solution may be obtained (as in the previous example) using numerical integration for the other integral. If neither integral can be solved with an antiderivative, the more general methods available for the numerical solution of differential equations should be used. These are given in Chapter 19.

The first order linear equation

$$dy/dx + Q(x)y = R(x) \qquad (13.11)$$

can also be solved in principle by evaluating two indefinite integrals (see Section 13.2). First $\int Q(x)\, dx$ gives the integrating factor

$$I(x) = \exp\left(\int Q(x)\, dx\right). \qquad (13.14)$$

If an explicit expression cannot be obtained for $I(x)$, then again numerical methods for the solution of differential equations are required. Assuming an antiderivative for Q, then the solution of equation (13.11) involves $\int I(x)R(x)\, dx$. It may be useful to evaluate this by quadrature when a particular solution is specified. The advantage of using quadrature, rather than more general numerical procedures for solving differential equations, is that error bounds are easier to obtain.

Example 15.43
If $dy/dx + xy = 2$, and $y = 0$ when $x = 0$, find y when $x = 1$, 2, and -1.

The differential equation is linear, and according to equation (13.14) an integrating factor is given by

$$I(x) = \exp\left(\int x\, dx\right) = \exp(\tfrac{1}{2}x^2).$$

Multiplying the equation by $I(x)\, dx$ gives

$$dy \exp(\tfrac{1}{2}x^2) + yx \exp(\tfrac{1}{2}x^2)\, dx = 2 \exp(\tfrac{1}{2}x^2)\, dx$$

$$d[y \exp(\tfrac{1}{2}x^2)] = 2 \exp(\tfrac{1}{2}x^2)\, dx.$$

The general solution has the form

$$y \exp(\tfrac{1}{2}x^2) = C + 2 \int \exp(\tfrac{1}{2}x^2)\, dx.$$

Using equation (15.20) to incorporate the given initial condition gives

$$y \exp(\tfrac{1}{2}x^2) = 2 \int_0^x \exp(\tfrac{1}{2}t^2)\, dt$$

and the required particular solution is

$$y = 2 \exp(-\tfrac{1}{2}x^2) \int_0^x \exp(\tfrac{1}{2}t^2) \, dt.$$

For the numerical evaluation of values of y, this can be written

$$y = \int_0^x 2 \exp(\tfrac{1}{2}t^2 - \tfrac{1}{2}x^2) \, dt$$

When $x = 1$,
$$y = \int_0^1 2 \exp(\tfrac{1}{2}t^2 - \tfrac{1}{2}) \, dt = 0.7248$$

When $x = 2$,
$$y = \int_0^2 2 \exp(\tfrac{1}{2}t^2 - 2) \, dt = 0.6400$$

When $x = -1$,
$$y = -\int_{-1}^0 2 \exp(\tfrac{1}{2}t^2 - \tfrac{1}{2}) \, dt = -0.7248.$$

The three numerical values were obtained from Simpson's rule with $n = 20$.   □

Exercises

15.4.1   A function is defined implicitly by

$$y^3 + y + 1 = \int_a^x (\sin t^2) \, dt.$$

Differentiate this equation, and obtain the first-order differential equation satisfied by this function.

15.4.2   Express in terms of an integral the solution $y = s(x)$ of

$$x \frac{dy}{dx} - \sin x = y^2 \sin x$$

which passes through $(1, 1)$, and hence find $s(2)$.

Answers to Exercises 15.1.1–15.4.2

15.1.1 $T_2 = 0.708$, $0.006 \leqslant \text{error} \leqslant 0.042$, $0.666 \leqslant \ln 2 \leqslant 0.702$
$T_4 = 0.697$, $0.002 \leqslant \text{error} \leqslant 0.011$, $0.686 \leqslant \ln 2 \leqslant 0.699$
$T_8 = 0.694$, $0.000 \leqslant \text{error} \leqslant 0.003$, $0.691 \leqslant \ln 2 \leqslant 0.694$.

15.2.1 $f^{(4)}(2) = 0.75 \leqslant f^{(4)}(x) \leqslant f^{(4)}(1) = 24$
Evaluate S_2 to 2D, S_4 to 3D, S_8 to 5D
$S_2 = 0.695$ (evaluating third place to compare with T_2)
$S_4 = 0.693$, $S_8 = 0.69316$, but equation (15.11) $\Rightarrow 0.69311 < \int_1^2 dx/x < 0.69316$.

15.3.1   58 (or more).

15.4.1 $\dfrac{dy}{dx} = \dfrac{\sin x^2}{3y^2 + 1}$.

15.4.2 $s(x) = \operatorname{Tan}\left[\dfrac{1}{4}\pi + \displaystyle\int_1^x \dfrac{\sin t}{t} \, dt\right]$, $s(2) = 7.9$.

Further Exercises on Chapter 15

15.1 Suppose $\{R_n\}$ is the Riemann sequence obtained (as in Section 9.1) by choosing the c_i at the left-end points of the n subintervals of $[a, b]$ of equal length $(b-a)/n$, and $\{R_n^*\}$ is the sequence obtained by choosing the c_i at the right end-points. Show that (equation (15.3) on p. 379) $T_n = \frac{1}{2}R_n + \frac{1}{2}R_n^*$, and deduce that $\mathrm{Lim}\, T_n = R_a^b(f)$ whenever $R_a^b(f)$ exists.

15.2 Define R_n and R_n^* as in Exercise 15.1, and let $\{M_n\}$ be the Riemann sequence obtained by choosing the c_i at the midpoints of the subintervals. Show (equation (15.10) on p. 382) $S_{2n} = \frac{1}{6}R_n + \frac{1}{6}R_n^* + \frac{2}{3}M_n$, and deduce that $\mathrm{Lim}\, S_n = R_a^b(f)$ whenever $R_a^b(f)$ exists. (The **midpoint rule** uses M_n as an integration formula.)

15.3 Verify that $\int_0^1 (ax^3 + bx + c)\, dx$ is evaluated exactly by Simpson's rule. Is this expected from the error formula?

15.4 Which of the reduction formulas on p. 253–4 are likely to show numerical instability if used with approximate values of definite integrals?

15.5 Express in terms of an integral the solution $y = s(x)$ of

$$dy/dx = (y^2 + 1)\sin(\tfrac{1}{2}\pi x^2)$$

which satisfies $s(0) = 1$, and obtain the value of $s(\tfrac{1}{2})$.

15.6 Express in terms of an integral the general solution of

$$dy/dx = y + 2xy + e^x.$$

For the particular solution which passes through $(0, 0)$, find the value of y when $x = 1$.

15.7 Let $y(x)$ denote the solution of

$$dy/dx = (y^2 + 1)\sin(1 + x^2)$$

determined by the condition $y = 2$ when $x = 0$. Express $y(1)$ in terms of a definite integral.

15.8 Evaluate $I = \int_0^4 x^3\, dx$ by using
(a) the trapezoidal rule (b) Simpson's rule, in each case using 4 subintervals.
Without assuming a knowledge of the exact value, calculate a bound on the truncation error in each approximation.

15.9 Evaluate $\int_{0.4}^{1.2} x^4\, dx$ by Simpson's rule with 8 subdivisions.
Compute the quantities in equation (15.11). What is the truncation error? What is the truncation error in the Simpson's rule approximation S_n to $\int_a^b f(x)\, dx$ when $f(x) = x^4 + ax^3 + \cdots$ is an arbitrary polynomial of degree 4?

15.10 The following results were obtained in either worked examples or exercises in Chapter 10. Use a numerical method to check them.

(i) $\displaystyle\int_1^2 \frac{dx}{\sqrt{(2x+1)}} = \sqrt{5} - \sqrt{3}$ 　　(ii) $\displaystyle\int_1^2 \frac{dx}{\sqrt{(9x^2-1)}} = 2(\sqrt{35} - \sqrt{8})/9$

(iii) $\displaystyle\int_1^2 x\, e^{-4x^2}\, dx = \frac{e^{-4} - e^{-16}}{8}$ 　　(iv) $\displaystyle\int_0^{\frac{1}{2}\pi} \cos^8 x\, dx = \frac{35\pi}{256}$

(v) $\displaystyle\int_0^{\pi/4} \sec^4 \theta\, d\theta = \frac{4}{3}$ 　　(vi) $\displaystyle\int_0^a \frac{dx}{(x^2+a^2)^2} = \frac{1 + \frac{1}{2}\pi}{4a^3}$

(vii) $\displaystyle\int_0^1 \sqrt{(2x+1)}\,dx = \sqrt{3}-(1/3)$ (viii) $\displaystyle\int_0^{\pi/4} x\sec^2 x\,dx = \tfrac14\pi - \tfrac12\ln 2$

(ix) $\displaystyle\int_0^\pi \sin^2 ax\,dx = \tfrac12\pi$ (x) $\displaystyle\int_0^1 \ln x\,dx = -1$ (xi) $\displaystyle\int_0^1 (x-1)\ln x\,dx = 3/4$

(xii) $\displaystyle\int_0^1 (1+x^2)^{-1}\,dx = \frac{\pi}{4}$ (xiii) $\displaystyle\int_0^1 x\log(2x+1)\,dx = \tfrac38\ln 3$

(xiv) $\displaystyle\int_0^4 \frac{2x^2+3x-1}{x^2-4x+8}\,dx = 8 + \frac{5\pi}{4}.$

16

Power Series and Fourier Series

16.1 Series of Functions

The convergence of series was considered in Chapter 8. The series with terms v_i converges if $\operatorname{Lim}_{n\to\infty} s_n$ exists, where $s_n = v_1 + v_2 + \cdots + v_n$. The value of the limit is called the sum of the series. In this chapter it will usually be convenient to let v_0 denote the first term, and correspondingly to write $\sum_{n=0}^{\infty} v_n$ for the value of the limit.

Example 16.10
(i) The series $1 + \frac{1}{2} + \frac{1}{4} + \frac{1}{8} + \cdots$, with terms $v_k = (\frac{1}{2})^k$, converges to the sum 2, i.e.

$$\sum_{n=0}^{\infty} v_n = \operatorname{Lim}_{m\to\infty} (1 + \tfrac{1}{2} + \cdots + (\tfrac{1}{2})^m) = 2.$$

(ii) The series $1 - 1 + 1 - 1 + 1 - 1 + \cdots$, with terms $v_k = (-1)^k$, does not converge. $\square$

If each term depends on a variable x, whether or not the series converges may depend on the value of x, and if the sum exists its value will also depend on x. The terms $v_n(x)$ and the sum $S(x)$ are functions of x.

Example 16.11
(i) If $v_n(x) = 1/(x+n)(x+n+1)$, the series is

$$\frac{1}{x(x+1)} + \frac{1}{(x+1)(x+2)} + \frac{1}{(x+2)(x+3)} + \cdots$$

which converges to the sum $S(x) = 1/x$ (see Exercise 8.5 on p. 192) provided $x \neq 0$, -1, -2, -3, ... This series converges for all values of x for which the terms are defined.
(ii) If $v_n(x) = kx^n$, the series

$$k + kx + kx^2 + kx^3 + \cdots$$

is a geometric series with ratio x. It converges if $|x| < 1$, and its sum is then $S(x) = k/(1-x)$. (See Example 8.13 on p. 180.)
The series in the previous example were the cases $x = \frac{1}{2}$ and $x = -1$, with $k = 1$. $\square$

A series of the form

$$a_0 + a_1 x + a_2 x^2 + \cdots + a_n x^n + \cdots,$$

where the coefficients a_n do not depend on x, is called a **power series**. The general term is $v_n(x) = a_n x^n$.

Sections 16.2–16.5 are devoted to examples, properties, and applications of power series. One example is the geometric series with ratio x.

Series of the form

$$a_0 + a_1 \cos x + b_1 \sin x + a_2 \cos 2x + b_2 \sin 2x + \cdots ,$$

called Fourier series, will be considered in Sections 16.7–16.10.

16.2   Properties of Power Series

Whether the power series $\sum a_k x^k$ converges will depend both on the form of the coefficients a_k and on the value of x. There are some power series which converge for all values of x.

Example 16.20

If $a_k = 1/k!$, the series is

$$1 + x + \frac{x^2}{2!} + \frac{x^3}{3!} + \frac{x^4}{4!} + \cdots ,$$

which is absolutely convergent for any value of x.

Note that $0! = 1$ is a conventional definition. The convergence can be shown by a modification of the method used in Exercise 8.1.4 on p. 185 for the case $x = 1$. $\square$

For the power series which do not converge for all values of x, there is a simple result on the values of x giving convergence:

associated with a power series is a number c such that it is absolutely convergent if $-c < x < c$, and does not converge if $x > c$ or if $x < -c$.

(There are power series which only converge (trivially) when $x = 0$; these are obviously not useful.)

Example 16.21

For the geometric series with ratio x (Example 16.11(ii)), $c = 1$. The series is absolutely convergent if $-1 < x < 1$, and does not converge if $x > 1$ or if $x < -1$. $\square$

The general result states that the power series converges absolutely if $|x| < c$, and does not converge if $|x| > c$, but there is no general result on the behaviour of the series when $x = \pm c$.

The number c is called the **radius of convergence** of the power series.

The reason for this term is that the result on convergence (in the form using $|x|$) remains true for a complex series $\sum a_n z^n$, and then $|z| < c$ is a disc in the complex plane (Fig. 16.1).

The radius of convergence c may be determined from the coefficients a_n. For example $c = \mathrm{Lim}_{n \to \infty} |a_n / a_{n+1}|$ if this limit exists. For any power series considered here the radius of convergence will be stated without derivation.

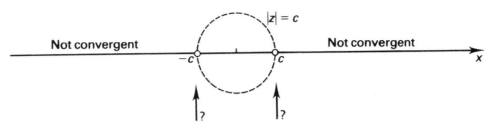

Figure 16.1   Power series converges if $-c < x < c$; does not converge if $|x| > c$

From a given power series, another power series may be formed by differentiating the terms. This new series has the same radius of convergence as the original series, and its sum is the derivative of that of the original series.

Example 16.22
From Example 16.11 (ii),

$$1 + x + x^2 + x^3 + \cdots + x^k + \cdots = (1-x)^{-1} \qquad \text{if } |x| < 1,$$

so

$$1 + 2x + 3x^2 + \cdots + kx^{k-1} + \cdots = \frac{d}{dx}(1-x)^{-1} \quad \text{if } |x| < 1.$$

The **general term** of the new series is $(k+1)x^k$, so the result is

$$\sum_{k=0}^{\infty} (k+1)x^k = (1-x)^{-2}, \qquad |x| < 1. \quad \square$$

The procedure in the previous example is called **term-by-term differentiation**.

Similarly **term-by-term integration** is valid.

Example 16.23
From

$$1 + x + x^2 + x^3 + \cdots = \frac{1}{1-x} \qquad (|x| < 1)$$

term-by-term integration gives

$$C + x + \frac{x^2}{2} + \frac{x^3}{3} + \frac{x^4}{4} + \cdots = -\ln(1-x) \qquad (|x| < 1).$$

The arbitrary integration constant C is determined by setting $x = 0$: $C + 0 + 0 + \cdots = 0$, $C = 0$. Thus

$$\sum_{k=1}^{\infty} \frac{x^k}{k} = -\ln(1-x) \qquad (|x| < 1) \tag{16.1}$$

(for $a_k = 1/k$ it is not convenient to start with $k = 0$). $\square$

Other operations yielding correct results are **multiplication of a power series by a polynomial**, or **by another power series**, or the **addition of two power series**.

Example 16.24

Multiply the geometric series by the polynomial $(1+x)$:

$$(1+x)(1+x+x^2+\cdots+x^{k-1}+x^k+\cdots) = (1+x)\left(\frac{1}{1-x}\right) \qquad (|x|<1).$$

Collecting terms gives

$$1+2x+2x^2+\cdots+2x^k+\cdots = \frac{1+x}{1-x}.$$

The coefficients are $a_k = 2$, except for $a_0 = 1$, so the result can be written

$$1+\sum_{k=1}^{\infty} 2x^k = \frac{1+x}{1-x} \qquad (|x|<1).$$

Check: the series is still geometric, so the left side is $1+2x/(1-x)$. □

Example 16.25

Multiplying the geometric series by itself gives

$$(1+x+x^2+\cdots+x^{k-1}+x^k+\cdots)(1+x+\cdots+x^{k-2}+x^{k-1}+x^k+\cdots)$$

and in this product x^k arises from $(1)(x^k)$, $x(x^{k-1})$, $(x^2)(x^{k-2}),\ldots(x^{k-1})x$, $x^k(1)$. The general term in the product is therefore $(k+1)x^k$, and the result is

$$\sum_{k=0}^{\infty} (k+1)x^k = \frac{1}{(1-x)(1-x)} \qquad (|x|<1).$$

This was previously obtained in Example 16.22. □

Example 16.26

$$1+2x+4x^2+8x^3+\cdots = \sum_{k=0}^{\infty} 2^k x^k \tag{16.2}$$

is a geometric series with ratio $2x$, so the sum is $1/(1-2x)$ provided $-1<2x<1$. This is $-\frac{1}{2}<x<\frac{1}{2}$, showing that the radius of convergence is $\frac{1}{2}$.

Similarly

$$\sum_{k=0}^{\infty} 3^k x^k = 1+3x+9x^2+27x^3+\cdots = \frac{1}{1-3x} \quad \text{if } -\tfrac{1}{3}<x<\tfrac{1}{3}. \tag{16.3}$$

Adding equations (16.2) and (16.3) shows that if $a_k = 2^k + 3^k$

$$\sum_{k=0}^{\infty} (2^k+3^k)x^k = 2+5x+13x^2+\cdots \tag{16.4}$$

has sum

$$\frac{1}{1-2x}+\frac{1}{1-3x} = \frac{2-5x}{1-5x+6x^2}.$$

For this to be valid both equations (16.2) and (16.3) must converge, so $-\frac{1}{3} < x < \frac{1}{3}$ is required. In other words $\frac{1}{3}$ is the radius of convergence of the series (16.4). $\square$

Since power series converge on an interval $-c < x < c$, replacement of x by $-x$ is always valid. This also follows from the fact that the convergence is absolute, and changing the sign of x merely changes the sign of alternate terms.

Example 16.27
Multiplying equation (16.1) by -1 gives

$$-x - \frac{x^2}{2} - \frac{x^3}{3} - \frac{x^4}{4} - \frac{x^5}{5} \cdots = \ln(1-x). \qquad (16.5)$$

Replacing x by $-x$:

$$x - \frac{x^2}{2} + \frac{x^3}{3} - \frac{x^4}{4} + \frac{x^5}{5} - \cdots = \ln(1+x). \qquad \textbf{(16.6)}$$

Subtracting (16.5) from (16.6):

$$2x + \tfrac{2}{3}x^3 + \tfrac{2}{5}x^5 + \cdots = \ln(1+x) - \ln(1-x)$$

or

$$x + \tfrac{1}{3}x^3 + \tfrac{1}{5}x^5 + \cdots = \tfrac{1}{2} \ln\left(\frac{1+x}{1-x}\right), \qquad |x| < 1.$$

If a series has only odd powers, the general term is usually specified in terms of x^{2k+1}. The above result is then written

$$\sum_{k=0}^{\infty} \frac{x^{2k+1}}{2k+1} = \tfrac{1}{2} \ln\left(\frac{1+x}{1-x}\right). \qquad \textbf{(16.7)}$$

$\square$

The sum function of a power series is continuous.

Its domain is the set of values of x for which the series converges, one of the intervals $(-c, c)$, $[-c, c]$, $[-c, c)$ or $(-c, c]$.

Example 16.28
Putting $x = 1$ in the result (16.6) gives a convergent series (Exercise 8.20, p. 193). The sum of the series is also given correctly by putting $x = 1$ in equation (16.6), because the sum of a power series is continuous:

$$1 - \tfrac{1}{2} + \tfrac{1}{3} - \tfrac{1}{4} + \tfrac{1}{5} - \cdots = \ln 2.$$

Similarly equation (16.5) converges to the sum $\ln 2$ when $x = -1$. However equation (16.7), which depends on (16.5) and (16.6), only converges for $-1 < x < 1$. $\square$

It can also be shown that **two power series with the same sum must be identical**, with the same coefficients for all n. This important result may be used either in the form

$$\sum_{n=0}^{\infty} a_n x^n = \sum_{n=0}^{\infty} b_n x^n \implies a_n = b_n \quad \text{for all } n,$$

or the equivalent form

$$\sum_{n=0}^{\infty} a_n x^n = 0 \implies a_n = 0 \quad \text{for all } n.$$

Exercises (answers on p. 433)

16.2.1 By differentiating the result of Example 16.22 find the power series with sums $(1-x)^{-3}$ and $(1-x)^{-4}$ for $-1 < x < 1$. Give the general term of each series, in the form $a_n x^n$. What power series has sum $(1+x)^{-2}$ on $(-1, 1)$?

16.2.2 Use equation (16.6) to find the general term of the power series with sum $(x^2 + 1) \ln(1+x)$.

16.2.3 Consider the geometric series

$$1 - y + y^2 - y^3 + \cdots + (-1)^k y^k + \cdots = \frac{1}{1+y} \qquad (-1 < y < 1).$$

(i) Substitute $y = x/a$, and hence obtain the general term of the power series with sum $(a+x)^{-1}$. What is the radius of convergence of this series?

(ii) Substituting $y = x^2$ gives the power series with sum $1/(1+x^2)$. Verify that this series of even powers can be written in the form $\sum_{n=0}^{\infty} a_n x^{2n}$, and give a formula for a_n.

(iii) By term-by-term integration of the series in (ii), obtain the series with sum $\text{Tan}^{-1} x$. What is the radius of convergence?

(iv) Show that substituting $y = -x^2$ and then integrating leads to equation (16.7).

16.3 Expansion of a Given Function

This section will discuss the problem of finding a power series with sum equal to a given function $F(x)$. This means finding the coefficients a_n such that $\sum_{n=0}^{\infty} a_n x^n = F(x)$ for all values of x for which the series converges. These values form an interval $(-c, c)$, possibly with one or both of the end-points. The series is then called the **power series expansion of F**. The given function F must certainly be continuous, at least in some neighbourhood of $x = 0$, because the sum of a power series is known to be continuous.

Example 16.30

Expand $F(x) = \ln(1+x)$ in a power series. This means find coefficients a_n such that $\sum_{n=0}^{\infty} a_n x^n = \ln(1+x)$ (in some neighbourhood of $x = 0$).

Assume

$$a_0 + a_1 x + a_2 x^2 + \cdots + a_n x^n + \cdots = \ln(1+x). \qquad (16.8)$$

Putting $x = 0$ shows that $a_0 = \ln 1 = 0$. Differentiating equation (16.8) gives

$$a_1 + 2a_2 x + 3a_3 x^2 + \cdots + na_n x^{n-1} + (n+1)a_{n+1}x^n + \cdots = (1+x)^{-1}. \qquad (16.9)$$

Putting $x = 0$ shows that $a_1 = 1$. Differentiating equation (16.9) gives

$$2a_2 + 6a_3 x + \cdots + n(n-1)a_n x^{n-2} + \cdots = -(1+x)^{-2}.$$

Putting $x = 0$ shows that $a_2 = -\frac{1}{2}$. Similarly another differentiation will give a_3 on setting $x = 0$, and continuing the process will determine as many of the coefficients as desired. In this example a_n can be expressed in terms of n. After equation (16.9) has been differentiated $(n-1)$ times the equation reads

$$n(n-1)(n-2) \cdots 3.2a_n + (n+1)n(n-1) \cdots 2a_{n+1}x + \cdots$$
$$= (-1)(-2) \cdots (-n+1)(1+x)^{-n}.$$

Putting $x = 0$ shows that

$$n! \, a_n = (-1)^{n-1}(n-1)! \, 1^{-n},$$

or

$$a_n = (-1)^{n-1}/n \quad (n > 0).$$

Together with $a_0 = 1$, these coefficients are just those found in equation (16.6) in Example 16.27. □

The above method does not show for what x the result is true, but once an expression for a_n is known, tests for convergence can be applied to determine the domain of validity of the result. It is only necessary to determine the radius of convergence c, and the behaviour of the series at $x = \pm c$. Here such results will be given without derivation.

The same method applies to any function F which has derivatives of all orders. If

$$a_0 + a_1 x + \cdots + a_n x^n + a_{n+1}x^{n+1} + \cdots = F(x),$$

differentiating n times gives (cf. the previous example)

$$n! \, a_n + (n+1)! \, a_{n+1}x + \cdots = F^{(n)}(x).$$

Putting $x = 0$ shows that

$$a_n = \frac{F^{(n)}(0)}{n!}. \qquad (16.10)$$

The power series expansion is therefore

$$F(x) = \sum_{n=0}^{\infty} \frac{F^{(n)}(0)}{n!} x^n, \qquad (16.11)$$

often called **Maclaurin's expansion** of F.

An explicit expression for a_n in terms of n is known if a formula is available giving $F^{(n)}(0)$ in terms of n. Then tests for convergence can be applied to determine the values of x for which Maclaurin's expansion is valid. Equation (16.11) is also called **Maclaurin's series**.

Example 16.31

Let $F(x) = \sin x$.

Then

$$F^{(0)}(x) = \sin x, \qquad F^{(1)}(x) = \cos x, \qquad F^{(2)}(x) = -\sin x, \quad F^{(3)}(x) = -\cos x,$$

$$F^{(4)}(x) = \sin x, \ldots \qquad \text{(repeating in the same way)},$$

and

$$F^{(0)}(0) = 0, \quad F^{(1)}(0) = 1, \quad F^{(2)}(0) = 0, \quad F^{(3)}(0) = -1,$$

$$F^{(4)}(0) = 0, \ldots \qquad \text{(repeating in the same way)}.$$

Substituting into equation (16.11) gives

$$\sin x = 0 + \frac{x}{1!} - 0 - \frac{x^3}{3!} + 0 + \frac{x^5}{5!} - 0 - \frac{x^7}{7!} + \cdots.$$

Since there are only odd powers, the general term can be written in the form $a_k x^{2k+1}$. Evidently $a_k = \pm 1/(2k+1)!$; the alternating sign is taken care of by a factor $(-1)^k$, as discussed on p. 189. Thus

$$\sin x = \sum_{k=0}^{\infty} \frac{(-)^k}{(2k+1)!} x^{2k+1}. \tag{16.12}$$

This series is absolutely convergent for any value of x.

Differentiation of equation (16.12) gives the power series expansion of $\cos x$:

$$\cos x = \sum_{k=0}^{\infty} \frac{(-)^k}{(2k)!} x^{2k} \tag{16.13}$$

$$= 1 - \tfrac{1}{2}x^2 + \frac{1}{24} x^4 - \frac{1}{720} x^6 + \cdots. \quad \square$$

The appearance in equation (16.12) of only odd powers stems from the fact that $\sin x$ is an odd function of x; similarly cos being even makes the expansion (16.13) have only even powers. Generally, if

$$F(x) = a_0 + a_1 x + a_2 x^2 + a_3 x^3 + \cdots$$

then

$$F(-x) = a_0 - a_1 x + a_2 x^2 - a_3 x^3 + \cdots.$$

If F is even, i.e. $F(-x) = F(x)$, the series must be the same, requiring $a_1 = a_3 = 0 = a_{2k+1}$. Similarly if $F(-x) = -F(x)$ then $a_0 = a_2 = 0 = a_{2k}$. (These results also follow from the argument in Exercise 6.23 on p. 156).

For most functions, $F^{(n)}(0)$ cannot be expressed in terms of n, but it is still possible and useful to calculate the first few coefficients. However the lack of a formula for a_n means that tests for convergence cannot be directly applied.

Example 16.32
The first few terms of the Maclaurin series expansion for $\tan x$ may be obtained using equation (16.10). However the labour of differentiating $\tan x$ several times may be avoided because $d(\tan x)/dx$ is $(1+\tan^2 x)$. Since $\tan$ is an odd function, the series has only odd powers.

Assuming $\tan x = a_0 x + a_1 x^3 + a_2 x^5 + a_3 x^7 + \cdots$,

$$\frac{d}{dx}(\tan x) = a_0 + 3a_1 x^2 + 5a_2 x^4 + 7a_3 x^6 + \cdots \qquad (16.14)$$

and

$$1 + \tan^2 x = 1 + (a_0 x + a_1 x^3 + a_2 x^5 + \cdots)(a_0 x + a_1 x^3 + a_2 x^5 + \cdots)$$

Since this must be the same power series as (16.14), equating coefficients of x^0, x^2, x^4, x^6, ... gives

$$a_0 = 1, \quad 3a_1 = a_0^2, \quad 5a_2 = 2a_0 a_1, \quad 7a_3 = 2a_0 a_2 + a_1^2, \ldots .$$

Hence

$$a_0 = 1, \quad a_1 = \tfrac{1}{3}, \quad a_2 = \tfrac{2}{15}, \quad a_3 = \tfrac{1}{7}(\tfrac{4}{15} + \tfrac{1}{9}) = \tfrac{17}{315}, \ldots$$

and

$$\boxed{\tan x = x + \tfrac{1}{3}x^3 + \tfrac{2}{15}x^5 + \tfrac{17}{315}x^7 + \cdots .} \qquad (16.15)$$

Although the general term has not been expressed in terms of n, it can be shown that $c = \tfrac{1}{2}\pi$ is the radius of convergence of this series. Note that one can say from equation (16.15) that c is not greater than $\tfrac{1}{2}\pi$ since (16.15) cannot be valid at $x = \tfrac{1}{2}\pi$ where the sum function $\tan x$ has a discontinuity. $\square$

A table of commonly used power series is given at the end of this chapter.

Exercises (answers on p. 433)
16.3.1 Find the Maclaurin series expansions of the following functions, giving the general term in each case:
  (i) e^x, by using equation (16.10);
  (ii) e^{-x}, by changing x to $-x$ in (i);
  (iii) $\sinh x$ and $\cosh x$, by using (i) and (ii).
  The result (i) is called the **exponential series**; from (p. 396) Example 16.20, it converges for all x, as do the series in (ii) and (iii).
16.3.2 Differentiate $F(x) = (1+x)^\lambda$ a few times, and by inspection of the results write down an expression for $F^{(n)}(x)$ (cf. Example 6.34, p. 116). From $F^{(n)}(0)$ obtain the series expansion of $(1+x)^\lambda$ in powers of x.
  The result is called the **binomial series**, and it converges if $|x| < 1$. If λ is a positive integer the series terminates with the x^λ term, because $a_n = 0$ for $n > \lambda$. Special cases of the binomial series were considered in Example 16.22 and Exercise 16.2.1. The result can be extended as in Exercise 16.2.3 (i) and (ii) (see p. 400).
16.3.3 Use the binomial series to obtain the first four terms of the series expansion of $(1+t)^{3/2}$ in powers of t.

16.4 Taylor's Series

One use of the power series expansion of a function is to approximate the function by the first few terms of the series. This truncates the series to a polynomial. The truncation error is the sum of all the neglected terms, and can only be small if successive terms decrease rapidly. Since

$$|x_1| < |x_2| \quad \Rightarrow \quad |a_n x_1^n| < |a_n x_2^n|$$

the error decreases as $|x|$ decreases. If $|x|$ is much less than 1, then $|x^{n+1}|$ is much less than $|x^n|$

$$(\text{this can be written } |x| \ll 1 \quad \Rightarrow \quad |x^{n+1}| \ll |x^n|),$$

and the terms $a_n x^n$ should decrease rapidly enough (as n increases).

Example 16.40
The following table shows values of the sum $(1-x)^{-1}$ of the geometric series, together with the approximations obtained by summing 2 or 3 terms:

x	0.01	0.02	0.03	0.04
$(1-x)^{-1}$	1.0101	1.0204	1.0309	1.0417
$1+x$	1.0100	1.0200	1.0300	1.0400
$1+x+x^2$	1.0101	1.0204	1.0309	1.0416

The approximation $(1+x)$ gives 3D accuracy for $x \leqslant 0.02$, but not for $x \geqslant 0.03$; the approximation $(1+x+x^2)$ gives 4D accuracy for $x \leqslant 0.03$, but not for $x = 0.04$. ☐

A few terms of $\sum a_n x^n$ thus give a good approximation to the sum for values of x near 0, because the terms contain powers of the small quantity x. To obtain a good approximation in some other region, say near $x = a$, one needs a series involving powers of the small quantity $(x - a)$. This suggests considering generalized power series of the form $\sum a_n (x-a)^n$, where a is some chosen number.

Example 16.41
Replacing x by ζ in equation (16.6) gives

$$\ln(1+\zeta) = \zeta - \frac{\zeta^2}{2} + \frac{\zeta^3}{3} - \frac{\zeta^4}{4} + \cdots \qquad (-1 < \zeta \leqslant 1).$$

Now substitute $\zeta = (x-1)$:

$$\ln x = (x-1) - \frac{(x-1)^2}{2} + \frac{(x-1)^3}{3} - \frac{(x-1)^4}{4} + \cdots \qquad (0 < x \leqslant 2).$$

This is an expansion of the function $\ln x$ in powers of $(x-1)$. It would give good approximations to ln for values of x near $x = 1$. ☐

An inspection of the derivation of Maclaurin's expansion shows that the same method finds the coefficients a_n in an assumed expansion

$$F(x) = \sum_{n=0}^{\infty} a_n (x-a)^n$$

where a is any chosen constant. Substituting $x = a$ gives

$$F(a) = a_0.$$

Differentiating k times gives

$$F^{(k)}(x) = a_k k! + a_{k+1}(k+1)!\,(x-a) + \cdots$$

so that $F^{(k)}(a) = a_k k!$, $a_k = F^{(k)}(a)/k!$, and

$$F(x) = \sum_{n=0}^{\infty} \frac{F^{(n)}(a)}{n!}(x-a)^n. \qquad (16.16)$$

This generalization of Maclaurin's series (16.11) is called a **Taylor series**. It is **the Taylor expansion of $F(x)$ about the point $x = a$.**

Example 16.42
Use a power series expansion to calculate $\tan 1$.

With $x = 1$ Maclaurin's series

$$x + \tfrac{1}{3}x^3 + \tfrac{2}{15}x^5 + \tfrac{17}{315}x^7 + \cdots \qquad (16.15)$$

converges slowly: $1 + \tfrac{1}{3} = 1.33$, $1 + \tfrac{1}{3} + \tfrac{2}{15} = 1.46$,

$$1 + \tfrac{1}{3} + \tfrac{2}{15} + \tfrac{17}{315} = 1.52, \ldots.$$

A Taylor series will converge better if a is close to 1. The coefficients in (16.16) require the derivatives of $\tan x$ evaluated at a, so a must also be chosen so that $\tan a$ and $\sec a$ have known values. Taking $a = \pi/3 = 1.047$ is a suitable choice; then $\tan a = \sqrt{3} = 1.732$ and $\sec^2 a = 4$.
If $F(x) = \tan x$, then $F'(x) = \sec^2 x$, and since

$$\frac{d}{dx}(\sec x) = \sec x \tan x, \qquad F''(x) = 2\sec^2 x \tan x,$$

$$F'''(x) = 4\sec^2 x \tan^2 x + 2\sec^4 x.$$

Hence $F(a) = \sqrt{3}$, $F'(a) = 4$, $F''(a) = 8\sqrt{3}$, $F'''(a) = 80$.
The first four terms of the Taylor expansion of $\tan x$ about $x = \pi/3$ are

$$\sqrt{3} + 4\left(x - \frac{\pi}{3}\right) + 4\sqrt{3}\left(x - \frac{\pi}{3}\right)^2 + \frac{40}{3}\left(x - \frac{\pi}{3}\right)^3.$$

At $x = 1$, the successive approximations are

$$\sqrt{3} = 1.732$$

$$1.732 + 4(-0.047) = 1.544$$

$$1.544 + 4\sqrt{3}(-0.047)^2 = 1.559$$

$$1.559 + \tfrac{40}{3}(-0.047)^3 = 1.558,$$

showing much better convergence than equation (16.15), and suggesting $\tan 1 = 1.56$. □

Note that the **Taylor** expansion ($a \neq 0$) of an odd or even function will generally contain *all* powers, and not just odd or even powers.

The Taylor series result (16.16) is often written in the form

$$F(a+h) = \sum_{n=0}^{\infty} \frac{F^{(n)}(a)}{n!} h^n, \qquad (16.17)$$

obtained from (16.16) by substituting $x = a+h$. Taylor's series can thus be considered alternatively as an expansion of $F(a+h)$ in powers of h. There will be a radius of convergence c such that the series converges for $-c < h < c$, i.e. $a - c < x < a + c$.

The above derivation of the Taylor's series shows that *if* there is a series of the form $\sum_{n=0}^{\infty} a_n(x-a)^n$ with sum $F(x)$, then $a_n = F^{(n)}(a)/n!$ For this to be true

$$F^{(n)}(a) \text{ must exist for all } n.$$

Example 16.43

(i) $F(x) = \ln x$ has no expansion about $x = 0$, since $\ln x$ is not defined at $x = 0$: there is no neighbourhood of 0 in which $\ln x$ is continuous.

(ii) $F(x) = x^{21/2}$ has no expansion about $x = 0$, because $F^{(11)}(0)$ does not exist. $\square$

Exercises (answers on p. 433)

16.4.1 Find the first three terms of the Taylor expansion of $\tan x$ about $x = \pi/4$.

16.4.2 Obtain the Taylor expansion of $\sin x$ about $x = -\pi/4$.

16.4.3 Obtain the general term in the Taylor expansion of $F(x) = 1/x^2$ about the point $a = 1$.

16.5 Errors

In Example 16.42 the value of $\tan 1$ was calculated using 4 terms of a Taylor series, but the error involved in truncating the series was not discussed. The object of this section is to obtain formulas giving exact bounds on such errors. To illustrate the methods, consider first series which are derived from the geometric series, for which a formula exists for the sum of n terms. From equation (8.1), on p. 180, replacing n by $(n+1)$:

$$s_{n+1} = a + ax + ax^2 + \cdots ax^n = a(1 - x^{n+1})/(1-x).$$

This can be rearranged to

$$\frac{a}{1-x} = s_{n+1} + \frac{ax^{n+1}}{1-x}, \qquad (16.18)$$

showing the sum as a polynomial s_{n+1} plus a remainder.

Example 16.50

Setting $a = 1$ and replacing x by t^2 in equation (16.18) gives

$$\frac{1}{1-t^2} = 1 + t^2 + t^4 + \cdots + t^{2n} + \frac{t^{2n+2}}{1-t^2}.$$

Integrate from $t = 0$ to $t = x$:

$$\tfrac{1}{2}\ln\left(\frac{1+t}{1-t}\right)\Big|_0^x = \left[t + \tfrac{1}{3}t^3 + \cdots + \frac{t^{2n+1}}{2n+1}\right]_0^x + \int_0^x \frac{t^{2n+2}}{1-t^2}\,dt,$$

$$\tfrac{1}{2}\ln\left(\frac{1+x}{1-x}\right) = x + \tfrac{1}{3}x^3 + \cdots + \frac{x^{2n+1}}{2n+1} + \int_0^x \frac{t^{2n+2}}{1-t^2}\,dt. \qquad (16.19)$$

The polynomial $(x + \tfrac{1}{3}x^3 + \cdots + x^{2n+1}/(2n+1))$ is just the first $(n+1)$ nonzero terms of the Maclaurin series (16.7) on p. 399. Thus the error in truncating the series to this polynomial is $-\int_0^x (t^{2n+2}/(1-t^2))\,dt$.

To use this integral expression for the error, it is no good trying an analytic evaluation (from an antiderivative), since this will inevitably involve values of ln, and the calculation of such values is the purpose of the approximation. (Obviously equation (16.19) can be rearranged to give the integral in terms of values of ln.) What is required is a bound on the error, so the procedure is to replace the integrand $t^{2n+2}/(1-t^2)$ by a function which is larger, and integrable without using ln.

In equation (16.19), $x < 1$ otherwise the integral does not exist (or because 1 is the radius of convergence of the series). Then

$$0 \leqslant t \leqslant x < 1 \;\Rightarrow\; t^2 \leqslant x^2 \leqslant 1$$

$$\Rightarrow\; -1 \leqslant -x^2 \leqslant -t^2 \;\Rightarrow\; 0 \leqslant 1 - x^2 \leqslant 1 - t^2$$

$$\Rightarrow\; \frac{1}{1-t^2} \leqslant \frac{1}{1-x^2} \;\Rightarrow\; \frac{t^{2n+2}}{1-t^2} \leqslant \frac{t^{2n+2}}{1-x^2}.$$

Hence

$$\int_0^x \frac{t^{2n+2}}{1-t^2}\,dt \leqslant \int_0^x \frac{t^{2n+2}}{1-x^2}\,dt = \frac{1}{1-x^2}\int_0^x t^{2n+2}\,dt = \frac{x^{2n+3}}{(2n+3)(1-x^2)}.$$

This is a **computable** bound, as it does not contain values of ln, which are the object of the approximation.

For instance, to calculate ln 2 with error less than 0.0005, by taking $x = \tfrac{1}{3}$, requires $\int_0^{1/3} (t^{2n+2}/(1-t^2))\,dt < 0.0005$. From the bound, this is ensured by choosing n so that

$$\frac{(\tfrac{1}{3})^{2n+3}}{(2n+3)(\tfrac{8}{9})} < 0.0005 \quad \text{or} \quad 3^{2n}(2n+3) > \tfrac{250}{3}.$$

Obviously $n = 1$ is not large enough, but $n = 2$ is sufficient. From equation (16.19), $\ln 2 = 2(\tfrac{1}{3} + \tfrac{1}{81} + \tfrac{1}{1215})$ has sufficient accuracy. Also, since the approximation improves when $|x|$ decreases, $\tfrac{1}{2}\ln((1+x)/(1-x))$ can be replaced by $(x + \tfrac{1}{3}x^3 + \tfrac{1}{5}x^5)$ for $-\tfrac{1}{3} \leqslant x \leqslant \tfrac{1}{3}$, with an error less than 0.0005 in magnitude. $\square$

Truncating the general Taylor series (16.16) gives the polynomial

$$P_n(x) = F(a) + F'(a)(x-a) + \cdots + \frac{F^{(n)}(a)}{n!}(x-a)^n$$

as an approximation for $F(x)$. Since the $(n+1)$th derivative of a polynomial of degree n is zero, the error in approximating F by P_n is expected to be proportional to the magnitude of $F^{(n+1)}(x)$. In fact a result similar to equation (16.19) can be derived, in which the integrand contains $F^{(n+1)}$. This is

Taylor's theorem:

$$F(x) = P_n(x) + \frac{1}{n!} \int_a^x (x-t)^n F^{(n+1)}(t) \, dt. \tag{16.20}$$

From this integral expression for the error, bounds on the error may be obtained as in the previous example: replace the integrand by a function which is larger, and integrable without using unknown values of F.

Example 16.51
Estimate the error in approximating e by

$$1 + 1 + \tfrac{1}{2} + \tfrac{1}{6} + \tfrac{1}{24} + \tfrac{1}{120} = 2.7167.$$

The approximation is obtained from the first 6 terms of the exponential series (S13 on p. 439) with $x = 1$. In equation (16.20), put $F(x) = e^x = F^{(n+1)}(x)$, and $n = 5$, $a = 0$, giving

$$e = 2.7167 + \tfrac{1}{120} \int_0^1 (1-t)^5 e^t \, dt. \tag{16.21}$$

Since $(d/dt) \, e^t = e^t > 0$, e^t is increasing, so on $[0, 1]$, $1 = e^0 \leq e^t \leq e$. This still involves the (unknown) value of e. However

$$e = 1 + 1 + \frac{1}{2} + \frac{1}{3 \cdot 2} + \frac{1}{4 \cdot 3 \cdot 2} + \frac{1}{5 \cdot 4 \cdot 3 \cdot 2} + \cdots$$

$$\leq 1 + 1 + \frac{1}{2} + \frac{1}{2 \cdot 2} + \frac{1}{2 \cdot 2 \cdot 2} + \frac{1}{2 \cdot 2 \cdot 2 \cdot 2} + \cdots \quad \text{(cf. Exercise 8.1.4 on p. 185)}$$

$$= 1 + \frac{1}{1 - \tfrac{1}{2}} \quad \text{(summing a geometric series with ratio } \tfrac{1}{2})$$

$$= 3.$$

Hence

$$0 \leq t \leq 1 \quad \Rightarrow \quad 1 \leq e^t < 3$$

$$\Rightarrow \quad (1-t)^5 \leq (1-t)^5 e^t \leq 3(1-t)^5$$

$$\Rightarrow \quad I \leq \int_0^1 (1-t)^5 \, e^t \, dt \leq 3I$$

where

$$I = \int_0^1 (1-t)^5 \, dt = -\int_1^0 u^5 \, du = \tfrac{1}{6} \quad (u = 1-t).$$

From equation (16.21), $\tfrac{1}{720} \leq e - 2.7167 \leq \tfrac{1}{240}$

$$2.7181 \leq e \leq 2.7209. \quad \square$$

Example 16.52
How many terms of the Taylor expansion of sin x about $x = \pi/3 = 1.047$ are required to calculate sin 1 with error less than 0.00005?

The stated error requirement should give sin 1 to 3S or 3 correct decimal places. For a maximum allowable error of 0.0005, n must be chosen so that

$$-0.0005 < \frac{1}{n!} \int_{\pi/3}^{1} (1-t)^n F^{(n+1)}(t)\, dt < 0.0005$$

(using equation (16.20) with $a = \pi/3$ and $x = 1$).
  Since $\pi/3 > 1$, it is convenient to write the integral as

$$-\int_{1}^{\pi/3} (1-t)^n F^{(n+1)}(t)\, dt = (-1)^{n+1} \int_{1}^{\pi/3} (t-1)^n F^{(n+1)}(t)\, dt.$$

The accuracy condition becomes

$$-0.0005 n! < \int_{1}^{\pi/3} (t-1)^n F^{(n+1)}(t)\, dt < 0.0005 n! \tag{16.22}$$

Since derivatives of sin are either $\pm\sin$ or $\pm\cos$,

$$-1 \leqslant F^{(n+1)}(t) \leqslant 1$$

and

$$-(t-1)^n \leqslant (t-1)^n F^{(n+1)}(t) \leqslant (t-1)^n.$$

(This step requires $(t-1)^n \geqslant 0$, and is the reason for the above change from $(1-t)^n$ to $(t-1)^n$.) Then

$$-I < \int_{1}^{\pi/3} (t-1)^n F^{(n+1)}(t)\, dt < I$$

where

$$I = \int_{1}^{\pi/3} (t-1)^n\, dt = \int_{0}^{0.047} u^n\, du = \frac{(0.047)^{n+1}}{n+1} \qquad (u = t-1).$$

So (16.22) is satisfied if n is chosen so that

$$(0.047)^{n+1} < 0.0005\, n!(n+1)$$

or

$$2000(0.047)^{n+1} < (n+1)!$$

This is satisfied for $n = 2$, so 3 terms of the Taylor expansion are required:

$$\sin(\pi/3) + \cos(\pi/3)\,(1 - \pi/3) - \tfrac{1}{2}\sin(\pi/3)\,(1 - \pi/3)^2 = 0.841. \quad \square$$

Example 16.53
For what values of x is the error in approximating $\cos x$ by $(1 - \tfrac{1}{2}x^2 + \tfrac{1}{24}x^4 - \tfrac{1}{720}x^6)$ less than 10^{-6}?

The approximation is the first four nonzero terms of the Maclaurin series expansion of $\cos x$, given in equation (16.13) on p. 402. This polynomial approximation is degree 6, suggesting $n = 6$ in equation (16.20), but as the next term in the series is $0x^7$, the approximation can be regarded as including this term. So the error is given by equation (16.20) with $n = 7$:

$$\cos x = 1 - \tfrac{1}{2}x^2 + \tfrac{1}{24}x^4 - \tfrac{1}{720}x^6 + \frac{1}{7!}\int_0^x (x-t)^7 F^{(8)}(t)\, dt.$$

Since

$$F^{(8)}(t) = \cos t, \qquad -1 \leqslant F^{(8)}(t) \leqslant 1 \quad \Rightarrow \quad -I \leqslant \int_0^x (x-t)^7 F^{(8)}(t)\, dt \leqslant I$$

where

$$I = \int_0^x (x-t)^7\, dt = -\int_x^0 u^7\, du = \frac{x^8}{8} \qquad (u = x - t).$$

The error is numerically less than $x^8/8!$, and so is less than 10^{-6} if

$$x^8 < 8!\,10^{-6} = 0.04032, \qquad x^4 < 0.2008, \qquad x^2 < 0.448,$$

$$-0.67 < x < 0.67. \quad \square$$

In the previous example, the bound obtained for the error was actually the next term of the series. It can be shown that

the first term after the truncation is a bound for the error in the special case when **the series is alternating.**

This result is only useful when the general term of the series is known, because only this knowledge can show that the terms are **always** alternating.

On the other hand the general bound given by equation (16.20) can be considered for particular values of n when the general term is not known, as in the case of the expansion of $\tan x$.

Exercises (answers on p. 433)

16.5.1   (cf. Exercise 16.2.3 (iii) on p. 400). Show that

$$\text{Tan}^{-1} x = P_{2n+1}(x) + (-1)^{n+1}\int_0^x \frac{t^{2n+2}}{1+t^2}\, dt$$

where

$$P_{2n+1}(x) = x - \frac{x^3}{3} + \frac{x^5}{5} - \cdots + (-1)^n \frac{x^{2n+1}}{2n+1}.$$

Show that

$$\frac{x^{2n+3}}{(2n+3)(1+x^2)} < \int_0^x \frac{t^{2n+2}}{1+t^2}\, dt < \frac{x^{2n+3}}{2n+3},$$

and hence obtain bounds on the value of $\text{Tan}^{-1}(0.2)$ by taking $n = 4$.

16.5.2   How many terms of the exponential series must be used to get e with error less than 0.0005?

16.5.3 Without assuming any values of sin x, find an interval on which the approximation of sin x by

$$\tfrac{1}{2}+\tfrac{1}{2}\sqrt{3}(x-\pi/6)-\tfrac{1}{4}(x-\pi/6)^2$$

gives values with error less than 0.05.

16.6 Evaluation of Limits

Consider $\mathrm{Lim}_{x\to a} f(x)/g(x)$ where $f(a)=g(a)=0$, and suppose f and g have Taylor expansions about $x=a$:

$$f(x)=0+f'(a)(x-a)+\tfrac{1}{2}f''(a)(x-a)^2+\cdots$$
$$g(x)=0+g'(a)(x-a)+\tfrac{1}{2}g''(a)(x-a)^2+\cdots.$$

Then, for $x\neq a$,

$$\frac{f(x)}{g(x)}=\frac{f'(a)+\tfrac{1}{2}f''(a)(x-a)+\cdots}{g'(a)+\tfrac{1}{2}g''(a)(x-a)+\cdots}\to\frac{f'(a)}{g'(a)}\quad\text{provided }g'(a)\neq0.\qquad(16.23)$$

It is not necessary to actually make the series expansions in order to use this result, which has already been mentioned in Exercise 4.16 on p. 93.

Example 16.60 (cf. Example 4.46 on p. 88).
Evaluate $\mathrm{Lim}_{x\to1} f(x)/g(x)$, where

$$f(x)=\sin(x-1),\qquad g(x)=x^2+2x-3.$$

Since $f(1)=g(1)=0$, the above method can be applied.

$$f'(x)=\cos(x-1),\qquad f'(1)=1,\qquad g'(x)=2x+2,\qquad g'(1)=4\neq0,$$

so the value of the limit is $f'(1)/g'(1)=1/4$. □

Suppose $g'(a)=0$. Then if $f'(a)\neq0$, equation (16.23) shows there is no limit. If also $f'(a)=0$, another factor $(x-a)$ can be cancelled in equation (16.23), giving $f''(a)/g''(a)$ unless $g''(a)=0$.

Example 16.61 (cf. Example 4.41 on p. 86).
Evaluate $\mathrm{Lim}_{x\to2} f(x)/g(x)$, where

$$f(x)=x^3-x^2-8x+12,\qquad g(x)=x^3-7x^2+16x-12.$$

Since $f(2)=g(2)=0$, the above method can be applied.

$$f'(x)=3x^2-2x-8,\qquad f'(2)=0,\qquad g'(x)=3x^2-14x+16,\qquad g'(2)=0,$$
$$f''(x)=6x-2,\qquad f''(2)=10,\qquad g''(x)=6x-14,\qquad g''(2)=-2\neq0.$$

The value of the limit is $f''(2)/g''(2)=-5$. □

The various possibilities arising in this method are all covered by the following statement, known as **L'Hopital's rule**:

If $f(a) = g(a) = 0$, then

$$\operatorname{Lim}_{x \to a} \frac{f(x)}{g(x)} = \operatorname{Lim}_{x \to a} \frac{f'(x)}{g'(x)}, \qquad \text{(16.24)}$$

if this exists.

This rule can be applied as many times as necessary, but it can only be used on a quotient which becomes an indeterminate form on substituting $x = a$. The previous example amounts to 2 applications of L'Hopital's rule.

Example 16.62

$$\operatorname{Lim}_{x \to a} \frac{x^3}{x} \neq \operatorname{Lim}_{x \to a} \frac{3x^2}{1}, \qquad \text{unless } a = 0. \quad \square$$

In some cases direct use of the series is better.

Example 16.63

$$\operatorname{Lim}_{x \to 0} \frac{\tan x - \sin x}{x^3} = \operatorname{Lim}_{x \to 0} \frac{(x + \frac{1}{3}x^3 + \cdots) - (x - \frac{1}{6}x^3 + \cdots)}{x^3} = \frac{1}{2}.$$

Using equation (16.24) would evidently require three differentiations before a nonzero value is obtained from $g(x) = x^3$. $\square$

Theorems on limits may still be useful.

Example 16.64

$$\operatorname{Lim}_{x \to 2\pi} \frac{(x^2 - \pi x - 2\pi^2) \sin^2 2x}{(x^2 - 3\pi x + 2\pi^2)(1 - \cos x)}$$

$$= \operatorname{Lim}_{x \to 2\pi} \frac{(d/dx)\{(x^2 - \pi x - 2\pi^2) \sin^2 2x\}}{(d/dx)\{(x^2 - 3\pi x + 2\pi^2)(1 - \cos x)\}}$$

is correct, but will be laborious. Alternatively, since the limit of a product is the product of the limits of the factors (Theorem 4.2(iii) on p. 83),

$$\operatorname{Lim}_{x \to 2\pi} \frac{(x^2 - \pi x - 2\pi^2)}{(x^2 - 3\pi x + 2\pi^2)} \operatorname{Lim}_{x \to 2\pi} \frac{\sin^2 2x}{(1 - \cos x)}$$

$$= \operatorname{Lim}_{x \to 2\pi} \left(\frac{2x - \pi}{2x - 3\pi} \right) \operatorname{Lim}_{x \to 2\pi} \frac{(2 \sin 2x)(2 \cos 2x)}{\sin x}, \qquad \text{using equation (16.24)}$$

$$= 3 \operatorname{Lim}_{x \to 2\pi} (8 \cos x \cos 2x), \qquad \text{by cancelling a factor } \sin x$$

$$= 24. \quad \square$$

Indeterminate forms of type $(\infty - \infty)$ can sometimes be rearranged as a quotient to which L'Hopital's rule can be applied.

Example 16.65

$$\operatorname*{Lim}_{x \to 1} \left(\frac{x}{x-1} - \frac{1}{\ln x} \right) = \operatorname*{Lim}_{x \to 1} \frac{x \ln x - x + 1}{(x-1) \ln x}$$

$$= \operatorname*{Lim}_{x \to 1} \frac{(\ln x) + 1 - 1}{(\ln x) + 1 - (1/x)}, \quad \text{from L'Hopital's rule (16.24)}$$

$$= \operatorname*{Lim}_{x \to 1} \frac{1/x}{1/x + 1/x^2}, \quad \text{from L'Hopital's rule}$$

$$= \tfrac{1}{2}. \quad \square$$

For indeterminate forms of type 0^0, ∞^0 or 1^∞, taking the logarithm may give a quotient.

Example 16.66
Evaluate $\operatorname*{Lim}_{x \to 0} (1-x)^{1/x}$ (type 1^∞).

If $y = (1-x)^{1/x}$, then $\ln y = \ln(1-x)/x$ (a quotient) and $\operatorname*{Lim}_{x \to 0} y = \operatorname*{Lim}_{x \to 0} \exp(\ln y) = \exp(\operatorname*{Lim}_{x \to 0} \ln y)$, since the exponential function is continuous.

$$\text{From L'Hopital's rule} \quad \operatorname*{Lim}_{x \to 0} \frac{\ln(1-x)}{x} = \operatorname*{Lim}_{x \to 0} \frac{-(1-x)^{-1}}{1} = -1.$$

So

$$\operatorname*{Lim}_{x \to 0} (1-x)^{1/x} = e^{-1} = \frac{1}{e}. \quad \square$$

By writing $f(x)/g(x) = (1/g(x))/(1/f(x))$, it can be shown that

L'Hopital's rule applies when $f(x) \to \pm\infty$ and $g(x) \to \pm\infty$ as $x \to a$

(type ∞/∞).

Example 16.67
$\operatorname*{Lim}_{x \to 0} f(x)/g(x)$ with $f(x) = \log(\tan x)$, $g(x) = \log(\tan 4x)$. Then, as $x \to 0$, $f(x) \to -\infty$ and $g(x) \to -\infty$.

$$\operatorname*{Lim}_{x \to 0} \frac{f(x)}{g(x)} = \operatorname*{Lim}_{x \to 0} \frac{f'(x)}{g'(x)} = \operatorname*{Lim}_{x \to 0} \frac{\sec^2 x / \tan x}{4 \sec^2 4x / \tan 4x}$$

$$= \operatorname*{Lim}_{x \to 0} \frac{\cos^2 4x}{4 \cos^2 x} \operatorname*{Lim}_{x \to 0} \frac{\tan 4x}{\tan x} = \frac{1}{4} \operatorname*{Lim}_{x \to 0} \frac{\tan 4x}{\tan x}$$

$$= \frac{1}{4} \operatorname*{Lim}_{x \to 0} \frac{4 \sec^2 4x}{\sec^2 x}, \quad \text{using L'Hopital's rule again,}$$

$$= 1. \quad \square$$

By writing $f(x)/g(x) = F(y)/G(y)$ with $F(y) = f(1/y)$ and $G(y) = g(1/y)$ it can also be shown that

L'Hopital's rule works for limits as $x \to \infty$

$(y \to 0)$.

Example 16.68
$\text{Lim}_{x \to \infty} x \, e^{-x} = \text{Lim}_{x \to \infty} f(x)/g(x)$, with $f(x) = x \to \infty$ and $g(x) = e^x \to \infty$ (as $x \to \infty$). From L'Hopital's rule, $\text{Lim}_{x \to \infty} f(x)/g(x) = \text{Lim}_{x \to \infty} 1/e^x = 0$. $\quad \square$

Exercises (answers on p. 433)
16.6.1 Use L'Hopital's rule to evaluate (if the limit exists):

(i) $\text{Lim}_{x \to 2} \dfrac{x^3 - x^2 - 8x + 12}{x^2 - 5x + 6}$ (ii) $\text{Lim}_{x \to 2} \dfrac{x^2 + x - 6}{x^3 - 7x^2 + 16x - 12}$

(iii) $\text{Lim}_{x \to 0} x \cot x$ (iv) $\text{Lim}_{x \to \pi} \dfrac{\sin x}{x - \pi}$ (v) $\text{Lim}_{x \to 0} \dfrac{\sin x}{x^2 + x}$

(vi) $\text{Lim}_{x \to 2} \dfrac{-3 + \sqrt{(1 + 4x)}}{-2 + \sqrt{(2x)}}$ (vii) $\text{Lim}_{x \to 0} \dfrac{\sin kx}{x}$

(viii) $\text{Lim}_{x \to \pi} \dfrac{1 + \cos x}{\sin x}$ (ix) $\text{Lim}_{x \to \frac{1}{2}\pi} (\tan \tfrac{1}{2}x)^{\tan x}$

16.6.2 Use series expansions to evaluate

(i) $\text{Lim}_{x \to 0} \dfrac{\sinh x - \sin x}{x^3}$ (ii) $\text{Lim}_{x \to 0} \dfrac{\cosh x - \cos x}{x^2}$

16.7 Fourier Series

If the nonhomogeneous term $R(x)$ in a constant coefficient linear equation

$$\frac{d^2 y}{dx^2} + 2a \frac{dy}{dx} + by = R(x)$$

is a combination of periodic trigonometric functions, then (see Exercise 13.54) a steady-state solution is a combination of terms with the same periods as those in $R(x)$. (Commonly x is time, so that period means frequency.) This means that for any periodic $R(x)$, useful information about the solution can be obtained from an expansion of $R(x)$ in terms of trigonometric functions. Such an expansion is called a Fourier series.

Periodic functions also often occur when it is convenient to use angular coordinates in problems involving two or more variables. When an ordinary differential equation is solved for a particular solution, say $y = s(x)$, the particular solution is specified by conditions at particular points, for example $y = y_1$ when $x = x_1$ (i.e. $y_1 = s(x_1)$). When solving a differential equation for a function of two variables, say $z = S(x, y)$, conditions to fix a particular solution must specify the value of the function at all points of a curve in the x-y plane. If this curve is a circle, then the condition is naturally expressed as a periodic function of angle.

Example 16.70

The temperature $T = S(x, y)$ across the circular cross-section of a pipe can be calculated by solving a differential equation known as the heat equation. Suppose the pipe is immersed in a cooling fluid flowing at right angles to it, maintaining the outside of the pipe at a temperature known to be given by the function

$$T = f(\theta) = 10 + \frac{\theta}{\pi} + \frac{\theta^2}{4\pi^2} - \frac{\theta^3}{\pi^3},$$

where the angle θ defines a point on the circular boundary (Fig. 16.2). If R is the radius of the pipe, axes can be chosen so that $x^2 + y^2 = R^2$ represents this boundary. The (boundary) condition can then be written

$$S(R \cos \theta, R \sin \theta) = f(\theta) = 10 + \frac{\theta}{\pi} + \frac{\theta^2}{4\pi^2} - \frac{\theta^3}{\pi^3} \qquad (-\pi \leqslant \theta \leqslant \pi).$$

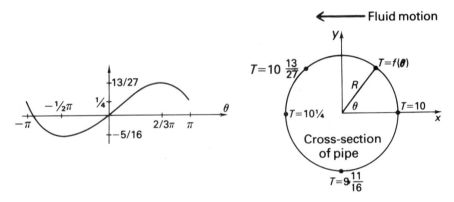

Figure 16.2   Temperature $T = f(\theta)$ on the outside of a circular pipe. Curve shows $T - 10$

When $f(\theta)$ is thus defined by the physical problem, its domain is evidently $[-\pi, \pi]$. However the natural domain of $S(R \cos \theta, R \sin \theta)$ is all real θ, giving a periodic function of θ with period 2π. Because of this it is useful to express the given form of $f(\theta)$ in terms of functions (such as $\cos \theta$) which have period 2π. □

The basic problem to be discussed in the rest of this chapter is to take a given function, defined on $(-\pi, \pi)$, and obtain a series expansion for it, the terms of the series being periodic trigonometric functions. For the application to problems with two variables, the expansion terms often also have to satisfy ordinary differential equations which are linear with constant coefficients. From Section 13.4, this implies trigonometric functions of the form $\sin c\theta$ and $\cos c\theta$, rather than powers of $\cos \theta$ and/or $\sin \theta$. However $\sin c\theta$ and $\cos c\theta$ have period 2π only if c is an integer.

A **Fourier series expansion** of a given function $f(\theta)$ is a series of the form

$$\sum_{n=0}^{\infty} \{a_n \cos n\theta + b_n \sin n\theta\} \qquad \text{(16.25)}$$

with sum equal to the given $f(\theta)$ for $-\pi < \theta < \pi$.

In the next example, a method of obtaining the coefficients a_n and b_n will be demonstrated. First some required integration results will be written down. From Example 10.35 (p. 234)

$$\int_0^\pi \sin mx \sin nx \, dx = \int_0^\pi \cos mx \cos nx \, dx = \begin{cases} 0 & \text{if } m \neq n \\ \frac{1}{2}\pi & \text{if } m = n \end{cases} \qquad (16.26)$$

giving

$$\int_{-\pi}^\pi \sin mx \sin nx \, dx = \int_{-\pi}^\pi \cos mx \cos nx \, dx = \begin{cases} 0 & \text{if } m \neq n \\ \pi & \text{if } m = n, \end{cases} \qquad (16.27)$$

since both integrands are even functions of x (cf. Exercise 10.35 on p. 256). Similarly, since the integrand is an odd function of x (cf. Exercise 10.35),

$$\int_{-\pi}^\pi \sin mx \cos nx \, dx = 0. \qquad (16.28)$$

In these results, m and n are any integers, not both zero. In the evaluation of definite integrals from $-\pi$ to π the values

$$\sin(m\pi) = \sin(-m\pi) = 0, \qquad \cos(m\pi) = \cos(-m\pi) = (-1)^m \qquad (16.29)$$

are required frequently. The following results (from Exercise 10.34) will also be used:

$$\int_{-\pi}^\pi x \sin mx \, dx = -2\pi(-1)^m/m \qquad (16.30)$$

$$\int_{-\pi}^\pi x^2 \cos mx \, dx = 4\pi(-1)^m/m^2 \qquad (16.31)$$

$$\int_{-\pi}^\pi x^3 \sin mx \, dx = 2\pi(-1)^m(6 - m^2\pi^2)/m^3 \qquad (16.32)$$

$$\int_{-\pi}^\pi x^4 \cos mx \, dx = 8\pi(-1)^m(m^2\pi^2 - 6)/m^4. \qquad (16.33)$$

Example 16.71
Obtain the Fourier series expansion of $f(x) = x^2 - 2x$.

This means find coefficients a_n and b_n so that (as in equation (16.25))

$$x^2 - 2x = \sum_{n=0}^\infty \{a_n \cos nx + b_n \sin nx\} \qquad (16.34)$$

is true in the interval $-\pi < x < \pi$.

Method: multiply each side of equation (16.34) by $\sin mx$, or by $\cos mx$, and integrate from $x = -\pi$ to π.

Assuming that term-by-term integration of the series is valid,

$$\int (x^2 - 2x) \sin mx \, dx = \sum_{n=0}^\infty \left\{ a_n \int \cos nx \sin mx \, dx + b_n \int \sin nx \sin mx \, dx \right\}.$$

For the integration limits $-\pi$ to π, equations (16.28) and (16.27) show all integrals from terms of the series are zero, except for $b_m \int_{-\pi}^{\pi} \sin mx \sin mx \, dx = b_m \pi$. Hence

$$b_m \pi = \int_{-\pi}^{\pi} (x^2 - 2x) \sin mx \, dx = \frac{4\pi(-1)^m}{m},$$

using equation (16.30) and $\int_{-\pi}^{\pi} x^2 \sin mx \, dx = 0$ (as $x^2 \sin mx$ is odd).

Similarly, multiply equation (16.34) by $\cos mx$, and integrate the series term-by-term from $x = -\pi$ to $x = \pi$. Equations (16.27) and (16.28) show that all terms give zero integrals except for $a_m \int_{-\pi}^{\pi} \cos mx \cos mx \, dx$. This has the value $a_m \pi$ if $m > 0$, and $2a_0 \pi$ if $m = 0$. Hence

$$2a_0 \pi = \int_{-\pi}^{\pi} (x^2 - 2x) \, dx = \tfrac{2}{3}\pi^3,$$

and for $m > 0$

$$\pi a_m = \int_{-\pi}^{\pi} (x^2 - 2x) \cos mx \, dx = \frac{4\pi(-1)^m}{m^2},$$

using equation (16.31) and the fact that $2x \cos mx$ is odd. Substituting these coefficients into equation (16.34) gives the required Fourier series expansion:

$$x^2 - 2x = \tfrac{1}{3}\pi^2 + \sum_{m=1}^{\infty} \left\{ 4(-1)^m \left(\frac{\cos mx}{m^2} + \frac{\sin mx}{m} \right) \right\}. \quad \square \qquad (16.35)$$

The term-by-term integration which was used in the previous example may be considered for a general function $f(x)$ to get the following results. Suppose coefficients a_n and b_n exist such that for $-\pi < x < \pi$

$$f(x) = a_0 + \sum_{n=1}^{\infty} \{a_n \cos nx + b_n \sin nx\} \qquad \textbf{(16.36)}$$

then

$$2\pi a_0 = \int_{-\pi}^{\pi} f(x) \, dx \qquad \textbf{(16.37)}$$

$$\pi a_m = \int_{-\pi}^{\pi} f(x) \cos mx \, dx \qquad \textbf{(16.38)}$$

$$\pi b_m = \int_{-\pi}^{\pi} f(x) \sin mx \, dx. \qquad \textbf{(16.39)}$$

These general formulas are obtained exactly as in the previous example, replacing $(x^2 - 2x)$ by $f(x)$.

Example 16.72

Obtain the Fourier series expansion of

$$f(x) = x^3 + x^2 - \pi^2 x - \pi^2. \qquad (16.40)$$

The required coefficients are obtained using equations (16.37), (16.38) and (16.39). Odd powers in $f(x)$ give zero contribution to (16.37) or (16.38), since the integrand will be odd. Similarly even powers in $f(x)$ give zero contribution to (16.39). Hence

$$2\pi a_0 = [\tfrac{1}{3}x^3 - \pi^2 x]^\pi_{-\pi} = -\tfrac{4}{3}\pi^3.$$

Using equation (16.31),

$$\pi a_m = \frac{4\pi(-1)^m}{m^2} - \int_{-\pi}^{\pi} \pi^2 \cos mx \, dx = \frac{4\pi(-1)^m}{m^2}.$$

Using equations (16.32) and (16.30)

$$\pi b_m = \frac{2\pi(-1)^m(6 - m^2\pi^2)}{m^3} + \frac{2\pi^3(-1)^m}{m} = \frac{12\pi(-1)^m}{m^3},$$

$$a_0 = -\tfrac{2}{3}\pi^2, \qquad a_m = \frac{4(-1)^m}{m^2}, \qquad b_m = \frac{12(-1)^m}{m^3},$$

and the Fourier series is

$$f(x) = -\tfrac{2}{3}\pi^2 + \sum_{m=1}^{\infty} \left\{ \frac{4(-1)^m}{m^3} (m \cos mx + 3 \sin mx) \right\}. \quad \square \qquad (16.41)$$

In the table of series at the end of Chapter 8, most of the sums of series of the form $\sum 1/n^p$ are obtained by substituting special values of x into suitable Fourier series. For example, from equations (16.31), (16.37) and (16.38), the Fourier series

$$x^2 = \tfrac{1}{3}\pi^2 + \sum_{n=1}^{\infty} \frac{4(-1)^n}{n^2} \cos nx \qquad (16.42)$$

can be written down. Substituting $x = 0$ gives

$$\sum_{n=1}^{\infty} \frac{(-1)^n}{n^2} = -\frac{\pi^2}{12},$$

and substituting $x = \pm\pi$ gives

$$\sum_{n=1}^{\infty} \frac{1}{n^2} = \frac{\pi^2}{6}.$$

Conversely, once such results have been established, other Fourier series expansions may be checked to some extent by considering particular values of x.

Example 16.73
Check equation (16.41) using suitable values of x.

Since $x = 0$ or $x = \pm\pi$ make $\sin mx = 0$, these values of x will not check the coefficients of $\sin mx$. However $x = \tfrac{1}{2}\pi$ gives

$$-\tfrac{2}{3}\pi^2 + 4 \sum_{m=1}^{\infty} \left\{ \frac{(-1)^m}{m^2} \cos \tfrac{1}{2}m\pi + \frac{3(-1)^m}{m^3} \sin \tfrac{1}{2}m\pi \right\}.$$

When m is odd, $\cos \frac{1}{2}m\pi = 0$ and $(-1)^m = -1$; when m is even, $\sin \frac{1}{2}m\pi = 0$, and $(-1)^m = 1$. The absolute convergence of the series allows a separation of even and odd terms to give

$$-\tfrac{2}{3}\pi^2 + 4 \sum_{\substack{even \\ m}} \frac{\cos \frac{1}{2}m\pi}{m^2} - 12 \sum_{\substack{odd \\ m}} \frac{\sin \frac{1}{2}m\pi}{m^3} \qquad (16.43)$$

$$= -\tfrac{2}{3}\pi^2 + 4\left(-\frac{1}{2^2} + \frac{1}{4^2} - \frac{1}{6^2} + \cdots \right) - 12\left(\frac{1}{1^3} - \frac{1}{3^3} + \frac{1}{5^3} - \cdots \right)$$

$$= -\tfrac{2}{3}\pi^2 + \frac{4}{4}\left(-\frac{\pi^2}{12} \right) - 12\left(\frac{\pi^3}{32} \right),$$

using the results on alternating series listed on p. 195. This value agrees with $f(\frac{1}{2}\pi) = \frac{1}{8}\pi^3 + \frac{1}{4}\pi^2 - \frac{1}{2}\pi^3 - \pi^2$ calculated from the given form (16.40).

Equation (16.43) can also be treated by putting $\cos \frac{1}{2}m\pi = (-1)^k$ when $m = 2k$ is even, and $\sin \frac{1}{2}m\pi = \sin(k\pi - \frac{1}{2}\pi) = -(-1)^k$ when $m = (2k-1)$ is odd. $\square$

Exercises

16.7.1 Show that the Fourier coefficients for $f(x) = x^3 - \pi^2 x$ are

$$a_n = 0, \qquad b_n = 12(-1)^n / n^3.$$

16.7.2 Show that the Fourier coefficients for $f(x) = 3x^2 + 2x$ are

$$a_0 = \pi^2, \qquad a_n = 12(-1)^n / n^2, \; b_n = 4(-1)^{n+1}/n.$$

16.7.3 Show that, for $-\pi \leqslant x \leqslant \pi$,

$$|x| = \tfrac{1}{2}\pi - \frac{4}{\pi} \sum_{n=0}^{\infty} \frac{1}{(2n+1)^2} \cos(2n+1)x.$$

16.7.4 Use the result $\sum_{m=1}^{\infty} 1/m^2 = \pi^2/6$ to verify that equation (16.41) is correct at $x = \pi$.

16.8 Properties of Fourier Series

Fourier series coefficients are found by evaluating integrals from $x = -\pi$ to $x = \pi$, so only depend on values in $(-\pi, \pi)$ of the given function f. The sum of the series is therefore not expected to be $f(x)$ when x is outside the interval $(-\pi, \pi)$. The sum of the Fourier series

$$a_0 + \sum_{n=1}^{\infty} \{a_n \cos nx + b_n \sin nx\}$$

is evidently a periodic function, since every term of the series is periodic. For example $x = \frac{5}{4}\pi$ and $x = -\frac{3}{4}\pi = \frac{5}{4}\pi - 2\pi$ give the same terms, and the same sum. Values of x in $(\pi, 3\pi)$ give the same sum as the corresponding values (2π less) in $(-\pi, \pi)$.

> Thus by taking the graph of $f(x)$ in $(-\pi, \pi)$, and repeating it in $(\pi, 3\pi)$, $(3\pi, 5\pi)$ etc., the resulting curve gives the sum of the series for any x. This sum function can be called a **periodic extension** of f.

Figures 16.3 and 16.4 illustrate this for the series (16.41) and (16.35).

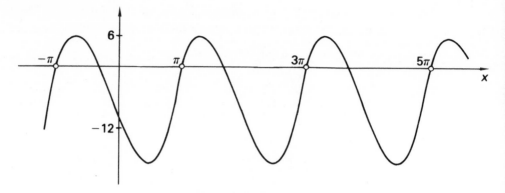

Figure 16.3   Periodic extension of $f(x)=x^3+x^2-\pi^2x-\pi^2$ $(-\pi<x<\pi)$

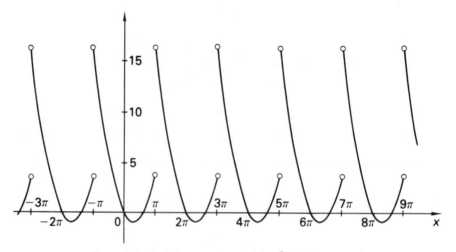

Figure 16.4   Periodic extension of $f(x)=x^2-2x$ $(-\pi<x<\pi)$

The above discussion has carefully avoided mentioning the sum of the series at $x=\pm\pi$, or any odd multiple of π. Examples 16.71 and 16.72 reveal a problem at these end-points: it is easy to verify that equation (16.41) is correct at $x=\pm\pi$, but in equation (16.35) $x=\pi$ gives

$$\tfrac{1}{3}\pi^2+\sum_{n=1}^{\infty}\frac{4}{n^2}(-1)^n\cos n\pi=\tfrac{1}{3}\pi^2+4\sum_{n=1}^{\infty}\frac{1}{n^2}=\tfrac{1}{3}\pi^2+\frac{4\pi^2}{6}=\pi^2,$$

not $f(\pi)=\pi^2-2\pi$. Figures 16.3 and 16.4 show how to recognize when the expected result is true at $x=\pm\pi$. In Example 16.71 the periodic extension (see Fig. 16.4) is discontinuous at $x=\pm\pi$, $\pm3\pi,\ldots$, because the given function x^2-2x has different values at $x=\pm\pi$. In Example 16.72 the given function has the same value (zero) at $x=\pm\pi$, so a continuous curve results when this value is included in the periodic extension (Fig. 16.3).

It can be shown that when there are discontinuities, as in Fig. 16.4,

the sum of the Fourier series is the average of the limiting values on either side of the discontinuity.

In Example 16.71, $f(-\pi) = \pi^2 + 2\pi$, $f(\pi) = \pi^2 - 2\pi$, giving the limiting values on either side of the discontinuities in Fig. 16.4. The average of the values is therefore π^2, which was calculated above as the sum of the series. Note that this result also applies to Example 16.72 because (Fig. 16.3) the limiting values on either side of $x = \pi$ are the same, and hence equal to their average.

In the above examples, the given function was continuous on $(-\pi, \pi)$. The formulas for the coefficients require f to be integrable rather than continuous, and

a Fourier series can be obtained if f has a number of finite discontinuities. Moreover, at the points of discontinuity, the sum of the series is given by the same average of limiting values on either side of the discontinuity.

Example 16.80

Let

$$f(x) = \begin{cases} 1 & \text{for } -\pi < x < -\tfrac{1}{2}\pi \\ 0 & \text{for } -\tfrac{1}{2}\pi < x < 0 \\ -1 & \text{for } 0 < x < \pi \end{cases}$$

Then the Fourier coefficients can be calculated from equations (16.37), (16.38), and (16.39):

$$2\pi a_0 = \int_{-\pi}^{-\pi/2} 1 \, dx + \int_{-\pi/2}^{0} 0 \, dx + \int_{0}^{\pi} (-1) \, dx = \tfrac{1}{2}\pi + 0 - \pi = -\tfrac{1}{2}\pi,$$

$$\pi a_m = \int_{-\pi}^{-\pi/2} \cos mx \, dx + \int_{0}^{\pi} -\cos mx \, dx = \frac{1}{m} \sin(-\tfrac{1}{2}m\pi) = -\frac{1}{m} \sin \tfrac{1}{2}m\pi,$$

$$\pi b_m = \int_{-\pi}^{-\pi/2} \sin mx \, dx - \int_{0}^{\pi} \sin mx \, dx = \frac{1}{m}(-\cos \tfrac{1}{2}m\pi + 2 \cos m\pi - 1).$$

The Fourier series is therefore

$$-\tfrac{1}{4} + \sum_{m=1}^{\infty} \frac{-1}{m\pi} \{ (\sin \tfrac{1}{2}m\pi)(\cos mx) + (1 + \cos \tfrac{1}{2}m\pi - 2 \cos m\pi)(\sin mx) \}.$$

When m is even, $\sin \tfrac{1}{2}m\pi = 0$, $\cos \tfrac{1}{2}m\pi = (-1)^{m/2}$, and $\cos m\pi = 1$. When m is odd, $\cos m\pi = -1$, $\cos \tfrac{1}{2}m\pi = 0$, and $\sin \tfrac{1}{2}m\pi = (-1)^{(m-1)/2}$. Thus the series has the form

$$-\tfrac{1}{4} - \frac{1}{\pi} \{ (\cos x + 3 \sin x) - \sin 2x + \tfrac{1}{3}(-\cos 3x + 3 \sin 3x)$$

$$+ \tfrac{1}{5}(\cos 5x + 3 \sin 5x) - \tfrac{1}{3} \sin 6x + \tfrac{1}{7}(-\cos 7x + 3 \sin 7x) + \cdots \}.$$

The series converges for all real x, the sum function being given by the periodic extension of $f(x)$, and the average of values on either side of any discontinuity. These averages are indicated by crosses ($\times$) in Fig. 16.5.

Putting $x = 0$, the series becomes

$$-\frac{1}{4} - \frac{1}{\pi} \left\{ 1 - \frac{1}{3} + \frac{1}{5} - \frac{1}{7} + \cdots \right\} = -\frac{1}{4} - \frac{1}{\pi} \left\{ \frac{\pi}{4} \right\} = -\frac{1}{2},$$

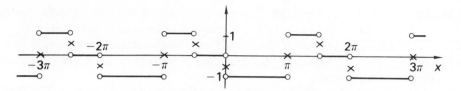

Figure 16.5   Sum of the series in Example 16.80

which is the average of the values 0 and -1 on either side of the discontinuity in $f(x)$ at $x = 0$. This checks the coefficients of cos mx. Putting $x = \frac{1}{2}\pi$, the series becomes

$$-\frac{1}{4} - \frac{1}{\pi}\left\{3\left(1 - \frac{1}{3} + \frac{1}{5} - \frac{1}{7} + \cdots\right)\right\} = -\frac{1}{4} - \frac{3}{\pi}\left(\frac{\pi}{4}\right) = -1 = f(\tfrac{1}{2}\pi),$$

checking the coefficients of sin mx when m is odd. There does not seem to be a simple check for the coefficients of sin mx when m is even. $\square$

In Section 16.2 it was stated that a power series can always be either differentiated or integrated term-by-term. For a Fourier series integration is expected to give correct results. Firstly the expandable functions $f(x)$ are certainly integrable, otherwise a_0 could not be calculated. Secondly, integration of the series terms sin nx and cos nx produces a factor $1/n$ in the coefficients, and this cannot destroy the convergence (in fact it should improve it).

Integration over any subinterval of $[-\pi, \pi]$ is valid.

Example 16.81
Consider

$$x^2 = \tfrac{1}{3}\pi^2 + \sum_{n=1}^{\infty} 4(-1)^n(1/n^2)\cos nx. \tag{16.42}$$

Multiplying by 3, replacing x by t, and integrating from $t = -\pi$ to $t = x$ gives

$$\int_{-\pi}^{x} 3t^2\,dt = \pi^2\int_{-\pi}^{x} dt + \sum_{n=1}^{\infty}\frac{12(-1)^n}{n^2}\int_{-\pi}^{x}\cos nt\,dt$$

$$x^3 + \pi^3 = \pi^2(x + \pi) + \sum_{n=1}^{\infty}\frac{12(-1)^n}{n^3}\sin nx,$$

since $\sin(-n\pi) = 0$. Rearranging:

$$x^3 - \pi^2 x = 12\sum_{n=1}^{\infty}\frac{(-1)^n}{n^3}\sin nx. \quad \square$$

On the other hand, differentiation is not always expected to give correct results. Firstly some expandable functions $f(x)$ have discontinuities, and are therefore not differentiable. Secondly differentiation of the series terms sin nx and cos nx produces a factor n in the coefficients, which may destroy the convergence.

Suppose

$$f(x) = a_0 + \sum_{n=1}^{\infty} (a_n \cos nx + b_n \sin nx) \qquad (-\pi \leqslant x \leqslant \pi)$$

where f is continuous on $[-\pi, \pi]$, and $f(-\pi) = f(\pi)$ so that the periodic extension is also continuous. Then differentiating gives a correct result at every point where $f'(x)$ exists.

Example 16.82
From Example 16.72

$$x^3 + x^2 - \pi^2 x = \frac{\pi^2}{3} + \sum_{m=1}^{\infty} \frac{4(-1)^m}{m^3} (m \cos mx + 3 \sin mx).$$

From the continuity (shown in Fig. 16.3), differentiation is valid, giving

$$3x^2 + 2x - \pi^2 = \sum_{m=1}^{\infty} \frac{4(-1)^m}{m^2} (3 \cos mx - m \sin mx). \quad \square$$

Section 16.5 considered the error when the sum of a power series is approximated by a polynomial obtained by adding the terms up to the $(x-a)^n$ term. This truncation error is zero at $x = a$, small near $x = a$, but increases with the distance of x from a. For a Fourier series truncation error does not vary much with x, except perhaps near discontinuities in the sum function.

Example 16.83
The following table shows errors, for various values of x and n, when $(x^3 + x^2 - \pi^2 x - \pi^2)$ is approximated by

$$S_n(x) = -\frac{2\pi^2}{3} + \sum_{m=1}^{n} \frac{4(-1)^m}{m^3} (m \cos mx + 3 \sin mx)$$

(cf. Example 16.72):

x	$n = 4$	$n = 6$	$n = 8$	$n = 10$	$x^3 + x^2 - \pi^2 x - \pi^2$
-3.1	-0.73	-0.44	-0.28	-0.19	0.55
-3.0	-0.39	-0.09	0.03	0.08	1.74
-1.0	0.06	0.04	-0.03	-0.004	0.0
1.0	-0.08	0.06	-0.01	-0.01	-17.74
3.0	0.04	0.13	0.15	0.13	-3.48
3.1	-0.54	-0.31	-0.19	-0.12	-1.06

(The value of a finite sum to n terms includes the error, for example $S_{10}(3.0) = -3.48 + 0.13$.) $\quad \square$

This example suggests that the error is greatest near $x = \pm \pi$. The next example shows that this feature is much worse when the sum function is discontinuous.

Example 16.84

The following table shows errors, for various values of x and n, when (x^2-2x) is approximated by

$$S_n(x) = \tfrac{1}{3}\pi^2 + \sum_{m=1}^{n} \frac{4(-1)^n}{n^2}(\cos nx + n \sin nx)$$

(cf. equation (16.35) in Example 16.71):

x	$n=4$	$n=6$	$n=8$	$n=10$	x^2-2x
−3.1	−6.2	−5.6	−5.1	−4.7	15.8
−2.5	1.3	0.54	−0.47	−0.55	11.25
0.0	0.10	0.05	0.03	0.02	0.0
2.5	−0.94	−0.70	0.32	0.57	1.25
3.1	4.9	4.8	4.6	4.4	3.41

The poor convergence near discontinuities is known as **Gibb's phenomenon**. It is expected because a continuous function $S_n(x)$ is used to approximate the discontinuous sum function. This is illustrated in Fig. 16.6 which shows $S_{10}(x)$ and the sum function.   □

Exercise (answer on p. 433–4)

16.8.1   Consider the Fourier series with the following sum functions on $(-\pi, \pi)$ (cf. Exercises 16.7.1–3): (i) $x^3 - \pi^2 x$ (ii) $3x^2 + 2x$ (iii) $|x|$. In each case give a diagram showing the sum function for $-3\pi \leqslant x \leqslant 3\pi$, and state what results can be obtained by differentiation.

16.9   Fourier Series with only Sine or only Cosine Terms

The derivation of the formulas

$$\pi a_m = \int_{-\pi}^{\pi} f(x) \cos mx \, dx, \qquad \pi b_m = \int_{-\pi}^{\pi} f(x) \sin mx \, dx$$

for the coefficients in the expansion

$$f(x) = a_0 + \sum_{n=1}^{\infty} (a_n \cos nx + b_n \sin nx)$$

depends only on the fact that the integral over the interval $(-\pi, \pi)$ of a product of two different expansion functions is zero (see equations (16.27) and (16.28) on p. 416). Equation (16.26)

$$\int_0^{\pi} \sin mx \sin nx \, dx = \int_0^{\pi} \cos mx \cos nx \, dx = 0 \quad \text{if } m \neq n$$

shows that the same is true on the interval $(0, \pi)$ for either the set of functions $\sin nx$, or for the set of functions $\cos nx$.

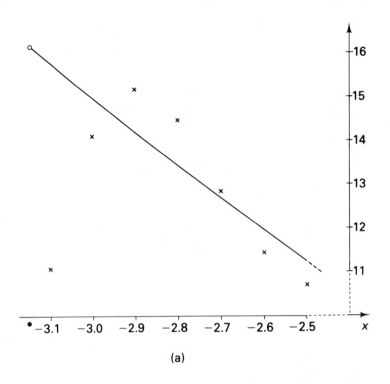

(a)

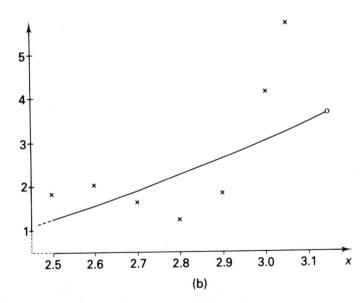

(b)

Figure 16.6   Sum function (solid curve and dot), and values (crosses) of the sum $S_{10}(x)$ of 11 terms of the
Fourier series

Expansions with only sine or cosine terms can therefore be obtained, but converge to the given function only on the interval $(0, \pi)$.

$$\text{If } f(x) = A_0 + \sum_{n=1}^{\infty} A_n \cos nx \quad \text{for } 0 < x < \pi,$$

then $\int_0^\pi f(x) \, dx = \pi A_0$, $\int_0^\pi f(x) \cos mx \, dx = \frac{1}{2} A_m \pi$, giving

$$A_0 = \frac{1}{\pi} \int_0^\pi f(x) \, dx, \qquad A_n = \frac{2}{\pi} \int_0^\pi f(x) \cos nx \, dx. \tag{16.44}$$

Similarly,

$$\text{if } f(x) = \sum_{n=1}^{\infty} B_n \sin nx \quad \text{for } 0 < x < \pi,$$

then

$$B_n = \frac{2}{\pi} \int_0^\pi f(x) \sin nx \, dx \tag{16.45}$$

To apply these formulas the integration results (cf. Exercise 10.36) in the following table are useful:

p	$\int_0^\pi x^p \sin nx \, dx$	$\int_0^\pi x^p \cos nx \, dx$	
0	$0 \quad (n \text{ even})$ $2/n \quad (n \text{ odd})$	0	(16.46)
1	$\dfrac{-\pi(-1)^n}{n}$	$0 \quad (n \text{ even})$ $-2/n^2 \quad (n \text{ odd})$	(16.47)
2	$-\pi^2/n \quad (n \text{ even})$ $(n^2\pi^2 - 4)/n^3 \quad (n \text{ odd})$	$\dfrac{2\pi(-1)^n}{n^2}$	(16.48)
3	$\dfrac{\pi(-1)^n(6 - n^2\pi^2)}{n^3}$	$3\pi^2/n^2 \quad (n \text{ even})$ $(12 - 3n^2\pi^2)/n^4 \quad (n \text{ odd})$	(16.49)

Example 16.90

Again consider $f(x) = x^2 - 2x$ (cf. Example 16.71). For an expansion in sine functions, valid on $(0, \pi)$, use equations (16.45), (16.47) and (16.48): for n even, $B_n = (4 - 2\pi)/n$

$$\text{for } n \text{ odd}, \quad B_n = -\frac{8}{\pi n^3} - \frac{4 - 2\pi}{n}.$$

The expansion is

$$x^2 - 2x = \sum_{n=1}^{\infty} B_n \sin nx = \left(-\frac{8}{\pi} + 2\pi - 4 \right) \sin x + (2 - \pi) \sin 2x$$

$$+ \left(-\frac{8}{27\pi} + \frac{2\pi - 4}{3} \right) \sin 3x + \frac{(2 - \pi)}{2} \sin 4x$$

$$+ \left(-\frac{8}{125\pi} + \frac{2\pi - 4}{5} \right) \sin 5x + \frac{(2 - \pi)}{3} \sin 6x + \cdots . \tag{16.50}$$

As a partial check, $x = \frac{1}{2}\pi$ gives

$$-\frac{8}{\pi} \left(1 - \frac{1}{3^3} + \frac{1}{5^3} - \cdots \right) + (2\pi - 4) \left(1 - \frac{1}{3} + \frac{1}{5} - \cdots \right) = -\frac{8}{\pi} \left(\frac{\pi^3}{32} \right) + (2\pi - 4) \frac{\pi}{4} = \frac{1}{4}\pi^2 - \pi$$

(using the results on alternating series given on p. 195).

For an expansion in cosine functions, valid on $(0, \pi)$, use equations (16.44), (16.47) and (16.48): $A_0 = (\pi^2/3) - \pi$;

$$\text{for } n \text{ even,} \quad A_n = \frac{4}{n^2}; \qquad \text{for } n \text{ odd,} \quad A_n = \frac{8 - 4\pi}{n^2\pi}.$$

The expansion is

$$x^2 - 2x = A_0 + \sum_{n=1}^{\infty} A_n \cos nx = \frac{\pi^2}{3} - \pi + 4 \left(\frac{2}{\pi} - 1 \right) \cos x + \frac{4}{2^2} \cos 2x$$

$$+ \frac{4}{3^2} \left(\frac{2}{\pi} - 1 \right) \cos 3x + \frac{4}{4^2} \cos 4x + \cdots . \quad \square \tag{16.51}$$

The coefficients A_n or B_n are found by evaluating integrals from $x = 0$ to $x = \pi$, so the sum of the series obtained can only equal the given function on $(0, \pi)$. The sum function, which has period 2π, can be obtained by a periodic extension once the sum in $(-\pi, \pi)$ is known. The extension from $(0, \pi)$ to $(-\pi, \pi)$ is made by observing that a

sine series must sum to an odd function, while a cosine series must sum to an even function.

Example 16.91
The sum of the series (16.51) is an even function, so has the value $x^2 + 2x$ on $(-\pi, 0)$ (Fig. 16.7(a)). The sum of the series (16.50) is an odd function, so has the value $-x^2 + 2x$ on $(-\pi, 0)$ (Fig. 16.7(b)). These two functions are the odd and even extensions of the given $x^2 - 2x$ on $(0, \pi)$. For values of x outside $(-\pi, \pi)$, the sum is given by the periodic extension, and by the average value rule at discontinuities (Fig. 16.8). $\square$

Exercises (answer on p. 434)
16.9.1 Check equation (16.51) in Example 16.90 by substituting $x = \frac{1}{2}\pi$.
16.9.2 Show that for $0 < x < \pi$,

$$x^2 = \frac{1}{3}\pi^2 + \sum_{n=1}^{\infty} \frac{4(-1)^n}{n^2} \cos nx = \sum_{n=1}^{\infty} (-1)^{n+1} \left(\frac{2\pi}{n} + c_n \right) \sin nx,$$

where $c_n = 0$ if n is even, and $c_n = 8/\pi$ when n is odd. Which one of these results is true on $[-\pi, \pi]$? What is the sum of the other series at $x = \pi$ and on $[-\pi, 0]$?

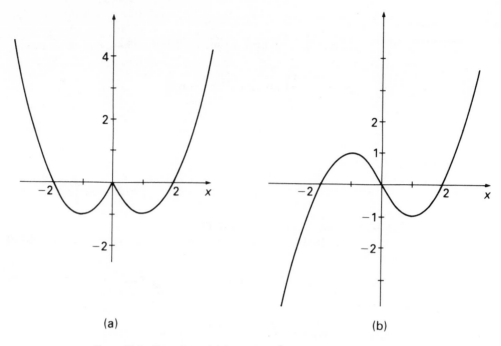

Figure 16.7　Extension onto $(-\pi, \pi)$ of $x^2 - 2x$ $(0 < x < \pi)$ (a) even (b) odd

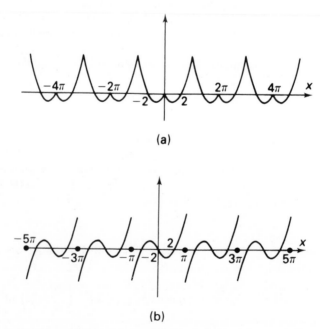

Figure 16.8　(a) Even, and (b) odd, periodic extensions of $x^2 - 2x$ $(0 < x < \pi)$. In (b), dots complete sum function of the series (16.50)

16.10 Complex Series

Much of Chapter 8 and the present chapter applies to series of complex terms without modification. When the terms v_k and $s_n = \sum_{k=1}^{n} v_k$ are complex numbers, the statement that the sum of the series $\sum v_k$ is L means that $|s_n - L| \to 0$ as $n \to \infty$. In the Argand diagram, $|s_n - L|$ is the distance between the points representing s_n and L.

A complex geometric series $\sum a\rho^{n-1}$ converges to the complex sum $a/(1-\rho)$ if $r = |\rho| < 1$. The ratio ρ is also complex, in general.

Example 16.100
The geometric series with $a = 1$ and ratio $\rho = \frac{1}{2}i$ converges to the sum

$$\frac{1}{1 - \frac{1}{2}i} = \frac{2}{2 - i} = \frac{4 + 2i}{4 + 1} = \frac{4}{5} + \frac{2}{5}i.$$

The terms $(1, \frac{1}{2}i, -\frac{1}{4}, -\frac{1}{8}i, \ldots)$ of this series can be represented by vectors in the Argand diagram. Placing these vectors end-to-end represents addition of the terms, constructing (Fig. 16.9) the points representing $S_1 = 1$, $S_2 = 1 + \frac{1}{2}i$, $S_3 = 1 + \frac{1}{2}i + (\frac{1}{2}i)^2 = S_2 - \frac{1}{4}$, $S_4 = 1 + (\frac{1}{2}i) + (\frac{1}{2}i)^2 + (\frac{1}{2}i)^3 = S_3 - \frac{1}{8}i$, etc.

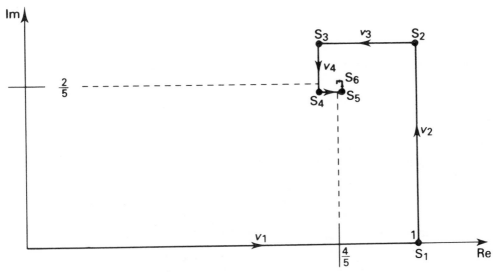

Figure 16.9 Terms $v_k = (\frac{1}{2}i)^{k-1}$ represented by vectors; point S_n represents sum of n terms $(n = 1, 2, \ldots)$

Multiplying a complex number by $\rho = \frac{1}{2}i$ multiplies the modulus by $|\frac{1}{2}i| = \frac{1}{2}$ and increases the argument by $\arg(\frac{1}{2}i) = \frac{1}{2}\pi$. The vector representing any term is therefore perpendicular to the vector representing the previous term, and half its length (Fig. 16.9). The convergence on to the sum is then obvious geometrically, the vectors v_k spiralling round and round the point $\frac{4}{5} + \frac{2}{5}i$ which represents the sum.

This series $\sum (\frac{1}{2}i)^{n-1}$ is absolutely convergent, because the series $\sum |(\frac{1}{2}i)^{n-1}| = \sum (\frac{1}{2})^{n-1}$ converges. $\square$

A complex series $\sum v_n$ is **absolutely convergent** if $\sum |v_n|$ converges.

It is then convergent, and its sum is unaffected by any rearrangement of the terms.

A complex series $\sum (x_n + iy_n)$ converges if and only if the two real series $\sum x_n$ and $\sum y_n$ converge. From a complex series with known sum, two real series with known sum may be obtained, and vice-versa.

In a **complex power series** $\sum a_n (z - a)^n$, the coefficients a_n, the variable z, and the number a can all be complex. Results given in Sections 16.2, 16.3, 16.4 and in the table at the end of this chapter remain true. The **radius of convergence** is a real number c such that the series converges if $|z - a| < c$, and does not converge if $|z - a| > c$. In the Argand diagram the region $|z - a| < c$ is the interior of the disc of radius c centred at $z = a$. Exponential-type series converge for all z.

Example 16.101

For any complex number z, the sum of the power series

$$\sum_{n=1}^{\infty} \frac{z^n}{n!} = 1 + z + \frac{z^2}{2!} + \frac{z^3}{3!} + \cdots \qquad (16.52)$$

is e^z.

This is consistent with

$$e^{it} = \cos t + i \sin t, \qquad (16.53)$$

obtained for real t in Section 6.11 from differentiation requirements. From equation (16.52), e^{it} is the sum of the series

$$1 + it + \frac{i^2 t^2}{2!} + \frac{i^3 t^3}{3!} + \cdots = 1 + it - \frac{t^2}{2!} - \frac{it^3}{3!} + \frac{t^4}{4!} + \frac{it^5}{5!} + \cdots.$$

The real parts of the terms, $1 + 0 - \frac{1}{2}t^2 + 0 + t^4/4! - \cdots$, have sum $\cos t$, and the imaginary parts have sum $\sin t$, demonstrating equation (16.53). □

Example 16.102
(i) The series $\sum v_n$ with $v_n = e^{in\theta}/n^2$ converges (absolutely), because $|v_n| = 1/n^2$, and $\sum 1/n^2$ converges.
(ii) The sum of the series $\sum_{n=1}^{\infty} e^{in\theta}/n^2$ can be written

$$\sum_{n=1}^{\infty} \frac{\cos n\theta}{n^2} + i \sum_{n=1}^{\infty} \frac{\sin n\theta}{n^2}.$$

The real part is the Fourier cosine series with sum $\frac{1}{4}\theta^2 - \frac{1}{2}\theta\pi + \frac{1}{6}\pi^2$ for $0 < \theta < \pi$. □

From equation (16.53) one obtains

$$\cos nx = \frac{e^{inx} + e^{-inx}}{2}, \qquad \sin nx = \frac{e^{inx} - e^{-inx}}{2i}. \qquad (16.54)$$

These equations allow Fourier series to be written in a complex form in which the expansion functions are complex exponential functions.

Example 16.103

The result of Example 16.72 can be written

$$x^3 + x^2 - \pi^2 x - \tfrac{1}{3}\pi^2 = \sum_{n=1}^{\infty} \left\{ \frac{4(-1)^n}{n^3}(n \cos nx + 3 \sin nx) \right\}$$

$$= 4 \sum_{n=1}^{\infty} (-1)^n \left\{ \frac{e^{inx} + e^{-inx}}{2n^2} + \frac{3e^{inx} - 3e^{-inx}}{2in^3} \right\}$$

$$= 4 \sum_{n=1}^{\infty} (-1)^n \frac{(n-3i)}{2n^3} e^{inx} + 4 \sum_{m=1}^{\infty} (-1)^m \frac{(m+3i)}{2m^3} e^{-imx}.$$

The summation variable has been changed to m in the second sum so that the substitution $m = -n$ can be made:

$$\sum_{m=1}^{\infty} (-1)^m \frac{(m+3i)}{2m^3} e^{-imx} = \sum_{n=-1}^{-\infty} (-1)^n \frac{(-n+3i)}{-2n^3} e^{inx}.$$

With this manipulation, the Fourier series can be written

$$x^3 + x^2 - \pi^2 x - \tfrac{1}{3}\pi^2 = 2 \sum_{n=-\infty}^{\infty}{}' (-1)^n \frac{(n-3i)}{n^3} e^{inx}, \qquad (16.55)$$

where the $\sum'$ indicates that $n = 0$ is omitted. □

Equation (16.55) is an example of the complex form of Fourier series, $\sum_{n=-\infty}^{\infty} c_n e^{inx}$. Obviously equation (16.53) can be used to write this as an expansion in $\cos nx$ and $\sin nx$. The required manipulations (like those in the previous example) are certainly correct when the series is absolutely convergent.

If $f(x)$ is given for $-\pi < x < \pi$, then the coefficients c_n in the expansion $\sum c_n e^{inx}$ can be found directly as follows. Since

$$\int_{-\pi}^{\pi} e^{ikx}\, dx = \frac{e^{ik\pi} - e^{-ik\pi}}{ik} \qquad \text{if } k \neq 0$$

$$= \frac{2}{k} \sin k\pi = 0 \quad \text{if } k \text{ is an integer,}$$

$$\int_{-\pi}^{\pi} e^{-imx} e^{inx}\, dx = \int_{-\pi}^{\pi} e^{i(n-m)x}\, dx = 0 \quad \text{if } n \neq m. \qquad (16.56)$$

Assume that, for some coefficients c_n to be found,

$$\boxed{f(x) = \sum_{n=-\infty}^{\infty} c_n e^{inx} \qquad (-\pi < x < \pi).}$$

Multiply by e^{-imx}, integrate from $x = -\pi$ to π, and use equation (16.56):

$$\boxed{\int_{-\pi}^{\pi} f(x) e^{-imx}\, dx = c_m \int_{-\pi}^{\pi} dx = 2\pi c_m.} \qquad (16.57)$$

Example 16.104
Obtain the coefficients for the complex Fourier series expansion of $f(x) = x^2 - 2x$.

From equation (16.57), the required coefficients are given by

$$2\pi c_n = \int_{-\pi}^{\pi} (x^2 - 2x)\, e^{-inx}\, dx \qquad \text{(integrate by parts)}$$

$$= \left[\frac{i}{n}(x^2 - 2x)\, e^{-inx}\right]_{-\pi}^{\pi} - \frac{i}{n}\int_{-\pi}^{\pi} (2x - 2)\, e^{-inx}\, dx \qquad (n \neq 0).$$

Since $e^{\pm in\pi} = \cos n\pi \pm i \sin n\pi = \cos n\pi = (-1)^n$,

$$2\pi c_n = -\frac{4i(-1)^n\pi}{n} + \frac{1}{n^2}\left[(2x - 2)\, e^{-inx}\right]_{-\pi}^{\pi} - \frac{2}{n^2}\int_{-\pi}^{\pi} e^{-inx}\, dx$$

$$= -\frac{4i(-1)^n\pi}{n} + \frac{4\pi(-1)^n}{n^2} \qquad (n \neq 0).$$

If $n = 0$,

$$2\pi c_0 = \int_{-\pi}^{\pi} (x^2 - 2x)\, dx = \tfrac{2}{3}\pi^3.$$

Thus $c_0 = \tfrac{1}{3}\pi^2$,

$$c_n = (-1)^n \frac{(2 - 2in)}{n^2},$$

where n is any positive or negative integer.   □

In the previous example, the integral (16.57) for c_n was explicitly evaluated in order to demonstrate one advantage of the complex form of the Fourier series: only one integral is required rather than two ((16.38) and (16.39)). The coefficients a_n and b_n in the real form of the series can be obtained from c_n, because

$$\pi(a_m - ib_m) = \int_{-\pi}^{\pi} f(x)(\cos mx - i \sin mx)\, dx,$$

from equations (16.38) and (16.39)

$$= 2\pi c_m, \quad \text{from (16.57)}.$$

Hence

$$a_m = 2\, \mathrm{Re}\ c_m, \quad b_m = -2\, \mathrm{Im}\ c_m, \qquad (m > 0) \tag{16.58}$$

and $a_0 = c_0$.

Exercises

16.10.1   Find the sum of the series $\sum_{n=0}^{\infty} (-2i/3)^n$. Draw an Argand diagram like Fig. 16.9 to illustrate the convergence to the sum.

16.10.2   Find the sum of the series $\sum_{n=0}^{\infty} (\tfrac{1}{2} + \tfrac{1}{2}i)^n$. Use De Moivre's theorem to find the real and imaginary parts of the general term. Write down the two real series and their sums obtained by taking real and imaginary parts.

16.10.3   Use equation (16.57) to show that if $x^2 = \sum_{n=-\infty}^{\infty} c_n e^{inx}$ $(-\pi < x < \pi)$, then $c_n = [2(-1)^n]/n^2$ for $n \neq 0$.

Answers to Exercises 16.2.1–16.10.2

16.2.1 $(1-x)^{-3} = 1+3x+6x^2+\cdots+\frac{1}{2}(n+1)(n+2)x^n+\cdots.$

$(1-x)^{-4} = 1+4x+10x^2+\cdots+\frac{1}{6}(n+1)(n+2)(n+3)x^n+\cdots.$

To check $(1+x)^{-2}$, replace x by $-x$ in the result of Example 16.22 (p. 397). See also S3 in the table of power series (p. 438).

16.2.2 $a_0 = 0$, $a_1 = 1$, $a_2 = -\frac{1}{2}$, $a_n = (-1)^{n-1}(1/(n-2)+1/n)$ for $n>2$.

16.2.3   (i) $(a+x)^{-1} = \dfrac{1}{a}-\dfrac{x}{a^2}+\dfrac{x^2}{a^3}-\cdots+\dfrac{(-1)^n}{a^{n+1}}x^n+\cdots$ $(-a<x<a)$

with radius of convergence a.

   (ii) $a_n = (-1)^n$.

   (iii) See S10 in the table of power series (p. 438).

16.3.1   (i) S12 in the table of power series.

   (ii) $e^{-x} = \sum_{n=0}^{\infty}(-)^n x^n/n!$

   (iii) S14 and S16 in the table of power series.

16.3.2   See S1 in the table of power series.

16.3.3 $1+\frac{3}{2}t+\frac{3}{8}t^2-\frac{1}{16}t^3$.

16.4.1 $1+2(x-\pi/4)+2(x-\pi/4)^2$.

16.4.2 $\sin x = \sqrt{\frac{1}{2}}[-1-(x+\pi/4)+\frac{1}{2}(x+\pi/4)^2+\frac{1}{6}(x+\pi/4)^3-\frac{1}{24}(x+\pi/4)^4$
$-\frac{1}{120}(x+\pi/4)^5+\cdots.$

16.4.3 $x^{-2} = 1-2(x-1)+3(x-1)^2-4(x-1)^3+\cdots+(-)^n(n+1)(x-1)^n+\cdots.$

16.5.1   Proceed as in Example 16.50 (p. 406) with $-t^2$ for t^2. The inequality follows from $1\leq 1+t^2\leq 1+x^2$. Taking $n=4$ gives
$0.19739555979\leq \text{Tan}^{-1}(0.2)\leq 0.19739555986.$

16.5.2   8.

16.5.3 $(\pi/6-0.7, \pi/6+0.7)$, or any subinterval.

16.6.1   (i) 0,   (ii) does not exist,   (iii) 1,   (iv) −1,   (v) 1,
   (vi) 4/3,   (vii) k,   (viii) 0,   (ix) e^{-1}.

16.6.2   (i) $\frac{1}{3}$,   (ii) 1.

16.8.1

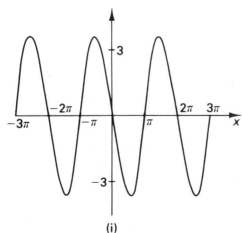

(i)

(i) $\displaystyle\sum_{n=1}^{\infty}\dfrac{12(-1)^n}{n^2}\cos nx = 3x^2-\pi^2$ $(|x|\leq \pi)$.

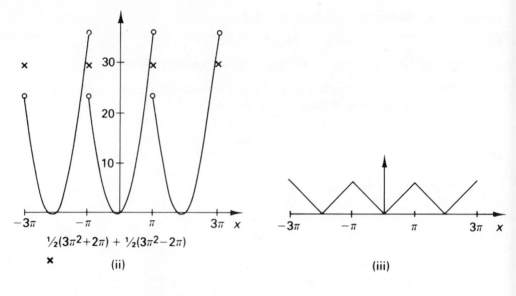

$$\tfrac{1}{2}(3\pi^2+2\pi) + \tfrac{1}{2}(3\pi^2-2\pi)$$

(ii)

(iii)

(ii) No result from differentiation.

(iii) $\dfrac{4}{\pi} \displaystyle\sum_{n=0}^{\infty} \dfrac{\sin(2n+1)x}{2n+1} = \operatorname{sgn} x \qquad (0<|x|<\pi).$

16.9.2 Cosine series gives x^2 on $[-\pi, \pi]$. Sine series gives $-x^2$ on $(-\pi, 0)$, and 0 at $x = \pm\pi$.
16.10.1 $(9-6i)/13$

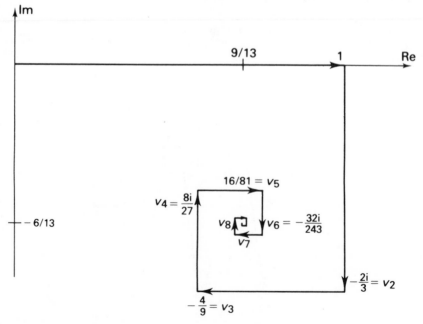

16.10.2 $1+i; \ \displaystyle\sum_{n=0}^{\infty} \dfrac{1}{(\sqrt{2})^n} \cos\!\left(\dfrac{n\pi}{4}\right) = 1 = \sum_{n=0}^{\infty} \dfrac{1}{(\sqrt{2})^n} \sin\!\left(\dfrac{n\pi}{4}\right).$

Further Exercises on Chapter 16

16.1 Find the power series with sum

$$x \, \text{Tan}^{-1} x - \ln\sqrt{(1+x^2)},$$

giving the general term. What is the radius of convergence c of this power series?

16.2 Find the coefficient of x^n in the (Maclaurin) power series expansion of the function

$$f(x) = \frac{6}{1+6x} + \frac{5}{(1-x)^2}.$$

What is the value of the radius of convergence?

16.3 Find the Taylor series expansion of the function $f(x) = x^{-3}$ about the point $a = 1$, giving the first three terms and the general term.

16.4 (i) Use series expansions to show that

$$\ln(1+x) \leqslant \text{Tan}^{-1} x$$

for $0 \leqslant x \leqslant \frac{1}{2}$.

(ii) Obtain the inequality in (i) by integration (cf. Exercise 9.11 on p. 221). For what values of x does this derivation prove the inequality?

16.5 For each of the following series, state the values of x for which they converge:

(a) $\displaystyle\sum_{n=1}^{\infty} (-)^{n+1} \frac{x^n}{n}$, (b) $\displaystyle\sum_{n=0}^{\infty} \frac{x^{2n}}{(2n)!}$, (c) $\displaystyle\sum_{n=0}^{\infty} \frac{3^{n+1} x^n}{5^n}$.

16.6 Calculate the first three terms of the Taylor series expansion of $F(x) = \sqrt{x}$ about $x = 4$. Is the series an alternating series?

Compute the approximation to $\sqrt{4.1}$ given by the three terms, and obtain bounds on the truncation error.

16.7 Calculate the first four terms in the Taylor expansion about $x = \pi/3$ of the function $F(x) = \cos x$.

In Exercises 16.8–16.18, either evaluate the given limit, or show that it does not exist.

16.8 $\text{Lim}_{x \to 0} \, x^{1/x}$.

16.9 $\text{Lim}_{s \to 1} \, s^{1/(s-1)}$.

16.10 $\text{Lim}_{t \to 1} \, t^{1/(t-1)}$.

16.11 $\text{Lim}_{x \to 0} \dfrac{\sin ax + \sin bx}{\sin cx + \sin dx}$ $(c + d \neq 0$, or any multiple of $2\pi)$.

16.12 $\text{Lim}_{x \to 0} \dfrac{\exp(x^n) - 1}{x}$.

16.13 $\text{Lim}_{x \to \infty} \dfrac{3x^2 + 7x + 9}{7x^2 + 3x + 5}$.

16.14 $\text{Lim}_{x \to -2} \dfrac{3x^2 + 7x + 9}{7x^2 + 3x + 5}$.

16.15 $\text{Lim}_{x \to 1} \dfrac{\ln x}{x^2 - 1}$.

16.16 $\displaystyle\lim_{x\to 1}\frac{1-x+\ln x}{x^2-2x+1}$.

16.17 $\displaystyle\lim_{x\to 0}(\cos ax)^{1/x}$.

16.18 $\displaystyle\lim_{x\to 0}\frac{1-e^{-x}-\ln(1+x)}{\sin x-\mathrm{Tan}^{-1}x}$.

16.19 Find values of r, s and t such that
$$\lim_{x\to 0}\frac{re^{-x^2}+s\cos 2x+t\ln(1+x^2)}{x^4}=1.$$

16.20 Use the logarithmic series (equations (16.5) and (16.6) on p. 399) to obtain the power series expansion of
$$F(x)=\tfrac{1}{2}[\ln(1+x)-\ln(1-x)+\ln(1-x^4)].$$

By evaluating $\lim_{x\to 1}F(x)$, find the sum of the series
$$1+\tfrac{1}{3}-\tfrac{1}{2}+\tfrac{1}{5}+\tfrac{1}{7}-\tfrac{1}{4}+\tfrac{1}{9}+\tfrac{1}{11}-\tfrac{1}{6}+\cdots$$
(cf. Example 8.45 on p. 190).

16.21 Use the exponential series to verify that $e^x e^y=e^{x+y}$.

16.22 (i) Obtain a geometric series with sum $1/(a+bx)$. What is the radius of convergence?

(ii) Express $f(x)=(13x-4)/(2+x-6x^2)$ in partial fractions, and hence use (i) to find a power series with sum $f(x)$ (cf. Example 16.26). What is the radius of convergence?

16.23 Apply the Ratio Test (see Exercise 8.25 on p. 194) to determine the values of x for which the following series converge, and so write down the radius of convergence of the series.

(i) $\displaystyle\sum_{n=1}^{\infty}nx^n$, (ii) $\displaystyle\sum_{n=1}^{\infty}\frac{nx^n}{2^n}$,

(iii) $\displaystyle\sum_{n=1}^{\infty}\frac{2^n x^n}{n!}$, (iv) $\displaystyle\sum_{n=1}^{\infty}n!x^n$.

16.24 Use the results in the table of series (p. 438) to find the power series expansions ($\sum a_n x^n$) of the following functions
(i) $x\log(1+x^2)$, (ii) $\mathrm{Tan}^{-1}(x^2)$, (iii) $(1+x^3)^{1/2}$,
(iv) $x^2\cos\sqrt{x}$, (v) $2\cos^2 x$.

16.25 Calculate the first three terms of the Taylor series expansion of $f(x)=x^4$ about the point $x=2$.

16.26 Evaluate the limits as $x\to 1$ of the following expressions:

(a) $\dfrac{\tan(x-1)}{x^2-x}$, (b) $\dfrac{(x^2-x+1)^{1/2}-(x^2+2x-2)^{1/2}}{x^2-1}$.

16.27 By using the Binomial series, or otherwise, obtain the general term of the Taylor series expansion of $F(x)=x^{-3}$ in powers of $(x-1)$, i.e. about the point $x=1$. For what values of x will this series converge?

16.28 Given that $1 < e^t < 2$ when $0 < t < \frac{1}{2}$, show that

$$\frac{1}{24} < \int_0^{1/2} (\tfrac{1}{2} - t)^2 e^t \, dt < \frac{1}{12},$$

without using any values of the exponential function. Use this result and Taylor's theorem to obtain bounds on the error in the approximation

$$e^{1/2} = 1 + \tfrac{1}{2} + \tfrac{1}{8}.$$

16.29 (i) Write down the general term of the (Maclaurin) power series expansions of the following functions:

(a) $\ln(1+x)$ $(|x|<1)$,

(b) $f(x) = \dfrac{e^x - 1}{x}, f(0) = 1,$

(c) $g(x) = \dfrac{\mathrm{Tan}^{-1} x}{x}$ $(0 < |x| < \tfrac{1}{2}\pi), g(0) = 1.$

(ii) Find the sums of the following series:

(a) $\displaystyle\sum_{n=1}^{\infty} \left(-\frac{1}{n3^n}\right)$, (b) $\displaystyle\sum_{n=1}^{\infty} \frac{(-1)^n}{2n+1}$, (c) $\displaystyle\sum_{n=1}^{\infty} \frac{1}{3^n(n+1)!}$

(π and values of the logarithmic and exponential functions need not be evaluated).

16.30 Calculate the first three terms of the Taylor series expansion of $f(x) = \cos x$ in powers of $(x - \tfrac{1}{3}\pi)$. Write down the truncation error as an integral when these three terms are used to calculate $\cos 61°$.

16.31 Find the limits as $x \to 3/2$ of

(a) $\dfrac{4x^3 - 7x - 3}{2x^2 + 3x - 9}$, (b) $\dfrac{\sqrt{(2x+4)} - \sqrt{7}}{4x^2 - 9}.$

16.32 Obtain the Fourier series expansion of the function

$$f(x) = (x + 2\pi)^2 \quad (-\pi < x < 0), f(x) = x^2 \quad (0 < x < \pi).$$

What is the sum of the series at $x = 0$?

16.33 Obtain the Fourier series expansion of the function

$$f(x) = 0 \quad (-\pi < x < 0), f(x) = x \quad (0 < x < \pi).$$

What is the sum of the series at $x = \pi$?

16.34 Find the Fourier sine series with sum $\cos x$ for $0 < x < \pi$. What is the sum of the series for $-\pi < x < 0$?

16.35 Find the Fourier cosine series with sum $(\tfrac{1}{2}\pi - x)$ for $0 < x < \pi$. What is the sum of the series for $-\pi < x < 0$?

16.36 Find the Fourier sine series with sum $(\tfrac{1}{2}\pi - \tfrac{1}{2}x)$ for $0 < x < \pi$. Show in a diagram the sum function $S(x)$ for $-3\pi \leqslant x \leqslant 3\pi$.

16.37 Assume that the solution of the linear differential equation

$$x\frac{dy}{dx} - y = x^2$$

has a power series expansion $y = \sum_{k=0}^{\infty} a_k x^k$. By substituting this into the differential equation, show that $a_k = 0$ unless $k = 1$ or 2, and find the value of a_2. (Note: a_1 is undetermined, and is the arbitrary constant in the solution).

16.38 By substituting an assumed series expansion $y = \sum_{k=0}^{\infty} a_k x^k$ into $dy/dx = y + 2xy + e^x$, and using the series for e^x, express a_1, a_2 and a_3 in terms of a_0. Check the results by differentiating the equation twice and using the Maclaurin formula (16.10).

Does this procedure give a method for solving the differential equation?

Table of Power Series

Binomial series (radius of convergence 1)

S1 $(1+x)^\lambda = 1 + \lambda x + \dfrac{\lambda(\lambda-1)}{2} x^2 + \dfrac{\lambda(\lambda-1)(\lambda-2)}{6} x^3 + \cdots$

$\qquad + \dfrac{\lambda(\lambda-1)\cdots(\lambda-n+1)}{n!} x^n + \cdots.$

Special Cases of S1

S2 $(1+x)^{-1} = 1 - x + x^2 - x^3 + \cdots + (-)^n x^n + \cdots$

S3 $(1+x)^{-2} = 1 - 2x + 3x^2 - 4x^3 + \cdots + (-)^n (n+1) x^n + \cdots$

S4 $(1+x)^{-3} = 1 - 3x + 6x^2 - 10x^3 + \cdots + (-)^n \tfrac{1}{2}(n+1)(n+2) x^n + \cdots$

S5 $(1+x)^{-4} = 1 - 4x + 10x^2 - 20x^3 + \cdots + (-)^n \tfrac{1}{6}(n+1)(n+2)(n+3) x^n + \cdots$

S6 $(1+x)^{-1/2} = 1 - \tfrac{1}{2}x + \dfrac{1\cdot 3}{2\cdot 4} x^2 - \dfrac{1\cdot 3\cdot 5}{2\cdot 4\cdot 6} x^3 + \dfrac{1\cdot 3\cdot 5\cdot 7}{2\cdot 4\cdot 6\cdot 8} x^4 - \cdots$

The general result S1 also gives

S7 $\dfrac{1}{(1+x)^\lambda} = 1 - \lambda x + \dfrac{\lambda(\lambda+1)}{2!} x^2 - \dfrac{\lambda(\lambda+1)(\lambda+2)}{3!} x^3 + \cdots$

$\qquad + (-)^n \dfrac{\lambda(\lambda+1)\cdots(\lambda+n-1)}{n!} x^n + \cdots.$

Logarithmic-type series (radius of convergence 1)

S8 $\log(1+x) = x - \dfrac{x^2}{2} + \dfrac{x^3}{3} - \cdots + (-)^{n-1}\dfrac{x^n}{n} + \cdots$

S9 $\tanh^{-1} x = \tfrac{1}{2}\log\left(\dfrac{1+x}{1-x}\right) = x + \dfrac{x^3}{3} + \dfrac{x^5}{5} + \cdots + \dfrac{x^{2n+1}}{2n+1} + \cdots$

S10 $\operatorname{Tan}^{-1} x = x - \dfrac{x^3}{3} + \dfrac{x^5}{5} - \cdots + (-)^n \dfrac{x^{2n+1}}{2n+1} + \cdots$

S11 $\sinh^{-1} x = \ln\{x + \sqrt{(1+x^2)}\} = x - \dfrac{1}{2}\dfrac{x^3}{3} + \dfrac{1\cdot 3}{2\cdot 4}\dfrac{x^5}{5} - \dfrac{1\cdot 3\cdot 5}{2\cdot 4\cdot 6}\dfrac{x^7}{7} + \cdots$

S12 $\sin^{-1} x = x + \dfrac{1}{2}\dfrac{x^3}{3} + \dfrac{1 \cdot 3}{2 \cdot 4}\dfrac{x^5}{5} + \cdots$

Exponential-type series (converge for all x)

S13 $e^x = 1 + x + \dfrac{x^2}{2} + \dfrac{x^3}{6} + \cdots + \dfrac{x^n}{n!} + \cdots$

S14 $\sinh x = x + \dfrac{x^3}{6} + \dfrac{x^5}{120} + \cdots + \dfrac{x^{2n+1}}{(2n+1)!} + \cdots$

S15 $\sin x = x - \dfrac{x^3}{6} + \dfrac{x^5}{120} - \cdots + \dfrac{(-)^n x^{2n+1}}{(2n+1)!} + \cdots$

S16 $\cosh x = 1 + \dfrac{x^2}{2} + \dfrac{x^4}{24} + \cdots + \dfrac{x^{2n}}{(2n)!} + \cdots$

S17 $\cos x = 1 - \dfrac{x^2}{2} + \dfrac{x^4}{24} - \cdots + (-)^n \dfrac{x^{2n}}{(2n)!} + \cdots$

S18 (**Bessel function** of order p)

$$J_p(x) = \frac{(\frac{1}{2}x)^p}{p!} - \frac{(\frac{1}{2}x)^{p+2}}{(p+1)!} + \frac{(\frac{1}{2}x)^{p+4}}{2(p+2)!} - \frac{(\frac{1}{2}x)^{p+6}}{3!(p+3)!} + \cdots$$

$$+ \frac{(-)^n (\frac{1}{2}x)^{p+2n}}{n!(p+n)!} + \cdots .$$

Series with no formula for the general term

S19 $\tan x = x + \frac{1}{3}x^3 + \frac{2}{15}x^5 + \frac{17}{315}x^7 + \frac{62}{2835}x^9 + \cdots \qquad (|x| < \frac{1}{2}\pi)$

S20 $\sec x = 1 + \frac{1}{2}x^2 + \frac{5}{24}x^4 + \frac{61}{720}x^6 + \frac{277}{8064}x^8 + \cdots \qquad (|x| < \frac{1}{2}\pi)$

Taylor's Series

$$F(x) = \sum_{n=0}^{\infty} \frac{F^{(n)}(a)}{n!}(x - a)^n$$

provided the nth derivative $F^{(n)}$ exists, in some neighbourhood of a, for every value of n. Alternatively

$$F(a + h) = \sum_{n=0}^{\infty} \frac{F^{(n)}(a)}{n!} h^n.$$

17

Linear Algebra

17.1 Geometrical Classification of Linear Equations

This chapter will discuss various topics which arise on considering the solution of the equations

$$a_{11}x_1 + a_{12}x_2 + a_{13}x_3 + \cdots + a_{1n}x_n = k_1$$
$$a_{21}x_1 + a_{22}x_2 + a_{23}x_3 + \cdots + a_{2n}x_n = k_2 \qquad (17.1)$$
$$\vdots \qquad\qquad \vdots \qquad\qquad \vdots \quad \vdots$$
$$a_{m1}x_1 + a_{m2}x_2 + a_{m3}x_3 + \cdots + a_{mn}x_n = k_m$$

i.e.

$$\sum_{j=1}^{n} a_{ij}x_j = k_i \qquad (i = 1, 2, \ldots, m).$$

There are m equations for the n unknowns x_i. They are **linear** because no term is higher than first degree in the unknowns.

Example 17.10·
The equations

$$2x + 3y = 5$$

$$xy + 2y = 1$$

are not linear because the xy term is **second** degree in the unknowns. □

When there are three unknowns, a geometrical interpretation may be obtained by considering (x_1, x_2, x_3) as Cartesian coordinates of a point in space. In this section this will be used to illustrate various possibilities which occur in the solution of linear equations.
If $m = 1$ and $n = 3$ there is just one equation:

$$a_{11}x_1 + a_{12}x_2 + a_{13}x_3 = k_1. \qquad (17.2)$$

This equation represents a plane; it is equation (2.4) on p. 25 in a different notation. If (x_1, x_2, x_3) is any point of the plane, then the numbers x_1, x_2, x_3 satisfy equation (17.2). Hence there are many solutions to 1 equation in 3 unknowns.
If $m = 2$ and $n = 3$ there are two equations:

$$a_{11}x_1 + a_{12}x_2 + a_{13}x_3 = k_1 \qquad (17.3)$$

$$a_{21}x_1 + a_{22}x_2 + a_{23}x_3 = k_2 \qquad (17.4)$$

and equations (17.3) and (17.4) each represent a plane. The numbers x_1, x_2 and x_3 satisfy both equations if the point (x_1, x_2, x_3) lies on both planes. In other words all points of the intersection of the planes provide solutions to the equations. The three geometrical possibilities were given on p. 29 at the end of Section 2.3: two planes intersect in a line unless they are parallel or identical. If they are parallel, then equations (17.3) and (17.4) have no solution; otherwise there are many solutions—corresponding to every point of a line or plane.

As discussed in Section 2.3, the three cases may be distinguished by inspection of the equations. This is not important here, because it does not extend to more equations and/or more unknowns, and general methods are required. However it is clear that, at least for some m and n, equations (17.1) may have either **no solution** or **many solutions**, depending on the coefficients.

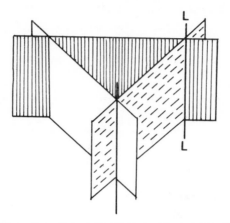

Figure 17.1   Three planes with no common point

If $m = n = 3$, there are 3 equations representing 3 planes, and the numbers x_1, x_2 and x_3 satisfy all three equations if the point (x_1, x_2, x_3) lies on all three planes. Suppose the first two planes intersect in a line L. This line may be parallel to the third plane, so that the three planes form a triangular prism (Fig. 17.1; in the figures, the shaded planes intersect in L and the third plane is unshaded). There are then no points on all three planes, and the equations have no solution. The line may cut through the third plane at a single point P (Fig. 17.2), which is then the only point on all three planes. The equations then have a unique solution. Finally the line L may lie in the third plane (Fig. 17.3); this means that the three planes have a common line. Then every point of the line gives a solution of the equations. There are other geometrical possibilities involving parallel or identical planes, but enough has been said to show that

> 3 equations in 3 unknowns may have **no solution**, a **unique solution**, or **innumerable solutions**.

If $m = 4$ and $n = 3$ there are 4 equations representing 4 planes. There is no point on all 4 planes if 3 form a triangular prism as in Fig. 17.1. In Fig. 17.2 or 17.3, a fourth plane could pass through the common point P or the common line L. Thus there are the same possibilities—no solution, a unique solution, or innumerable solutions.

In the general case (17.1) the same possibilities will arise. Note that no case has appeared with a **finite** number of **different** solutions. The problem of solving the equations includes the question of how to distinguish these possibilities, and how to specify the

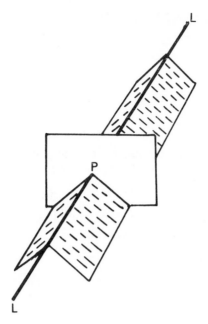

Figure 17.2   Three planes with common point P

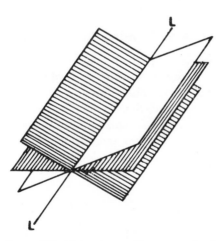

Figure 17.3   Three planes with common line L

solutions when there are many. It is also important that the process should involve as little computation as possible, even if a programmable calculating machine is available, because more arithmetic operations involve more rounding errors.

The way to specify many solutions is shown by the geometrical interpretation in the case where the solutions correspond to the points of a line. Then the parametric equations of the line give all the solutions by allowing the parameter to take all values. In most cases (see p. 41, Exercise 2.20) the equations of the line can be arranged so that any one of x_1, x_2, x_3 is set equal to the parameter.

Example 17.11 (cf. Example 2.32 on p. 28)
The solution of

$$x_1 + x_2 + x_3 = 5 \tag{17.5}$$

$$4x_1 + x_2 + 2x_3 = 15 \tag{17.6}$$

may be written

$$x_1 = 3 + t, \qquad x_2 = 1 + 2t, \qquad x_3 = 1 - 3t$$

where t is arbitrary. (These are the parametric equations of the line found in Example 2.32.) Changing the parameter to $s = 1 - 3t$, so that $t = (1 - s)/3$, gives

$$x_1 = \tfrac{10}{3} - \tfrac{1}{3}s, \; x_2 = \tfrac{5}{3} - \tfrac{2}{3}s, \; x_3 = s \quad (s \text{ arbitrary}).$$

Check: on substituting into equations (17.5) and (17.6), the equations are satisfied for any value of s (the terms containing s cancel).   □

Exercises (answer on p. 467)
17.1.1 By considering lines in a plane as a geometrical interpretation, draw diagrams which show that 3 linear equations in 2 unknowns may have no solution, a unique solution, or an infinity of solutions.
17.1.2 For three plane equations, list the geometrical possibilities involving parallel or coincident planes, and state the corresponding possibilities for the solution of 3 linear equations in 3 unknowns.

17.2   Solution by Gaussian Elimination

Solving simultaneous equations by eliminating unknowns is probably a familiar process, but a systematic method is necessary in order to distinguish whether equations have a unique solution, many solutions, or no solution. It is sufficient to use an abbreviated notation which shows only the coefficients a_{ij} and the constants k_i in equations (17.1).

In the first example to follow, the full equations are written out line by line on the left, and the abbreviated notation representing these equations on the right.

Example 17.20
Solve

$$3x_2 - 4x_3 = 2$$
$$4x_1 + 26x_2 \qquad = 40$$
$$x_1 + \quad x_2 + 7x_3 = 6$$

Abbreviated notation

$$\begin{array}{ccc|c} 0 & 3 & -4 & 2 \\ 4 & 26 & 0 & 40 \\ 1 & 1 & 7 & 6 \end{array}$$

Step 1: make first equation contain first unknown with coefficient $\neq 0$. Since the given first equation does not contain x_1, this requires **interchanging equations**, say the first and third:

$$x_1 + \quad x_2 + 7x_3 = 6$$
$$4x_1 + 26x_2 \qquad = 40$$
$$3x_2 - 4x_3 = 2$$

$$\begin{array}{ccc|c} 1 & 1 & 7 & 6 \\ 4 & 26 & 0 & 40 \\ 0 & 3 & -4 & 2 \end{array}$$

In the abbreviated notation, row R_i represents the ith equation, and the operations used on equations are operations on the rows of the array. Thus we can write $R_1 \leftrightarrow R_3$ to denote the above interchange.

Step 2: Eliminate first unknown from all equations after the first by adding (or subtracting) multiples of the first. This requires subtracting 4 times the first equation from the second:

$$x_1 + x_2 + 7x_3 = 6 \qquad \begin{array}{ccc|c} 1 & 1 & 7 & 6 \\ \end{array}$$
$$22x_2 - 28x_3 = 16 \qquad \begin{array}{ccc|c} 0 & 22 & -28 & 16 \\ \end{array} \quad (R_2 - 4R_1)$$
$$3x_2 - 4x_3 = 2 \qquad \begin{array}{ccc|c} 0 & 3 & -4 & 2 \\ \end{array}$$

This operation can be denoted by $(R_2 - 4R_1)$. After this elimination of the first unknown, the first equation is not used again for eliminations. The two steps are now repeated, with second replacing first; make second equation contain second unknown with coefficient $\neq 0$, and eliminate second unknown from all subsequent equations:

$$x_1 + x_2 + 7x_3 = 6 \qquad \begin{array}{ccc|c} 1 & 1 & 7 & 6 \\ \end{array}$$
$$22x_2 - 28x_3 = 16 \qquad \begin{array}{ccc|c} 0 & 22 & -28 & 16 \\ \end{array}$$
$$-(2/11)x_3 = -2/11 \qquad \begin{array}{ccc|c} 0 & 0 & -2/11 & -2/11 \\ \end{array} \quad (R_3 - (3/22)R_2)$$

The operation used can be denoted by $(R_3 - (3/22)R_2)$. The equations are now in **triangular form**: all numbers below the diagonal of the array of coefficients are zero. (If there were more equations, the two steps would be repeated, with third replacing second, etc., until this form was obtained.) From the triangular form, the solution can be read off, starting from the last equation and working up (at this stage, it may be helpful to use the full equations):

$$x_3 = 1, \qquad x_2 = (16 + 28)/22 = 2, \qquad x_1 = 6 - 2 - 7 = -3.$$

Check: substitute $x_1 = -3$, $x_2 = 2$, $x_3 = 1$ in the *given* equations. □

Example 17.21

$$2x + y + 3z = 1$$
$$x + 2z = 1$$
$$-x + 2y - 4z = \alpha \quad \text{where } \alpha \text{ is a known constant.}$$

$$\begin{array}{ccc|c} 2 & 1 & 3 & 1 \\ 1 & 0 & 2 & 1 \\ -1 & 2 & -4 & \alpha \end{array} \quad \begin{array}{l} \\ (R_2 - \tfrac{1}{2}R_1) \\ (R_3 + \tfrac{1}{2}R_1) \end{array} \quad \to \quad \begin{array}{ccc|c} 2 & 1 & 3 & 1 \\ 0 & -0.5 & 0.5 & 0.5 \\ 0 & 2.5 & -2.5 & \alpha + 0.5 \end{array}$$

$$\begin{array}{ccc|c} 2 & 1 & 3 & 1 \\ 0 & -0.5 & 0.5 & 0.5 \\ 0 & 0 & 0 & \alpha + 3 \end{array} \quad (R_3 + 5R_2)$$

(triangular form)

In the triangular form, the last equation reads $0x + 0y + 0z = \alpha + 3$, which is impossible unless $\alpha = -3$. Thus the given equations are **inconsistent** and have **no solution** if $\alpha \neq -3$.

In the previous example, the last equation in the triangular form determined the value of the last unknown x_3. If $\alpha = -3$ in this example, the last equation of the triangular form reads $0z = 0$, which is true for any value of z. Example 17.11 showed how to present the general solution in this situation. Put $z = s$, where the value of the parameter s is arbitrary, and then use the other equations of the triangular form to determine x and y in terms of s:

$$y = z - 1 = s - 1, \qquad x = -\tfrac{1}{2}y - \tfrac{3}{2}z + \tfrac{1}{2} = -2s + 1.$$

The solution is $x = 1 - 2s$, $y = -1 + s$, $z = s$ (s arbitrary).

Check: on substituting into the given equations, they are satisfied for any value of s.

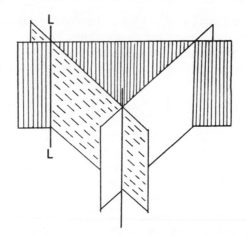

Figure 17.4   Third plane parallel to L

The geometrical interpretation of this example is seen in Fig. 17.4. The equations represent three planes, no two of which are parallel, by inspection (of the normals). For $\alpha \neq -3$, the planes are as in Fig. 17.4, with no common point. When the value of α is changed, the third plane becomes a parallel plane, as the normal is unaltered. In Fig. 17.4 there is obviously just one plane parallel to the third plane which contains the line of intersection L of the other two. Thus a solution with an arbitrary parameter (a line of solutions) is expected for just one value of α, as found algebraically.   □

Example 17.22

$$
\begin{array}{rrr|r}
1 & -2 & 3 & -2 \\
3 & -6 & 1 & -14 \\
-2 & 4 & -4 & 6
\end{array}
\quad
\begin{array}{c}
 \\
(R_2 - 3R_1) \\
(R_3 + 2R_1)
\end{array}
\quad \rightarrow \quad
\begin{array}{rrr|r}
1 & -2 & 3 & -2 \\
0 & 0 & -8 & -8 \\
0 & 0 & 2 & 2
\end{array}
$$

(triangular form)

The last equation gives $x_3 = 1$. Then the second equation reduces to $0x_2 = 0$, showing that x_2 is arbitrary, say $x_2 = s$. The first equation gives $x_1 = 2x_2 - 3x_3 - 2 = 2s - 5$, so the general solution is

$$x_1 = 2s - 5, \qquad x_2 = s, \qquad x_3 = 1 \quad (s \text{ arbitrary}).$$

Check: substitute into the given equations, which should be satisfied for any value of s.   □

Example 17.23
Find the value of β for which

$$v - w - y - z = 1$$
$$w - x + 2y + z = 1$$
$$-2v - w + x + z = 1$$
$$-v + x + y + z = 1$$
$$v - 2w - x - 3y - 2z = \beta$$

are consistent, and give the general solution for this value of β.

Consistent means that the equations have a solution. This is just like Example 17.21 but with 5 equations in 5 unknowns.

Starting from

$$\begin{array}{ccccc|c} 1 & -1 & 0 & -1 & -1 & 1 \\ 0 & 1 & -1 & 2 & 1 & 1 \\ -2 & -1 & 1 & 0 & 1 & 1 \\ -1 & 0 & 1 & 1 & 1 & 1 \\ 1 & -2 & -1 & -3 & -2 & \beta \end{array}$$

the operations
(i) $R_3 + 2R_1$, $R_4 + R_1$, $R_5 - R_1$
(ii) $R_3 + 3R_2$, $R_4 + R_2$, $R_5 + R_2$
(iii) $R_5 - R_3$
(iv) $R_5 + 2R_4$
produce the triangular form

$$\begin{array}{ccccc|c} 1 & -1 & 0 & -1 & -1 & 1 \\ & 1 & -1 & 2 & 1 & 1 \\ & & -2 & 4 & 2 & 6 \\ & & & 2 & 1 & 3 \\ & & & & 0 & \beta \end{array}$$

(zeros below the diagonal are omitted without confusion).
The equations are consistent only if $\beta = 0$, and then the general solution is

$$z = t, \quad y = \tfrac{3}{2} - \tfrac{1}{2}t, \quad x = 0, \quad w = -2, \quad v = \tfrac{1}{2}t + \tfrac{1}{2} \quad (t \text{ arbitrary}).$$

Note that checking the given fifth equation also checks that $\beta = 0$ is the value for consistency. □

Example 17.24 (cf. Example 17.11)

$$\begin{array}{cc|c} 1 & 1 & 1 & 5 \\ 4 & 1 & 2 & 15 \end{array} \quad \xrightarrow{(R_2 - 4R_1)} \quad \begin{array}{ccc|c} 1 & 1 & 1 & 5 \\ 0 & -3 & -2 & -5 \end{array}$$

$$x_3 = s \text{ (arbitrary)}, \qquad -3x_2 = 2s - 5, \qquad x_2 = -\tfrac{2}{3}s + \tfrac{5}{3}$$

$$x_1 = -x_2 - x_3 + 5 = -\tfrac{1}{3}s + \tfrac{10}{3}. \quad \square$$

When the number of equations is less than the number of unknowns, the last equation in the 'triangular form' always allows one of the unknowns to be given an arbitrary value.

Thus m linear equations in n unknowns cannot have a unique solution if $m < n$.

Example 17.25

Find the value of α for which

$$x - 2y = 5, \qquad 3y - z = -6, \qquad y + z = \alpha, \qquad 2x + 3y = 10$$

are consistent, and give the general solution when it exists.

$$
\begin{array}{ccc|c}
1 & -2 & 0 & 5 \\
0 & 3 & -1 & -6 \\
0 & 1 & 1 & \alpha \\
2 & 3 & 0 & 10
\end{array}
\quad
\begin{array}{c}
\\ \\ \\ (R_4 - 2R_1)
\end{array}
\rightarrow
\begin{array}{ccc|c}
1 & -2 & 0 & 5 \\
0 & 3 & -1 & -6 \\
0 & 1 & 1 & \alpha \\
0 & 7 & 0 & 0
\end{array}
$$

$$
\begin{array}{c}
\\ \\ (R_3 - R_2/3) \\ (R_4 - \tfrac{7}{3}R_2)
\end{array}
\begin{array}{ccc|c}
1 & -2 & 0 & 5 \\
0 & 3 & -1 & -6 \\
0 & 0 & 4/3 & \alpha + 2 \\
0 & 0 & 7/3 & 14
\end{array}
$$

The fourth equation $\frac{7}{3}z = 14$ gives $z = 6$, which is consistent with the third equation $\frac{4}{3}z = \alpha + 2$ only if $\alpha = 8 - 2 = 6$. The solution is then unique: $y = 0$ from the second equation (of the triangular form), and $x = 5$ from the first equation.

Check: substitute $x = 5$, $y = 0$, $z = 6$ into the *given* equations.

In the above work, the last form obtained was not quite a triangular form, although it allowed the necessary results to be obtained. The further operation $(R_4 - \frac{7}{4}R_3)$ reduces the last row to

$$0 \quad 0 \quad 0 \mid (42 - 7\alpha)/4, \quad \text{completing the reduction}$$

to triangular form, which makes obvious the consistency requirement $\alpha = 6$. $\square$

Back substitution from the triangular form is avoided in **Gauss–Jordan elimination** which makes the coefficients above the diagonal zero as well as those below. This is possible provided the triangular form has no zeros on the diagonal, i.e. the solution is unique.

Example 17.26 (cf. previous example)

$$
\begin{array}{ccc|c}
1 & -2 & 0 & 5 \\
0 & 3 & -1 & -6 \\
0 & 1 & 1 & 6
\end{array}
\quad
\begin{array}{c}
(R_1 + 2R_2/3) \\ \rightarrow \\ (R_3 - R_2/3)
\end{array}
\begin{array}{ccc|c}
1 & 0 & -2/3 & 1 \\
0 & 3 & -1 & -6 \\
0 & 0 & 4/3 & 8
\end{array}
$$

$$
\begin{array}{c}
(R_1 + \frac{1}{2}R_3) \\ \downarrow (R_2 + 3R_3/4)
\end{array}
$$

$$
\begin{array}{ccc|c}
1 & 0 & 0 & 5 \\
0 & 1 & 0 & 0 \\
0 & 0 & 1 & 6
\end{array}
\quad
\begin{array}{c}
(\frac{1}{3}R_2) \\ \leftarrow \\ (\frac{3}{4}R_3)
\end{array}
\begin{array}{ccc|c}
1 & 0 & 0 & 5 \\
0 & 3 & 0 & 0 \\
0 & 0 & 4/3 & 8
\end{array}
$$

The final form is just a statement of the solution. $\square$

The final array produced by Gauss–Jordan elimination may be called **unit diagonal form**. This reduction involves more arithmetic operations than reduction to triangular form followed by back substitution.

Reduction to triangular form in the above examples involves using the number occurring on the diagonal of the matrix of coefficients to eliminate the unknown below the diagonal. For each elimination, the coefficient on the diagonal is called the **pivot**. During elimination, the row (i.e. equation) containing the pivot is divided by the pivot; for instance the operation $R_2/22$ appears in Example 17.20, and $R_2/3$ appears in Example 17.26. This means that it is impossible to proceed using a zero pivot, and a zero on the diagonal is removed by interchanging equations, as in the first step of Example 17.20.

A zero on the diagonal could also be removed by interchanging the order of the unknowns.

Example 17.27 (cf. Example 17.20)

$$
\left.\begin{array}{ccc|c}
0 & 3 & -4 & 2 \\
4 & 26 & 0 & 40 \\
1 & 1 & 7 & 6
\end{array}\right.
\rightarrow
\left.\begin{array}{ccc|c}
3 & 0 & -4 & 2 \\
26 & 4 & 0 & 40 \\
1 & 1 & 7 & 6
\end{array}\right.
$$

by interchanging (the positions of) x_1 and x_2. This operation on the columns of the matrix of coefficients can be denoted by $(C_1 \leftrightarrow C_2)$. □

The possible operations of interchanging rows or of interchanging columns allow any coefficient (in equations i to m) to be used for the ith pivot. This possibility may be used to minimize rounding error in the arithmetic.

An example of a computer program for solution by Gaussian elimination is given in Appendix C, based on Procedure B8 in Appendix B. On encountering a small pivot (or zero) this program simply stops and prints out the stage that has been reached. To complete the reduction to triangular form, the remaining array could be re-entered after a suitable interchange. Small pivots are best avoided owing to the likely increase in rounding error on dividing by the pivot, which would be equivalent to multiplying by a large number.

Exercises (check on p. 467)

17.2.1 Use Gaussian elimination to solve the following sets of equations:

(i) $2x + 4y + z = 5$
    $x + y + z = 6$
    $2x + 3y + z = 6$

(ii) $2x + 4y + z = 1$
    $3x + 5y = 1$
    $5x + 13y + 7z = 4$

(iii) $2x + 3y + 4z = 1$
    $5x + 6y + 7z = 2$
    $8x + 9y + 10z = 3$

(iv) $2x_1 + 3x_2 + 4x_3 = 1$
    $5x_1 + 6x_2 + 7x_3 = 2$

In each case interpret geometrically, and state whether reduction to unit diagonal form is possible.

17.2.2 By applying row operations to reduce the left side of the array

$$\begin{array}{ccc|cc} 1 & 1 & 1 & 5 & 4 \\ 1 & 2 & 3 & 11 & 9 \\ 3 & 1 & 4 & 13 & 17 \end{array}$$

to triangular form, solve the two sets of equations

$$\begin{array}{ll} x+ y+ z = 5 & x+ y+ z = 4 \\ x+2y+3z = 11 \quad \text{and} & x+2y+3z = 9 \\ 3x+ y+4z = 13 & 3x+ y+4z = 17. \end{array}$$

17.3   The Inverse of a Matrix

The general set (17.1) of linear equations can be written in the matrix form $Ax = k$, where the elements of the $m \times n$ matrix A are the coefficients a_{ij}, the column vector x contains the n unknowns x_j, and the column vector k contains the m constants k_i.

Example 17.30
The equations

$$x-2y = 5, \qquad 3y-z = -6, \qquad y+z = 6, \qquad 2x+3y = 10$$

can be written

$$\begin{bmatrix} 1 & -2 & 0 \\ 0 & 3 & -1 \\ 0 & 1 & 1 \\ 2 & 3 & 0 \end{bmatrix} \begin{bmatrix} x \\ y \\ z \end{bmatrix} = \begin{bmatrix} 5 \\ -6 \\ 6 \\ 10 \end{bmatrix} \quad (m=4, n=3) \quad \square$$

$$A(4\times 3) \quad x(3\times 1) \quad k(4\times 1)$$

For the rest of this section it will be assumed that $m = n$, and that the triangular form has no zeros on the diagonal, so that unit diagonal form may be obtained. The coefficient matrix of this form is just a unit matrix, and the reduction is equivalent to pre-multiplying the matrix form of the equations by a certain matrix called the inverse of A.

Example 17.31 (cf. Example 17.20)
Multiply each side of

$$\begin{bmatrix} 0 & 3 & -4 \\ 4 & 26 & 0 \\ 1 & 1 & 7 \end{bmatrix} \begin{bmatrix} x \\ y \\ z \end{bmatrix} = \begin{bmatrix} 2 \\ 40 \\ 6 \end{bmatrix} \quad \text{by } G = \tfrac{1}{4} \begin{bmatrix} 182 & -25 & 104 \\ -28 & 4 & -16 \\ -22 & 3 & -12 \end{bmatrix}.$$

$$\quad A \qquad\quad x \qquad k$$

Since

$$GA = \begin{bmatrix} 1 & 0 & 0 \\ 0 & 1 & 0 \\ 0 & 0 & 1 \end{bmatrix}$$

and

$$Gk = \begin{bmatrix} -3 \\ 2 \\ 1 \end{bmatrix},$$

this gives

$$\begin{bmatrix} 1 & 0 & 0 \\ 0 & 1 & 0 \\ 0 & 0 & 1 \end{bmatrix} \begin{bmatrix} x \\ y \\ z \end{bmatrix} = \begin{bmatrix} -3 \\ 2 \\ 1 \end{bmatrix} \quad \text{or} \quad x = -3, \qquad y = 2, \qquad z = 1.$$

The essential property of G is that $GA = I_3$, the 3×3 unit matrix. $\square$

In general, if A is a square matrix, then a matrix G is a **left-inverse** of A if $GA = I$, and a matrix H is a **right-inverse** of A if $AH = I$. Here I (the unit matrix), and G and H are of the same order as A.

Theorem: if a left-inverse and a right-inverse of A both exist, they are unique and equal.

Proof: Given $GA = I = AH$, then
(i) $G = GI = G(AH) = (GA)H = IH = H$
(ii) If G' is another left-inverse, then the same steps give $G' = H$, so $G' = G$.
When G and H both exist, then $G = H$ is written A^{-1} and called the **inverse** of A, so that

$$\boxed{A^{-1}A = AA^{-1} = I.} \tag{17.7}$$

Example 17.32
In Example 17.31 it is easy to verify that $AG = I_3$, i.e. that G is also a right-inverse. Then G is written A^{-1}, and is the inverse of A. $\square$

In general n equations in n unknowns $Ax = k$ can be solved as in Example 17.31 if A^{-1} is calculated (assuming A^{-1} exists). Premultiplying the equations by A^{-1} gives

$$x = A^{-1}k \tag{17.8}$$

since $A^{-1}Ax = Ix = x$. Equation (17.8) shows that the solution is unique.
The calculation of A^{-1} from A will now be illustrated using a general 3×3 matrix

$$A = \begin{bmatrix} a & b & c \\ d & e & f \\ g & h & k \end{bmatrix}.$$

Let

$$A^{-1} = \begin{bmatrix} r & u & x \\ s & v & y \\ t & w & z \end{bmatrix}.$$

Then

$$\begin{bmatrix} a & b & c \\ d & e & f \\ g & h & k \end{bmatrix}\begin{bmatrix} r & u & x \\ s & v & y \\ t & w & z \end{bmatrix} = \begin{bmatrix} 1 & 0 & 0 \\ 0 & 1 & 0 \\ 0 & 0 & 1 \end{bmatrix}, \tag{17.9}$$

since A^{-1} is a right-inverse.

In any product of 2 matrices, the first column of the product comes from the first column only of the right factor. In equation (17.9) the multiplication giving the first column of the product is

$$\begin{bmatrix} a & b & c \\ d & e & f \\ g & h & k \end{bmatrix}\begin{bmatrix} r \\ s \\ t \end{bmatrix} = \begin{bmatrix} 1 \\ 0 \\ 0 \end{bmatrix}.$$

Since A is given, this is a set of 3 equations for 3 unknowns r, s, t.

Similarly in equation (17.9) the multiplication giving the second column is

$$\begin{bmatrix} a & b & c \\ d & e & f \\ g & h & k \end{bmatrix}\begin{bmatrix} u \\ v \\ w \end{bmatrix} = \begin{bmatrix} 0 \\ 1 \\ 0 \end{bmatrix},$$

a set of 3 equations for the 3 unknowns u, v, w. From the third column in equation (17.9),

$$A\begin{bmatrix} x \\ y \\ z \end{bmatrix} = \begin{bmatrix} 0 \\ 0 \\ 1 \end{bmatrix}$$

are equations for x, y, and z.

Thus the inverse of a 3×3 matrix can be found by solving 3 sets of 3 simultaneous linear equations. Since the 3 sets have the same coefficient matrix A, the same operations reduce the 3 sets to unit diagonal form. This means that all 3 sets can be solved together, starting from

$$A|I = \begin{array}{ccc|ccc} a & b & c & 1 & 0 & 0 \\ d & e & f & 0 & 1 & 0 \\ g & h & k & 0 & 0 & 1 \\ (1) & (2) & (3) \end{array}$$

where column (i) contains the constants of the ith set ($i = 1, 2, 3$) (cf. Exercise 17.2.2).

When the reduction to unit diagonal form is complete, the solutions appear in place of the original column of constants (cf. Example 17.26). Thus the final array is

$$\begin{array}{ccc|ccc} 1 & 0 & 0 & r & u & x \\ 0 & 1 & 0 & s & v & y \\ 0 & 0 & 1 & t & w & z \end{array} = I|A^{-1}.$$

The reduction changes $A|I$ to $I|A^{-1}$.

Example 17.33
Find the inverse of

$$A = \begin{bmatrix} 1 & 2 & 2 \\ 3 & 0 & 3 \\ 2 & -1 & 2 \end{bmatrix}.$$

$$
\left[\begin{array}{rrr|rrr}
1 & 2 & 2 & 1 & 0 & 0 \\
3 & 0 & 3 & 0 & 1 & 0 \\
2 & -1 & 2 & 0 & 0 & 1
\end{array}\right]
\quad
\begin{array}{l}
\rightarrow \\
(R_2 - 3R_1) \\
(R_3 - 2R_1)
\end{array}
\quad
\left[\begin{array}{rrr|rrr}
1 & 2 & 2 & 1 & 0 & 0 \\
0 & -6 & -3 & -3 & 1 & 0 \\
0 & -5 & -2 & -2 & 0 & 1
\end{array}\right]
$$

$$\downarrow \quad (-R_2/6)$$

$$
\left[\begin{array}{rrr|rrr}
1 & 0 & 1 & 0 & \frac{1}{3} & 0 \\
0 & 1 & \frac{1}{2} & \frac{1}{2} & -\frac{1}{6} & 0 \\
0 & 0 & \frac{1}{2} & \frac{1}{2} & -\frac{5}{6} & 1
\end{array}\right]
\quad
\begin{array}{l}
(R_1 - 2R_2) \\
\leftarrow \\
(R_3 + 5R_2)
\end{array}
\quad
\left[\begin{array}{rrr|rrr}
1 & 2 & 2 & 1 & 0 & 0 \\
0 & 1 & \frac{1}{2} & \frac{1}{2} & -\frac{1}{6} & 0 \\
0 & -5 & -2 & -2 & 0 & 1
\end{array}\right]
$$

$$\downarrow \quad (2R_3)$$

$$
\left[\begin{array}{rrr|rrr}
1 & 0 & 1 & 0 & \frac{1}{3} & 0 \\
0 & 1 & \frac{1}{2} & \frac{1}{2} & -\frac{1}{6} & 0 \\
0 & 0 & 1 & 1 & -\frac{5}{3} & 2
\end{array}\right]
\quad
\begin{array}{l}
(R_1 - R_3) \\
(R_2 - \frac{1}{2}R_3) \\
\rightarrow
\end{array}
\quad
\left[\begin{array}{rrr|rrr}
1 & 0 & 0 & -1 & 2 & -2 \\
0 & 1 & 0 & 0 & \frac{2}{3} & -1 \\
0 & 0 & 1 & 1 & -\frac{5}{3} & 2
\end{array}\right] = I \,|\, A^{-1}.
$$

Check: verify that $A^{-1}A = I$, i.e. that the right-inverse found is also a left-inverse. In connection with the previous general discussion, note that the columns

$$
\begin{bmatrix} r \\ s \\ t \end{bmatrix} = \begin{bmatrix} -1 \\ 0 \\ 1 \end{bmatrix}, \quad
\begin{bmatrix} u \\ v \\ w \end{bmatrix} = \begin{bmatrix} 2 \\ \frac{2}{3} \\ -\frac{5}{3} \end{bmatrix}, \quad
\begin{bmatrix} x \\ y \\ z \end{bmatrix} = \begin{bmatrix} -2 \\ -1 \\ 2 \end{bmatrix}
$$

have been obtained as the solutions of

$$
A\begin{bmatrix} r \\ s \\ t \end{bmatrix} = \begin{bmatrix} 1 \\ 0 \\ 0 \end{bmatrix}, \quad
A\begin{bmatrix} u \\ v \\ w \end{bmatrix} = \begin{bmatrix} 0 \\ 1 \\ 0 \end{bmatrix}, \quad
A\begin{bmatrix} x \\ y \\ z \end{bmatrix} = \begin{bmatrix} 0 \\ 0 \\ 1 \end{bmatrix}. \quad \square
$$

Once the inverse has been calculated and checked, it may be used to solve any sets of linear equations $Ax = k$ with the same coefficient matrix A. This method is only more efficient than direct elimination if more than 3 sets of such equations (with different k) have to be solved. Rounding errors may require careful consideration, because (cf. Example 17.31) the elements of the inverse matrix may be an order of magnitude larger than the given coefficients.

However it is sometimes useful to be able to write down $x = A^{-1}k$ as a formal solution of $Ax = k$, and it is then important to know whether A^{-1} exists. The method just given for constructing A^{-1} shows that it exists when the triangular form of A has no zeros on the diagonal, so that unit diagonal form exists. Then the calculation produces a right-inverse $H: A\,|\,I \rightarrow I\,|\,H$. The operations used in the calculation convert A into I, and are equivalent to multiplying A on the left by a matrix G (see Exercise 17.7 for an example). Then $GA = I$, and G is a left-inverse. From the theorem proved above, $G = H$.

If the triangular form of A does have a zero on the diagonal, equations $Ax = k$ have either no solution or many solutions. So A^{-1} does not exist, because if it did then $Ax = k$ would have the unique solution $x = A^{-1}k$.

Exercise

17.3.1   Calculate A^{-1} for

$$A = \begin{bmatrix} 1 & 2 & -1 \\ 1 & 1 & 1 \\ 3 & 1 & 4 \end{bmatrix},$$

and verify that $AA^{-1} = A^{-1}A = I_3$.

17.4   Determinants and Homogeneous Equations

If all the constants k_i on the right sides of the equations (17.1) $(Ax = k)$ are zero, then the equations are **homogeneous**. There is then an obvious solution with all the unknowns zero. This is called the **trivial** solution, and usually homogeneous equations are only of interest when there is a different (non-trivial) solution. Whether this is so depends on the coefficients a_{ij}.

Example 17.40

(i) The only (i.e. unique) solution of

$$2x + y = 0, \qquad 3x + y = 0$$

is the trivial solution $x = y = 0$.

(ii) The general solution of

$$2x - y = 0, \qquad -4x + 2y = 0$$

is $x = s$, $y = 2s$ where s is arbitrary.   ☐

If $x = a$, $y = b$, $z = c, \ldots$ is a solution of a set of linear, homogeneous equations, then $x = sa$, $y = sb$, $z = sc, \ldots$ is also a solution for any s. Thus a non-trivial solution is never unique.

When the coefficients are given numbers, as in Example 17.40, the solution may be found as before by Gaussian elimination. If some of the coefficients are parameters with values not yet assigned, it is often necessary to find values which will give a non-trivial solution.

Example 17.41

The equations $2x - y = 0$, $\alpha x + 2y = 0$ (cf. Example 17.40 (ii)) have a non-trivial solution if (and only if) $\alpha = -4$.   ☐

With non-numerical coefficients, the operations needed to get triangular form become complicated, also giving different cases for special values of the parameters in order to avoid division by zero. The purpose of this section is to give an alternative method for finding the parameter values which allow homogeneous equations to have a non-trivial solution. This method assumes n equations in n unknowns, i.e. that the matrix of coefficients is square.

Consider first 2 equations:

$$ax + by = 0 \quad (*)$$

$$cx + dy = 0 \quad (**).$$

Then $d \times (*) - b \times (**)$ is $(ad - bc)x = 0$; if there is a non-trivial solution with $x \neq 0$, then $(ad - bc) = 0$. The same condition must hold if there is a non-trivial solution with $x = 0$, $y \neq 0$, because $a \times (**) - c \times (*)$ is $(ad - bc)y = 0$. Thus, unless $(ad - bc) = 0$, $(*)$ and $(**)$ only have the trivial solution.

Check: in Example 17.40, $(ad - bc)$ is -1 in (i) and 0 in (ii).

The number $(ad - bc)$ is called the **determinant** of the matrix $\begin{bmatrix} a & b \\ c & d \end{bmatrix}$.

The determinant is denoted by the symbol $\begin{vmatrix} a & b \\ c & d \end{vmatrix}$, and in connection with $(*)$ and $(**)$ is referred to as the determinant of the coefficients (meaning the determinant of the matrix of coefficients).

Unless the determinant of the coefficients is zero the homogeneous equations have only the trivial solution.

Next consider 3 equations:

$$a_1 x + b_1 y + c_1 z = 0 \quad (*)$$

$$a_2 x + b_2 y + c_2 z = 0 \quad (**)$$

$$a_3 x + b_3 y + c_3 z = 0 \quad (***)$$

$$c_3 \times (**) - c_2 \times (***) \quad \text{is} \quad (a_2 c_3 - c_2 a_3)x + (b_2 c_3 - c_2 b_3)y = 0 \quad (17.10)$$

$$b_3 \times (**) - b_2 \times (***) \quad \text{is} \quad (a_2 b_3 - b_2 a_3)x + (c_2 b_3 - b_2 c_3)z = 0. \quad (17.11)$$

If $(b_2 c_3 - b_3 c_2) \neq 0$, these two equations can be used to express y and z in $(*)$ in terms of x, giving $\Delta_3 x = 0$, where

$$\Delta_3 = [a_1(b_2 c_3 - c_2 b_3) - b_1(a_2 c_3 - c_2 a_3) + c_1(a_2 b_3 - b_2 a_3)]. \quad (17.12)$$

Suppose there is a non-trivial solution with $x \neq 0$. Then $\Delta_3 = 0$. If $b_2 c_3 - b_3 c_2 = 0$ and $x \neq 0$, then equation (17.10) gives $(a_2 c_3 - c_2 a_3) = 0$ and equation (17.11) gives $(a_2 b_3 - b_2 a_3) = 0$, so that again $\Delta_3 = 0$.

If there is a non-trivial solution with $x = 0$, then either y or z is non-zero, and the same condition $\Delta_3 = 0$ can be derived using $-a_3 \times (**) + a_2 \times (***)$,
i.e. $(a_2 b_3 - b_2 a_3)y + (a_2 c_3 - c_2 a_3)z = 0$.

The number Δ_3 is called the determinant of the matrix

$$A = \begin{bmatrix} a_1 & b_1 & c_1 \\ a_2 & b_2 & c_2 \\ a_3 & b_3 & c_3 \end{bmatrix},$$

and denoted by the symbol $|A|$ or by

$$\begin{vmatrix} a_1 & b_1 & c_1 \\ a_2 & b_2 & c_2 \\ a_3 & b_3 & c_3 \end{vmatrix}.$$

Three homogeneous equations in three unknowns only have the trivial solution unless the determinant of the coefficients is zero.

The **order of a determinant** is that of the corresponding matrix, i.e. Δ_3 is third order, and $\Delta_2 = \begin{vmatrix} a & b \\ c & d \end{vmatrix} = (ad - cb)$ is second order.

In equation (17.12), the terms in round brackets may be written as second order determinants, giving

$$\begin{vmatrix} a_1 & b_1 & c_1 \\ a_2 & b_2 & c_2 \\ a_3 & b_3 & c_3 \end{vmatrix} = a_1 \begin{vmatrix} b_2 & c_2 \\ b_3 & c_3 \end{vmatrix} - b_1 \begin{vmatrix} a_2 & c_2 \\ a_3 & c_3 \end{vmatrix} + c_1 \begin{vmatrix} a_2 & b_2 \\ a_3 & b_3 \end{vmatrix}. \tag{17.13}$$

Example 17.42

Find the value of α for which the planes

$$x + y + 2z = 0$$

$$2x + \alpha y - z = 0$$

$$3x - y + 4z = 0$$

have a common line.

For any α, the three planes have the origin $(0, 0, 0)$ as a common point, corresponding to the trivial solution of the homogeneous equations. Requiring a common line is the same as requiring a non-trivial solution. The condition is

$$0 = \begin{vmatrix} 1 & 1 & 2 \\ 2 & \alpha & -1 \\ 3 & -1 & 4 \end{vmatrix} = \begin{vmatrix} \alpha & -1 \\ -1 & 4 \end{vmatrix} - \begin{vmatrix} 2 & -1 \\ 3 & 4 \end{vmatrix} + 2 \begin{vmatrix} 2 & \alpha \\ 3 & -1 \end{vmatrix},$$

using equation (17.13)

$$= (4\alpha - 1) - (8 + 3) + 2(-2 - 3\alpha) = -2\alpha - 16.$$

The planes have a common line, i.e. the equations have a non-trivial solution, if $\alpha = -8$.

Check:

1	1	2	$\rightarrow$	1	1	1	$\rightarrow$	1	1	1
2	-8	-1	$(R_2 - 2R_1)$	0	-10	-5	$(-R_2/10)$	0	1	$\frac{1}{2}$
3	-1	4	$(R_3 - 3R_1)$	0	-4	-2	$(R_3 - 2R_2/5)$	0	0	0

showing that there is a solution with z arbitrary.

An alternative check is to re-arrange the order of the equations and/or unknowns, and then evaluate the determinant of the new coefficients. □

Similarly the condition for 4 homogeneous equations in 4 unknowns to have a non-trivial solution will be $\Delta_4 = 0$ where Δ_4 is a suitably defined expression in the coefficients called the determinant of the matrix of coefficients. The expression can be derived by eliminating unknowns as above. This derivation will not be given here, but the general form of the expression can be seen as follows: on eliminating one unknown from the last 2 equations, the coefficients are second order determinants as in equations (17.10) and (17.11); using the second equation to eliminate another unknown, its coefficients multiply these second order determinants (as in equation (17.12)), giving third order determinants; the final elimination multiplies the coefficients of the first equation by these third order determinants. The actual expression for a fourth order determinant must therefore involve products of numbers from the first row with third order determinants formed from numbers in the other rows.

The following rule for writing down equation (17.13) extends to determinants of any higher order:

$$\Delta = \sum_m (\pm mM),$$

where the m are the numbers in the first row of Δ, and M is the determinant (order one less) obtained by deleting the row and column in Δ containing m, and the signs are alternating.

The next case after Δ_3 is

$$\Delta_4 = \begin{vmatrix} a_1 & b_1 & c_1 & d_1 \\ a_2 & b_2 & c_2 & d_2 \\ a_3 & b_3 & c_3 & d_3 \\ a_4 & b_4 & c_4 & d_4 \end{vmatrix}$$

$$= a_1 \begin{vmatrix} b_2 & c_2 & d_2 \\ b_3 & c_3 & d_3 \\ b_4 & c_4 & d_4 \end{vmatrix} - b_1 \begin{vmatrix} a_2 & c_2 & d_2 \\ a_3 & c_3 & d_3 \\ a_4 & c_4 & d_4 \end{vmatrix} + c_1 \begin{vmatrix} a_2 & b_2 & d_2 \\ a_3 & b_3 & d_3 \\ a_4 & b_4 & d_4 \end{vmatrix} - d_1 \begin{vmatrix} a_2 & b_2 & c_2 \\ a_3 & b_3 & c_3 \\ a_4 & b_4 & c_4 \end{vmatrix} \qquad (17.14)$$

Exercises (answers on p. 468)

17.4.1 Find the values of λ for which the equations

$$(\lambda + 1)x + 3y + z = 0$$
$$2x + \lambda y - z = 0$$
$$x - 2y + 3z = 0$$

have non-trivial solutions.

17.4.2 Evaluate

$$\begin{vmatrix} 2 & 1 & -1 & -1 \\ 1 & 0 & 2 & 1 \\ 0 & 2 & 1 & 2 \\ 1 & 1 & 0 & 2 \end{vmatrix}.$$

17.5   Properties of Determinants

Equation (17.13) is usually called the expansion of Δ_3 on the first row, while

$$\Delta_3 = a_1 b_2 c_3 - a_1 c_2 b_3 - b_1 a_2 c_3 + b_1 c_2 a_3 + c_1 a_2 b_3 - c_1 b_2 a_3 \qquad (17.12)$$

may be called the full expansion of Δ_3. The full expansion of Δ_2 contains 2 terms; from equation (17.13), the full expansion of Δ_3 contains $3 \times 2 = 3!$ terms; from equation (17.14), the full expansion of Δ_4 contains $4 \times 3! = 4!$ terms; and in the general case the expansion of Δ_n on the first row contains n determinants of order $(n-1)$, so the full expansion contains $n \times (n-1)! = n!$ terms.

In equation (17.12), the 3! terms of Δ_3 are shown explicitly; each is a product of three elements of the array, one from each row and one from each column; and exactly half the terms are prefixed by a minus sign. These statements remain true for the $n!$ terms of the full expansion of Δ_n. Apart from the signs, the terms are precisely all the possible products of n elements of the array taking just one from each row and taking just one from each column. With a suitable rule for the signs, this allows a definition of a determinant which is symmetric with respect to rows and columns. This symmetry implies that **interchanging rows and columns does not change the value of a determinant (∗).**

Example 17.50
The previous example obtained

$$\begin{vmatrix} 1 & 1 & 2 \\ 2 & \alpha & -1 \\ 3 & -1 & 4 \end{vmatrix} = -2\alpha - 16.$$

Interchanging rows and columns gives

$$\begin{vmatrix} 1 & 2 & 3 \\ 1 & \alpha & -1 \\ 2 & -1 & 4 \end{vmatrix} = (4\alpha - 1) - 2(4+2) + 3(-1 - 2\alpha), \quad \text{using equation (17.13)}$$

$$= -2\alpha - 16. \quad \square$$

Example 17.51

$$\begin{vmatrix} a & b & d \\ 0 & c & e \\ 0 & 0 & f \end{vmatrix} = \begin{vmatrix} a & 0 & 0 \\ b & c & 0 \\ d & e & f \end{vmatrix} = a \begin{vmatrix} c & 0 \\ e & f \end{vmatrix} = acf.$$

Alternatively, consider forming a nonzero product taking just one element from each row and column of

$$\begin{vmatrix} a & b & d \\ 0 & c & e \\ 0 & 0 & f \end{vmatrix}.$$

This requires f from the last row, which also uses the last column. So c is the only nonzero possibility from the centre row, and similarly a is the only possibility from the first row, i.e. fca is the only nonzero product. $\square$

If two rows are interchanged, the same products will be obtained on choosing one element from each row, but consideration of the signs shows that **all terms change sign**.

Example 17.52
Interchanging the first two rows in

$$\begin{vmatrix} a_1 & b_1 & c_1 \\ a_2 & b_2 & c_2 \\ a_3 & b_3 & c_3 \end{vmatrix}$$

gives

$$\begin{vmatrix} a_2 & b_2 & c_2 \\ a_1 & b_1 & c_1 \\ a_3 & b_3 & c_3 \end{vmatrix} = a_2(b_1c_3 - c_1b_3) - b_2(a_1c_3 - c_1a_3) + c_2(a_1b_3 - b_1a_3),$$

from equation (17.13)

$$= -\Delta_3, \quad \text{by comparing with equation (17.12).} \quad \square$$

If two rows are the same, the value must be zero, because interchanging the two rows changes the sign, yet leaves the value unaltered.

Next consider adding a multiple of the second row to the first. For the third order case, $(R_1 + \lambda R_2)$ gives

$$\begin{vmatrix} a_1 + \lambda a_2 & b_1 + \lambda b_2 & c_1 + \lambda c_2 \\ a_2 & b_2 & c_2 \\ a_3 & b_3 & c_3 \end{vmatrix}$$

$$= (a_1 + \lambda a_2)\begin{vmatrix} b_2 & c_2 \\ b_3 & c_3 \end{vmatrix} - (b_1 + \lambda b_2)\begin{vmatrix} a_2 & c_2 \\ a_3 & c_3 \end{vmatrix} + (c_1 + \lambda c_2)\begin{vmatrix} a_2 & b_2 \\ a_3 & b_3 \end{vmatrix},$$

from equation (17.13)

$$= a_1\begin{vmatrix} b_2 & c_2 \\ b_3 & c_3 \end{vmatrix} - b_1\begin{vmatrix} a_2 & c_2 \\ a_3 & b_3 \end{vmatrix} + c_1\begin{vmatrix} a_2 & b_2 \\ a_3 & b_3 \end{vmatrix} + \lambda\left\{a_2\begin{vmatrix} b_2 & c_2 \\ b_3 & c_3 \end{vmatrix} - b_2\begin{vmatrix} a_2 & c_2 \\ a_3 & c_3 \end{vmatrix} + c_2\begin{vmatrix} a_2 & b_2 \\ a_3 & b_3 \end{vmatrix}\right\}$$

$$= \begin{vmatrix} a_1 & b_1 & c_1 \\ a_2 & b_2 & c_2 \\ a_3 & b_3 & c_3 \end{vmatrix} + \lambda.0$$

since the curly bracket is the expansion of

$$\begin{vmatrix} a_2 & b_2 & c_2 \\ a_2 & b_2 & c_2 \\ a_3 & b_3 & c_3 \end{vmatrix}$$

which has 2 identical rows. Hence Δ_3 is unaltered by adding a multiple of the second row to the first row. The given demonstration obviously extends to any order; and since any pair of rows can be put in the first two positions, with appropriate changes of sign, the value is unaltered by adding to any row a multiple of another row.

The expansion on the first row, such as equation (17.13) or (17.14), shows that multiplying the first row through by a number λ multiplies the value by λ. The result remains true for any other row, since it can be put in the first position to show the property. This allows factors to be removed from rows.

Example 17.53

$$\begin{vmatrix} 10101 & 20202 \\ 59 & 177 \end{vmatrix} = (10101)\begin{vmatrix} 1 & 2 \\ 59 & 177 \end{vmatrix} = (10101)(59)\begin{vmatrix} 1 & 2 \\ 1 & 3 \end{vmatrix} = 595959. \quad \square$$

Since the value of a determinant is unchanged when rows and columns are interchanged, the properties demonstrated above for rows must also hold for columns.

Summary

The value of a determinant is
  (i) unaltered by interchanging rows and columns;
 (ii) unaltered by adding a multiple of one row to another row, or by adding a multiple of one column to another column;
(iii) multiplied by (-1) on interchanging two rows, or interchanging two columns;
(iv) multiplied by λ on multiplying each element of a row (or column) by λ.

Exercises (answers on p. 468)
17.5.1 Given that

$$\begin{vmatrix} a & b & c \\ d & e & f \\ g & h & k \end{vmatrix} = 5,$$

write down the values of the following determinants:

(i) $\begin{vmatrix} a & d & g \\ b & e & h \\ c & f & k \end{vmatrix}$ (ii) $\begin{vmatrix} a & b+3c & c \\ d & e+3f & f \\ g & h+3k & k \end{vmatrix}$ (iii) $\begin{vmatrix} g & h & k \\ d & e & f \\ a & b & c \end{vmatrix}$

(iv) $\begin{vmatrix} d & g & a \\ e & h & b \\ f & k & c \end{vmatrix}$ (v) $\begin{vmatrix} a & b & c \\ 2d & 2e & 2f \\ -g & -h & -k \end{vmatrix}$ (vi) $\begin{vmatrix} a & 3b & 2c \\ 2d & 6e & 4f \\ g & 3h & 2k \end{vmatrix}$

(vii) $\begin{vmatrix} d & e & f \\ a & b & c \\ d & e & f \end{vmatrix}$ (viii) $\begin{vmatrix} 3a & 3b & 3c \\ 2d-a & 2e-b & 2f-c \\ -g+a & -h+b & -k+c \end{vmatrix}$

17.5.2 In Example 17.20 the array

$$\begin{array}{ccc} 0 & 3 & -4 \\ 4 & 26 & 0 \\ 1 & 1 & 7 \end{array}$$

is converted to triangular form by row operations. The effect of each row operation on the corresponding determinant is given in (ii)–(iv) of the above summary.

Consider the effect of each operation in Example 17.20 on the value of the determinant, and hence find the relation between

$$\begin{vmatrix} 0 & 3 & -4 \\ 4 & 26 & 0 \\ 1 & 1 & 7 \end{vmatrix} \quad \text{and} \quad \begin{vmatrix} 1 & 1 & 7 \\ 0 & 22 & -28 \\ 0 & 0 & -2/11 \end{vmatrix}.$$

17.5.3   Evaluate

$$\begin{vmatrix} 2 & 7 & -6 & 12 \\ 0 & -1 & 4 & -8 \\ 0 & 0 & 3 & 17 \\ 0 & 0 & 0 & 1 \end{vmatrix}$$

by interchanging rows and columns, and then using equation (17.14).

17.5.4   What is the value of a determinant which has all numbers in one row zero?

17.6 Applications of Determinants

The formulas (1.26) and (1.31) for the cross product of two vectors and the triple scalar product of three vectors were given on pages 14 and 17. Some other geometrical applications will be given in the exercises at the end of this chapter. The use of determinants to investigate the existence of solutions to homogeneous equations can be given various geometrical flavours, as indicated in Example 17.42. The next three examples concern plane geometry.

Example 17.60
Find the condition for 3 lines, say $a_i x + b_i y + c_i = 0$ ($i = 1, 2, 3$), to intersect in a point.

If the lines intersect at (X, Y), then the 3 equations

$$a_i x + b_i y + c_i = 0 \qquad (17.15)$$

have the simultaneous solution $x = X$, $y = Y$. The homogeneous equations

$$a_1 x + b_1 y + c_1 z = 0 \quad (*)$$
$$a_2 x + b_2 y + c_2 z = 0 \quad (**)$$
$$a_3 x + b_3 y + c_3 z = 0 \quad (***)$$

then have a non-trivial solution $x = X$, $y = Y$, $z = 1$. Hence

$$\begin{vmatrix} a_1 & b_1 & c_1 \\ a_2 & b_2 & c_2 \\ a_3 & b_3 & c_3 \end{vmatrix} = 0.$$

However this condition is not sufficient, because although it means the homogeneous equations have a non-trivial solution, this solution could have $z = 0$, and could not then lead to a solution of the three equations (17.15).   □

Example 17.61

Express the area of a triangle in terms of the Cartesian coordinates (x_i, y_i) of the vertices P_i.

(i) If $P_3(x_3, y_3)$ is the origin O (Fig. 17.5) then

$$\text{area } OP_1P_2 = OM_2P_2 + M_2P_2P_1M_1 - OP_1M_1$$

$$= \tfrac{1}{2}x_2y_2 + (x_1 - x_2)\tfrac{1}{2}(y_1 + y_2) - \tfrac{1}{2}x_1y_1$$

$$= \tfrac{1}{2}(x_1y_2 - x_2y_1) = \frac{1}{2}\begin{vmatrix} x_1 & x_2 \\ y_1 & y_2 \end{vmatrix}. \tag{17.16}$$

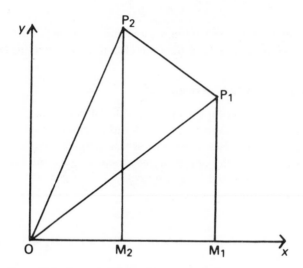

Figure 17.5   Area of triangle with vertices O, $P_1(x_1, y_1)$, $P_2(x_2, y_2)$

(ii) In the general case (Fig. 17.6),

$$\text{area } P_1P_2P_3 = OP_2P_3 - OP_1P_3 + OP_1P_2 = \frac{1}{2}\begin{vmatrix} x_2 & x_3 \\ y_2 & y_3 \end{vmatrix} - \frac{1}{2}\begin{vmatrix} x_1 & x_3 \\ y_1 & y_3 \end{vmatrix} + \frac{1}{2}\begin{vmatrix} x_1 & x_2 \\ y_1 & y_2 \end{vmatrix},$$

using equation (17.16);

$$\text{area } P_1P_2P_3 = \frac{1}{2}\begin{vmatrix} 1 & 1 & 1 \\ x_1 & x_2 & x_3 \\ y_1 & y_2 & y_3 \end{vmatrix}. \tag{17.17}$$

Alternatively, the construction in Fig. 17.5 can be used in the general case (Fig. 17.7). In Fig. 17.5, $x_i = OM_i$, $y_i = P_iM_i$, so equation (17.16) can be written

$$\frac{1}{2}\begin{vmatrix} OM_1 & OM_2 \\ P_1M_1 & P_2M_2 \end{vmatrix}.$$

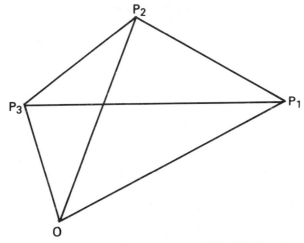

Figure 17.6   Area of general triangle $P_1P_2P_3$: P_i is (x_i, y_i)

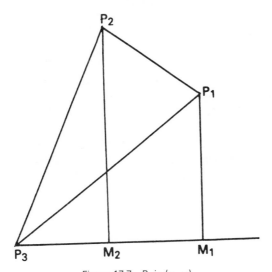

Figure 17.7 P_i is (x_i, y_i)

Since Figs 17.5 and 17.7 are the same geometrically,

$$\text{area } P_1P_2P_3 = \frac{1}{2}\begin{vmatrix} P_3M_1 & P_3M_2 \\ P_1M_1 & P_2M_2 \end{vmatrix} = \frac{1}{2}\begin{vmatrix} (x_1-x_3) & (x_2-x_3) \\ (y_1-y_3) & (y_2-y_3) \end{vmatrix}$$

$$= \frac{1}{2}\begin{vmatrix} 0 & 0 & 1 \\ x_1-x_3 & x_2-x_3 & x_3 \\ y_1-y_3 & y_2-y_3 & y_3 \end{vmatrix}$$

which becomes equation (17.17) on adding column 3 to column 1 and to column 2. Note that in Fig. 17.5, $x_1 = OM_1 > OM_2 = x_2$, and $y_2 = M_2P_2 > M_1P_1 = y_1$, so equation (17.16) has a positive value, as does equation (17.17). Interchanging columns of the determinants would change the sign, so the formulas give a positive value for the area when the points are taken in counter-clockwise order. □

Example 17.62
Show that the equation of the line through (x_1, y_1) and (x_2, y_2) is

$$\begin{vmatrix} x & y & 1 \\ x_1 & y_1 & 1 \\ x_2 & y_2 & 1 \end{vmatrix} = 0. \tag{17.18}$$

(i) By interchanging rows with columns, and then making two row interchanges, equation (17.18) may be written

$$\begin{vmatrix} 1 & 1 & 1 \\ x & x_1 & x_2 \\ y & y_1 & y_2 \end{vmatrix} = 0.$$

From equation (17.17), the area of the triangle formed by (x, y), (x_1, y_1) and (x_2, y_2) is zero. This means the three points are collinear. Thus any point (x, y) satisfying equation (17.18) lies on the line joining (x_1, y_1) and (x_2, y_2), i.e. (17.18) is the equation of this line.
(ii) A more elegant argument, which does not use the result of Example 17.61, is as follows. Expanding the determinant in equation (17.18) on the first row shows that (17.18) is first degree in x and y, i.e. is the equation of some line. Substituting either $(x, y) = (x_1, y_1)$ or $(x, y) = (x_2, y_2)$ satisfies the equation, because a determinant with 2 identical rows is zero. Thus the line represented by equation (17.18) is the one through (x_1, y_1) and (x_2, y_2). □

If n equations in n unknowns have a unique solution, then formulas for this solution can be given using determinants formed from the coefficients. Consider 3 equations in 3 unknowns, say

$$a_1 x + b_1 y + c_1 z = k_1$$
$$a_2 x + b_2 y + c_2 z = k_2 \tag{17.19}$$
$$a_3 x + b_3 y + c_3 z = k_3.$$

Then, assuming equations (17.19) have a solution,

$$\begin{vmatrix} k_1 & b_1 & c_1 \\ k_2 & b_2 & c_2 \\ k_3 & b_3 & c_3 \end{vmatrix} = \begin{vmatrix} a_1 x + b_1 y + c_1 z & b_1 & c_1 \\ a_2 x + b_2 y + c_2 z & b_2 & c_2 \\ a_3 x + b_3 y + c_3 z & b_3 & c_3 \end{vmatrix},$$

$$= \begin{vmatrix} a_1 x & b_1 & c_1 \\ a_2 x & b_2 & c_2 \\ a_3 x & b_3 & c_3 \end{vmatrix}$$

by adding to the first column $(-y)$ times the second, and $(-z)$ times the third,

$$= x \begin{vmatrix} a_1 & b_1 & c_1 \\ a_2 & b_2 & c_2 \\ a_3 & b_3 & c_3 \end{vmatrix},$$

removing a factor x from the first column.

$$\text{Provided } \Delta_3 = \begin{vmatrix} a_1 & b_1 & c_1 \\ a_2 & b_2 & c_2 \\ a_3 & b_3 & c_3 \end{vmatrix} \neq 0, \qquad x = \frac{\begin{vmatrix} k_1 & b_1 & c_1 \\ k_2 & b_2 & c_2 \\ k_3 & b_3 & c_3 \end{vmatrix}}{\Delta_3}.$$

(17.20)

Note that the determinant in the numerator is obtained from Δ_3 by replacing the coefficients of x, in the equations, by the constants on the right hand side. Similarly one can investigate the determinants obtained from Δ_3 when the constants k_i replace the b_i (coefficients of y) or the c_i (coefficients of z), and obtain

$$y = \frac{\begin{vmatrix} a_1 & k_1 & c_1 \\ a_2 & k_2 & c_2 \\ a_3 & k_3 & c_3 \end{vmatrix}}{\Delta_3}, \qquad z = \frac{\begin{vmatrix} a_1 & b_1 & k_1 \\ a_2 & b_2 & k_2 \\ a_3 & b_3 & k_3 \end{vmatrix}}{\Delta_3}.$$

(17.21)

The solution of equations (17.19) given by (17.20) and (17.21) is known as **Cramer's Rule**. The equations given here extend in an obvious way to n equations in n unknowns, using nth order determinants.

Cramer's rule is not used to solve linear equations when all the coefficients are known numbers, because the number of arithmetic operations increases exponentially with the number of equations. Gaussian elimination is therefore both quicker and less affected by rounding error. To solve 8 equations in 8 unknowns by Cramer's rule would require 986 399 arithmetic operations, compared to 428 using Gaussian elimination. (An average computer can solve several hundred equations by Gaussian elimination—the computer time required using Cramer's rule might exceed the age of the universe.) However Cramer's rule is used if it is desirable to write down an algebraic solution in which the values of the coefficients need not be known. In particular, it gives algebraic expressions for the elements of the inverse matrix (see Exercise 17.11).

The above derivation of Cramer's rule shows that **if the determinant of coefficients is not zero, then any solution is unique.** Hence **if there is a non-unique solution, the determinant of coefficients must be zero.** A special case (used above to introduce determinants) is when homogeneous equations have a non-trivial solution (which is never unique). The converse result will now be shown: **if there is a unique solution then the determinant of coefficients is not zero; if the determinant is zero, there is either no solution or many solutions.**

In Gaussian elimination, there is a unique solution if and only if the triangular form has no zeros on the diagonal. The determinant of a triangular form is just the product of the diagonal elements. (Note that the methods in Example 17.51 and Exercise 17.5.3

will extend to a triangular form of any order.) So there is a unique solution when the determinant of the triangular form is non-zero, and no solution or many solutions if the determinant of the triangular form is zero.

The summary at the end of the previous section shows how the row operations used in Gaussian elimination affect the value of the determinant (cf. Exercise 17.5.2). The value is changed by interchanging rows, or by multiplying a row by λ, but the operations cannot change the value from zero to nonzero, or vice-versa.

> So if the determinant of coefficients is non-zero, so is the determinant of the triangular form, and the solution is unique. If the determinant of coefficients is zero, so is that of the triangular form, and the equations are either inconsistent or the solution is not unique.

Example 17.63
Investigate the types of solution of the equations

$$x+ \quad y+2z = \beta$$

$$2x+\alpha y- \quad z = \gamma$$

$$3x- \quad y+4z = \delta$$

for different values of α, β, γ, and δ.

From Example 17.42, the determinant of coefficients is $(-2\alpha - 16)$. So, if $\alpha \neq -8$, the equations have a unique solution for any values of β, γ and δ.

For $\alpha = -8$, the operations to reduce to triangular form were given in the check to Example 17.42. This reduction gives

$$\begin{array}{ccc|c} 1 & 1 & 2 & \beta \\ 2 & -8 & -1 & \gamma \\ 3 & -1 & 4 & \delta \end{array} \rightarrow \begin{array}{ccc|c} 1 & 1 & 1 & \beta \\ 0 & 1 & \frac{1}{2} & (2\beta - \gamma)/10 \\ 0 & 0 & 0 & (-11\beta - 2\gamma + 5\delta)/5 \end{array}$$

The equations have no solution when $\alpha = -8$ and $11\beta + 2\gamma \neq 5\delta$. The solution is not unique when $\alpha = -8$ and $11\beta + 2\gamma = 5\delta$. □

> The fact that the determinant of the triangular form is zero if and only if the determinant of coefficients is zero also gives the **condition for the existence of an inverse A^{-1} of a square matrix A.**

(i) If the determinant $|A| \neq 0$, the triangular form has no zero on the diagonal, so unit diagonal form can be obtained, giving A^{-1} by the calculation $A|I \rightarrow I|A^{-1}$. Alternatively, the n sets of equations for the columns of A^{-1} all have unique solutions.

(ii) If $|A| = 0$, the triangular form has a zero on the diagonal, and the n sets of equations for the columns of A^{-1} could only all be consistent if there was a corresponding row of zeros on the right side:

$$A|I \rightarrow \begin{array}{ccccc} * & & & & \\ & * & & & \\ & & 0 & \ldots & \ldots \\ & & & * & \ldots \\ & & & & * \end{array} \left| \begin{array}{ccccc} \ldots & \ldots & \ldots & \ldots & \ldots \\ \ldots & \ldots & \ldots & \ldots & \ldots \\ 0 & 0 & 0 & \ldots & 0 \\ \ldots & \ldots & \ldots & \ldots & \ldots \\ \ldots & \ldots & \ldots & \ldots & \ldots \end{array} \right.$$

But then the determinant of the right array is zero (Exercise 17.5.4), which is impossible because the array is obtained from I which has determinant 1. Hence A^{-1} does not exist.

Note that when $|A| \neq 0$, the operations which change A to I change the determinant from $|A|$ to 1, i.e. multiply the determinant by $1/|A|$. The same operations change I to A^{-1}, with the same effect on the determinant, changing it from 1 to $1/|A|$. Thus

$$\boxed{|A^{-1}| = 1/|A|.}$$ (17.22)

Exercises (answers on p. 468)

17.6.1 Find the area of the triangle with vertices at

$$P_1(-3, -2), P_2(-1, 4), P_3(2, 2).$$

17.6.2 If

$$2x + y - z - w = 3$$

$$x + 2z + w = 1$$

$$2y + z + 2w = -1$$

$$x + y + 2w = 2,$$

use Cramer's rule to find z (cf. Exercise 17.4.2).

17.6.3 Derive the result of Example 17.60 by solving two of equations (17.15) using Cramer's rule, and substituting the result into the third equation.

17.6.4 The following statements refer to the system of linear equations $Ax = k$, where A is order $n \times n$, x and k are column vectors. Which of the statements are correct?

(i) If $|A| \neq 0$, there is a unique solution for any k.
(ii) If for some particular k there is a unique solution, then $|A| \neq 0$.
(iii) If there is a unique solution for any k, then $|A| \neq 0$.
(iv) If for some particular k there is no solution, then $|A| = 0$.
(v) If for some particular k there is more than one solution, then $|A| = 0$.
(vi) If for some particular k there is a unique solution, then there is a unique solution for any k.
(vii) If for some particular k there is no solution, there is no solution for any k.
(viii) If for some particular k there are many solutions, then there are many solutions for any k.

Answers (or checks) for Exercises 17.1.2–17.6.4

17.1.2

Geometric case	Solution of equations
3 coincident	Many solutions
2 coincident, third parallel	None
2 parallel, third distinct	None
2 coincident, third not parallel	Many solutions

17.2.1–2 Check by substituting into the given equations. Any arbitrary parameters in the solutions must cancel.

17.4.1 $\lambda = \pm 3.$ **17.4.2** $-20.$
17.5.1   (i)   5 (interchange rows and columns)
          (ii)   5 $(C_2 - 3C_3)$
          (iii) -5 $(R_1 \leftrightarrow R_3)$
          (iv)   5 $(C_1 \leftrightarrow C_2)$ and $(C_1 \leftrightarrow C_3)$
          (v) -10 (factors 2 from R_2, -1 from R_3)
          (vi)   60 (factors 2 from R_2, 3 from C_2, 2 from C_3)
          (vii)   0 $(R_1 = R_3)$
          (viii) -30 $(R_2 + \frac{1}{3}R_1, R_3 - \frac{1}{3}R_1,$ then factors 3 from R_1, 2 from R_2, -1 from R_3)
17.5.2 $R_1 \leftrightarrow R_3$ changes sign
          $R_2 - 4R_1$ does not change value
          $R_3 - (3/22)\ R_2$ does not change value

$$\text{Hence}\ \begin{vmatrix} 1 & 1 & 7 \\ 0 & 22 & -28 \\ 0 & 0 & -2/11 \end{vmatrix} = - \begin{vmatrix} 0 & 3 & -4 \\ 4 & 26 & 0 \\ 1 & 1 & 7 \end{vmatrix}$$

17.5.3. -6 (product of diagonal elements).   **17.5.4**   0.
17.6.1   11.   **17.6.2** $-3/5.$
17.6.4   (i)–(vi) correct; (vii), (viii) incorrect (cf. Examples 17.21, 17.23).

Further Exercises on Chapter 17

17.1   (i) Show that Example 2.40 on p. 30 gives a geometrical interpretation of Example 17.20.
     (ii) Show that the lines (1) and (4) in Example 2.50 on p. 32 give a geometrical interpretation of the consistent case $(\alpha = 6)$ of Example 17.25.
17.2   (i) Use Gaussian elimination (on 3 equations) to solve Exercise 2.8 (p. 40).
     (ii) Use Gaussian elimination (on 2 equations) to solve Exercise 2.9.
     (iii) Use Gaussian elimination on 2 equations (for s and u or for s and t) to solve Exercise 2.10 (i) and (iii).
     (iv) Use Gaussian elimination (on 4 equations) to solve Exercise 2.12.
17.3   Use Gaussian elimination to solve

(i) $2x + y + 3z + 5w = 6$ (ii) $3x + y - 2z - w = 2$

$\quad\ \ 3x + 2y + 4z + 6w = 8$ $\qquad 15x + 5y + 4z + 3w = 4$

$\ \ -x + 3y + 2z + 7w = -3$ $\qquad\ \ 6x + 2y + 3z + w = 0$

17.4   Find the value of β for which the equations

$$x + 4y - 2z + 3w = \beta$$
$$3x + 5y \qquad + 2w = 5$$
$$7y - 6z + 7w = 13$$

have a solution.

17.5   Find inverses for the following matrices:

(i) $\begin{bmatrix} 1 & 5 & 2 \\ 1 & 1 & 7 \\ 0 & -3 & 4 \end{bmatrix}$ (ii) $\begin{bmatrix} 1 & 2 & 0 & 0 \\ 4 & 9 & 0 & 0 \\ 0 & 0 & -3 & 1 \\ 0 & 0 & -8 & 3 \end{bmatrix}$

(iii) $\begin{bmatrix} 1 & 1 & 1 & 1 \\ 1 & 2 & 3 & 4 \\ 1 & 3 & 6 & 10 \\ 1 & 4 & 10 & 20 \end{bmatrix}$ (iv) $\begin{bmatrix} 1 & 0 & 1 & 0 \\ 0 & 1 & 0 & 1 \\ 0 & 0 & 1 & 1 \\ 2 & 1 & 2 & 2 \end{bmatrix}$ (v) $\begin{bmatrix} -1 & -1 & -1 & 1 \\ 2 & 2 & 0 & -1 \\ 2 & 1 & 1 & -1 \\ -2 & -1 & 0 & 1 \end{bmatrix}$.

17.6   The equations considered in Example 17.22 have coefficient matrix

$$A = \begin{bmatrix} 1 & -2 & 3 \\ 3 & -6 & 1 \\ -2 & 4 & -4 \end{bmatrix}$$

and have a non-unique solution. What can be said about $|A|$?
   Show that the equations

$$x - 2y + 3z = \alpha$$
$$3x - 6y + z = \beta$$
$$-2x + 4y - 4z = \gamma$$

are consistent only if $\beta + 4\gamma + 5\alpha = 0$, and that when this holds $z = \frac{1}{2}\gamma + \alpha$ in any solution.

17.7   (i) If

$$P = \begin{bmatrix} 0 & 0 & 1 \\ 0 & 1 & 0 \\ 1 & 0 & 0 \end{bmatrix},$$

write out the product PA for an arbitrary 3×3 matrix A, and compare the rows of A and PA.
   (ii) Repeat (i) with P replaced by

(a) $E = \begin{bmatrix} 1 & 0 & 0 \\ -4 & 1 & 0 \\ 0 & 0 & 1 \end{bmatrix}$ (b) $S = \begin{bmatrix} 1 & 0 & 0 \\ 0 & \frac{1}{22} & 0 \\ 0 & 0 & 1 \end{bmatrix}$ (c) $F = \begin{bmatrix} 1 & 0 & 0 \\ 0 & 1 & 0 \\ 0 & -3 & 1 \end{bmatrix}$.

   (iii) If

$$A = \begin{bmatrix} 0 & 3 & -4 \\ 4 & 26 & 0 \\ 1 & 1 & 7 \end{bmatrix}$$

(the coefficient matrix in Example 17.20), write down the matrices PA, EPA, $SEPA$, $FSEPA$.

(iv) Suppose

$$A = \begin{bmatrix} 1 & -2 & 0 \\ 0 & 3 & -1 \\ 0 & 1 & 1 \end{bmatrix},$$

the coefficient matrix in Example 17.26. By considering the reduction to unit diagonal form in Example 17.26, find matrices E, S and F such that

$$FSEA = I.$$

17.8   (i) If the planes $a_i x + b_i y + c_i z = 0$ $(i = 1, 2, 3)$ have a common line, what 3×3 determinant must be zero?

(ii) If the planes $a_i x + b_i y + c_i z + d_i = 0$ $(i = 1, 2, 3, 4)$ have a common point, what determinant must be zero?

17.9   If the two lines $(\alpha = 1, 2)$

$$r = r_\alpha + t_\alpha v_\alpha = x_\alpha i + y_\alpha j + z_\alpha k + t_\alpha (l_\alpha i + m_\alpha j + n_\alpha k)$$

intersect in a point, deduce that the scalar triple product of $r_1 - r_2$, v_1 and v_2 is zero. Use Equation (1.31) on p. 17 to write down a determinant which is zero.

If this determinant is zero, do the lines necessarily intersect? Can the determinant be used to distinguish intersecting, skew, and coincident lines? Check your answer against Example 2.50 on p. 32 and Exercises on pp. 40–1.

17.10 Express the equation of the plane through 3 given points (x_i, y_i, z_i) $(i = 1, 2, 3)$ as a fourth order determinant equated to zero (cf. Example 17.62).

17.11 Use Cramer's rule to solve the 3 sets of linear equations for the inverse matrix, and express each solution as a quotient of a second order determinant and $|A|$.

Verify the following algorithm for calculating

$$A^{-1} = \begin{bmatrix} a & b & c \\ d & e & f \\ g & h & k \end{bmatrix}^{-1}$$

(i) change the signs of b, d, f and h

(ii) interchange rows and columns

(iii) replace each element by the 2nd order determinant obtained by deleting the row and column containing the element

(iv) divide by $|A|$.

17.12 For what value of k does the following set of equations fail to have a unique solution:

$$x + y - z = 3, \qquad kx - y + 2z = 5, \qquad x + 2y - z = 4.$$

17.13 Investigate the solutions of

$$3y - 4z = 2, \qquad 4x + 26y = 40, \qquad kx + 5y + 2z = 1$$

for different values of k. Interpret your results geometrically.

17.14 Suppose the columns of a 3×3 matrix A are a set of 3 orthogonal, unit vectors.

(i) If A^T is obtained from A by interchanging columns and rows, show that $A^T A = I$.

(ii) Use equation (1.31) on p. 17 to show that $|A| = 1$.

Note: in general A^T is called the **transpose** of A; and A is an **orthogonal** matrix if $A^T = A^{-1}$, as in (i).

17.15 Find the value of k for which the equations

$$x+2y-z=1, \qquad x+y+z=2, \qquad kx+y+4z=5$$

fail to have a unique solution. Find the general solution of the equations with this value of k, and also for the case $k=3$.

17.16 Find the value of k for which the equations

$$x+\ z+\ w=0$$
$$y+\ z+2w=0$$
$$kx+3z+4w=0$$
$$-x+y+5z+7w=0$$

have a non-trivial solution.

17.17 Verify that $x=y=1$, $z=-1$ is a solution of

$$x+\ y-\ 3z=5$$
$$2x+\ y-\ 6z=9$$
$$4x-7y-12z=9$$

Find the general solution of these equations.

17.18 Find the value of t for which the equations $2x-y=3$, $x+y=t$, $4x+5y=1$ have a solution.

17.19 Find the values of α for which the matrix

$$\begin{bmatrix} 1 & 1 & 2 \\ 2 & \alpha & -1 \\ 3 & -1 & 4 \end{bmatrix}$$

has an inverse. Also find the values of α and β for which the planes

$$x+\ y+2z=1$$
$$2x+\alpha y-\ z=4$$
$$3x-\ y+4z=\beta$$

have a common line.

17.20 Find the condition on the constants α, β, γ for the equations

$$x-2y+3z=\alpha$$
$$3x-6y+\ z=\beta$$
$$-2x+4y-4z=\gamma$$

to be consistent.

17.21 Find the value of t for which the equations

$$x + y + 2z = 0$$
$$2x + 3y + z = t + 2$$
$$3x + z = 2$$
$$5x - 2y + 3z = t$$

are consistent, and give the solution when t has this value.

17.22 Find the value of α for which the equations

$$x - y - 5z = 7$$
$$\alpha x + 3z = -4$$
$$y + z = \beta$$

may be inconsistent.

With this value of α, find the value of β with which the equations are consistent, and give the general solution.

17.23 Calculate the inverse of the matrix

$$\begin{bmatrix} 1 & 0 & 1 & 1 \\ 0 & 1 & 1 & 2 \\ 0 & 0 & 3 & 4 \\ -2 & 2 & 10 & 14 \end{bmatrix}.$$

17.24 Find the solutions, if any, of the equations

$$x + y + z = 1$$
$$x - y - 2z = 0$$
$$x + 2y + 3z = 1$$
$$3x - y - 5z = 1.$$

18

Functions of Three Variables

18.1 Level Curves

The derivative $f'(x)$ of a function of one variable can be interpreted as the slope of a tangent to the curve, say $w = f(x)$, which the function f represents. Differentials dx and dw are components of a displacement along a tangent. The partial derivatives f_x and f_y of a function f of two variables were interpreted in Chapter 14 as the slopes of tangents to the surface, say $w = f(x, y)$, which the function f represents. Differentials dx, dy and dw are components of a displacement in the tangent plane. These pictures use two-dimensional (plane) geometry for functions of one variable, and three-dimensional (solid) geometry for functions of two variables. To extend such geometric interpretations to a function of three variables would evidently require four-dimensional geometry. This abstraction has been considered by mathematicians, and indeed extended to n-dimensional spaces. However three-dimensional pictures of the calculus of functions of three variables are clearly desirable. This chapter therefore begins by reconsidering functions of two variables in a way that only uses two-dimensional pictures, to obtain a treatment that can easily be extended to functions of three variables.

If $f(x, y)$ is a function of two variables, then $f(x, y) = c$ is the equation, usually implicit, of a plane curve. The function f has the same value c at every point of this curve, which is called a **level curve** of the function. This name indicates that the corresponding points of the surface $w = f(x, y)$ all have the same height $w = c$ above the x-y plane. A plot of the level curve gives the same information about the function f, using only a two-dimensional picture.

Example 18.10
Let $f(x, y) = 2 + x^2 + 2y^2$.

Then $f(x, y) = 4$ is a level curve, the ellipse $x^2 + 2y^2 = 2$ shown in Fig. 18.1(a). The corresponding values in the three-dimensional picture give the ellipse (Fig. 18.1(b))

$$x^2 + 2y^2 = 2, \ z = 4$$

lying on the surface $z = 2 + x^2 + 2y^2$. □

A two-dimensional picture of a function $f(x, y)$ is obtained by sketching a number of level curves, labelling each with the appropriate value c of the function.

Example 18.11
Fig. 18.2 shows several level curves of the function $f(x, y) = x^2 + xy + y^2$, namely $x^2 + xy + y^2 = c$ with $c = 0.36$, 1.0, 1.7, 2.0, 4.0, 6.0, and 9.0. The function evidently has a minimum value zero at $(0, 0)$, and generally increases along any displacement directed outward, i.e. moving away from the origin.

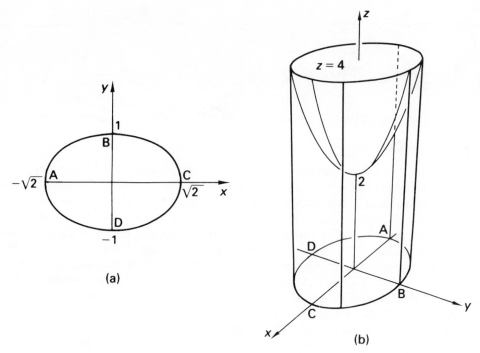

Figure 18.1   (a) Level curve (b) corresponding curve on surface

The partial derivative $f_x(P)$ is the rate of change of the function in a displacement from P in the positive x-direction. The level curve diagram gives information on the value of this derivative. Consider $P(1, 0)$ on the level curve with $c = 1$. The adjacent level curves shown ($c = 0.36$ and 1.7) intersect the x-axis at $Q(0.6, 0)$ and $R(1.3, 0)$. Then

$$\frac{f(R) - f(P)}{RP} = \frac{1.7 - 1}{1.3 - 1} = 2.3 \quad \text{and} \quad \frac{f(Q) - f(P)}{QP} = \frac{0.36 - 1}{0.6 - 1} = 1.6$$

indicate that $1.6 < f_x(P) < 2.3$. (In the surface picture, these bounds are the slopes of chords.)

In the direction of the level curve, the rate of change of the function is zero. For example, the level curve through $S(0, 2)$ is $x^2 + xy + y^2 = 4$. Differentiating (implicitly),

$$2x\,dx + x\,dy + y\,dx + 2y\,dy = 0.$$

At $S(0, 2)$, differentials satisfying $2\,dx + 4\,dy = 0$ give the direction of the level curve at S (i.e. the gradient of the tangent to this curve). Taking $dx = 2$, $dy = -1$ gives $2i - j$ as a vector along the tangent. At $S(0, 2)$ the rate of change of f is zero in the directions $\pm 2i \mp j$. □

Level curves with equally spaced values $f(x, y) = c,\ c + h,\ c + 2h, \ldots$ are called **contours** of the function. If P and Q are on adjacent contours, then h/PQ is an estimate of the rate of change of f at P in the direction $\overrightarrow{PQ}$. The function changes rapidly (corresponding to a steep surface) if PQ is small, i.e. in regions where the contours are close together.

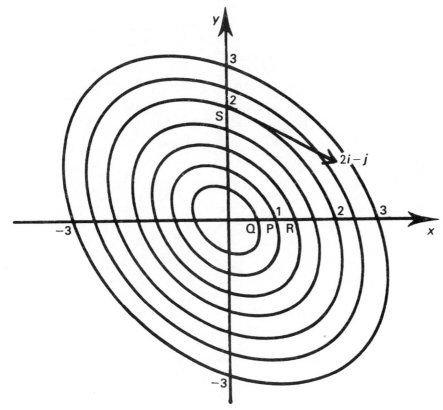

Figure 18.2   Level curves; vector at S(0, 2) is $2i - j$ (along level curve)

Example 18.12
Contours on a map are level curves of the function H where $H(x, y)$ is the height above sea level of the point (x, y).

Figure 18.3 shows contours for the Mount Dandenong (Victoria, Australia) region, the unit of height and distance being 1000 ft. The coordinates (x, y) represent the distance east and north of the origin (One Tree Hill).

The contours indicate a maximum (Mount Dandenong) near M (10, 16). Moving away from M in any direction $ai + bj$ with $a < 0$ and $b > 0$, the function decreases rapidly, as shown by the close contours.

There is a local maximum near L(19, −1), and another somewhere in the shaded region.

At any point of a contour, the direction of the contour shows the direction in which the rate of change of H (i.e. the slope of the ground surface) is zero. This direction can change rapidly, for example from i at P to j at Q near (13, 10). □

Exercises (answers on p. 490)
18.1.1   Sketch level curves for each of the following functions $f(x, y)$:
   (i) $y - 2x - 1$ (ii) $x^2 + y^2$ (iii) $(y - 2x - 1)^2$
   (iv) $\sqrt{\{1 - (x^2 + y^2)\}}$ (v) $\ln \sqrt{(x^2 + y^2)}$.

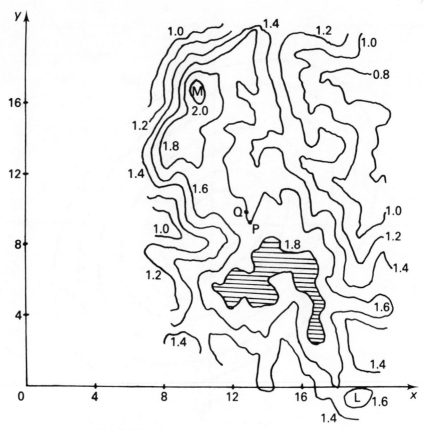

Figure 18.3   Numbers show height (unit 1000 feet)

18.1.2   For each of the following give a vector showing the direction at P in which the rate of change of the function f is zero:

(i) $f(x, y) = y - 2x - 1$, P(1, 1)

(ii) $f(x, y) = y - 2x - 1$, P(a, b)

(iii) $f(x, y) = (y - 2x - 1)^2$, P(a, b)

(iv) $f(x, y) = (2x - 3y + 1)^2(x + 2y - 2)$, P(2, 1)

(v) $f(x, y) = (2x - 3y + 1)^2(x + 2y - 2)$, P(1, 1)

18.2   Differentials and Directional Derivatives

The definition of differentials in Section 14.3 can be written

$$df = \frac{\partial f}{\partial x} dx + \frac{\partial f}{\partial y} dy. \tag{18.1}$$

The interpretation of this equation in terms of first-order changes in the variables remains the same: with $\partial f/\partial x$ and $\partial f/\partial y$ evaluated at (a, b), df is the first-order approximation to the change in f from (a, b) to $(a + dx, b + dy)$, where the increments dx and dy are arbitrary. Thus df is an approximation to

$$f(a + dx, b + dy) - f(a, b).$$

The work in Section 14.4 on finding the slope of the surface (or tangent line) in an arbitrary direction may now be regarded as finding the rate of change of the function f from a given point in a given direction. This quantity is called the **directional derivative** at the point in the given direction.

Example 18.20
Find the directional derivative of the function $f(x, y) = 3x^2y^2 + x^3 + 2y^2$ at the point $(-1, -1)$ in the direction $3i + 4j$.

This is just Example 14.40 re-interpreted (see p. 365). From equation (18.1)

$$df = (6xy^2 + 3x^2)\, dx + (6x^2y + 4y)\, dy = -3\, dx - 10\, dy \text{ at } (-1, -1).$$

The directional derivative is the differential of f corresponding to a displacement of unit length in the given direction. Taking $dx = \frac{3}{5}$ and $dy = \frac{4}{5}$, $df = -\frac{49}{5}$. $\square$

Exercises (answers on p. 490)
18.2.1 Find the directional derivative of $f(x, y) = e^{xy}\cos(x + y)$ at $(\pi, 0)$ in the direction $i + j$.
18.2.2 At (a, b) a function $f(x, y)$ has directional derivatives zero in the direction $i - j$ and 1 in the direction $i + j$. Calculate $f_x(a, b)$ and $f_y(a, b)$, assuming that f is differentiable at (a, b). What can be said about the level curve of f through (a, b)?

18.3 Gradient Vector (Two-dimensional)

The equation

$$df = \frac{\partial f}{\partial x}\bigg|_P dx + \frac{\partial f}{\partial y}\bigg|_P dy \qquad (18.1)$$

gives an approximation to $f(Q) - f(P)$, where the displacement

$$\vec{PQ} = i\, dx + j\, dy = d\mathbf{r} \qquad (18.2)$$

is in the x-y plane. The right side of equation (18.1) has the form of a scalar product of the vector (18.2) with a vector whose components are the partial derivatives. This vector, called the **gradient** of f, or **grad** f, is defined at all points where f is differentiable:

$$\nabla f = \frac{\partial f}{\partial x} i + \frac{\partial f}{\partial y} j. \qquad (18.3)$$

Then equation (18.1) becomes

$$df = \nabla f \cdot d\mathbf{r}. \qquad (18.4)$$

Example 18.30
For $f(x, y) = x^3 - xy + y^2$ at $(1, 2)$,

$$f_x(1, 2) = 1, \qquad f_y(1, 2) = 3$$

$$\nabla f = i + 3j \text{ at } (1, 2), \text{ or } \nabla f(1, 2) = i + 3j. \quad \square$$

The value of a directional derivative depends on both the function f and the direction considered. Equation (18.4) cleanly separates these: ∇f comes from the function only, and $d\mathbf{r}$ comes from the displacement only.

If $d\mathbf{r}$ is a unit vector, then df is the directional derivative in that direction.

Example 18.31
Consider Example 18.20 again.

$$\nabla f = (6xy^2 + 3x^2)\mathbf{i} + (6x^2y + 4y)\mathbf{j} = -3\mathbf{i} - 10\mathbf{j} \quad \text{at } (-1, -1).$$

$d\mathbf{r} = \frac{3}{5}\mathbf{i} + \frac{4}{5}\mathbf{j}$ is a unit vector in the given direction. The directional derivative is $\nabla f \cdot d\mathbf{r} = -49/5$. $\square$

In general, the directional derivative of f at P in the direction specified by a unit vector $\mathbf{e}$ is $\nabla f(\mathrm{P}) \cdot \mathbf{e}$, which is just the component of ∇f in the direction $\mathbf{e}$. As the direction $\mathbf{e}$ varies (Fig. 18.4),

the maximum value of the component is $|\nabla f|$, when $\mathbf{e}$ is the direction of ∇f. The minimum value is $-|\nabla f|$ when $\mathbf{e}$ is in the opposite direction to ∇f. The directional derivative is zero in the direction $\mathbf{e}$ which is perpendicular to ∇f.

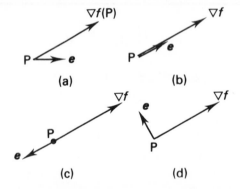

Figure 18.4   Directional derivative at P in direction of unit vector $\mathbf{e}$: (a) $0 < \nabla f \cdot \mathbf{e} < |\nabla f|$ (b) $\nabla f \cdot \mathbf{e} = |\nabla f|$ (c) $\nabla f \cdot \mathbf{e} = -|\nabla f|$ (d) $\nabla f \cdot \mathbf{e} = 0$

Example 18.32
For $f(x, y) = x^3 - xy + y^2$, $\nabla f(1, 2) = \mathbf{i} + 3\mathbf{j}$ (Example 18.30). Then the maximum directional derivative at $(1, 2)$ is $|\nabla f| = \sqrt{10}$ in the direction $\mathbf{i} + 3\mathbf{j}$. In the opposite direction $(-\mathbf{i} - 3\mathbf{j})$ the directional derivative is $-\sqrt{10}$. The directional derivative is zero in the directions $\pm(3\mathbf{i} - \mathbf{j})$, which are perpendicular to ∇f. $\square$

Since the directional derivative is zero along the level curve, the direction of $\nabla f(\mathrm{P})$ is perpendicular to the level curve through P.

Exercises (answers on p. 490)

18.3.1 Find the value of the maximum directional derivative at $(2, 1)$ of $f(x, y) = x^3 - xy + 3y^2$, and give a vector showing the direction required for this maximum derivative.

18.3.2 Consider $f(x, y) = x^2 + x + 4xy + y^2$ at the point $(1, 1)$. Find (i) the value and direction of the maximum directional derivative; (ii) the direction in which the directional derivative is zero; (iii) the directional derivative in the direction $i + 2j$.

18.3.3 Find a vector which is perpendicular to the curve $x^2 + 2y^2 = 3$ at the point $(1, 1)$.

18.4 Functions of Three Variables

For a function of two variables the total differential

$$df = \frac{\partial f}{\partial x} dx + \frac{\partial f}{\partial y} dy \tag{18.1}$$

is the sum of two terms (partial differentials) corresponding to the separate variation of each independent variable. This formula is evidently extended to a function of three variables by adding the appropriate term for the third independent variable: for $f(x, y, z)$,

$$df = \frac{\partial f}{\partial x} dx + \frac{\partial f}{\partial y} dy + \frac{\partial f}{\partial z} dz. \tag{18.5}$$

With the partial derivatives evaluated at (a, b, c), df is the first-order approximation to $f(a + dx, b + dy, c + dz) - f(a, b, c)$.

Example 18.40
The length x, width y, and height z of an open rectangular box are measured as 12 ± 0.2 cm, 10 ± 0.1 cm, and 8 ± 0.3 cm. Estimate the error in the calculated external surface area $S = 472$ cm^2.

The function

$$S(x, y, z) = xy + 2xz + 2yz$$

gives the surface area of any open box. From equation (18.5),

$$dS = (y + 2z) dx + (x + 2z) dy + 2(x + y) dz$$

$$= 26 dx + 28 dy + 44 dz \quad \text{if } x = 12, y = 10, z = 8.$$

For $dx = 0.2$, $dy = 0.1$, and $dz = 0.3$ (the indicated maximum errors), $dS = 21.2$ is the first-order estimate of the possible resulting error in S. Thus $S = (472 \pm 21)$ cm^2. □

In the formula (18.5), the displacement from (a, b, c) can have any direction in three-dimensional space, and is given by the vector $dr = i\, dx + j\, dy + k\, dz$. Then df is written as a scalar product by defining the gradient of f as

$$\text{grad}\, f = \nabla f = \frac{\partial f}{\partial x} i + \frac{\partial f}{\partial y} j + \frac{\partial f}{\partial z} k,$$

so that (as before)

$$df = \nabla f \cdot dr. \qquad (18.4)$$

If dr is a unit vector, then df is the directional derivative of f in the direction dr.

Example 18.41

Find the directional derivative at $(1, 1, 0)$ of $f(x, y, z) = 2x^2 e^{yz}$ in the direction $2i - j - 2k$.

$$\nabla f = 4x\, e^{yz} i + 2x^2 z\, e^{yz} j + 2x^2 y\, e^{yz} k = 4i + 2k \quad \text{at } (1, 1, 0).$$

A unit vector in the given direction is $e = \tfrac{2}{3}i - \tfrac{1}{3}j - \tfrac{2}{3}k$.
The required directional derivative is $\nabla f \cdot e = \tfrac{4}{3}$.   □

The directional derivative of f at P in the direction of the unit vector e is $\nabla f(P) \cdot e$, which has greatest value $|\nabla f|$ when e is in the direction of ∇f, minimum value $-|\nabla f|$ in the opposite direction, and is zero in any direction perpendicular to ∇f.

The only difference from the case of two variables is that the directional derivative is now zero in any direction in the **plane** perpendicular to ∇f, instead of in just two directions.

Example 18.42

Find the direction in which the directional derivative of $f(x, y, z) = xyz$ at $(1, 2, 3)$ is a maximum, and obtain the value of this maximum derivative.

$$\nabla f = yz\, i + xz\, j + xy\, k = 6i + 3j + 2k \text{ at } (1, 2, 3).$$

This is the direction of the greatest directional derivative at $(1, 2, 3)$. The value of this maximum derivative is $|6i + 3j + 2k| = 7$.   □

Example 18.43

Find the direction at $(1, 1, 1)$ for the greatest rate of decrease of the function

$$G(x, y, z) = 3x^2 z + 3y^2 z - 2z^3.$$

$$\nabla G = 6xzi + 6yzj + (3x^2 + 3y^2 - 6z^2)k$$

$$\nabla G(1, 1, 1) = 6i + 6j.$$

The opposite direction $-i - j$ gives the greatest rate of decrease from $(1, 1, 1)$.   □

Example 18.44

Find the equation of the plane through $P(3, 5, -4)$ which contains all directions in which the directional derivative of

$$V(x, y, z) = x^2 + y^2 - z^2$$

at P is zero.

$$\nabla V = 2xi + 2yj - 2zk$$

$$\nabla V(3, 5, -4) = 6i + 10j + 8k.$$

This vector is normal to the required plane, since the plane contains all directions perpendicular to ∇V. The plane is

$$6x + 10y + 8z = D$$

where $D = 18 + 50 - 32$, since the plane contains P. The plane is

$$6x + 10y + 8z = 36$$

or

$$3x + 5y + 4z = 18. \quad \square$$

Corresponding to the level curves of a function of two variables, the surfaces on which a function of three variables is constant are its **level surfaces**.

Example 18.45
(i) The level surfaces of $f(x, y, z) = 2x - 3y + z$ are the parallel planes $2x - 3y + z = c$.
(ii) The level surfaces of $g(x, y, z) = (x^2 + y^2 + z^2)^2$ are the concentric spheres $x^2 + y^2 + z^2 = c$ $(c > 0)$. $\quad \square$

The level surface of f through P(a, b, c) has the equation $f(x, y, z) = f(a, b, c)$. Moving away from P on this surface gives no change in f. Moving away in any direction in the tangent plane to the level surface will give zero rate of change of f. Thus the tangent plane at P to the level surface is the plane containing all the directions at P in which f has zero directional derivative. This means that

$\nabla f(P)$ is normal to the level surface through P.

Exercises (answers on p. 491)
18.4.1 Find ∇f when $f(x, y, z) = x^2 e^{2y} \cos 4z$, and show that $\nabla f = 0$ at every point of a certain plane.
18.4.2 Find the directional derivative of the function

$$F(x, y, z) = x^4 + 4y^4 + 9z^4 + 4x^2 y^2 + 6x^2 z^2 + 12 y^2 z^2$$

at $(1, 1, 1)$ in the direction $i + j + k$.
18.4.3 Find the direction in which the directional derivative of $f(x, y, z) = xy^2 z^3$ at P$(2, 1, 1)$ is a maximum. What is the maximum value?
18.4.4 Find the equation of the plane through P$(2, 1, 3)$ which contains all directions in which the directional derivative of

$$f(x, y, z) = 2x^2 + 3y^2 + z^2$$

at P is zero.
18.4.5 The length, width and height of a rectangular box are measured as 12 ± 0.03 cm, 4 ± 0.01 cm, and 3 ± 0.01 cm. Estimate the possible error when the length of a diagonal (between opposite corners) is calculated from these measurements.

18.5 Implicit Differentiation

In Examples 6.63, 6.64 and 6.65 (see p. 126), equations implicitly defining y as a function of x were differentiated to obtain relations between the differentials dy and dx, and hence the derivative of the implicit function:

$$4x^4 + y^2 = 4x^2 \quad \Rightarrow \quad 16x^3\,dx + 2y\,dy = 8x\,dx$$

$$\ln x + \ln y - y = 0 \quad \Rightarrow \quad dx/x + dy/y - dy = 0$$

$$(2x-3y+1)^2(x+2y-2) = C \quad \Rightarrow \quad (6x+5y-7)\,dx - 2(x+9y-7)\,dy = 0.$$

In general, an equation of the form $F(x, y) = C$ implicitly defines y as a function of x. The curve represented by the equation is a level curve of F, and the required derivative is just the slope of this level curve (Fig. 18.5). The relation between differentials must be such that the directional derivative of F in the corresponding direction is zero. From equation (18.1), this relation is given by $F_x\,dx + F_y\,dy = 0$.

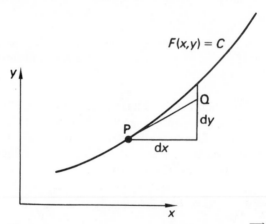

Figure 18.5   Directional derivative of F is zero along $\overrightarrow{PQ}$

Example 6.63 (again)
Find the derivative of the function defined implicitly by $4x^4 + y^2 = 4x^2$.

Let

$$F(x, y) = 4x^4 + y^2 - 4x^2.$$

Then $F_x = 16x^3 - 8x$, $F_y = 2y$, so $dF = 0$ if

$$(16x^3 - 8x)\,dx + 2y\,dy = 0. \quad \square$$

Example 6.65 (again)
Find the derivative of the function defined implicitly by

$$(2x-3y+1)^2(x+2y-2) = C.$$

As previously, logarithmic differentiation is convenient, so the given relation is written $F(x, y) = k$ with

$$F(x, y) = 2\ln(2x-3y+1) + \ln(x+2y-2), \qquad k = \ln C.$$

$$\frac{\partial F}{\partial x} = \frac{4}{2x-3y+1} + \frac{1}{x+2y-2}, \qquad \frac{\partial F}{\partial y} = \frac{-6}{2x-3y+1} + \frac{2}{x+2y-2}.$$

On multiplication by $(2x-3y+1)(x+2y-2)$,

$$dF = \frac{\partial F}{\partial x} dx + \frac{\partial F}{\partial y} dy = 0$$

becomes

$$\{4(x+2y-2)+(2x-3y+1)\} dx + \{-6(x+2y-2)+2(2x-3y+1)\} dy = 0.$$

So

$$\frac{dy}{dx} = \frac{6x+5y-7}{2(x+9y-7)}$$

as before. ☐

(Logarithmic differentiation need not be used—see Example 6.101 on p. 146.)

> In general the required derivative of the function $y(x)$ defined implicitly by $F(x, y) = C$ is given by $dF = 0$,

which justifies the procedures used in Section 6.6. When $dF = 0$, the resulting differentials dx and dy correspond to variations of x and y along the level curve, i.e. to values obtained in the implicit function.

A function $z(x, y)$ of two variables may be defined implicitly by an equation $F(x, y, z) = C$. This represents a level surface of F, which is also the surface representing $z = z(x, y)$. Equating to zero dF ($= F_x\, dx + F_y\, dy + F_z\, dz$) constrains the differentials so that $i\, dx + j\, dy + k\, dz$ is a displacement in the tangent plane to the surface. Thus any differentials satisfying

$$F_x\, dx + F_y\, dy + F_z\, dz = 0$$

give a displacement in the tangent plane to the surface representing $z = z(x, y)$.

If $dy = 0$, the displacement gives the slope of $z = z(x, y)$ in the x-direction, which is $\partial z/\partial x$; if $dx = 0$, the displacement gives $\partial z/\partial y$:

$$\frac{\partial z}{\partial x} = -\frac{F_x}{F_z}, \qquad \frac{\partial z}{\partial y} = -\frac{F_y}{F_z}$$

are the partial derivatives of the implicit function of two variables.

Example 18.50
Find the partial derivatives $(\partial z/\partial x)_y$ and $(\partial z/\partial y)_x$ of the function $z(x, y)$ defined implicitly by

$$F(x, y, z) = x^3 + y^3 + z^3 - 3xyz = C.$$

$$F_x = 3x^2 - 3yz, \qquad F_y = 3y^2 - 3xz, \qquad F_z = 3z^2 - 3xy.$$

In general, $dF = F_x\, dx + F_y\, dy + F_z\, dz$. Putting $dF = 0$ gives differentials in the tangent plane to the level surface which is represented by the implicit function. Solving $dF = 0$ for dz gives

$$dz = \frac{x^2 - yz}{xy - z^2} dx + \frac{y^2 - xz}{xy - z^2} dy \qquad (xy \ne z^2).$$

In this relation between differentials of the variables in the implicit function, the differentials of the independent variables x and y are arbitrary. If $dy = 0$, y is constant, so

$$\left(\frac{\partial z}{\partial x}\right)_y = \frac{x^2 - yz}{xy - z^2}.$$

Similarly

$$\left(\frac{\partial z}{\partial y}\right)_x = \frac{y^2 - xz}{xy - z^2}, \text{ the coefficient of } dy.$$

The condition $xy \neq z^2$ shows that if $xy = z^2$ the tangent plane to the level surface is then a vertical plane. For $F(x, y, z) = C$ to define a function $z(x, y)$, rather than a relation, the domain must be restricted. □

Exercises (answers on p. 491)

18.5.1 Obtain dF for $F(x, y) = xy - e^y$, and deduce the derivative of the function $y(x)$ defined implicitly by $xy = e^y$.

18.5.2 Find the derivative of the function defined implicitly by

$$2y^3 + xy^3 - x^2y^3 + x^2 + x = 2.$$

18.5.3 Find the partial derivatives of the function $z(x, y)$ defined implicitly by $z^2 - x^2y + zy^2 = 1$.

18.6 Composite Functions

If $w = f(x)$ where x is a function of t, then $dw = f'(x)\,dx$, and simply dividing by dt gives the correct formula for the rate of change of w with respect to t. This same procedure gives the derivative of a composite function of one variable when f is a function of several variables.

Example 18.60
$w = x^2y^3$ where $x = t^2$, $y = t^3$.

$$dw = 2xy^3\,dx + 3x^2y^2\,dy$$

$$\frac{dw}{dt} = 2xy^3\frac{dx}{dt} + 3x^2y^2\frac{dy}{dt} = 4t^{12} + 9t^{12} = 13t^{12}.$$

In this example the result is easily checked by first expressing w in terms of t and then differentiating. □

Example 18.61
If $w = f(x, y)$ with $x = a + bt$, $y = ct^2$, then

$$dw = f_x\,dx + f_y\,dy$$

$$= f_x b\,dt + f_y 2ct\,dt$$

$$\frac{dw}{dt} = bf_x(a + bt, ct^2) + 2ctf_y(a + bt, ct^2).$$

In this result, f is any (differentiable) function of 2 variables. □

Example 18.62
If $w = axy + yz^2 + x^2z$, where

$$x = a \cos bt, \qquad y = a \sin bt, \qquad z = abt,$$

then

$$dw = w_x\, dx + w_y\, dy + w_z\, dz \qquad (18.6)$$
$$= (ay + 2xz)\, dx + (ax + z^2)\, dy + (2yz + x^2)\, dz,$$

and $dx = -ab \sin bt\, dt$, $dy = ab \cos bt\, dt$, $dz = ab\, dt$. So

$$\frac{dw}{dt} = a^3b(2 \cos^2 bt - \sin^2 bt - bt \sin 2bt + b^2t^2 \cos bt + 2bt \sin bt). \quad \square$$

A special case of such composite functions is w, a function of x, given either as $f(x, y)$ where y is a function of x, or as $f(x, y, z)$ where y and z are functions of x.

Example 18.63
If $w = x^2y^3 + yz^2$, where $y = a \sin bx$, and $z = 3x^2 + 2x$, then

$$dw = 2xy^3\, dx + (3x^2y^2 + z^2)\, dy + 2yz\, dz,$$

where

$$dz = (6x + 2)\, dx, \qquad \text{and} \qquad dy = ab \cos bx\, dx.$$

Hence

$$\frac{dw}{dx} = 2xy^3 + (3x^2y^2 + z^2)ab \cos bx + 2yz(6x + 2). \quad \square$$

In Examples 18.60, 18.62 and 18.63, the results could have been obtained by first expressing w in terms of the single variable and then differentiating. This may not be possible when functions are defined implicitly.

Example 18.64
Suppose z is defined implicitly as a function of x and y by $z^3 + 3xyz + x^2 + y^2 = 0$, and y is defined as a function of x by $y^3 + 2xy^2 + x^3 = 0$. The two relations together define z as a function of x, and to get dz/dx the two relations are differentiated:

$$3z^2\, dz + 3yz\, dx + 3xz\, dy + 3xy\, dz + 2x\, dx + 2y\, dy = 0$$
$$3y^2\, dy + 2y^2\, dx + 4xy\, dy + 3x^2\, dx = 0.$$

Eliminating dy leads to

$$\frac{dz}{dx} = \frac{(3xz + 2y)(3x^2 + 2y^2)}{(3y^2 + 4xy)(3z^2 + 3xy)} - \frac{3yz + 2x}{3z^2 + 3xy}. \quad \square$$

Example 18.65
Given a first-order differential equation for y,

$$\frac{dy}{dx} = f(x, y),$$

express d^2y/dx^2 in terms of f and its partial derivatives.

Put $w = dy/dx$, so that $w = f(x, y)$ where y is a function of x, and $d^2y/dx^2 = dw/dx$ is required.

$$dw = f_x\,dx + f_y\,dy$$

$$\boxed{\frac{d^2y}{dx^2} = \frac{dw}{dx} = f_x + f_y\frac{dy}{dx} = f_x + f_yf.} \quad \square$$

(18.7)

The general rule for differentiating a composite function $w = f(x(t), y(t), z(t))$, that is

$$\boxed{\frac{dw}{dt} = \frac{\partial f}{\partial x}\frac{dx}{dt} + \frac{\partial f}{\partial y}\frac{dy}{dt} + \frac{\partial f}{\partial z}\frac{dz}{dt}}$$

(18.8)

is often called the **chain rule**.

Since equation (18.7) gives d^2y/dx^2 as a function of x and y, where y is a function of x, the differentiation can be repeated to obtain d^3y/dx^3. This extends to higher derivatives, allowing the computation of the coefficients of a Taylor series expansion of a solution of the differential equation $dy/dx = f(x, y)$.

Exercises (answers on p. 491)

18.6.1   If $w = f(x, y)$ with $x = a\cos t$, $y = a\sin t$, express dw/dt in terms of f_x and f_y.

18.6.2   If $w = (x^2 + 4y^2)$ where x and y are functions of t, find dw/dt at $t = 0$ given that $x = 1$, $dx/dt = 2$, $y = -1$ and $dy/dt = 1$ at $t = 0$.

18.6.3   If $w = xy^2z^3$ where $x = t^3$, $y = \sqrt{t}$, $z = t^2$, use equation (18.6) to calculate dw/dt, and check the result by expressing w in terms of t and differentiating.

18.7   Conservative Functions

In Section 11.3 the line integral $\int_A^B F \cdot dr$ of a vector field F along a given path from A to B was evaluated using parametric equations of the path. Suppose first that the given path is in the Oxy plane. Then the result (11.7) on p. 267 becomes

$$\int_A^B F \cdot dr = \int_\alpha^\beta \{F_1(t)x'(t) + F_2(t)y'(t)\}\,dt$$

in which $F_i(t)$ are components of F expressed in terms of the parameter t, $x'(t) = dx/dt$ and $y'(t) = dy/dt$ are obtained from the path equations, and α, β are the parameters of A and B. If the components F_1 and F_2 are given in terms of the coordinates x and y, the functions in equation (11.7) are composite functions $F_i(x(t), y(t))$, where $x = x(t)$, $y = y(t)$ are the parametric equations of the path.

Now suppose F is the gradient of a scalar field $u(x, y)$, i.e. there is a function $u(x, y)$ such that $F = \nabla u$. Then

$$F_1(x, y) = u_x(x, y), \qquad F_2(x, y) = u_y(x, y). \tag{18.9}$$

On the curve, the composite function $u(x(t), y(t))$ gives u as a function of t. The derivative of such a function was obtained in equation (18.8) of Section 18.6:

$$\frac{du}{dt} = u_x \frac{dx}{dt} + u_y \frac{dy}{dt} = F_1 \frac{dx}{dt} + F_2 \frac{dy}{dt}, \quad \text{from equation (18.9).}$$

Hence the integrand (in curly brackets) in equation (11.7) above is du/dt, and

$$\int_A^B \boldsymbol{F} \cdot d\boldsymbol{r} = \int_\alpha^\beta \frac{du}{dt} dt = u(t) \Big|_\alpha^\beta = u(\beta) - u(\alpha) = u(B) - u(A). \tag{18.10}$$

The first consequence of this equation is that the value of the line integral can be written down if u is known.

Example 18.70 (cf. Exercise 11.3 on p. 289)
Let $\boldsymbol{F}(x, y) = (e^y + y^2 e^x)\boldsymbol{i} + (xe^y + 2ye^x)\boldsymbol{j}$. Then

$$F_1 = u_x \quad \text{and} \quad F_2 = u_y \quad \text{if } u(x, y) = xe^y + y^2 e^x.$$

The two integrals set in Exercise 11.3 were

$$\int_{A(1,1)}^{B(3,4)} \boldsymbol{F} \cdot d\boldsymbol{r} = u(B) - u(A) \quad \text{from equation (18.9)}$$

$$= u(3, 4) - u(1, 1) = 3e^4 + 16e^3 - 2e. \quad \square$$

The second, and more important, consequence of equation (18.10) is suggested by this example. If u exists giving $\boldsymbol{F} = \nabla u$, then $\int_A^B \boldsymbol{F} \cdot d\boldsymbol{r}$ depends only on A and B, and is the same for *any* path taken between A and B.

To extend this work to the line integral along a space curve of a three-component vector field, it is only necessary to include in each equation a term corresponding to the third component. The function $u(x, y, z)$ must give $F_1 = u_x$, $F_2 = u_y$, $F_3 = u_z$ so that from equation (18.8) $du/dt = F_1 \, dx/dt + F_2 \, dy/dt + F_3 \, dz/dt$, the integrand in equation (11.7).

A vector field $\boldsymbol{F}(x, y, z)$ is called **conservative** if it is the gradient of a scalar field $u(x, y, z)$. **A line integral of a conservative field depends only on the end-points of the path**, having the same value for any path joining these end-points. This value is the change in value of the scalar field u.

Example 18.71

$$\int_{A(0,0,0)}^{B(1,1,1)} \boldsymbol{F} \cdot d\boldsymbol{r} \quad \text{where } \boldsymbol{F} = y^2 z^3 \boldsymbol{i} + 2xyz^3 \boldsymbol{j} + 3xy^2 z^2 \boldsymbol{k},$$

does not depend on the path from A to B because $\boldsymbol{F} = \nabla u$ with $u(x, y, z) = xy^2 z^3$. The value of this line integral is $u(B) - u(A) = u(1, 1, 1) - u(0, 0, 0) = 1$. $\quad \square$

Example 18.72
If $u(x, y, z) = p(x) + q(y) + r(z)$, then $\nabla u = p'(x)\boldsymbol{i} + q'(y)\boldsymbol{j} + r'(z)\boldsymbol{k}$. Hence any vector field of the form $\boldsymbol{F}(x, y, z) = f(x)\boldsymbol{i} + g(y)\boldsymbol{j} + h(z)\boldsymbol{k}$ is conservative, taking $p' = f$, etc. (cf. Exercise 11.6 on p. 290). $\quad \square$

For a conservative **force field** $F(x, y, z)$, a **potential function** $V(x, y, z)$ is defined by $F = -\nabla V$. Then

$$\int_A^B F \cdot dr = -V(B) + V(A). \qquad (18.11)$$

To test whether a given vector field is conservative, note that in the two-component case $F_1 = u_x$, $F_2 = u_y$, and therefore

$$\boxed{F_{1y} = u_{yx} = u_{xy} = F_{2x}.} \qquad (18.12)$$

Example 18.73
Test whether (cf. Example 18.70)

$$F(x, y) = (e^y + y^2 e^x)i + (xe^y + 2ye^x)j$$

is conservative.

$$F_{1y} = \frac{\partial}{\partial y}(e^y + y^2 e^x) = e^y + 2ye^x$$

$$F_{2x} = \frac{\partial}{\partial x}(xe^y + 2ye^x) = F_{1y}, \quad \text{so } F \text{ is conservative.} \quad \square$$

For the three-component case, there is a relation like equation (18.12) for each pair of components:

$$F_{1y} = u_{yx} = u_{xy} = F_{2x}$$

$$F_{1z} = u_{zx} = u_{xz} = F_{3x} \qquad (18.13)$$

$$F_{2z} = u_{zy} = u_{yz} = F_{3y}.$$

All three relations must hold for F to be conservative.

The final question to be considered is the determination of the scalar function u for a given conservative F. In the two-component case, the problem is to find u from $u_x = F_1$ and $u_y = F_2$. Since u_x is the derivative of u with respect to x, keeping y constant, u can be found by integrating u_x with respect to x, keeping y constant. The only complication is that because any function of y is treated as constant, the arbitrary 'constant' of integration is a function of y.

Example 18.74
Given the (conservative) vector field

$$F(x, y) = (4x^3 + 2xy^2)i + (2x^2y + 4y^3)j,$$

find $u(x, y)$ such that $F = \nabla u$.

u must satisfy

$$\partial u / \partial x = 4x^3 + 2xy^2 \qquad (18.14)$$

and

$$\partial u/\partial y = 2x^2 y + 4y^3. \tag{18.15}$$

Integrating equation (18.14) with respect to x, with y constant, gives

$$u = x^4 + x^2 y^2 + A(y) \tag{18.16}$$

where A is an unknown function of y. Differentiating with respect to y, keeping x constant, gives

$$\partial u/\partial y = 2x^2 y + A'(y).$$

Comparing with equation (18.15) shows that $A'(y) = 4y^3$. Hence $A(y) = y^4 + C$. Substituting into (18.16) gives

$$u(x, y) = x^4 + x^2 y^2 + y^4 + C.$$

Check: then $\nabla u = (4x^3 + 2xy^2)\boldsymbol{i} + (2x^2 y + 4y^3)\boldsymbol{j} = \boldsymbol{F}$.
   Alternatively, equation (18.15) can be integrated with respect to y, and the result differentiated with respect to x and compared with equation (18.14):

$$u = x^2 y^2 + y^4 + B(x)$$

$$\partial u/\partial x = 2xy^2 + B'(x).$$

From (18.14), $B'(x) = 4x^3$, giving $B(x) = x^4 + C$. $\square$

When the comparison is made with the second equation, it must give $A'(y)$ as a function of y *only*, or $B'(x)$ as a function of x *only*. If the comparison appears to require $A(y)$ or $B(x)$ to be a function of x *and* y, then either a mistake has been made, or the given vector field is not conservative, i.e. u does not exist. Unless $\boldsymbol{F}$ is known to be conservative, the test $F_{1y} = F_{2x}$ should be verified before attempting to obtain u.
   The same method can be used to obtain u in the three-dimensional case.

Example 18.75
Given the (conservative) vector field

$$\boldsymbol{F}(x, y, z) = (3x^2 + 4xy + 3yz)\boldsymbol{i} + (3y^2 + 3xz + 2x^2)\boldsymbol{j} + (3z^2 + 3xy)\boldsymbol{k},$$

find $u(x, y, z)$ such that $\boldsymbol{F} = \nabla u$.

u must satisfy

$$\partial u/\partial x = 3x^2 + 4xy + 3yz \tag{18.17}$$

$$\partial u/\partial y = 3y^2 + 3xz + 2x^2 \tag{18.18}$$

$$\partial u/\partial z = 3z^2 + 3xy. \tag{18.19}$$

Integrate equation (18.17) with respect to x, keeping y, z constant:

$$u = x^3 + 2x^2 y + 3xyz + A(y, z) \tag{18.20}$$

where A is a function of y and z to be found. Then

$$\frac{\partial u}{\partial y} = 2x^2 + 3xz + \frac{\partial A}{\partial y}, \qquad \frac{\partial u}{\partial z} = 3xy + \frac{\partial A}{\partial z}.$$

Comparing with equations (18.18) and (18.19),

$$\frac{\partial A}{\partial y} = 3y^2, \qquad \frac{\partial A}{\partial z} = 3z^2.$$

In general, these derivatives will depend on y and z; A is now obtained as in the previous example:

$$\frac{\partial A}{\partial y} = 3y^2 \quad \Rightarrow \quad A = y^3 + B(z)$$

$$\Rightarrow \quad \frac{\partial A}{\partial z} = B'(z).$$

But $\partial A/\partial z = 3z^2$, so $B'(z) = 3z^2$, $B(z) = z^3 + C$. Hence $A = y^3 + z^3 + C$. Substituting into equation (18.20) gives

$$u(x, y, z) = x^3 + 2x^2 y + 3xyz + y^3 + z^3 + C.$$

Check: $\nabla u = F$. $\square$

Exercises (answers on p. 491)

18.7.1 If $f(x, y) = 2x^2 - y^2$, and $A = \nabla f$, evaluate the line integral $\int_{(-1,1)}^{(1,2)} A \cdot dr$

18.7.2 Show that there is no function $u(x, y)$ such that $\nabla u = 3xyi - y^2j$.

18.7.3 If $F(x, y) = (1 + 4xy)i + 2(x^2 + y)j$, find $u(x, y)$ such that $F = \nabla u$.

18.7.4 If $u(x, y, z) = (xy + yz + zx)^3$, and $A = \nabla u$, evaluate the line integral $\int A \cdot dr$ along a path from $(0, 0, 0)$ to $(2, -1, -1)$.

18.7.5 Show that there is no function $u(x, y, z)$ such that

$$\nabla u = (1 + 4xyz)i + 2x^2 zj + 4xyk.$$

18.7.6 Suppose L denotes the path along the straight line from $A(-1, -1)$ to $B(1, 1)$, and C denotes a path from A to B around the circle $x^2 + y^2 = 2$. Which of the following statements are correct?

(i) If $F(x, y) = \nabla u$ for some differentiable $u(x, y)$, then $\int_L F \cdot dr = \int_C F \cdot dr$

(ii) If $\int_L F \cdot dr = \int_C F \cdot dr$ then a function $u(x, y)$ exists such that $F = \nabla u$.

(iii) If $F = F_1 i + F_2 j$, and $\partial F_1/\partial y = \partial F_2/\partial x$, then $\int_L F \cdot dr = \int_C F \cdot dr$.

(iv) If $F = F_1 i + F_2 j$, and $\partial F_1/\partial y \neq \partial F_2/\partial x$, then $\int_L F \cdot dr \neq \int_C F \cdot dr$.

Answers to Exercises 18.1.1–18.7.6

18.1.1 (i) and (iii) Parallel lines with slope 2. (ii), (iv) and (v) Concentric circles centred on the origin, with maximum radius 1 in (iv) which has domain $\{(x, y): x^2 + y^2 \leqslant 1\}$.

18.1.2 (i) (ii) and (iii) $i + 2j$ (iv) $4i + 5j$ (v) $3i + 2j$ (or any non-zero multiples of these vectors). See Example 6.65 (p. 126) for the differentiation of the function in (iv) and (v).

18.2.1 $-\pi/\sqrt{2}$ (cf. Exercise 6.22 on p. 156).

18.2.2 $f_x(a, b) = f_y(a, b) = \sqrt{\tfrac{1}{2}}$ (cf. Example 14.41 on p. 366). The level curve through (a, b) has slope 1 at (a, b).

18.3.1 $\sqrt{137}$ in the direction $11i + 4j$ ($= \nabla f(2, 1)$).

18.3.2 (i) $\sqrt{85}$ in the direction $7i + 6j$; (ii) $-6i + 7j$ or $6i - 7j$; (iii) $19/\sqrt{5} = 8.50$.

In (i) and (ii), any multiple of the given vectors can be used to specify the direction.

18.3.3 Any non-zero multiple of $2i+4j = \nabla(x^2+2y^2)|_{1,1}$ (cf. Example 14.21 on p. 359).

18.4.1 $\nabla f = (2x\,e^{2y}\cos 4z)i + (2x^2\,e^{2y}\cos 4z)j - (4x^2\,e^{2y}\sin 4z)k$ which is zero on the plane $x = 0$.

18.4.2 $48\sqrt{3}$.   **18.4.3** $i+4j+6k$; $\sqrt{53}$.   **18.4.4** $4x+3y+3z=20$.

18.4.5 (13 ± 0.03) cm.

18.5.1 $dy/dx = y/(xy-x)$ (cf. Example 6.64 on p. 126).

18.5.2 $dy/dx = (y^3 - 2xy^3 + 2x + 1)/3y^2(x^2 - x - 2)$.

18.5.3 $\left(\dfrac{\partial z}{\partial x}\right)_y = \dfrac{2xy}{2z+y^2}$, $\left(\dfrac{\partial z}{\partial y}\right)_x = \dfrac{x^2 - 2yz}{2z+y^2}$ $(z \neq -\tfrac{1}{2}y^2)$.

18.6.1 $f_x(x, y)(-a \sin t) + f_y(x, y)(a \cos t)$.

18.6.2 $\dfrac{dw}{dt} = 2x\dfrac{dx}{dt} + 8y\dfrac{dy}{dt}$, $\dfrac{dw}{dt}\Big|_{t=0} = -4$.

18.7.1 $f(1, 2) - f(-1, 1) = -3$.   **18.7.2** $\dfrac{\partial}{\partial y}(3xy) \neq \dfrac{\partial}{\partial x}(-y^2)$.

18.7.3 Check that $u_x = 1+4xy$, $u_y = 2x^2+2y$.

18.7.4 $u(2, -1, -1) - u(0, 0, 0) = -27$.

18.7.5 $\dfrac{\partial}{\partial z}(2x^2 z) \neq \dfrac{\partial}{\partial y}(4xy)$.   **18.7.6** (i) and (iii) are correct.

Further Exercises on Chapter 18

18.1 For each of the following vector fields $F(x, y, z)$, determine whether the field is conservative, and if so find a scalar function $u(x, y, z)$ so that $u = \nabla f$
  (i) $3xyz\,i + (3xz+4y)j + 3xy\,k$
  (ii) $(2i - j + 3k)e^{2x-y+3z}$
  (iii) $(y+z)i + (z+x)j + (x+y)k$
  (iv) $(2xyz + z^3 + 2xy^2)i + (x^2 z + 3y^2 z^2 + 2x^2 y)j + (x^2 y + 2y^3 z + 3xz^2)k$
  (v) $2xy\,i + (x^2 - 2yz)j - (z + y^2)k$.

18.2 The area A of a triangle with sides x, y, z is

$$A(x, y, z) = \tfrac{1}{4}[(x+y+z)(x+y-z)(x-y+z)(-x+y+z)]^{1/2}.$$

Suppose the sides of a triangle are measured as (1 ± 0.001) m, (2 ± 0.002) m, (2 ± 0.002) m. Use differentials to estimate the possible error in the calculated area resulting from the given errors in the lengths.

18.3 Evaluate $\nabla(e^{2x-y+3z})$.
Find a point P at which the direction of $\nabla(e^{2x-y+3z})$ is the same as the direction it has at the origin.

18.4 Find the directional derivative of the function

$$f(x, y, z) = x^2 z - y^3$$

at the point $(1, 1, 6)$ in the direction $3i - 6j + 2k$.

18.5 Determine whether the following vector function is conservative:

$$A(x, y, z) = (yz + x)i + (zx + y)j + (xy + z)k.$$

Evaluate $\int A \cdot d\mathbf{r}$ along the path from $(-1, 0, 0)$ to $(1, 0, 0)$ consisting of the semi-circular arc with equations

$$x^2 + y^2 = 1, \qquad z = 0.$$

18.6 Find the directional derivative of the function

$$F(x, y, z) = x^2 z^2 + 2xy + y^3 z$$

at the point $P(1, 2, -1)$ in the direction of $\overrightarrow{OP}$.

In what direction from P is the rate of increase of $F(x, y, z)$ a maximum? What is the value of this maximum rate of increase? Determine whether $Q(-1, 2, -1)$ lies on the level surface of F which passes through P.

18.7 Find the directional derivative of $F(x, y, z) = x^2 y^3 z^2$ at the point $(2, 1, 2)$ in the direction of $i + 2j + k$.

18.8 Determine whether the following vector function is conservative:

$$A(x, y, z) = (x^2 + z)i + (y^2 + 2z^2)j + (yz^2 + x)k.$$

What does your result imply for line integrals $\int A \cdot d\mathbf{r}$? Evaluate $\int A \cdot d\mathbf{r}$ along the straight line from $(0, 0, 0)$ to $(1, 0, 0)$.

19

Numerical Solution of Differential Equations

19.1 Introduction

In Chapter 13 differential equations were solved by finding a formula giving the general solution, which contains one or more arbitrary constants. Particular solutions were then determined from given conditions which require particular values to be assigned to the arbitrary constants.

Example 19.10
For the differential equation

$$\frac{d^2y}{dx^2} - 2\frac{dy}{dx} + y = x + e^x, \tag{19.1}$$

the general solution is (*A* and *B* are arbitrary constants)

$$y = (A + Bx + \tfrac{1}{2}x^2)\, e^x + x + 2.$$

The particular solution satisfying

$$y = 1 \quad \text{and} \quad dy/dx = 0 \quad \text{when } x = 0 \tag{19.2}$$

is

$$y = (-1 + \tfrac{1}{2}x^2)e^x + x + 2. \tag{19.3}$$

It is the general solution with the values $A = -1$ and $B = 0$ for the arbitrary constants. ☐

However only particular types of differential equations have general solutions that can be expressed in terms of known functions. In other cases a formula cannot be given for the function (or relation) that is the desired solution. What can be obtained is a numerical table of values of this function. Such a table can only pertain to a particular solution, so conditions that determine a particular solution must be known before a numerical method can be applied.

Example 19.11
Given the differential equation (19.1) and the conditions (19.2) in Example 19.10, a numerical method might produce the table

x	0	0.1	0.2	0.3	0.4	0.5
y	1.000	1.000	1.003	1.011	1.028	1.057

which are approximate values of the solution (19.3). ☐

When calculating such a table by the methods to be discussed in this chapter, the interval in x at which the solution is tabulated can be chosen. This is called the **steplength** and will be denoted by h. For instance $h = 0.1$ in the previous example. One of the values in the table will be known from a given condition, say $y = y_0$ at $x = x_0$. The objective of the numerical method is then to calculate approximate values $y_1, y_2, y_3, \ldots$

$$y_1 \text{ at } x = x_1 = x_0 + h \qquad (\text{or perhaps } x_0 - h)$$

$$y_2 \text{ at } x = x_2 = x_0 + 2h \qquad (\text{or perhaps } x_0 - 2h)$$

$$y_3 \text{ at } x = x_3 = x_0 + 3h, \quad \text{etc.}$$

Any particular method will be a prescription, usually an explicit formula, which calculates y_1 from the known x_0 and y_0 (the first step). After this first step, the formula is repeated: y_2 is calculated from y_1 and x_1 (the second step), y_3 is calculated from y_2 and x_2 (the third step), etc.

In the following sections, various formulas are derived and their accuracy considered. As calculation proceeds, errors build up because the error in y_1 increases the error in y_2, the error in y_2 affects y_3, etc. The error in any step is reduced if the steplength h is chosen smaller, but then more steps are required to tabulate y over a given interval in x. This also increases rounding error, so it may not actually give an improvement. A larger number of steps also requires more time and/or effort for the computation.

19.2   Euler Formulas

Suppose the given differential equation is first-order, say

$$\frac{dy}{dx} = f(x, y), \tag{19.4}$$

and that the given condition is $y = y_0$ when $x = x_0$. The required particular solution represents a curve passing through $K(x_0, y_0)$, and equation (19.4) shows that its slope at K is $f(x_0, y_0)$.

The tangent to the curve at K is therefore known. **Euler's formula** approximates the solution curve by this tangent in the first step from $x = x_0$ to $x = x_1 = x_0 + h$. If y_1 is the resulting value of y, then from Fig. 19.1,

$$\frac{y_1 - y_0}{h} = \frac{\text{LR}}{\text{KR}} = \text{slope of tangent} = f(x_0, y_0),$$

giving

Euler's formula

$$y_1 = y_0 + hf(x_0, y_0). \tag{19.5}$$

Repetition of this formula then gives the required table of approximate values, i.e. $y_2 = y_1 + hf(x_1, y_1)$ and generally $y_{n+1} = y_n + hf(x_n, y_n)$.

Example 19.20

$$\frac{dy}{dx} = 2 \cos x - y \cot x, \qquad y = 0 \quad \text{when } x = \tfrac{1}{2}.$$

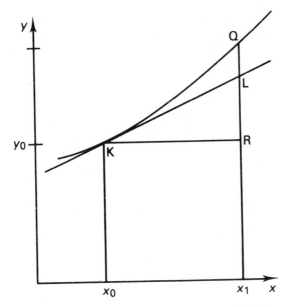

Figure 19.1   Euler's formula approximates QR by LR

Euler's formula (19.5) gives $y_1 = 0 + 2h \cos \frac{1}{2}$,

$$y_2 = y_1 + h\{2 \cos x_1 - y_1 \cot x_1\} = y_1 + h\{2 \cos (\tfrac{1}{2} + h) - y_1 \cot(\tfrac{1}{2} + h)\} \quad \text{etc.}$$

The following table shows results from integrating from $x = 0.5$ to $x = 1.0$, comparing the use of different steplengths h, and also giving exact values from the solution $y = \sin x - \sin^2 \frac{1}{2} / \sin x$ obtained in Example 13.20.

x	0.5	0.6	0.7	0.8	0.9	1.0	
y	0					$y_1 = 0.88$	$(h = 0.5)$
	0	$y_1 = 0.176$	$y_2 = 0.315$	$y_3 = 0.430$	$y_4 = 0.528$	$y_5 = 0.610$	$(h = 0.1)$
	0	$y_2 = 0.166$	$y_4 = 0.300$	$y_6 = 0.413$	$y_8 = 0.508$	$y_{10} = 0.589$	$(h = 0.05)$
	0	$y_5 = 0.161$	$y_{10} = 0.292$	$y_{15} = 0.403$	$y_{20} = 0.497$	$y_{25} = 0.576$	$(h = 0.02)$
	0	0.158	0.287	0.397	0.490	0.568	(exact)

These results confirm that error is reduced by making the steplength smaller, and that error increases with the number of steps. ☐

Euler's formula (19.5) can also be written

$$y_1 = y_0 + h y'_K, \qquad y'_K = f(x_0, y_0) = f(K). \tag{19.6}$$

With this notation, $y'_K = f(K)$ is the slope of the line by which the approximate solution passes from K to L. One way of increasing the accuracy is to improve the slope of this line. From Fig. 19.1, using the slope of the chord KQ would give the exact value of y at $x = x_1$, and the mean value theorem shows that there is some tangent between K and Q with this slope. An improvement might therefore be expected by crossing the interval using the average of the slopes at K and Q. This is not actually possible, because Q is unknown, but one can use the nearest known point L as an approximation to Q. Since $dy/dx = f(x, y)$, the average of the slopes at K and L is $\frac{1}{2}\{f(K) + f(L)\}$. Using this gives the

---

improved Euler formula

$$y_1 = y_0 + \tfrac{1}{2}h\{f(K) + f(L)\} \tag{19.7}$$

$$= y_0 + \tfrac{1}{2}h(y'_K + y'_L) \tag{19.8}$$

$$= y_0 + \tfrac{1}{2}h\{f(x_0, y_0) + f(x_0 + h, y_0 + hy'_K)\}. \tag{19.9}$$

The next step starts from (x_1, y_1) and calculates

$$y_2 = y_1 + \tfrac{1}{2}h\{f(x_1, y_1) + f(x_1 + h, y_1 + hy'_1)\}, \qquad y'_1 = f(x_1, y_1).$$

Example 19.21

Again consider

$$\frac{dy}{dx} = f(x, y) = 2\cos x - y\cot x, \qquad x_0 = \tfrac{1}{2}, y_0 = 0.$$

Then $y'_K = 2\cos\tfrac{1}{2}$, and equation (19.9) gives

$$y_1 = \tfrac{1}{2}h\{2\cos\tfrac{1}{2} + 2\cos(\tfrac{1}{2} + h) - 2h\cos\tfrac{1}{2}\cot(\tfrac{1}{2} + h)\}.$$

The following table compares results from equations (19.5) and (19.9), using $h = 0.01$.

	$x_0 = 0.5$	$x_{10} = 0.6$	$x_{20} = 0.7$	$x_{30} = 0.8$	$x_{40} = 0.9$	$x_{50} = 1.0$	
y	0	0.1591	0.2899	0.4000	0.4934	0.5723	from (19.5)
	0	0.157571	0.287427	0.396941	0.489895	0.568313	from (19.9)
	0	0.157573	0.287430	0.396945	0.489900	0.568320	exact

Note that only values after every 10 steps are shown $(y_{10}, y_{20}, \ldots)$.   □

19.3 Comparison of Formulas

The table in the previous example shows the expected improvement using equation (19.9) rather than (19.5), evaluating f at two points K, L, and taking an average slope $\frac{1}{2}\{f(K) + f(L)\}$ in the step. Other possibilities for improving the slope are to use different points, to weight the average, or to average slopes over three or more points. Note that for any point M, the value of $f(M)$ is the slope of the particular solution of $dy/dx = f(x, y)$ that passes through M. Thus if M is any known point near to the desired solution curve, $f(M)$ may be a suitable approximate slope. For example if M is the midpoint of KL in Fig. 19.1, using the slope $f(M)$ gives a possible formula:

$$y_1 = y_0 + hf(M) = y_0 + hf(x_0 + \tfrac{1}{2}h, y_0 + \tfrac{1}{2}hy'_K). \tag{19.10}$$

Alternatively, the fact that the starting point K is known, while L is an approximation, might be reflected by using a weighted average such as $y_1 = y_0 + h\{\frac{2}{3}f(K) + \frac{1}{3}f(L)\}$. In general one may consider

$$y_1 = y_0 + h\{vf(x_0, y_0) + wf(x_0 + \alpha h, y_0 + \beta h y'_K)\} \tag{19.11}$$

in which v and w are arbitrary weights averaging the slopes at K and at M$(x_0 + \alpha h, y_0 + \beta h y'_K)$. Since α and β have yet to be specified, M is an arbitrary point. The form chosen for the coordinates of M is suggested by the previous special cases: equation (19.9) has $\alpha = \beta = 1$, while equation (19.10) has $\alpha = \beta = \frac{1}{2}$ and $v = 0$. The unspecified constants v, w, α, β in equation (19.11) now have to be chosen to give the most accurate formula.

One criterion for this choice results from expanding equation (19.11) in powers of h, and comparing the result with the Taylor expansion of the exact solution. To expand (19.11), consider $g(h) = f(x_0 + \alpha h, y_0 + \beta h y'_K)$ as a composite function of h. Then

$$g(h) = g(0) + hg'(0) + \frac{1}{2}h^2 g''(0) + \cdots$$

where $g(0) = f(x_0, y_0) = f(K)$. Derivatives of g can be calculated from f as in Section 14.5 or Section 18.6:

$$\frac{dg}{dh} = f_x \frac{dx}{dh} + f_y \frac{dy}{dh} = f_x \alpha + f_y \beta y'_K$$

since $x = x_0 + \alpha h$, $y = y_0 + \beta h y'_K$. Thus

$$g'(0) = \frac{dg}{dh}\bigg|_{h=0} = \alpha f_x(x_0, y_0) + \beta y'_K f_y(x_0, y_0) = \alpha f_x(K) + \beta f(K) f_y(K).$$

The expansion of equation (19.11) in powers of h, up to the h^2 term, is therefore

$$y_1 = y_0 + h(v + w)f(K) + h^2 w\{\alpha f_x(K) + \beta f(K) f_y(K)\} + \cdots. \tag{19.12}$$

On the other hand the required solution has a Taylor expansion about $x = x_0$ (in powers of $h = x - x_0$) of the form

$$y = y_0 + \frac{dy}{dx}\bigg|_K (x - x_0) + \frac{1}{2}\frac{d^2 y}{dx^2}\bigg|_K (x - x_0)^2 + \cdots.$$

The exact value of y at $x_1 = x_0 + h$ is therefore the sum of the series

$$y_0 + \frac{dy}{dx}\bigg|_K h + \frac{1}{2}\frac{d^2 y}{dx^2}\bigg|_K h^2 + \cdots. \tag{19.13}$$

But $dy/dx|_K = f(K)$, and from equation (18.7) on p. 486, $d^2 y/dx^2|_K = f_x(K) + f_y(K)f(K)$. Hence equation (19.12) agrees with (19.13) up to the h^2 term if

$$v + w = 1 \quad \text{and} \quad \alpha w = \beta w = \frac{1}{2}. \tag{19.14}$$

A formula for the numerical integration of differential equations is said to be **second-order** if its expansion in powers of the steplength h agrees with the exact Taylor series as far as the h^2 term. Substituting conditions (19.14) into equation (19.11) shows that

$$y_1 = y_0 + h(1 - w)f(x_0, y_0) + whf\left(x_0 + \frac{h}{2w}, y_0 + \frac{hy'_K}{2w}\right)$$

is second-order for any choice of w. This includes equations (19.9) and (19.10) which are obtained when $w = \frac{1}{2}$ or $w = 1$ respectively.

The Euler formula (19.5) is **first-order** because it agrees with equation (19.13) up to the h term only.

This comparison with the exact Taylor series shows that the error in each step when using the first-order formula (19.5) is proportional to h^2, while the error when using a second-order formula will be proportional to h^3. The total error depends on the number of steps also; over a fixed interval this number varies as $1/h$. In general therefore

the error using a first-order formula is proportional to h, while the error using a second-order formula is proportional to h^2.

Example 19.30

The following table shows the error when the calculation in Example 19.21 is repeated using the second-order formula (19.10), using four different values of h (all errors in units of 10^{-4}).

h	$x = 0.6$	$x = 0.7$	$x = 0.8$	$x = 0.9$	$x = 1.0$
|Error| when $h = 0.1$	14	19	21	22	22
|Error| when $h = 0.05$	3.2	4.5	5.0	5.2	5.3
|Error| when $h = 0.02$	0.49	0.69	0.77	0.80	0.81
|Error| when $h = 0.01$	0.12	0.17	0.19	0.20	0.20
cf. (19.9) when $h = 0.01$	0.02	0.03	0.04	0.05	0.07

The last line shows that equation (19.9) is significantly more accurate than equation (19.10), but this cannot be predicted from the simple error analysis given above. However the deduction that the error is proportional to h^2 does allow the prediction that halving the steplength will reduce the error by a factor of about 4, and that the error with $h = 0.01$ should be about $\frac{1}{100}$ of the error with $h = 0.1$, etc. This prediction is verified in the above table. □

In principle the given equation $dy/dx = f(x, y)$ can be differentiated as many times as required, to give any number of terms of the Taylor series (19.13). In practice this is too complicated to be useful, and is not a suitable basis for a numerical method, for which it is convenient to only have to evaluate the given function f and not also various derivatives of f.

Exercise (answer on p. 504)

19.3.1 Consider $dy/dx = x^2 + y^3$, $y = y_0$ when $x = x_0$. Find the Taylor series expansion of y_1 (the value at $x = x_0 + h$) in powers of h as far as the h^3 term. Show that the improved Euler formula (19.9) is

$$y_1 = y_0 + \tfrac{1}{2}hy'_K + \tfrac{1}{2}h(x_0 + h)^2 + \tfrac{1}{2}h(y_0 + hy'_K)^3.$$

Verify that this agrees with the Taylor expansion up to the h^2 term.

19.4 Fourth-Order Runge Formula

> A formula is fourth-order if its expansion in powers of the steplength agrees with the exact Taylor expansion up to the h^4 term. The error in each step is then expected to be proportional to h^5, and the total error proportional to h^4.

The formulas can be obtained by extending equation (19.11) to use a slope which is a weighted average over 4 points. So suppose equation (19.11) is generalized to

$$y_1 = y_0 + h\{tf(K) + uf(L) + vf(M) + wf(N)\} \tag{19.15}$$

where the weights t, u, v, w and the points L, M, N are to be chosen so that the formula is fourth-order.

In the previous section the expansion of equation (19.11) showed that one of the weights w in the average was arbitrary, and that once w was fixed the remaining weight and the coordinates of the second point were determined by the condition that the formula was second-order. For equation (19.15) the Taylor series comparison again leads to relations between the weights and the coordinates of the points. These relations show that two of the weights are arbitrary. When these are fixed, the other two weights and the coordinates of L, M, and N are determined by the condition that the formula is fourth-order.

The details of this demonstration will not be given here, but three of the possible resulting formulas will be described.

A common choice of v and w is $v = \frac{1}{3}$, $w = \frac{1}{6}$ leading to $t = \frac{1}{6}$, $u = \frac{1}{3}$ and the points

$$L(x_0 + \tfrac{1}{2}h, \, y_0 + \tfrac{1}{2}hy'_K), \, M(x_0 + \tfrac{1}{2}h, \, y_0 + \tfrac{1}{2}hy'_L), \, N(x_0 + h, \, y_0 + hy'_M). \tag{19.16}$$

Substituting into equation (19.15) gives the **Runge formula**

$$y_1 = y_0 + \tfrac{1}{6}h\{f(K) + 2f(L) + 2f(M) + f(N)\} \tag{19.17}$$

$$= y_0 + \tfrac{1}{6}h\{y'_K + 2y'_L + 2y'_M + y'_N\}$$

where K is the known point (x_0, y_0), and L, M, N are given in equation (19.16). The y-coordinate of each point is obtained using the value of f calculated at the previous point, e.g. $y'_L = f(L) = f(x_0 + \tfrac{1}{2}h, \, y_0 + \tfrac{1}{2}hy'_K)$.

Example 19.40

Repeating the calculation in Example 19.21 using equation (19.17) gives results with 9D accuracy when $h = 0.01$, and 5D accuracy when $h = 0.1$. The following table compares various errors:

	$x = 0.6$	$x = 0.7$	$x = 0.8$	$x = 0.9$	$x = 1.0$
(19.17) with $h_1 = 0.01$	0.67 E−10	1.0 E−10	1.3 E−10	1.5 E−10	1.7 E−10
(19.17) with $h_2 = 0.1$	0.50 E−6	0.74 E−6	0.86 E−6	0.94 E−6	1.0 E−6
(19.9) with $h_1 = 0.01$	−2 E−6	−3 E−6	−4 E−6	−5 E−6	−7 E−6

The second-order formula (errors in last line) evidently gives a greater build-up of error. The ratios of the errors in the first two lines are approximately $(h_1/h_2)^4 = 10^{-4}$, as expected. □

The weights $u = v = \frac{3}{8}$, $t = w = \frac{1}{8}$ give the $\frac{3}{8}$ **rule or Kutta's formula**. The points in equation (19.15) are then $L(x_0 + \frac{1}{3}h, y_0 + \frac{1}{3}hy_K')$, $M(x_0 + \frac{2}{3}h, y_0 - \frac{1}{3}hy_K' + hy_L')$ and $N(x_0 + h, y_0 + hy_K' - hy_L' + hy_M')$.

The weights $u = \frac{1}{3}(1 - \sqrt{\frac{1}{2}})$, $v = \frac{1}{3}(1 + \sqrt{\frac{1}{2}})$, $t = w = \frac{1}{6}$ are called Gill's coefficients. The points in equation (19.15) are then $L(x_0 + \frac{1}{2}h, y_0 + \frac{1}{2}hy_K')$, $M(x_0 + \frac{1}{2}h, y_0 + h(-\frac{1}{2} + \sqrt{\frac{1}{2}})y_K' + h(1 - \sqrt{\frac{1}{2}})y_L')$, and $N(x_0 + h, y_0 - h\sqrt{\frac{1}{2}}y_L' + h(1 + \sqrt{\frac{1}{2}})y_M')$.

Exercise (answer on p. 504)

19.4.1   Consider $dy/dx = x + y$, $y = y_0$ when $x = x_0$. Express the following in terms of x_0, y_0 and h:

  (i) the Taylor expansion in powers of h, to the h^4 term;
  (ii) the coordinates of the points used in the Runge formula (19.17);
  (iii) the coordinates of the points used in the Kutta formula;
  (iv) the coordinates of the points used with Gill's coefficients.
  Verify that the three formulas are fourth-order.

19.5   Computer Implementation

Any of the above formulas can be programmed as a subroutine with parameters x, y and h. On entering the subroutine, $x = x_0$ and $y = y_0$; the new values $x = x_1 = x_0 + h$ and $y = y_1$ are returned to the main program. The formulas require evaluation of the function f which appears in the differential equation $dy/dx = f(x, y)$, so a function subroutine is also convenient. The input to the main program will be the given initial condition (x_0, y_0), the chosen steplength h, and the final value of x at which the program is terminated.

A possible flowchart of these operations is:

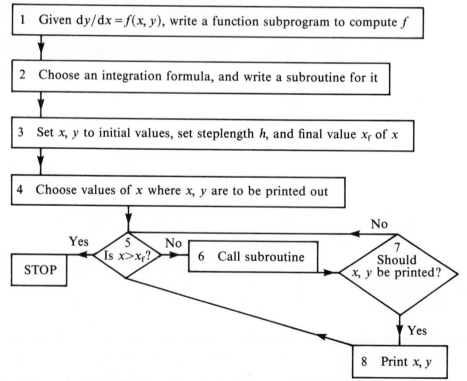

The programs in Appendix C are based on this sequence of operations.

19.6 Second-Order Equations

The above methods can be extended to second-order equations because a second-order equation is always equivalent to two first-order equations. A rather natural example of this decomposition is provided by Newton's second law of motion

$$m\frac{d^2s}{dt^2} = F(s, t), \tag{19.18}$$

where $s(t)$ is the position at time t of a particle of mass m, and $F(s, t)$ gives the force acting on the particle. This equation arises from

$$m\frac{dv}{dt} = F, \quad \text{where } v = \frac{ds}{dt} \text{ is the velocity.}$$

Similarly,

a general second-order equation, say

$$\frac{d^2y}{dx^2} = f\left(x, y, \frac{dy}{dx}\right)$$

is equivalent to the two first-order equations

$$\frac{dp}{dx} = f(x, y, p), \quad \frac{dy}{dx} = p. \tag{19.19}$$

Example 19.60

$$\frac{d^2y}{dx^2} + 4\frac{dy}{dx} + 3y = 0$$

becomes

$$\frac{dp}{dx} = -4p - 3y, \quad \frac{dy}{dx} = p. \quad \square$$

A particular solution of a second-order equation is usually fixed by two given conditions, since there are two arbitrary constants in a general solution. These conditions are called **initial conditions** if they are the values of y and $p = dy/dx$ at the same point K, i.e.

$$y = y_0 \quad \text{and} \quad p = p_0 \quad \text{at } x = x_0 \tag{19.20}$$

The name 'initial conditions' comes from the mechanics application (19.18) in which values of s and v at $t = 0$ are often given. Provided the two given conditions have the form (19.20), the two equations (19.19) can be integrated together by the methods already described.

For example, the Euler formula is

$$y_1 = y_0 + hf(x_0, y_0) \tag{19.5}$$

for the integration of $dy/dx = f(x, y)$. This can be extended to the pair of equations

$$\frac{dy}{dx} = p, \quad \frac{dp}{dx} = f(x, y, p) \tag{19.19}$$

giving

$$y_1 = y_0 + hp_0, \qquad p_1 = p_0 + hf(x_0, y_0, p_0) \tag{19.21}$$

$$y_2 = y_1 + hp_1, \qquad y_2 = p_1 + hf(x_1, y_1, p_1), \quad \text{etc.}$$

Before writing down the higher-order formulas, suitable extensions of the previous notation will be given. In the formulas for integrating $dy/dx = f(x, y)$, a value of the derivative of y was denoted by y'_L or by $f(L)$. Similarly formulas for integrating $dp/dx = f(x, y, p)$ involve values of the derivative of p that will be denoted by p'_L, or by $f(L')$, where L' is a point in a 3-dimensional space in which the third coordinate is p. Formulas for integrating $dy/dx = p$ use values of the derivative of y, which can be denoted by y'_L as before. This value y'_L is the third coordinate of L'.

For example the Euler formula (19.21) can be written either $y_1 = y_0 + hy'_K$, $p_1 = p_0 + hp'_K$ or $y_1 = y_0 + hy'_K$, $p_1 = p_0 + hf(K')$, where K' is $K'(x_0, y_0, p_0)$ and $y'_K = p_0$ is the third coordinate of K'.

Now consider the extension of the **improved Euler formula** (19.9). The Euler formula (19.21) gives the point $L'(x_0 + h, y_0 + hy'_K, p_0 + hp'_K)$, in which the third coordinate is a predicted value of $p = dy/dx$, i.e. $y'_L = p_0 + hp'_K$. The improved Euler formula corresponding to equation (19.7) or (19.8) is then

$$y_1 = y_0 + \tfrac{1}{2}h(y'_K + y'_L),$$

$$p_1 = p_0 + \tfrac{1}{2}h\{f(K') + f(L')\} = p_0 + \tfrac{1}{2}h(p'_K + p'_L) \tag{19.22}$$

where K' is $K'(x_0, y_0, p_0 = y'_K)$ and L' is $L'(x_0 + h, y_0 + hy'_K, p_0 + hp'_K = y'_L)$.

Finally the **fourth-order Runge formulas** will be written down. There are two equations, as in (19.22), but each uses an average over four derivatives in analogy to equations (19.16) and (19.17):

$$y_1 = y_0 + \tfrac{1}{6}h(y'_K + 2y'_L + 2y'_M + y'_N),$$

$$p_1 = p_0 + \tfrac{1}{6}h\{f(K') + 2f(L') + 2f(M') + f(N')\} \tag{19.23}$$

where y'_K, y'_L, y'_M, y'_N are the third coordinates of $K'(x_0, y_0, p_0)$, L', M' and N'. The coordinates of L', M', N' are calculated in succession as in equation (19.16):

$$L' \text{ is } (x_0 + \tfrac{1}{2}h, y_0 + \tfrac{1}{2}hy'_K, p_0 + \tfrac{1}{2}hp'_K = y'_L) \text{ with } y'_K = p_0 \text{ and } p'_K = f(K');$$

$$M' \text{ is } (x_0 + \tfrac{1}{2}h, y_0 + \tfrac{1}{2}hy'_L, p_0 + \tfrac{1}{2}hp'_L = y'_M) \text{ with } y'_L = p_0 + \tfrac{1}{2}hp'_K, p'_L = f(L'); \tag{19.24}$$

and

$$N' \text{ is } (x_0 + h, y_0 + hy'_M, p_0 + hp'_M) \text{ with } y'_M = p_0 + \tfrac{1}{2}hp'_L, p'_M = f(M').$$

In equation (19.24), each y-coordinate is obtained using the derivative of y at the previous point (its third coordinate), and each p-coordinate is obtained using the second derivative (i.e. value of f) at the previous point.

Example 19.61

Consider $d^2y/dx^2 + 2xy \, dy/dx = x^2$ with the initial conditions $y = 1$, $dy/dx = -1$ at $x = 1$.

Take steplength $h = 0.1$. The two first-order equations are

$$\frac{dy}{dx} = p \tag{19.25}$$

$$\frac{dp}{dx} = x^2 - 2xyp. \tag{19.26}$$

Applying Euler's formula to equation (19.25), using the given initial conditions, gives

$$y_1 = 1 + (0.1)(-1) = 0.9 \quad \text{at } x = 1.1.$$

From equation (19.26), $dp/dx = 1 + 2 = 3$ at $x = 1$, so applying Euler's formula gives

$$p_1 = -1 + (0.1)(3) = -0.7 \quad \text{at } x = 1.1.$$

These calculated values y_1 and p_1 are input for the next step: application of Euler's formula to equation (19.25) gives

$$y_2 = 0.9 + (0.1)(-0.7) = 0.83;$$

calculation of dp/dx at $x = 1.1$ gives

$$(1.1)^2 - 2(1.1)(0.9)(-0.7) = 2.596;$$

application of Euler's formula to equation (19.26) gives

$$p_2 = -0.7 + (0.1)(2.596) = -0.4404$$

The information obtained consists of points and slopes at these points (Fig. 19.2).   □

    The computer implementation of the improved Euler formulas (19.22) and the Runge formulas (19.23) is given in Appendix C. The flowchart in Section 19.5 requires minor changes: $d^2y/dx^2 = f(x, y, dy/dx)$ in 1; x, y, p (instead of just x, y) in 3, 4, 7 and 8.

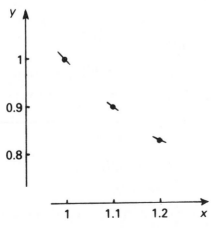

Figure 19.2   Integration of equation (19.26) from $(x, y, p) = (1, 1, -1)$

Exercises (answers on p. 505)

19.6.1 Express each of the following equations as two coupled first-order equations in the form required for numerical integration:

(i) $x^2 \dfrac{d^2y}{dx^2} + x\dfrac{dy}{dx} + (x^2 - n^2)y = 0$ (Bessel's equation)

(ii) $(1-x^2)\dfrac{d^2y}{dx^2} - 2x\dfrac{dy}{dx} + n(n+1)y = 0$ (Legendre's equation)

19.6.2 Write down formulas for the integration of $dy/dx = p$, $dp/dx = f(x, y, p)$ which are an extension of the second-order formula

$$y_1 = y_0 + hf(x_0 + \tfrac{1}{2}h, \, y_0 + \tfrac{1}{2}hy_0') \qquad\qquad (19.10)$$

for the integration of $dy/dx = f(x, y)$. ($y_0' = f(x_0, y_0)$.)

19.6.3 Consider the equation $d^2y/dx^2 + 4\, dy/dx + 3y = 0$ with the initial conditions $y = 1$ and $dy/dx = 2$ at $x = x_0$. Show that two steps with Euler's formula give

$$y_2 = 1 + 4h - 11h^2, \quad p_2 = 2 - 22h + 38h^2. \qquad\qquad (*)$$

What feature of the equation ensures that these results are independent of x_0?
  For $x_0 = 0$, the solution is $y = -\tfrac{3}{2}e^{-3x} + \tfrac{5}{2}e^{-x}$. Expand this in powers of x to the x^3 term, and compare with $(*)$ at $x = 2h$.

19.6.4 Consider $d^2y/dx^2 + 2xy\, dy/dx = x^2$ with the initial conditions $y = 2$, $dy/dx = \tfrac{1}{2}$ at $x = 3$. Express in terms of h the approximations y_1 and p_1 obtained from the improved Euler formulas (19.22).

19.6.5 Consider $d^2y/dx^2 = x^2 + y^2$ with the initial conditions $y = 2$, $dy/dx = \tfrac{1}{2}$ at $x = 0$. Express in terms of h the approximation y_1 obtained from the Runge formulas (19.23) and (19.24).

Answers to Exercises 19.3.1–19.6.5

19.3.1 The Taylor series is ($y' = y_K' = x_0^2 + y_0^3$)

$$y_1 = y_0 + hy' + (x_0 + \tfrac{3}{2}y_0^2 y')h^2 + (2 + 6x_0 y_0^2 + 6x_0^2 y_0 y' + 15 y_0^4 y')h^3.$$

19.4.1 Taylor series $y_1 = y_0 + (x_0 + y_0)h + (1 + x_0 + y_0)(\tfrac{1}{2}h^2 + \tfrac{1}{6}h^3 + \tfrac{1}{24}h^4)$.

Runge: $L(x_0 + \tfrac{1}{2}h, \, y_0 + \tfrac{1}{2}h\{x_0 + y_0\})$,

$\qquad\quad M(x_0 + \tfrac{1}{2}h, \, y_0 + \tfrac{1}{2}h\{x_0 + y_0\} + \tfrac{1}{4}h^2\{1 + x_0 + y_0\})$,

$\qquad\quad N(x_0 + h, \, y_0 + h\{x_0 + y_0\} + \{\tfrac{1}{2}h^2 + \tfrac{1}{4}h^3\}\{1 + x_0 + y_0\})$.

Kutta: $L(x_0 + \tfrac{1}{3}h, \, y_0 + \tfrac{1}{3}h\{x_0 + y_0\})$,

$\qquad\quad M(x_0 + \tfrac{2}{3}h, \, y_0 + \tfrac{2}{3}h\{x_0 + y_0\} + \tfrac{1}{3}h^2\{1 + x_0 + y_0\})$,

$\qquad\quad N(x_0 + h, \, y_0 + h\{x_0 + y_0\} + \{\tfrac{1}{3}h^2 + \tfrac{1}{3}h^3\}\{1 + x_0 + y_0\})$.

Gill: $L(x_0 + \tfrac{1}{2}h, \, y_0 + \tfrac{1}{2}h\{x_0 + y_0\})$,

$\qquad\quad M(x_0 + \tfrac{1}{2}h, \, y_0 + \tfrac{1}{2}h\{x_0 + y_0\} + \tfrac{1}{2}h^2(1 - \sqrt{\tfrac{1}{2}})\{1 + x_0 + y_0\})$,

$\qquad\quad N(x_0 + h, \, y_0 + h\{x_0 + y_0\} + \{\tfrac{1}{2}h^2 + \tfrac{1}{4}h^3\}\{1 + x_0 + y_0\})$.

19.6.1 (i) $\dfrac{dy}{dx} = p, \dfrac{dp}{dx} = -\dfrac{p}{x} + \left(\dfrac{n^2}{x^2} - 1\right) y$

(ii) $\dfrac{dy}{dx} = p, \dfrac{dp}{dx} = \dfrac{2xp - n^2 y - ny}{1 - x^2}$

19.6.2 $y_1 = y_0 + h y_L'$ with $y_L' = p_0 + \frac{1}{2} h p_K' = p_0 + \frac{1}{2} h f(x_0, y_0, p_0)$

$p_1 = p_0 + h f(L') = p_0 + h f(x_0 + \frac{1}{2}h, y_0 + \frac{1}{2}h y_K', p_0 + \frac{1}{2}h p_K')$

with $y_K' = p_0$.

19.6.3 Equation does not depend on x. At $x = 2h$, series expansions give

$$y = 1 + 4h - 22h^2, \qquad p = 2 - 22h + 19h^2.$$

19.6.4 $y_1 = 2 + \frac{1}{2}h + \frac{3}{2}h^2$, $p_1 = \frac{1}{2} + 3h - \frac{67}{4}h^2 - \frac{41}{4}h^3 - \frac{3}{2}h^4$.

19.6.5 $y_1 = 2 + \frac{1}{2}h + 2h^2 + \frac{5}{24}h^3 + \frac{37}{48}h^4 + \frac{1}{12}h^5 + \frac{1}{6}h^6$.

Further Exercises on Chapter 19

19.1 The solution of

$$x \frac{dy}{dx} = y + x^2, \qquad y = 12 \quad \text{when} \quad x = 3$$

is $y = x + x^2$ (Exercise 13.2.2). Verify that the approximations given by equations (19.9) and (19.10) agree with this to second-order.

19.2 If $y = s(x)$ and $y = t(x)$ are two (distinct) particular solutions of a first-order linear equation $dy/dx = R(x) - yQ(x)$, show that $y = (1 - A)s(x) + At(x)$ is a form of the general solution.

The following table shows two numerical solutions of $dy/dx = y + 2xy + e^x$ (obtained for $y = 0$ when $x = 0$ and $y = -1$ when $x = 0$):

x	0	0.2	0.4	0.6	0.8	1.0
s	0	0.251	0.665	1.40	2.78	5.52
t	-1	-1.02	-1.09	-1.21	-1.44	-1.87

By finding A in the general solution, calculate from the values of s and t the corresponding values of the solutions determined by (i) $y = -\frac{1}{2}$ when $x = 0$ (ii) $y = 0$ when $x = 1$.

19.3 Write down Euler-type formulas for the numerical integration of the coupled equations

$$\frac{dx}{dt} = f(x, y, t), \qquad \frac{dy}{dt} = g(x, y, t),$$

from the initial conditions $x = x_0$ and $y = y_0$ at $t = t_0$.

19.4 Write down the formulas corresponding to the $\frac{3}{8}$ rule (Kutta's formula) for the second-order equation

$$\frac{d^2 y}{dx^2} = f\left(x, y, \frac{dy}{dx}\right)$$

with $y = y_0$ and $\dfrac{dy}{dx} = p_0$ at $x = x_0$.

19.5 If $y = s(x)$, $y = t(x)$ and $y = u(x)$ are three particular solutions of a second-order linear equation

$$\frac{d^2 y}{dx^2} + f(x)\frac{dy}{dx} + g(x)y = r(x),$$

and there is no c such that $s(x) = (1 + c)t(x) - cu(x)$, then (Exercise 13.51) $y = As(x) + (B + 1 - A)t(x) - Bu(x)$ is a form of the general solution.

The following table shows numerical values for three solutions of

$$(1 - x^2)\frac{d^2 y}{dx^2} - 2x\frac{dy}{dx} + 2y = 1 - 2x^2.$$

x	$s(x)$	$s'(x)$	$t(x)$	$t'(x)$	$u(x)$	$u'(x)$
0	0	1	0	2	1	0
0.25	0.28	1.25	0.53	2.25	0.9674	−0.2723
0.5	0.625	1.5	1.125	2.5	0.8504	−0.7166

Calculate the value at $x = 0.25$ of the solution determined by the boundary conditions $y = 0.5$ at $x = 0$ and at $x = 0.5$.

19.6 The following results appeared as exercises after Chapter 13. Use a numerical method to check them.

(i) $y = -\frac{1}{4}e^x + x e^x - \frac{1}{2}\sin x + \frac{1}{4}e^{-x}$ is the solution of $d^2 y/dx^2 - 2\,dy/dx + y = \cos x + e^{-x}$ satisfying $y = dy/dx = 0$ at $x = 0$;

(ii) $y = \frac{1}{2}(x + 2)^3$ is the solution of $x^2\,d^2 y/dx^2 - 2x\,dy/dx + 2y = x^3 + 8$ satisfying $y = dy/dx = \frac{27}{2}$ when $x = 1$;

(iii) $y = \frac{1}{290}(-81\,e^{-3t} + 92\,e^{-2t} - 11\,e^{3t}\cos 2t + 13\,e^{3t}\sin 2t)$ is the solution of $d^2 y/dt^2 + 5\,dy/dt + 6y = 2\,e^{3t}\sin 2t$ satisfying $y = dy/dt = 0$ at $x = 0$.

19.7 If $g(h) = f(x_0 + h, y_0 + hp_0, p_0 + hp'_K)$, where $p'_K = f(K') = f(x_0, y_0, p_0)$ does not depend on h, show that (cf. Section 18.6, e.g. Example 18.62)

$$g'(0) = f_x(K') + p_0 f_y(K') + f(K')f_p(K').$$

Use this to expand the improved Euler formulas (19.22) in powers of h up to the h^2 term.

By differentiating the equation $d^2 y/dx^2 = f(x, y, dy/dx)$, show that

$$y = y_0 + p_0(x - x_0) + \tfrac{1}{2}f(K')(x - x_0)^2$$
$$+ \tfrac{1}{6}\{f_x(K') + p_0 f_y(K') + f(K')f_p(K')\}(x - x_0)^3 + \cdots$$

is the Taylor expansion of the solution ($y = y_0$, $p = p_0$ when $x = x_0$). Hence verify that equation (19.22) is second-order.

20

Laplace Transforms

20.1   Definition of the Laplace Transform

If $f(x)$ is defined for $x > 0$, then the Laplace transform of f is a function F defined by

$$F(p) = \int_0^\infty e^{-px} f(x)\, dx. \tag{20.1}$$

The domain of the transform function F is the set of real values of p for which the (improper) integral exists. Since e^{-px} is a decreasing function of p, this domain is $p > p_0$ for some p_0 determined by f.

Example 20.10
If n is a non-negative integer, then (Example 10.75)

$$\int_0^\infty e^{-t} t^n\, dt = n! \qquad \text{(Note: } 0! = 1\text{)}$$

Substituting $t = px$, where $p > 0$:

$$\int_0^\infty e^{-px} p^n x^n p\, dx = n!$$

Taking p^{n+1} outside the integral, and dividing by p^{n+1}, shows that the Laplace transform of $f(x) = x^n$ is $F(p) = n!/p^{n+1}\,(p > 0)$. □

Example 20.11

(i) $\displaystyle \int_0^\infty e^{-px} e^{ax}\, dx = \left[\frac{e^{-px+ax}}{-p+a}\right]_{x=0}^\infty = 0 - \frac{1}{-p+a} \qquad (p > a).$

The Laplace transform of $f(x) = e^{ax}$ is therefore $F(p) = 1/(p-a)$.
(ii) If in (i) ia replaces a, the real and imaginary parts of $1/(p-ia) = (p+ia)/(p^2+a^2)$ give the Laplace transforms of the functions $\cos ax$ and $\sin ax$. □

The symbol L will be used to denote the operation of taking the Laplace transform, so that

$$Lf(x) = \int_0^\infty e^{-px} f(x)\, dx = F(p). \tag{20.2}$$

The statement that L is a **linear operator** means that

$$L\{cf(x)\} = c\{Lf(x)\} \quad \text{and} \quad L\{f(x)+g(x)\} = L\{f(x)\} + L\{g(x)\}. \qquad (20.3)$$

These equations follow from basic properties of any integral (equations (9.6) and (9.7) in Section 9.3).

Example 20.12

From Example 20.11,

$$L(\cos 3x) = \frac{p}{p^2+9}, \qquad L(\sin 3x) = \frac{3}{p^2+9}.$$

From the linear property (20.3),

$$L(k \cos 3x) = \frac{kp}{p^2+9}, \qquad L(\cos 3x + \sin 3x) = \frac{p+3}{p^2+9}. \quad \square$$

Further examples of Laplace transforms are given in the table at the end of the chapter. These results can be extended by

Theorem 20.1   If $F(p) = Lf(x)$, then $L\{e^{-bx}f(x)\} = F(p+b)$.

This follows from the definition (20.2):

$$L\{e^{-bx}f(x)\} = \int_0^\infty e^{-px}\, e^{-bx}f(x)\, dx = \int_0^\infty e^{-(p+b)x}f(x)\, dx = F(p+b),$$

on changing p to $(p+b)$ in equation (20.2).

Example 20.13

From the results (Examples 20.10, 20.12)

$$L(x^3) = \frac{6}{p^4}, \qquad L(\cos 3x) = \frac{p}{p^2+9},$$

Theorem 20.1 gives results such as

$$L(x^3 e^{-2x}) = \frac{6}{(p+2)^4}, \qquad L(e^{-x}\cos 3x) = \frac{p+1}{p^2+2p+10}. \quad \square$$

Exercises (answers on p. 514)

20.1.1   Evaluate $\int_0^\infty x\, e^{(-p+ia)x}\, dx$ $(p>0)$ by integrating by parts. Deduce the Laplace transforms of $x \cos ax$ and $x \sin ax$ (see the table at the end of this chapter).

20.1.2   The following results can be written down using the table of Laplace transforms at the end of the chapter and the general properties already given. For each result below, state which table formula and which general property has been used:

(i) $L(x^3+x^2) = \dfrac{6}{p^4} + \dfrac{2}{p^3}$

(ii) $L(3e^{ax}) = \dfrac{3}{p-a}$

(iii) $L(e^x \sin ax) = \dfrac{a}{p^2 - 2p + 1 + a^2}$

(iv) $L(e^{-2x} \cos 3x + 2e^{-2x} \sin 3x) = \dfrac{p+8}{p^2 + 4p + 13}.$

20.2 Inversion of Transforms

In order to use Laplace transforms it is usually necessary to be able to recover the function $f(x)$ when $Lf(x) = F(p)$ is known. This is called inverting the transform, and can be regarded as the action on $F(p)$ of an operator L^{-1} which is the inverse of L. A general method of inversion involves a complex integral which is beyond the scope of this book, which will therefore use known transforms as a basis for inversion.

Example 20.20
From the results in Exercise 20.1.2 above, one has the inverse results

(i) $L^{-1}\left(\dfrac{6}{p^4} + \dfrac{2}{p^3}\right) = x^3 + x^2,$ (ii) $L^{-1}\left(\dfrac{3}{p-a}\right) = 3e^{ax}$, etc. □

Because L is a linear operator, as expressed by the properties in equation (20.3), it follows that L^{-1} is also linear, i.e.

$$L^{-1}\{cF(p)\} = cL^{-1}\{F(p)\},$$

$$L^{-1}\{F(p) + G(p)\} = L^{-1}\{F(p)\} + L^{-1}\{G(p)\}.$$

(20.4)

Example 20.21 (cf. Example 20.20)

$$L^{-1}\left(\dfrac{6}{p^4} + \dfrac{2}{p^3}\right) = L^{-1}\left(\dfrac{6}{p^4}\right) + L^{-1}\left(\dfrac{2}{p^3}\right), \quad L^{-1}\left(\dfrac{3}{p-a}\right) = 3L^{-1}\left(\dfrac{1}{p-a}\right). □$$

The inverse of Theorem 20.1 can also be written down:

Theorem 20.2 If $L^{-1}F(p) = f(x)$, then $L^{-1}F(p+b) = e^{-bx}f(x).$

Example 20.22
Invert the Laplace transform $(3p+7)/(p^2 + 4p + 13).$

The table of transforms gives the inverses of $p/(p^2 + a^2)$ and $1/(p^2 + a^2)$, suggesting a completion of the square in the given denominator: $(3p+7)/(p^2 + 4p + 13) = (3(p+2)+1)/((p+2)^2 + 9).$ Evidently Theorem 20.2 can be used with $b = 2$. So consider first

$$L^{-1}\left(\dfrac{3p+1}{p^2+9}\right) = 3L^{-1}\left(\dfrac{p}{p^2+9}\right) + L^{-1}\left(\dfrac{1}{p^2+9}\right) \quad \text{from equations (20.4)}$$

$$= 3\cos 3x + \tfrac{1}{3}\sin 3x \quad \text{(from the table on p. 515)}.$$

Finally Theorem 20.2 gives
$$L^{-1}((3(p+2)+1)/((p+2)^2 + 9)) = e^{-2x}(3\cos 3x + \tfrac{1}{3}\sin 3x). □$$

The table at the end of the chapter shows that the invertible functions are just the basic partial fractions into which any rational function can be decomposed (cf. Section 10.4) so any rational function of p can be inverted.

Example 20.23
Invert the Laplace transform $F(p) = (5p^2 - 11p + 8)/(p^3 - 3p^2 + 2p)$.

Method: Express the given rational function in partial fractions.

$$F(p) = \frac{4}{p} + \frac{3}{p-2} - \frac{2}{p-1}.$$

(For the algebraic details, see Example 10.45.) Then

$$L^{-1}F(p) = 4L^{-1}\left(\frac{1}{p}\right) + 3L^{-1}\left(\frac{1}{p-2}\right) - 2L^{-1}\left(\frac{1}{p-1}\right), \quad \text{using equation (20.4)}$$

$$= 4 + 3e^{2x} - 2e^x, \quad \text{using L4 in the table of transforms.}   \quad\square$$

Example 20.24
Invert the Laplace transform $F(p) = 16/(p^3 - 2p^2 - 4p + 8)$.

The partial fractions expression (see Example 10.46) is

$$F(p) = \frac{4}{(p-2)^2} - \frac{1}{p-2} + \frac{1}{p+2}.$$

From L1 in the table of transforms, $L^{-1}(1/p^2) = x$. Then Theorem 20.2 with $b = -2$ gives $L^{-1}(1/(p-2)^2) = x\, e^{2x}$. Using also L4 from the table,

$$L^{-1}F(p) = 4x\, e^{2x} - e^{2x} + e^{-2x}.   \quad\square$$

Example 20.25
Invert the Laplace transform $F(p) = (4p^2 - 9p + 10)/(p^3 - 4p^2 + 5p)$.

The partial fractions expression (see Example 10.47) is

$$F(p) = \frac{2}{p} + \frac{2p-1}{p^2 - 4p + 5} = \frac{2}{p} + \frac{2(p-2)+3}{(p-2)^2 + 1}.$$

Using L1, L2 and L3 from the table, and Theorem 20.2 with $b = -2$:

$$L^{-1}F(p) = 2 + e^{2x} \cos x + 3\, e^{2x} \sin x.   \quad\square$$

Since $e^{-px} \to 0$ as $p \to \infty$,

$$\boxed{\; F(p) = \int_0^\infty e^{-px} f(x)\, dx \to 0 \quad \text{as } p \to \infty. \;}$$

This property of the transforms is evident in the table, and $F(p)$ cannot be inverted unless it has this property. A rational function must have the degree of the numerator less than that of the denominator.

Exercises (answers on p. 515)

20.2.1 Use the table at the end of the chapter, together with Theorem 20.2 and equation (20.4), to write down inverses of the following Laplace transforms:

(i) $\dfrac{2}{p^4}$ (ii) $\dfrac{3}{p-1}$ (iii) $\dfrac{2p+3}{p^2+4}$ (iv) $\dfrac{2p+3}{p^2-4}$ (v) $\dfrac{2p+3}{(p^2+4)^2}$

(vi) $\dfrac{p-1}{(p-2)^2}$ (vii) $\dfrac{4p}{p^2-2p+2}$ (viii) $\dfrac{p^2+p+1}{p^3}$.

20.2.2 Obtain the following results by expressing the given transform in partial fractions:

(i) $L^{-1}\left(\dfrac{5p-3}{p^2-2p-3}\right)=2e^{-x}+3e^{3x}$

(ii) $L^{-1}\left(\dfrac{1}{p^3+p}\right)=1-\cos x$

(iii) $L^{-1}\left(\dfrac{5p^2-11p+8}{p^3-2p^2+2p}\right)=4+e^x(\cos x-2\sin x).$

20.3 Solution of Differential Equations using Laplace Transforms

For some linear differential equations, a solution may be obtained as follows:

(i) apply the operator L to the equation;
(ii) solve the resulting equation for the transform of the solution;
(iii) invert the transform.

This method is straightforward for constant coefficient equations such as

$$\frac{d^2y}{dx^2}+2a\frac{dy}{dx}+by=R(x), \tag{20.5}$$

provided the transform of $R(x)$ can be obtained. A glance at the table of transforms shows that the $R(x)$ allowed by this condition are just those nonhomogeneous terms that allowed a particular solution to be found by using trial functions (in Section 13.4). The examples presented below thus illustrate the method rather than give solutions not previously obtained.

In order to transform equation (20.5), the relation between the transforms of $f(x)$ and $f'(x)$ is required.

Theorem 20.3 If $F(p)=Lf(x)$, then $Lf'(x)=-f(0)+pF(p)$.

This is demonstrated by the following integration by parts:

$$Lf'(x)=\int_0^\infty e^{-px}f'(x)\,dx=[e^{-px}f(x)]_0^\infty+\int_0^\infty p\,e^{-px}f(x)\,dx$$

$$=-f(0)+pF(p) \qquad (p>0).$$

The corresponding result for the second derivative is obtained by integrating $Lf''(x)$ by parts twice.

Theorem 20.4 If $F(p) = Lf(x)$, then $Lf''(x) = -f'(0) - pf(0) + p^2 F(p)$.

Because $f(0)$ and $f'(0)$ appear in these results, the Laplace transform method is most useful if a particular solution satisfying given initial conditions is required. Then $f(0)$ and $f'(0)$ are prescribed.

Example 20.30
Find the solution of

$$\frac{d^2y}{dx^2} - 5\frac{dy}{dx} - 6y = 14\,e^{-x}$$

satisfying $y = 3$ and $dy/dx = 9$ at $x = 0$.

The required solution $y = f(x)$ has $f(0) = 3$, $f'(0) = 9$. Taking the Laplace transform of each side of the differential equation gives

$$L\left(\frac{d^2y}{dx^2} - 5\frac{dy}{dx} - 6y\right) = L(14\,e^{-x}) = 14\,L(e^{-x}) = \frac{14}{p+1}.$$

Using Theorems 20.3 and 20.4, the left side is

$$L\{f''(x) - 5f'(x) - 6f(x)\} = -9 - 3p + p^2 F(p) - 5\{-3 + pF(p)\} - 6F(p),$$

so the transformed equation can be written

$$(p^2 - 5p - 6)F(p) + 6 - 3p = \frac{14}{p+1},$$

$$(p^2 - 5p - 6)F(p) = 3p - 6 + \frac{14}{p+1} = \frac{3p^2 - 3p + 8}{p+1}.$$

The Laplace transform of the required particular solution is therefore

$$F(p) = \frac{3p^2 - 3p + 8}{(p+1)^2(p-6)}.$$

To invert this transform, it is expressed in partial fractions:

$$F(p) = \frac{-2}{(p+1)^2} + \frac{1}{p+1} + \frac{2}{p-6}. \tag{20.6}$$

(Substituting $p = 1$ will check this partial fraction expression.) From L4 in the table, $L^{-1}(1/(p+1)) = e^{-x}$, $L^{-1}(2/(p-6)) = 2\,e^{6x}$. From L1 in the table, $L^{-1}(-2/p^2) = -2x$, and Theorem 20.2 with $b = 1$ gives $L^{-1}(-2/(p+1)^2) = -2x\,e^{-x}$. Thus the required solution, the inverse of equation (20.6), is

$$y = f(x) = -2x\,e^{-x} + e^{-x} + 2\,e^{6x}. \quad \square$$

The advantages of the Laplace transform method can now be seen. There is no need to determine a general solution and then have to determine values for arbitrary constants. The given initial conditions are included automatically when the transform is taken. The whole process is quite definite in the sense that there is no step (such as the selection of a trial function for a particular integral) requiring intuition from the solver.

If initial conditions are given at a point $x = a \neq 0$, then the change of variable $x = t + a$ will allow Theorems 20.3 and 20.4 to be used.

Example 20.31
Find the solution of $dy/dx + 2y = e^{2x}$ satisfying $y = 2$ when $x = \ln 2$.

If $t = x - \ln 2$, then $dy/dx = dy/dt$, $e^{2x} = e^{2t} e^{2\ln 2} = 4 e^{2t}$, and the given condition is $y = 2$ when $t = 0$. From Theorem 20.3, applying the Laplace transform operator to

$$\frac{dy}{dt} + 2y = 4 e^{2t}, \qquad y = 2 \quad \text{when } t = 0,$$

gives

$$-2 + pF(p) + 2F(p) = \frac{4}{p-2}.$$

Hence $F(p) = 2p/(p^2 - 4)$, which inverts (L5 in table) to $2 \cosh 2t$. The required solution is obtained by setting $t = x - \ln 2$, $e^{2t} = \frac{1}{4} e^{2x}$:

$$y = \frac{1}{4} e^{2x} + 4 e^{-2x}. \quad \square$$

In principle, the general solution of a differential equation could be obtained by regarding the values of $f(0)$ and $f'(0)$ as arbitrary constants.

Example 20.32
Find the general solution of $dy/dx + 2y = e^{2x}$.

The Laplace transform of the equation is

$$-A + pF(p) + 2F(p) = \frac{1}{p-2},$$

where A is an arbitrary constant. Then $F(p) = (Ap + 1 - 2A)/(p^2 - 4)$ and the general solution can be written

$$y = A \cosh 2x + \tfrac{1}{2}(1 - 2A) \sinh 2x. \quad \square$$

In practice this procedure may be difficult. Special cases, depending on the values of the arbitrary constants, may arise when the transform is inverted. It is also necessary to be sure that the differential equation does allow solutions with arbitrary values at $x = 0$. This is true for constant coefficient linear equations, for which boundary value problems where $f(0)$ is known but $f'(0)$ unknown may be considered.

Example 20.33
Find the solution of $d^2y/dx^2 + 4y = 2 \cos 2x$ which satisfies $y = -1$ when $x = 0$ and $y = \pi/4$ when $x = \pi/4$.

Taking the Laplace transform, using Theorem 20.4, gives

$$-f'(0)+p+p^2F(p)+4F(p)=\frac{2p}{p^2+4},$$

$$F(p)=\frac{2p}{(p^2+4)^2}+\frac{f'(0)}{p^2+4}-\frac{p}{p^2+4}.$$

The inverse is (L8, L3 and L2 in the table)

$$f(x)=\tfrac{1}{2}x\sin 2x+\tfrac{1}{2}f'(0)\sin 2x-\cos 2x.$$

This equation gives a family of solutions all having $f(0)=-1$; the slope $f'(0)$ is arbitrary and still to be chosen. Then

$$f(\tfrac{1}{4}\pi)=\tfrac{1}{8}\pi+\tfrac{1}{2}f'(0),$$

so choosing $f'(0)=\tfrac{1}{4}\pi$ gives the required particular solution, i.e.

$$y=\tfrac{1}{8}(4x+\pi)\sin 2x-\cos 2x.$$

(This method of solving the boundary value problem corresponds to the 'shooting' method for numerical solution, in which the equation is integrated from $x=0$ using trial values for the initial slope.)   □

Exercises (answers on p. 515)
   Use the Laplace transform method to solve the following differential equations with the given conditions.

20.3.1 $2\dfrac{dy}{dx}-y=e^{x/2}$, $y=1$ when $x=0$.

20.3.2 $\dfrac{dy}{dx}+2y=e^{-x}$, $y=-1$ when $x=0$.

20.3.3 $\dfrac{d^2y}{dx^2}+\dfrac{dy}{dx}=x$, $y=0$ and $\dfrac{dy}{dx}=-2$ when $x=0$.

20.3.4 $\dfrac{d^2y}{dx^2}+4\dfrac{dy}{dx}+5y=10$, $y=3$ and $\dfrac{dy}{dx}=0$ when $x=0$.

20.3.5 $\dfrac{dx}{dt}+x=3\,e^{-t}$, $x=2$ when $t=0$.

20.3.6 $\dfrac{dy}{dx}=y+2e^x$, $y=3e$ when $x=1$.

20.3.7 $\dfrac{d^2y}{dx^2}+y=\cos x$, $y=0$ at $x=0$, $y=\dfrac{3\pi}{4}$ at $x=\tfrac{1}{2}\pi$.

Answers to Exercises 20.1.1–20.3.7

20.1.1 $(p+ia)^2/(p^2+a^2)^2$; see L7 and L8 in table.
20.1.2   (i) Equation (20.3) and L1   (ii) Equation (20.3) and L4   (iii) L3 and Theorem 20.1   (iv) Equation (20.3), L2, L3 and Theorem 20.1.

20.2.1 (i) $\frac{1}{3}x^3$ (ii) $3e^x$ (iii) $2\cos 2x + \frac{3}{2}\sin 2x$
(iv) $2\cosh 2x + \frac{3}{2}\sinh 2x$ (v) $\frac{1}{2}x\sin 2x + \frac{3}{16}\sin 2x - \frac{3}{8}\cos 2x$
(vi) $e^{2x} + x e^{2x}$ ($p - 1 = p - 2 + 1$) (vii) $4e^{-x}(\cos x + \sin x)$ ($4p = 4p - 4 + 4$)
(viii) $1 + x + \frac{1}{2}x^2$.

20.3.1 $y = \frac{1}{2}(x + 2)e^{x/2}$ **20.3.2** $y = e^{-x} - 2e^{-2x}$

20.3.3 $y = \frac{1}{2}x^2 - x - 1 + e^{-x}$ **20.3.4** $y = e^{-2x}(\cos x + 2\sin x) + 2$

20.3.5 $x = (2 + 3t)e^{-t}$ **20.3.6** $y = (1 + 2x)e^x$

20.3.7 $y = \frac{1}{2}(\pi + x)\sin x$

Table of Laplace Transforms and Inversions

		Transforms			Inversions	
	$f(x)$	$Lf(x) = F(p)$		$F(p)$		$L^{-1}F(p) = f(x)$
L1	$x^n \ (n \geqslant 0)$	$\dfrac{n!}{p^{n+1}}$	$(p > 0)$	$\dfrac{1}{p^n}$	$(p > 0, n \geqslant 1)$	$\dfrac{x^{n-1}}{(n-1)!}$
L2	$\cos ax$	$\dfrac{p}{p^2 + a^2}$	$(p > 0)$	$\dfrac{p}{p^2 + a^2}$	$(p > 0)$	$\cos ax$
L3	$\sin ax$	$\dfrac{a}{p^2 + a^2}$	$(p > 0)$	$\dfrac{1}{p^2 + a^2}$	$(p > 0)$	$\dfrac{\sin ax}{a}$
L4	e^{ax}	$\dfrac{1}{p - a}$	$(p > a)$	$\dfrac{1}{p + a}$	$(p > -a)$	e^{-ax}
L5	$\cosh ax$	$\dfrac{p}{p^2 - a^2}$	$(p > \lvert a\rvert)$	$\dfrac{p}{p^2 - a^2}$	$(p > \lvert a\rvert)$	$\cosh ax$
L6	$\sinh ax$	$\dfrac{a}{p^2 - a^2}$	$(p > \lvert a\rvert)$	$\dfrac{1}{p^2 - a^2}$	$(p > \lvert a\rvert)$	$\dfrac{\sinh ax}{a}$
L7	$x\cos ax$	$\dfrac{p^2 - a^2}{(p^2 + a^2)^2}$	$(p > 0)$	$\dfrac{1}{(p^2 + a^2)^2}$	$(p > 0)$	$\dfrac{\sin ax - ax\cos ax}{2a^3}$
L8	$x\sin ax$	$\dfrac{2ap}{(p^2 + a^2)^2}$	$(p > 0)$	$\dfrac{p}{(p^2 + a^2)^2}$	$(p > 0)$	$\dfrac{x\sin ax}{2a}$

For comprehensive tables of transforms and inverses see compilations such as
Erdelyi, Magnus, Oberhettinger and Tricomi, *Tables of Integral Transforms* (Bateman Manuscript Project, McGraw-Hill, 1954);
Oberhettinger and Badii, *Tables of Laplace Transforms* (Springer Verlag, 1973).

Further Exercises on Chapter 20

20.1 Invert the following Laplace transforms:

(i) $\dfrac{a^2}{p(p^2 + a^2)}$ (ii) $\dfrac{a^3}{p^2(p^2 + a^2)}$

(iii) $\dfrac{2a^3}{(p^2 + a^2)^2}$ (iv) $\dfrac{1}{p(p-1)(p-2)(p-3)}$

(v) $\dfrac{1}{(p-1)^3(p^3 + 1)}$ (vi) $\dfrac{2}{p(p+1)(p^2 + 1)}$ (vii) $\dfrac{4}{p^4 + 4}$.

20.2   Use Laplace transforms to obtain solutions of the following differential equations satisfying the given conditions:

(i) $\dfrac{d^2y}{dx^2} + 5\dfrac{dy}{dx} + 6y = 0$, $y = 2$ and $\dfrac{dy}{dx} = -3$ at $x = 0$.

(ii) $\dfrac{d^2y}{dx^2} + 5\dfrac{dy}{dx} + 6y = e^{-2x}$, $y = 1$ and $\dfrac{dy}{dx} = -2$ at $x = 0$.

(iii) $\dfrac{d^2y}{dx^2} + 4\dfrac{dy}{dx} + 5y = 40\sin 3x$, $y = \dfrac{dy}{dx} = 0$ when $x = 0$.

20.3   Find the Laplace transform of the function

$$f(x) = 0 \quad \text{for } 0 < x < a \quad \text{and} \quad x > b, \qquad f(x) = 1 \quad \text{for } a < x < b.$$

20.4   Suppose $F(p)$ is the Laplace transform of $f(x)$. Show that the Laplace transform of $g(x)$ where

$$g(x) = 0 \quad \text{for } 0 < x < a, \qquad g(x) = f(x) \quad \text{for } x > a$$

is $G(p) = e^{-pa}F(p)$. Hence, or otherwise, invert the following Laplace transforms:

(i) $\dfrac{e^{-pa}}{p^2 + 1}$ (ii) $\dfrac{e^{-2pa}}{p^4}$ (iii) $\dfrac{p\,e^{-p}}{p^2 + b^2}$.

Appendix A
Complex Numbers

A.1 Introduction

Complex numbers were invented about 400 years ago in connection with the solution of polynomial equations. The quadratic equation

$$ax^2 + bx + c = 0 \qquad \text{(A.1)}$$

has solutions

$$x = \{-b \pm \sqrt{(b^2 - 4ac)}\}/2a \qquad \text{(A.2)}$$

provided that $b^2 \geq 4ac$. If $b^2 < 4ac$ then equation (A.2) cannot be evaluated since it would require the square root of a negative number.

Example 1A
(i) $x^2 + 6x - 3 = 0$ if $x = -3 + \sqrt{12}$, or if $x = -3 - \sqrt{12}$. The graph $y = x^2 + 6x - 3$ cuts the x-axis at the two points $(-3 \pm \sqrt{12}, 0)$. (ii) $x^2 - 2x + 5 = (x-1)^2 + 4 \geq 4$, so $x^2 - 2x + 5 = 0$ has no solution. The graph $y = x^2 - 2x + 5$ does not intersect the x-axis. Substituting into equation (A.2) would give $(b^2 - 4ac) = -16$. ☐

When equation (A.1) does have roots, say r and s given by equation (A.2), then

$$ax^2 + bx + c = a(x - r)(x - s)$$
$$= a(x^2 - rx - sx + rs)$$

and so

$$r + s = -b/a, \qquad rs = c/a. \qquad \text{(A.3)}$$

The idea of a complex number arose by postulating the existence of a quantity i such that $i^2 = -1$.

Then equation (A.2) can be used when $b^2 < 4ac$, in the sense that the formula can be evaluated in terms of i.

Example 2A
Putting $a = 1$, $b = -2$ and $c = 5$ in equation (A.2) leads to $\sqrt{(-16)} = \sqrt{16(-1)} = \sqrt{16}\sqrt{(-1)} = 4i$, assuming that the quantity i can be manipulated as though it were an ordinary number. Then (A.2) gives

$$x = 1 + 2i \quad \text{or} \quad x = 1 - 2i$$

as solutions of $x^2 - 2x + 5 = 0$ (cf. Example 1A). ☐

Since the graph $y = x^2 - 2x + 5$ does not intersect the x-axis, these solutions were considered to be imaginary. (The notation i was derived from the initial letter of imaginary; however, in the extensive applications of complex numbers to electric circuit theory, j is used instead of i, which is the traditional symbol for current.) In the algebra, only the symbol i need be regarded as imaginary, so the solutions $1 \pm 2i$ are said to have **real part** 1 and **imaginary part** ± 2. The imaginary part is the coefficient of i.

> In general, if p and q are numbers, then $p + qi$ is called a **complex number.** Its real part is p and its imaginary part is q.

By contrast p, q, -1, $\sqrt{12}$ etc. may be called **real** numbers. A common convention reserves the symbols x and y for real numbers, and the symbols w and z for complex numbers.

The solution of the quadratic equation (A.1) then depends on whether complex solutions are admitted. If so then equation (A.2) always gives solutions. A notational convention distinguishing real and complex numbers can also be used to indicate what types of solution are allowed.

Example 3A

(i) The equation $x^2 - 2x + 5 = 0$ has no solution (assuming that the use of the symbol x for the unknown means that solutions must be real numbers).

(ii) The equation $z^2 - 2z + 5 = 0$ has two solutions $z = 1 \pm 2i$ (assuming that the use of the symbol z for the unknown means that complex solutions are required).

(iii) The equation $z^2 - 6z + 8 = 0$ has solutions $2 + 0i$ and $4 + 0i$. More generally, if $b^2 \geqslant 4ac$, the solutions of $az^2 + bz + c = 0$ have zero imaginary part. $\square$

Since equations (A.3) can be obtained from the explicit formula (A.2), they remain true when the roots r and s are complex numbers. Indeed the factorization method previously used to get (A.3) remains valid when x is replaced by z.

Example 4A

The roots $1 \pm 2i$ of $z^2 - 2z + 5 = 0$ give

$$r + s = (1 + 2i) + (1 - 2i) = 2 = -b/a$$

$$rs = (1 + 2i)(1 - 2i) = 1 - 4i^2 = 1 + 4 = 5 = c/a.$$ $\square$

Exercises (answers on p. 538)

A1.1 Find the complex numbers which are solutions of the following equations:
  (a) $z^2 - 3z + 2 = 0$ (b) $w^2 - w + 9 = 0$ (c) $z^2 = 2z$

A1.2 Use complex numbers to factorize the following quadratic expressions:
  (a) $w^2 + 2w - 8$ (b) $z^2 + 2z + 8$ (c) $z^2 + 2iz - 5$

A1.3 Construct the quadratic equations having the following roots:
  (a) $3 + i, 3 - i$ (b) $1 + 0i, 2 + 0i$ (c) $1, 2$ (d) $1 + 0i$
  (e) $1 + i\sqrt{2}, 1 - i\sqrt{2}$ (f) $1 + \sqrt{2}, 1 - \sqrt{2}$.

A.2   Complex Algebra

In the above introduction to complex numbers, the quantity i was assumed to have some of the properties of real numbers, because algebraic manipulations were carried out in the usual manner that is familiar through working with real quantities. This assumption gives formulas for the basic operations of addition and multiplication of two complex numbers, say $z = x + iy$ and $w = u + iv$:

$$z + w = (x + u) + i(y + v) \tag{A.4}$$

$$zw = xu + xiv + iyu + i^2 yv$$

$$= (xu - yv) + i(xv + yu). \tag{A.5}$$

These formulas have been arranged so as to display the real and imaginary parts of the sum and the product. Another way of expressing these equations is to use the operation of taking the real part x of $z = x + iy$ to define a function Re:

$$\text{Re } z = \text{Re}(x + iy) = x \tag{A.6}$$

Similarly the value of the function Im z is the imaginary part of z:

$$\text{Im } z = \text{Im}(x + iy) = y \tag{A.7}$$

Then equations (A.4) and (A.5) can be rewritten

$$\text{Re}(z + w) = \text{Re } z + \text{Re } w, \qquad \text{Im}(z + w) = \text{Im } z + \text{Im } w \tag{A.4}$$

$$\text{Re}(zw) = (\text{Re } z)(\text{Re } w) - (\text{Im } z)(\text{Im } w)$$

$$\text{Im}(zw) = (\text{Re } z)(\text{Im } w) + (\text{Im } z)(\text{Re } w) \tag{A.5}$$

Either form of the equations serves as the **definition** of addition and multiplication of complex numbers.

Note that such definitions are only sensible if the real and imaginary parts of z are unique real numbers, which is also implicit in saying that equations (A.6) and (A.7) define functions. This further means that two complex numbers are *equal* if, and only if, they have the same real parts and the same imaginary parts:

$$w = z \quad \Leftrightarrow \quad \text{Re } w = \text{Re } z \quad \text{and} \quad \text{Im } w = \text{Im } z \tag{A.8}$$

or, if $w = u + iv$ and $z = x + iy$

$$w = z \quad \Leftrightarrow \quad u = x \quad \text{and} \quad v = y.$$

The complex number **zero** is $0 + 0i$, and will simply be written as 0. (This has already been done on the right sides of quadratic equations in the previous section.) It has the defining property of a zero, namely $z + 0 = z$ for all complex numbers z. The **negative** of z, written $-z$, is the unique number giving zero when added to z:

$$z + (-z) = 0. \tag{A.9}$$

If $z = x + iy$, then $-z = -x + i(-y)$ which can be written $-x - iy$. **Subtraction** of z is defined as the addition of $-z$:

$$w - z = w + (-z). \tag{A.10}$$

The **unit** complex number is $1+0i$, and will simply be written as 1. It has the defining property of a unit, namely $z1 = z$ for all complex numbers z:

$$\text{Re}[(x+iy)(1+i0)] = x - y0 = x$$
$$\text{Im}[(x+iy)(1+i0)] = y + x0 = y.$$

The **reciprocal** of z, written $1/z$ (or z^{-1}), is the unique number giving 1 when multiplied by z. If $z = x+iy$, then $\text{Re}(1/z)$ and $\text{Im}(1/z)$ can be expressed as functions of x and y, as follows:

if $\qquad\qquad\qquad\qquad z = x+iy, \quad \text{let } 1/z = u+iv;$

then $\qquad\qquad\qquad\qquad (u+iv)(x+iy) = 1 + i0.$

But $\qquad\qquad\qquad (u+iv)(x+iy) = (ux - vy) + i(vx + uy),$ $\qquad$ (A.11)

so $\qquad\qquad\qquad\qquad xu - yv = 1, \qquad yu + xv = 0.$ $\qquad\qquad$ (A.12)

These are two (linear) equations for two unknowns u and v, where the coefficients x and y are regarded as known. Their solution is

$$u = x/(x^2+y^2), \qquad v = (-y)/(x^2+y^2),$$ $\qquad$ (A.13)

provided x and y are not both zero. This shows that the reciprocal of z exists and is unique, for all $z \neq 0$. A convenient procedure for the actual calculation of a reciprocal in the form $u+iv$ is

$$\boxed{\frac{1}{x+iy} = \frac{x-iy}{(x+iy)(x-iy)} = \frac{x-iy}{x^2+y^2}.}$$

Example 5A
Find the reciprocal of $1+2i$.

$$\frac{1}{1+2i} = \frac{1-2i}{(1+2i)(1-2i)} = \frac{1-2i}{5} = \tfrac{1}{5} - \tfrac{2}{5}i \quad (u = \tfrac{1}{5}, \ v = -\tfrac{2}{5}).$$

Check:

$$(\tfrac{1}{5} - \tfrac{2}{5}i)(1+2i) = \tfrac{1}{5} - \tfrac{2}{5}i + \tfrac{2}{5}i - \tfrac{4}{5}i^2 = \tfrac{1}{5} + \tfrac{4}{5} + 0i = 1. \qquad \square$$

Finally **division** by z is defined as multiplication by $1/z$ $(z \neq 0)$.

The real and imaginary parts of a quotient can be found as for the reciprocal.

Example 6A
Evaluate $(1+2i)/(1-i)$.

Here 'evaluate' means express in the form $x+iy$ (which displays the real and imaginary parts).

$$\frac{(1+2i)}{(1-i)} = \frac{(1+2i)(1+i)}{(1-i)(1+i)} \quad \text{(cf. Example 5A)}$$

$$= \frac{1+3i+2i^2}{1-i^2} = \frac{-1+3i}{2} = -\tfrac{1}{2} + \tfrac{3}{2}i.$$

Check:

$$(1-i)(-\tfrac{1}{2}+\tfrac{3}{2}i) = -\tfrac{1}{2}+\tfrac{3}{2}i+\tfrac{1}{2}i-\tfrac{3}{2}i^2 = 1+2i. \qquad \square$$

The above definitions of addition, multiplication, negative, subtraction, reciprocal and division give laws of algebra which are the same as for real numbers. The only extra feature has been illustrated in the passage from equation (A.11) to (A.12). Any equation involving complex numbers, such as (A.11), is true provided the real parts on each side are equal and the imaginary parts on each side are equal.

A complex equation is thus equivalent to two real equations,

such as (A.12).

Example 7A
Putting $z = x+iy$ in $z^2 - 2z + 5 = 0$ gives

$$x^2 - y^2 + 2ixy - 2x - 2iy + 5 = 0 + 0i$$

and

$$x^2 - y^2 - 2x + 5 = 0 \quad \text{(equating real parts)}$$

$$2xy - 2y = 0 \quad \text{(equating imaginary parts)}.$$

These two real equations may be solved to get $x = 1$, $y = \pm 2$, agreeing with the result of Example 2A. $\square$

The algebraic properties of complex numbers can all be expressed using the real and imaginary parts, which are two real numbers. The modern approach to complex numbers is therefore to **define** a complex number z as an **ordered pair of real numbers** (x, y). The above definitions become

Equality:	$(x, y) = (u, v) \iff x = u$ and $y = v$	
Addition:	$(x, y) + (u, v) = (x+u, y+v)$	
Negative:	$-(x, y) = (-x, -y)$	
Multiplication:	$(x, y)(u, v) = (xu - yv, xv + yu)$	etc.

The notation $x+iy$ for (x, y) is convenient because the algebra resulting from these definitions is then obtained using the same manipulative techniques as for real numbers together with the rule $i^2 = -1$. In terms of the pairs, this rule is

$$(0, 1)(0, 1) = (-1, 0). \tag{A.14}$$

This equivalence of $x+iy$ to (x, y) implies that the complex numbers $(x, 0)$ behave like the real numbers x. They need not be distinguished from the real numbers in applications and calculations.

Example 3A
(iii) the roots of $z^2-6z+8=0$ may be given as $z=2$ and $z=4$. $\square$

In general $x+i0$ is called **real**, and simply written x. Similarly $0+yi$, which has zero real part, is called **pure imaginary**, and written yi or iy.

Then multiplication of a complex number $x+iy$ by a real number b means $(b+0i)(x+iy)=bx+iby$.

Exercises (answers on p. 538)

A2.1 If $z=2+3i$ and $w=3-i$, evaluate the following (in the form $a+ib$ where a and b are real):
(i) $z-w$ (ii) z^2 (iii) z/w (iv) w/z
(v) $(z+w)(z-w)$ (vi) z^2-w^2.

A2.2 Evaluate (a) i^3 (b) i^4 (c) i^5 (d) $(1+i)^2$ (e) $(1-i)^2$ (f) i^{-1} (g) i^{-3}.

A2.3 If $z=\cos\theta+i\sin\theta$, show that (a) $z^2=\cos 2\theta+i\sin 2\theta$ (b) $1/z=\cos\theta-i\sin\theta$.

A2.4 (a) By substituting $z=x+iy$ into $z^2-4z+13=0$, obtain equivalent simultaneous equations for x and y. Solve these equations.
(b) Solve $z^2-4z+13=0$ by completing the square on z.

A2.5 Solve $z^2+10z+6iz+30i=0$.

A2.6 Use equation (A.2) and the result of Exercise A2.2(d) to solve

$$z^2+(4+2i)z+(3+2i)=0.$$

A2.7 If $z=x+iy$ with x and y real, let $\bar{z}$ denote $x-iy$. Show that $z+\bar{z}$ and $z\bar{z}$ are real, and express x and y in terms of z and $\bar{z}$.

A2.8 Express $\mathrm{Re}(iz)$ and $\mathrm{Im}(iz)$ in terms of $\mathrm{Re}\,z$ and $\mathrm{Im}\,z$.

A.3 Complex Conjugates

The **complex conjugate** of the number $z=x+iy$ is $\bar{z}=x-iy$. It can also be denoted by z^*. From the definitions of addition, multiplication, and division, it can be shown that the conjugate of a sum, product or quotient is the sum, product or quotient of the conjugates:

$$(z+w)^*=z^*+w^*, \qquad (zw)^*=z^*w^*, \qquad (z/w)^*=z^*/w^* \qquad (\text{A.15})$$

For example, from equation (A.5)

$$(zw)^*=(xu-yv)-i(xv+yu),$$

which is

$$(x-iy)(u-iv)=z^*w^*.$$

Also two complex numbers are equal if and only if their conjugates are equal. Equations (A.15) imply that the complex conjugate of any algebraic expression is obtained by changing every quantity in the expression to its conjugate. Any real quantity is unchanged.

Example 8A

If a, b and c are real

$$(az^2 + bz + c)^* = a^* z^* z^* + b^* z^* + c^*$$

$$= a(z^*)^2 + bz^* + c.$$

Suppose $az^2 + bz + c = 0$. Then $0^* = 0 = a(z^*)^2 + bz^* + c$. Thus if z is a root of a quadratic with real coefficients, so is z^*. This could also be deduced from the two explicit solutions given in (A.2), which are obviously complex conjugates if complex. However the method used in this example extends to any polynomial equation with real coefficients. $\square$

Example 9A

If r, s and t are real, then

$$\left[\frac{(r^2 + ir - s)(it^2 - 3ist + r^3)}{r^2 s^2 - ist + s^2 t^2 + 2i} \right]^* = \frac{(r^2 - ir - s)(-it^2 + 3ist + r^3)}{r^2 s^2 + ist + s^2 t^2 - 2i},$$

merely by changing the sign of i throughout. $\square$

Example 10A

If $w\bar{w} = 1$, then $w = \cos\theta + i\sin\theta$ for some θ: if $w = u + iv$, $w\bar{w} = u^2 + v^2$, and if $u^2 + v^2 = 1$, θ can be chosen so that $u = \cos\theta$, $v = \sin\theta$. $\square$

One property of the conjugate has been indicated in Exercise A2.7:

$$\text{Re } z = \tfrac{1}{2}(z + \bar{z}), \qquad \text{Im } z = -\tfrac{1}{2}i(z - \bar{z}). \tag{A.16}$$

Exercises

A3.1 Show that $(1/w)^* = 1/w^*$.

A3.2 Show that $(\bar{z}/z) = \cos\Psi + i\sin\Psi$ for some Ψ.

A.4 The Interpretation of Complex Numbers

Ordered pairs (x, y) of real numbers correspond to the points of a plane by regarding (x, y) as the Cartesian coordinates of a point relative to some chosen axes. The interpretation (or representation) of complex numbers as points in a plane was proposed by Wessel and by Argand at the beginning of the nineteenth century. Examples are shown in Fig. A.1(b). The plane is called the **complex plane**, and illustrations of complex equations or functions are called **Argand diagrams**.

An equivalent representation associates the vector $x\mathbf{i} + y\mathbf{j}$ with the complex number $z = x + iy$, as in Fig. A.1(a). The axes in the complex plane are referred to as the **real axis** and the **imaginary axis**, and labelled accordingly.

In the vector representation, the components of the vector corresponding to z are the real and imaginary parts of z. It follows that the condition for equality is the same for complex numbers as for vectors:

$$u = x \quad \text{and} \quad v = y \quad \Leftrightarrow \quad u + iv = x + iy \quad \Leftrightarrow \quad u\mathbf{i} + v\mathbf{j} = x\mathbf{i} + y\mathbf{j}.$$

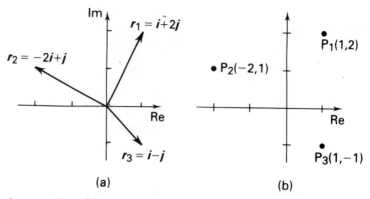

Representations, (a) by vectors, (b) by points, of the complex numbers $z_1 = 1 + 2i$, $z_2 = -2 + i$, $z_3 = 1 - i$.

Figure A.1

Similarly the operations of changing the sign (Fig. A.2), addition and subtraction (Fig. A.3), and multiplication by a real number (Fig. A.4), are represented in the complex plane by the same operations on the vectors. For example, if

$$\boldsymbol{r} = x\boldsymbol{i} + y\boldsymbol{j} \quad \leftrightarrow \quad x + iy = z,$$

$$t\boldsymbol{r} = (tx)\boldsymbol{i} + ty(\boldsymbol{j}) \quad \leftrightarrow \quad tx + ity = tz.$$

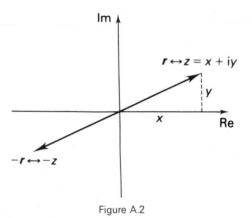

Figure A.2

Note that in the Argand diagrams the vectors are identified with the complex numbers. Where convenient, the vector can be translated to any position in the complex plane, i.e. it need not start at the origin. Deleting the arrows in the diagrams gives the pictures corresponding to the point representation of the complex numbers.

Some vector problems can be reconsidered in terms of complex numbers.

Example 11A

Suppose A, B, C are collinear points in the complex plane, representing the complex numbers α, γ, β respectively (see Fig. A.5). If $CB = \lambda AB$, then

$$\beta = \lambda\alpha + (1 - \lambda)\gamma. \tag{1.2}$$

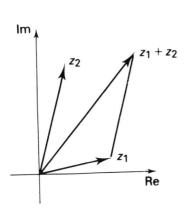

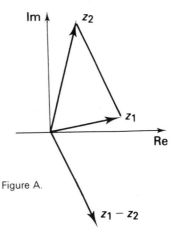

Figure A.

(a) Addition of complex numbers   **(b)** Subtraction of complex numbers

Figure A.3

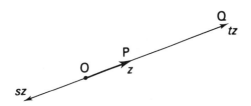

Multiplication of a complex number z by a
real number (s or t)

Figure A.4

This result is just a re-interpretation of Example 1.10 on vectors in Section 1.1. If C is between A and B, then $0 < \lambda < 1$, but taking $\lambda > 1$ or $\lambda < 0$ allows C to be outside the segment AB. Figure A.5 is merely a relabelling of Figs 1.6 and 1.7. □

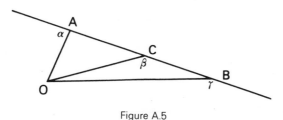

Figure A.5

The interpretation in the complex plane of multiplication and division will be given in Section A.6.

Complex numbers may also be interpreted as 2×2 matrices, through the correspondence

$$x + iy \leftrightarrow \begin{bmatrix} x & -y \\ y & x \end{bmatrix}. \tag{A.17}$$

These matrices behave like complex numbers for all operations so far defined, for example

$$i^2 \leftrightarrow \begin{bmatrix} 0 & -1 \\ 1 & 0 \end{bmatrix}\begin{bmatrix} 0 & -1 \\ 1 & 0 \end{bmatrix} = \begin{bmatrix} -1 & 0 \\ 0 & -1 \end{bmatrix} \leftrightarrow -1.$$

Exercises (answers on p. 539)

A4.1 Show on an Argand diagram the points of the complex plane corresponding to the following complex numbers:

$$z_1 = 3 + 2i, \qquad z_2 = i, \qquad z_3 = -2i, \qquad z_4 = -3, \qquad z_5 = -1 - 3i.$$

Show on another diagram the vectors corresponding to these numbers. Give a diagram illustrating the equation

$$z_1 + z_3 + z_4 = 0.$$

Interpret geometrically the equation $z_2 = \frac{1}{2}z_4 + \frac{1}{2}z_1$.

A4.2 Show on an Argand diagram either the points or the vectors corresponding to z, z^2 and z^{-1} in Exercise A2.3.

A4.3 (i) Describe geometrically the relation between the vectors represented by z and iz (cf. Exercise A2.8).

(ii) Suppose the points O, A, B, C in the complex plane are the corners of a square in *counter-clockwise* order. If O is the origin, and z represents A, what complex numbers represent B and C?

(iii) Repeat (ii) for the case where OABC are in *clockwise* order.

A4.4 Illustrate equations (A.16) in the complex plane.

A4.5 Interpret geometrically the points in the complex plane represented by $z = z_0 + tw$, where z_0 and w are fixed complex numbers, and t a parameter taking all real values.

A4.6 The points A, B, C, D, E in the complex plane are consecutive, equally spaced points in a straight line $(AB = BC = CD = DE)$. If z represents B and w represents D, what numbers represent A, C and E?

A4.7 Verify that equations (A.13) give the inverse of (A.17).

A4.8 (i) Find a 2×2 matrix W satisfying $W^2 - W + 9I = 0$, where I is the 2×2 unit matrix, and 0 the 2×2 zero matrix.

(ii) Find a 2×2 matrix Z such that $Z^{-1} = \frac{1}{5}(Z + 2iI)$.

A4.9 If $z = 1 + 2i$, evaluate z^2, and show in an Argand diagram the vectors represented by z^2 and $-2z$. Verify from the diagram that $z^2 + (-2z) = -5$ (cf. Example 2A).

A4.10 (i) If $z = -1 - 3i$, evaluate z^2 and $(10 + 6i)z$, and show the corresponding vectors in the complex plane. Verify from the diagram that $z^2 + (10 + 6i)z = -30i$.

(ii) Repeat (i) for $z = -9 - 3i$ (cf. Exercise A2.5).

A.5   Polar Form of Complex Numbers

Complex numbers may be regarded as representing vectors in the complex plane. Vectors are quantities with magnitude and direction. The plane vector $x\mathbf{i} + y\mathbf{j}$ has magnitude $\sqrt{(x^2 + y^2)}$, and its direction may be specified by giving the angle the vector makes with the positive x-direction. The correspondence with vectors makes it useful to define the analogous quantities for complex numbers.

If $z = x + iy$, the **modulus** of z is the non-negative real number $|z| = \sqrt{(x^2 + y^2)}$. This is zero if and only if $z = 0$, and if $z \neq 0$ then $|z| > 0$. In the complex plane the modulus

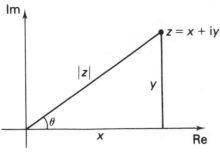

Figure A.6

represents the distance from the origin of the point represented by z, or the length of the vector represented by z.

The **argument** of z, written arg z, is a number θ such that

$$\sin \theta = \frac{y}{\sqrt{(x^2+y^2)}} = \frac{y}{|z|}, \qquad \cos \theta = \frac{x}{\sqrt{(x^2+y^2)}} = \frac{x}{|z|}.$$

Then

$$x = |z| \cos \theta, \qquad y = |z| \sin \theta,$$

and

$$z = x + iy = |z|(\cos \theta + i \sin \theta) \tag{A.18}$$

(see Fig. A.6)

This is called a **polar form** of z,

since $|z|$ and θ are **polar coordinates** of the point represented by z.

Example 12A

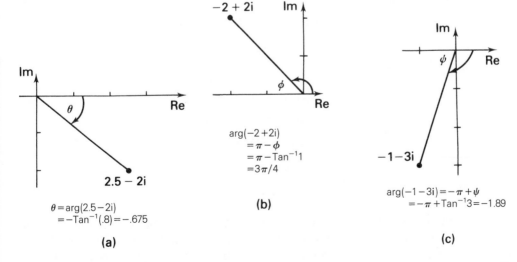

arg$(-2+2i)$
$= \pi - \phi$
$= \pi - \text{Tan}^{-1}1$
$= 3\pi/4$

(b)

$-1-3i$

arg$(-1-3i) = -\pi + \psi$
$= -\pi + \text{Tan}^{-1}3 = -1.89$

(c)

$2.5 - 2i$

$\theta = \arg(2.5-2i)$
$= -\text{Tan}^{-1}(.8) = -.675$

(a)

Figure A.7

Because the functions sin and cos have period 2π, the number θ can be changed by any integer multiple of 2π without affecting equation (A.18), and any of the values $\theta + 2n\pi$ can be taken for arg z. The **principal value** of arg z satisfies $-\pi < \theta \leqslant \pi$; this is sometimes written Arg z (with a capital A). The negative values of Arg z are angles measured clockwise from the positive real direction, corresponding to vectors pointing into the lower half of the complex plane.

Example 13A

Express the following complex numbers in polar form: $1+i$, $-\sqrt{3}+i$, $-5i$, $-2-3i$.

To find the argument of a complex number it is always advisable to use an Argand diagram to locate the correct quadrant of the complex plane. Figure A.8 shows the arguments of the given numbers.

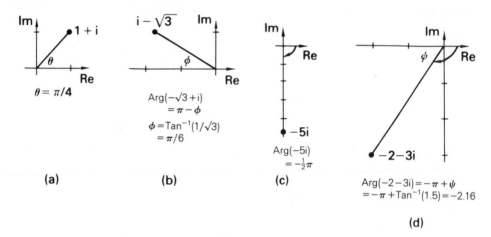

Figure A.8

The moduli of the numbers are

$$|1+i| = \sqrt{(1^2+1^2)} = \sqrt{2}, \qquad |-\sqrt{3}+i| = \sqrt{\{(-\sqrt{3})^2+1^2\}} = 2$$
$$|-5i| = \sqrt{\{0^2+(-5)^2\}} = 5, \qquad |-2-3i| = \sqrt{\{(-2)^2+(-3)^2\}} = \sqrt{13},$$

and (using Fig. A.8)

$$(1+i) = \sqrt{2}\{\cos \pi/4 + i \sin \pi/4\}$$
$$-\sqrt{3}+i = 2\{\cos 5\pi/6 + i \sin 5\pi/6\}$$
$$-5i = 5\{\cos(-\pi/2) + i \sin(-\pi/2)\}$$
$$-2-3i = \sqrt{13}\{\cos(-2.16) + i \sin(-2.16)\}$$

are polar forms.   □

If a, b, and c are real numbers, then $a(b+ic)$ gives a polar form of a complex number if $b^2+c^2=1$ and $a \geqslant 0$. Since a polar form contains $\cos \theta$ and $\sin \theta$ rather than θ itself, it is permissible to express θ in degrees rather than radians. This angle is also called the **phase** of the complex number.

If two complex numbers are equal, they have the same modulus, but their arguments could differ by an integral multiple of 2π. For example,

$$-5i = 5\{\cos(-\pi/2) + i \sin(-\pi/2)\} = 5\{\cos(3\pi/2) + i \sin(3\pi/2)\}.$$

Example 14A
The polar form of $\zeta = -\frac{6}{5} - \frac{8}{5}i$ is not (cf. Fig. A.9)

$$-2(\tfrac{3}{5} + \tfrac{4}{5}i) = -2(\cos 0.925 + i \sin 0.925),$$

but $2\{\cos(-2.22) + i \sin(-2.22)\}$ and $2\{\cos(4.06) + i \sin(4.06)\}$ are polar forms of ζ (Fig. A.10).

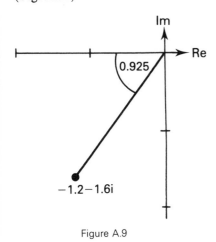

Figure A.9

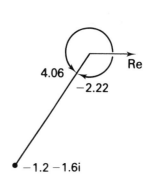

Figure A.10

From equation (A.18),

$$z^2 = |z|^2(\cos^2 \theta - \sin^2 \theta + 2i \sin \theta \cos \theta)$$
$$= |z|^2(\cos 2\theta + i \sin 2\theta).$$

This is a polar form, so $|z^2| = |z|^2$, arg $z^2 = 2$ arg z, showing that squaring a number doubles the argument and squares the modulus. Conversely, **a square root** can be obtained by halving the argument and taking the square root of the modulus.

Example 15A
Evaluate $\sqrt{(2i)}$.

Since $|2i| = 2$ and $\arg(2i) = \frac{1}{2}\pi$, a square root has modulus $\sqrt{2}$ and argument $\pi/4$. Its polar form is therefore $\sqrt{2}(\cos \pi/4 + i \sin \pi/4)$, i.e. $1 + i$ (cf. Exercise A2.2(d)). $\square$

This method allows the evaluation of $\sqrt{(b^2 - 4ac)}$ for any complex values of a, b and c, and so equation (A.2) may be used to solve any quadratic equation (A.1) with complex number coefficients. There is an alternative method of calculating the square root, by separating $(x + iy)^2 = (b^2 - 4ac)$ into two real simultaneous equations for x and y (cf. Example 7A).

Example 16A
To evaluate $\sqrt{(2i)}$, let $(x+iy)^2 = 2i$.

$$x^2 - y^2 = 0, \qquad 2xy = 2.$$

$$y = 1/x, \qquad x^2 - x^{-2} = 0, \qquad x^4 = 1, \qquad x = \pm 1, \qquad y = \pm 1. \qquad \square$$

Note that two square roots are obtained, differing only in sign. But unlike in the real case, there is no convention denoting a particular one of these by $\sqrt{(2i)}$.

Example 17A
Solve $z^2 - (5+i)z + 8 + i = 0$.

From equation (A.2), $z = \frac{1}{2}\{5 + i \pm \sqrt{(24 + 10i - 32 - 4i)}\}$, requiring evaluation of $\sqrt{(-8+6i)}$.

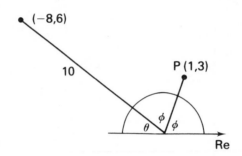

Figure A.11

Either (i) $|-8+6i| = \sqrt{(64+36)} = 10$, and

$$\arg(-8+6i) = \pi - \theta \qquad \text{(Fig. A.11)}$$

$$= \pi - \text{Tan}^{-1}(0.75) = 2.498.$$

$$\sqrt{(-8+6i)} = \sqrt{10}(\cos 1.249 + i \sin 1.249) = 1 + 3i$$

or (ii) if $(x+iy)^2 = -8+6i$, $x^2 - y^2 = -8$, $2xy = 6$.
 Substituting $y = 3/x$ into $x^2 - y^2 = -8$ gives

$$x^4 + 8x^2 - 9 = 0, \qquad x^2 = 1, \qquad (x^2 \neq -9 \text{ since } x \text{ real})$$

$$x = \pm 1, \qquad y = 3/x = \pm 3.$$

$$x + iy = \pm 1 \pm 3i$$

$$z = \frac{1}{2}\{5 + i \pm 1 \pm 3i\} = 3 + 2i \quad \text{or} \quad 2 - i. \qquad \square$$

Exercises (answers on p. 540)
A5.1 Show that the following complex numbers have modulus 1. Find the principal value of their arguments, and write them in polar form:
(i) i (ii) -1 (iii) $(1+i)/\sqrt{2}$ (iv) $\frac{1}{2}(\sqrt{3}-i)$.
A5.2 Find the modulus and the principal value of the argument of
(a) $\sqrt{3}+i$ (b) $-1+i\sqrt{3}$ (c) $-2\sqrt{3}+2i$.

A5.3 Write the following complex numbers in polar form, using the principal value of the argument
(a) 3i (b) $-2(\sqrt{3}+i)$ (c) $1-2i$ (d) $4-4i$ (e) -2.

A5.4 Express $|\bar{z}|$ and Arg $\bar{z}$ in terms of $|z|$ and Arg z.

A5.5 Show that
(a) $z^2+|z|^2=2z$ Re z (b) $z^2-|z|^2=2iz$ Im z.

A5.6 Evaluate $\sqrt{(-16)}$ by halving the argument and taking the square root of the modulus. Draw an Argand diagram to illustrate the calculation.

A5.7 If $\tan\theta=7/5$, calculate $\tan 2\theta$. Use the result to evaluate $\sqrt{(-12+35i)}$ and $\sqrt{(12-35i)}$. Illustrate the calculations by vectors in the complex plane.

A5.8 Find the square roots of $3+4i$, $-3+4i$, and $-2i$ by solving simultaneous equations for the real and imaginary parts.

A.6 Geometric Interpretation of Multiplication and Division

Multiplying z by z doubles the argument, so the direction of the vector represented by z^2 is obtained by rotating the vector represented by z through the angle arg z (Fig. A.12). For a unit vector, this is the complete interpretation, since the modulus 1 is unchanged by squaring.

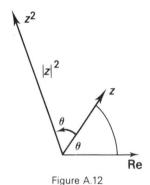

Figure A.12

   This suggests that the geometric interpretation of any product will involve rotating vectors, so it is convenient to consider first what happens to a unit vector $e=i\cos\phi+j\sin\phi$ when it is rotated through an angle θ. If this changes i, j and e to i', j' and e' respectively, evidently (see Fig. A.13)

$$e'=i'\cos\phi+j'\sin\phi.$$

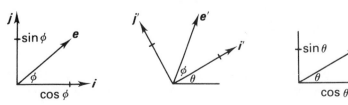

Figure A.13

But $i' = i \cos \theta + j \sin \theta$, and $j' = -i \sin \theta + j \cos \theta$, so $e' = i(\cos \theta \cos \phi - \sin \theta \sin \phi) + j(\sin \theta \cos \phi + \cos \theta \sin \phi)$. Also $e' = i \cos(\theta + \phi) + j \sin(\theta + \phi)$; equating components of the two forms for e' gives the trigonometric addition formulas

$$\cos(\theta + \phi) = \cos \theta \cos \phi - \sin \theta \sin \phi$$

$$\sin(\theta + \phi) = \sin \theta \cos \phi + \cos \theta \sin \phi. \tag{A.19}$$

Now consider the product zw of any two complex numbers, with polar forms ($r \geqslant 0$, $s \geqslant 0$)

$$z = r(\cos \theta + i \sin \theta) \quad \text{and} \quad w = s(\cos \phi + i \sin \phi).$$

Then

$$zw = rs\{\cos \theta \cos \phi - \sin \theta \sin \phi + i(\sin \theta \cos \phi + \cos \theta \sin \phi)\}$$

$$= rs\{\cos(\theta + \phi) + i \sin(\theta + \phi)\}, \quad \text{using equations (A.19).}$$

Since $rs \geqslant 0$, this is a polar form of the product, and so

$$\boxed{|zw| = rs = |z||w|, \qquad \arg(zw) = \theta + \phi = \arg z + \arg w.} \tag{A.20}$$

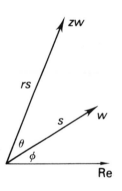

Figure A.14

Thus **to take the product of two complex numbers given in polar form, one multiplies their moduli and adds their arguments**. Figure A.14 can be interpreted as follows: when w is multiplied by z, the vector represented by w is rotated through an angle $\theta = \arg z$, and its length is multiplied by $r = |z|$. (The rotation is clockwise if $\arg z$ is negative.)

Example 18A

If OPQ is an equilateral triangle in the complex plane (Fig. A.15), it is evident geometrically that $\overrightarrow{OQ}$ is $\overrightarrow{OP}$ rotated through $\pi/3$, and $\overrightarrow{PQ}$ is $\overrightarrow{OP}$ rotated through $2\pi/3$. Also $\overrightarrow{PQ} = \overrightarrow{OQ} - \overrightarrow{OP}$.

If z and w are the complex numbers representing P and Q, then w must be obtained from z by multiplying by the complex number with modulus 1 and argument $\pi/3$:

$$w = 1(\cos \pi/3 + i \sin \pi/3)z = (\tfrac{1}{2} + \tfrac{1}{2}i\sqrt{3})z.$$

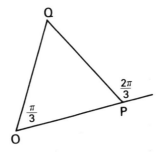

Figure A.15

So $\overrightarrow{PQ} = \overrightarrow{OQ} - \overrightarrow{OP}$ is represented by

$$w - z = (-\tfrac{1}{2} + \tfrac{1}{2}i\sqrt{3})z$$

$$= 1(\cos 2\pi/3 + i \sin 2\pi/3)z,$$

checking also that $\overrightarrow{PQ}$ is $\overrightarrow{OP}$ rotated through $2\pi/3$. □

Special cases of the interpretation of multiplication in terms of rotating and stretching a vector are:

(i) Multiplying by a positive real number, which has argument zero, does not change the direction of the vector.

(ii) Multiplying by a negative real number, which has argument π, reverses the direction of the vector by rotating through π.

(iii) Multiplying by a purely imaginary number, which has argument $\pm\pi/2$, rotates the vector through a right angle (cf. Exercise A4.3).

(iv) The complex number i represents the unit vector in the imaginary direction. Multiplying i by i rotates the unit vector through a right angle to point in the negative real direction, corresponding to the number -1 (see Fig. A.16).

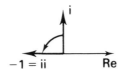

Figure A.16

The polar form of a quotient, say w/z, may be obtained by considering the polar form of the reciprocal $1/z$. If $z = r(\cos\theta + i \sin\theta)$, then putting $x = r\cos\theta$ and $y = r\sin\theta$ into equation (A.13) on p. 520 gives ($z \neq 0$)

$$\frac{1}{z} = \frac{1}{r}\cos\theta - i\frac{1}{r}\sin\theta$$

$$= (1/r)\{\cos(-\theta) + i\sin(-\theta)\} \quad \text{in polar form.}$$

i.e.

$$|1/z| = 1/|z|, \qquad \arg(1/z) = -\arg z \qquad\qquad (A.21)$$

Since w/z is w multiplied by $1/z$, equations (A.21) and (A.20) give

$$|w/z| = |w|/|z|, \qquad \arg(w/z) = \arg w - \arg z. \qquad \textbf{(A.22)}$$

Exercises (answers on p. 540)

A6.1   Evaluate $(\sqrt{3}+i)(-1+i\sqrt{3})$. Use Exercise A5.2 to verify equation (A.20).

A6.2   Use equation (A.5) to verify that $|zw| = |z||w|$.

A6.3   (i) If OPQ are the corners of an equilateral triangle taken in clockwise order, and z and w represent P and Q, express w in terms of z (cf. Example 18A).
(ii) Solve

$$w^2 - zw + z^2 = 0 \qquad (*)$$

for w in terms of z, and deduce that $(*)$ is the condition for O and the points represented by z and w to form an equilateral triangle.

A6.4   The points OABC in the complex plane are the corners of a parallelogram taken in counter-clockwise order. The angle AOC is $45°$, and $OC = 2OA$. If z represents the point A, express in terms of z the numbers representing C and B.

A6.5   (i) How are the modulus and argument of z^3 related to those of z?
(ii) Find a cube root of 8i (a solution of $z^3 = 8i$).
(iii) Factorize $(z^3 - 8i)$ into three linear factors.

A6.6   Find a complex cube root of -1.

A6.7   If $M(\theta) = \begin{bmatrix} \cos\theta & -\sin\theta \\ \sin\theta & \cos\theta \end{bmatrix}$, show that $M(\theta)M(\phi) = M(\theta + \phi)$.

A.7   Sets of Points in the Complex Plane

In elementary two-dimensional geometry using Cartesian coordinates, the points (x, y) satisfying a given relation, such as $x^2 = y + 1$, may lie on a curve. Points satisfying two given relations which represent curves must lie on both curves, and are generally a finite number of points which are the intersections of the two curves.

Example 19A
Points satisfying (see Fig. A.17)

$$y^2 - (x-1)^2 = 4 \qquad \text{(A.23)}$$

and

$$(x-1)y = 0 \qquad \text{(A.24)}$$

are the two intersections $(1, \pm 2)$ of the hyperbola (A.23) and the line-pair (A.24). $\square$

Since one complex equation for z is equivalent to two real relations between Re z and Im z, generally the solution set of one equation for z represents a finite number of points in the complex plane.

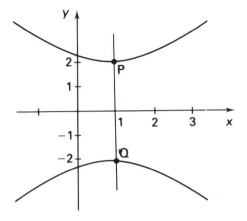

Figure A.17

Example 20A
$z^2 - 2z + 5 = 0$ is satisfied by $z = 1 \pm 2i$. $\square$

(cf. Example 7A and Example 19A).

However one equation for $|z|$, or for arg z, is equivalent to one relation between x and y, and so may represent a curve in the complex plane.

Example 21A
(i) The equation $|z| = 1$ is satisfied by any number z representing a point at unit distance from the origin. Thus $|z| = 1$ represents the unit circle, which has centre O and radius 1 (Fig. A.18).

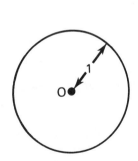

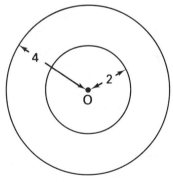

Figure A.18   Figure A.19

(ii) Similarly, if R is real and positive, $|z| = R$ represents the circle centre O and radius R.
(iii) If $|z|^2 - 6|z| + 8 = 0$, then $|z| = 2$ or $|z| = 4$. The equation represents a pair of concentric circles, centre O, radii 2 and 4 (Fig. A.19).
(iv) The equation $|z|^2 + |z| - 2 = 0$ represents the unit circle only, since there are no numbers z with $|z| = -2$. $\square$

Example 22A

Consider the equation $|z - c| = 2$, where c is complex.

If z and c represent P and Q, then the vector represented by $z - c$ is $\overrightarrow{OP} - \overrightarrow{OQ} = \overrightarrow{QP}$ (see Fig. A.20). So $|z - c| = QP$, and the equation represents every point P distant 2 from Q, i.e. a circle of radius 2, centre Q.

Check: if $z = x + iy$ and $c = a + ib$, then $z - c = (x - a) + i(y - b)$, and $|z - c|^2 = (x - a)^2 + (y - b)^2$, and $(x - a)^2 + (y - b)^2 = 2^2$ is the equation for the circle of radius 2 centred on $Q(a, b)$. □

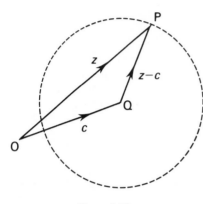

Figure A.20

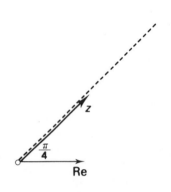

Figure A.21

Example 23A

(i) The equation $\arg z = \pi/4$ is satisfied by any number z representing a vector making an angle $\pi/4$ with the positive real direction (Fig. A.21). The vector can be any length, so the equation represents a radial (half) line making an angle $\pi/4$ with the real axis. The origin is not included.

(ii) The positive and negative portions of the real axis are represented by $\arg z = 0$ and $\arg z = \pi$ respectively.

(iii) The upper and lower portions of the imaginary axis are represented by $\arg z = \pi/2$ and $\arg z = -\pi/2$ respectively. The equation $|\arg z| = \pi/2$ represents the imaginary axis with the origin removed.

(iv) The equation $\arg(z - c) = \pi/4$ represents a half-line parallel to $\arg z = \pi/4$, emanating from the point Q represented by c. □

If an equation for $|z|$ or $\arg z$ is changed to an inequality, the solution set is a region of the complex plane; generally the equality represents the boundary of the region, which may or may not be included.

Example 24A

(i) The inequality $|z| < 1$ is satisfied by any number z representing a point within unit distance of the origin. Thus $|z| < 1$ represents the interior of the unit circle (Fig. A.22).

(ii) The region represented by $|z| \leqslant 1$ is the interior of the unit circle plus the boundary (i.e. the circle).

(iii) The inequality $|z| > 1$ represents that part of the complex plane lying outside the unit circle. □

Figure A.22

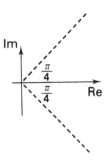

Figure A.23

Example 25A

The inequality $2<|z|<4$ represents the annulus lying between circles of radius 2 and 4 centred on the origin. (cf. Example 21A(iii) and Fig. A.19: the annular region could also be represented by $|z|^2-6|z|+8<0$). ☐

Example 26A

(i) The inequality $0<\arg z<\frac{1}{2}\pi$ represents the positive quadrant of the complex plane. The boundaries formed by the real and imaginary axes are not included.

(ii) The inequality $|\arg z|<\frac{1}{2}\pi$ represents the right half of the complex plane.

(iii) The inequality $|\arg z|<\frac{1}{4}\pi$ represents a quarter segment of the complex plane, enclosed by the radial lines $\arg z=\pm\pi/4$ (Fig. A.23). ☐

Example 27A

Solve the inequality $|z+iz-2+i|<2$.

An inequality of the form $|z-c|<R$ represents the interior of the circle of radius R centred on c (cf. Example 22A). Now

$$z+iz-2+i=(1+i)\left(z-\frac{2-i}{1+i}\right),$$

so $|z+iz-2+i|=|1+i||z-c|$ with

$$c=\frac{2-i}{1+i}=\tfrac{1}{2}(1-3i), \quad\text{and}\quad |z+iz-2+i|<2 \iff |z-c|<\sqrt{2},$$

since $|1+i|=\sqrt{2}$. The solution set represents the interior of a circle of radius $\sqrt{2}$ centred on $(\tfrac{1}{2}, -\tfrac{3}{2})$, the point represented by c. ☐

Exercises (answers on pp. 541–2)

A7.1 Show on an Argand diagram what set of points each of the following equations represents in the complex plane.

(i) $z-1-3i=0$ (ii) $z^2+z=1+3i$ (iii) $|z|^2=4$
(iv) $|z|^2+3|z|+2=0$ (v) $z^2+3z+2=0$ (vi) $|z-3+2i|=4$
(vii) $z\bar{z}=i(\bar{z}-z)$ (viii) $\arg z=3\pi/4$ (ix) $|\arg z|=\pi/3$.

A7.2 Give equations for z, $|z|$, or $\arg z$, which represent the following curves in the complex plane:

(i) a circle of radius 2, centre $(-1, -1)$.

(ii) the radial half-line passing through $(-1, -1)$, bisecting the angle between the negative real and negative imaginary directions.

(iii) the radial half-line in the positive quadrant, making an angle $\beta\,(\beta < \frac{1}{2}\pi)$ with the positive imaginary direction.

A7.3 Show on an Argand diagram the regions which are the solution sets of the following inequalities (using full lines for included boundaries, and dotted lines for boundaries not included):

(i) $|z| \leqslant 6$ (ii) $|z| > 3$ (iii) $|z| > 0$ (iv) $|z+i| < 1$
(v) $0 \leqslant \arg z \leqslant \pi$ (vi) $-\pi < \arg z < \pi$ (vii) $\arg z > 0$
(viii) $\operatorname{Arg} z > 0$ (ix) $|\operatorname{Arg} z| > 3\pi/4$
(x) $-\frac{1}{2}\pi < \arg(z-i) < \pi$.

A7.4 Give inequalities which represent the following regions in the complex plane:

(i) the interior of a circle centre $(-1, 2)$ and radius 3
(ii) the region outside a circle centre $(2, 4)$ and radius $\frac{1}{2}$.
(iii) the upper half of the complex plane, lying above the real axis.

Answers to Exercises A1.1–A7.4

A1.1 (a) $1+0i, 2+0i$ (b) $\frac{1}{2}(1 \pm i\sqrt{35})$ (c) $2+0i, 0+0i$.

A1.2 (a) $(w+4+0i)(w-2+0i)$ (b) $(z+1+i\sqrt{7})(z+1-i\sqrt{7})$
(c) $(z+2+i)(z-2+i)$.

A1.3 (a) $z^2-6z+10=0$ (b) $z^2-3z+2=0$ (c) $x^2-3x+2=0$
(d) $z^2-2z+1=0$ (e) $z^2-2z+3=0$ (f) $x^2-2x-1=0$.

A2.1 (i) $-1+4i$ (ii) $-5+12i$ (iii) $0.3+1.1i$ (iv) $\frac{3}{13}-\frac{11}{13}i$
(v) and (vi) $-13+18i$. (The agreement of (v) and (vi) checks (i) and (ii).)

A2.2 (a) $0-i$ (b) $1+0i$ (c) $0+i$ (d) $0+2i$ (e) $0-2i$
(f) $0-i$ (g) $0+i$.

A2.4 $2 \pm 3i$,   **A2.5** $-1-3i$ or $-9-3i$.

A2.6 $-1+0i$ or $-3-2i$.   **A2.7** See equation (A.16).

A2.8 $\operatorname{Re}(iz) = -\operatorname{Im} z$, $\operatorname{Im}(iz) = \operatorname{Re} z$.

A4.1

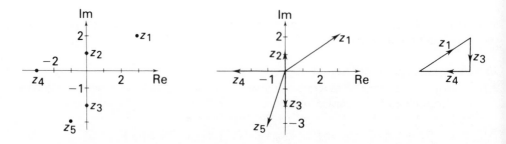

From Example 11A, $z_2 = \frac{1}{2}z_4 + \frac{1}{2}z_1$ shows that the point (represented by) z_2 is the midpoint of the line joining the points (represented by) z_4 and z_1.

A4.2

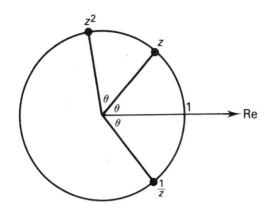

A4.3   (i) See (ii)
(ii) iz represents C, and $z+iz=(1+i)z$ represents B
(iii) $-iz$ represents C, and $z-iz=(1-i)z$ represents B.

A4.4

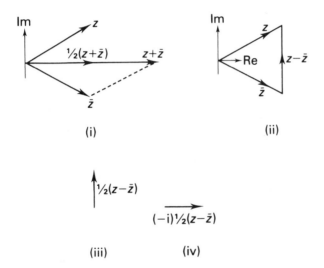

(i)   (ii)

(iii)   (iv)

Note that multiplying the purely imaginary number $\frac{1}{2}(z-\bar{z})$ by $(-i)$ rotates the vector clockwise through a right angle, giving a real number.

A4.5   The points lie on the line through the point represented by z_0 having the direction of the vector represented by w (cf. equation (2.5) and Fig. 2.4).

A4.6 $\frac{3}{2}z-\frac{1}{2}w$, $\frac{1}{2}z+\frac{1}{2}w$, $-\frac{1}{2}z+\frac{3}{2}w$ (cf. Example 11A).

A4.8   (i) $W=\begin{bmatrix} u & -v \\ v & u \end{bmatrix}$ where $u+iv$ is a complex solution of $w^2-w+9=0$; i.e. $u=\frac{1}{2}$, $v=\frac{1}{2}\sqrt{35}$.

(ii) Multiply by $5Z$: i.e. consider $Z^2+2iZ-5I=0$ as in (i).

A4.9

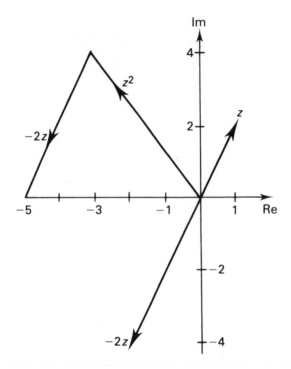

A4.10 $(-1-3i)^2 = -8+6i$, $(-9-3i)^2 = 72+54i$.

A5.1 (i) $i = 1(\cos\frac{1}{2}\pi + i\sin\frac{1}{2}\pi)$ (ii) $-1 = 1(\cos\pi + i\sin\pi)$

(iii) $(1+i)/\sqrt{2} = 1(\cos\pi/4 + i\sin\pi/4)$

(iv) $\frac{1}{2}(\sqrt{3}-i) = 1(\cos\{-\pi/6\} + i\sin\{-\pi/6\})$.

A5.2 (a) $2, \pi/6$ (b) $2, 2\pi/3$ (c) $4, 5\pi/6$.

A5.3 (a) $3(\cos\frac{1}{2}\pi + i\sin\frac{1}{2}\pi)$ (b) $4(\cos\{-5\pi/6\} + i\sin\{-5\pi/6\})$

(c) $\sqrt{5}(\cos\{-1.107\} + i\sin\{-1.107\})$

(d) $4\sqrt{2}(\cos\{-\pi/4\} + i\sin\{-\pi/4\})$ (e) $2(\cos\pi + i\sin\pi)$.

A5.4 $|\bar{z}| = |z|$, Arg $\bar{z} = \pm$Arg z, where the $+$ sign is taken if z is real.

A5.6 $-16 = 16(\cos\{\pm\pi\} + i\sin\{\pm\pi\})$,

$$\sqrt{(-16)} = 4(\cos\{\pm\tfrac{1}{2}\pi\} + i\sin\{\pm\tfrac{1}{2}\pi\}) = \pm 4i.$$

A5.7 (see facing page)

A5.8 See Example 17A(ii). Check solutions by squaring them.

A6.3 (i) $w = (\cos\{-\pi/3\} + i\sin\{-\pi/3\})z = \frac{1}{2}(1 - i\sqrt{3})z$

(ii) The two solutions are the results of (i) and Example 18A.

A6.4 C represented by $2(\cos 45° + i\sin 45°)z = \sqrt{2}(1+i)z$. $\overrightarrow{OB} = \overrightarrow{OA} + \overrightarrow{OC}$ so B is represented by $(1 + \sqrt{2} + i\sqrt{2})z$.

A6.5 (i) $|z^3| = |z|^3$, arg $z^3 = 3$ arg z

(ii) Take cube root of modulus, divide argument by 3

(iii) $(z - \sqrt{3} - i)(z + \sqrt{3} - i)(z + 2i)$, which also displays the three possible answers to (ii).

A6.6 $\frac{1}{2}(1 \pm i\sqrt{3})$ **A6.7** Use equation (A.19)

A5.7

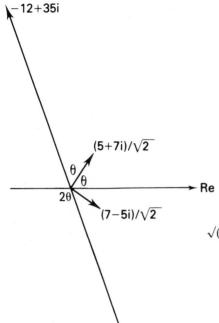

$$\tan 2\theta = \frac{2\tan\theta}{1-\tan^2\theta} = -\frac{35}{12}$$

$$\sqrt{(-12+35i)} = \sqrt{37}(\cos\theta + i\sin\theta)$$

$$\arg(12-35i) = 2\theta - \pi$$

$$\sqrt{(12-35i)} = \sqrt{37}(\cos\{\theta-\tfrac{1}{2}\pi\} + i\sin\{\theta-\tfrac{1}{2}\pi\}).$$

A7.1

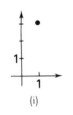

(i)

(ii)

(iii)

(iv) no points

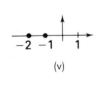

(v)

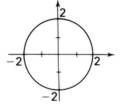

(vi)

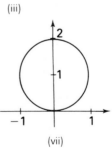

(vii)

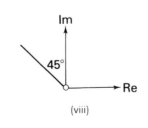

(viii)

(ix)

A7.2   (i) $|z+1+i| = 2$ (ii) $\text{Arg } z = -3\pi/4$ (iii) $\text{Arg } z = \frac{1}{2}\pi - \beta$.

A7.3

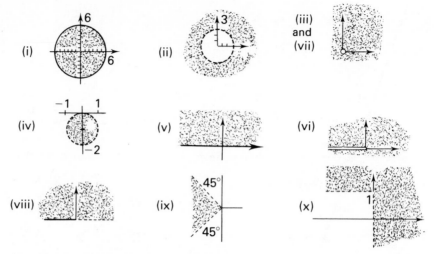

(i)

(ii)

(iii) and (vii)

(iv)

(v)

(vi)

(viii)

(ix)

(x)

In (v)–(ix), $z = 0$ is not included; similarly $z \neq i$ in (x).

A7.4   (i) $|z+1-2i| < 3$ (ii) $|z-2-4i| > \frac{1}{2}$
(iii) $\text{Im } z > 0$ (or $0 < \text{Arg } z < \pi$)

Appendix B
Flow Diagrams or Summaries of Mathematical Procedures

B1 Newton's method for finding a root r of $f(x) = 0$

B2 Antiderivative of $(x + \alpha)/(x^2 + \beta x + \gamma)^\lambda$, λ integer or half-integer

B3 Antiderivative of a rational function

B4 Systematic antiderivation: find F given F'

B5 Evaluation of a line integral along a given path

B6 Integration of a first-order linear differential equation

B7 Trial functions for particular solution of a second-order linear equation with constant coefficients

B8 Reduction of m linear equations in n unknowns to (upper) triangular form

B9 Trapezoidal rule approximation to $\int_A^B F(x)\, dx$

B1   Newton's Method for Finding a Root *r* of *f(x)*=0

1   Select one of the alternative criteria in 4.
2   Choose initial approximation x_0 and accuracy parameter ε.

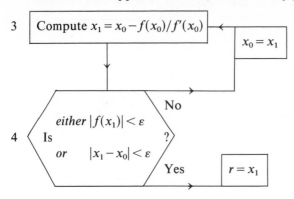

B2   Antiderivatives of $(x+\alpha)/(x^2+\beta x+\gamma)^\lambda$ (2λ an integer)

1   Substitute $u = x + \frac{1}{2}\beta$.
2   $\int u\,du/(u^2 \pm a^2)^\lambda = \frac{1}{2}\int w^{-\lambda}\,dw$ $(w = u^2 \pm a^2)$.
3   If $\lambda = \frac{1}{2}$ or 1, $\int du/(u^2 \pm a^2)^\lambda$ is a standard form.
4   Otherwise use reduction formula (10.11) to reduce P_λ to $P_{1/2}$ or P_1 or $P_{3/2}$

B3   Antiderivative of a Rational Function *N(x)/D(x)*

1   If the degree of N is not less than that of D, divide out:

$$\frac{N}{D} = (\text{polynomial}) + \frac{N_1}{D}$$

where the degree of N_1 is less than that of D.
2   Factorize D into linear and quadratic factors.
3   Express N_1/D in partial fractions.
4   Integrate, using procedure B2 for partial fractions corresponding to quadratic factors (see Examples 10.45–10.49).

B4   Systematic Antiderivation: find **F** given **F'**

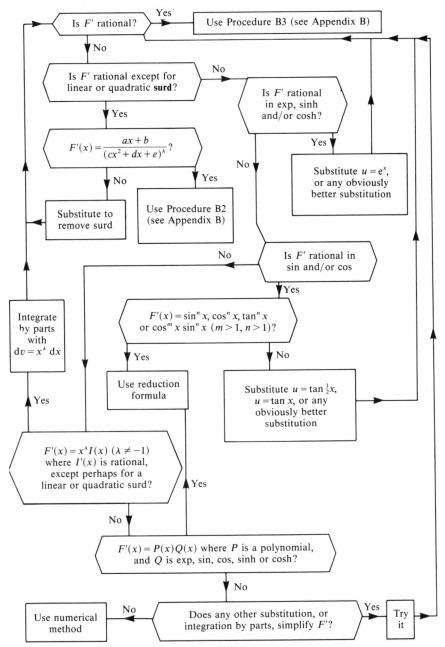

B5   Evaluation of $W = \int_A^B F(x, y, z) \cdot dr$, along a given path from A to B

1   $W = \int_A^B (F_1\,dx + F_2\,dy + F_3\,dz)$, where $F_1 i + F_2 j + F_3 k = F$.
2   If necessary, obtain equations representing the given path.
3   Use these equations (differentiating if necessary) to express each of $F_1\,dx$, $F_2\,dy$ and $F_3\,dz$ in terms of one variable only, using variables which are either increasing or decreasing along the path.
4   Evaluate each integral between limits corresponding to the values of the variable at A and B.
5   To check, repeat steps 3 and 4, expressing $F_1\,dx$ etc. in terms of a different variable.

B6   Integration of a First-order Linear Differential Equation

1   Write equation in the form $\dfrac{dy}{dx} + Q(x)y = R(x)$.
2   Multiply by $I(x)$, where $\ln I = \int Q(x)\,dx$.
3   Integrate: $Iy = \int I(x)R(x)\,dx + C$.

B7   Trial Functions for Particular Solutions of $\dfrac{d^2 y}{dx^2} + 2a\dfrac{dy}{dx} + by = R(x)$

$$(*)$$

Greek letters indicate constants to be determined by substituting the trial form into (*), while p, q, r indicate given constants occurring in $R(x)$.

1   If $R = R_1 + R_2 + \cdots$, then $y = y_1 + y_2 + \cdots$, where each y_i is a solution of (*) with R_i replacing R.
2   If a trial function suggested in steps 3–6 below already appears in the complementary function, multiply by x, repeating the multiplication if necessary.
3   If $R(x) = p\,e^{rx}$, $y = \lambda\,e^{rx}$.

4   If $R(x) = \displaystyle\sum_{i=0}^{n} a_i x^i$ $\Big\}$ (polynomials of degree n).

   $y = \displaystyle\sum_{i=0}^{n} \lambda_i x^i$

5   If $R(x) = p\,e^{qx}\cos rx$ or $p\,e^{qx}\sin rx$, consider $y = \lambda\,e^{(q+ir)x}$, with λ complex, and take Re y or Im y.
   Alternatively $y = e^{qx}(\lambda\cos rx + \mu\sin rx)$.

6   If $P(x) = \displaystyle\sum_{i=0}^{n} a_i x^i$ is a polynomial of degree n,
   and $R(x) = P(x)\,e^{rx}$ or $P(x)\,e^{qx}\cos rx$ or $P(x)\,e^{qx}\sin rx$,
   then $y = \rho(x)\,e^{rx}$ or Re$[\rho(x)\,e^{(q+ir)x}]$
                or Im$[\rho(x)\,e^{(q+ir)x}]$

   where $\rho(x) = \displaystyle\sum_{i=0}^{n} \rho_i x^i$ is a polynomial of degree n.
   Alternatively, for $R(x) = P(x)\,e^{qx}\cos rx$ or $P(x)\,e^{qx}\sin rx$,
   $y = \rho(x)\,e^{qx}\{\lambda\sin rx + \mu\cos rx\}$, with $\rho_0 = 1$.

B8 Reduction of *m* Linear Equations in *n* Unknowns to (Upper) Triangular Form

a_{ij} denotes the jth coefficient in the ith equation at the current stage of the reduction.
For $i = 1$ to max(m, n)
1 If $a_{ii} = 0^*$, interchange equations i and j $(j > i)$ so that $a_{ii} \neq 0$. $(R_i \leftrightarrow R_j)$.
2 Divide equation i through by a_{ii} (R_i / a_{ii})
3 For† $j = (i+1)$ to m, subtract a_{ji} times equation i from equation j $(R_j - a_{ji} R_i)$.

B9 Trapezoidal Rule Approximation to $\int_A^B F(x)\,dx$

(see equation (15.3) on p. 379)

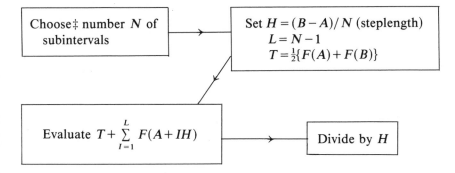

* To reduce rounding error, this interchange should be made whenever the magnitude of a_{ii} is much smaller than that of a_{ji} $(j > i)$.
  † To get unit diagonal form, also take $j = 1$ to $(i - 1)$.
  ‡ See Example 15.30 on p. 386 for choice of N to give a prescribed accuracy.

Appendix C
Computer Programs

C1 Newton's Method of finding a solution of $f(x) = 0$

C2 Bisection Method (half-interval or binary search) for solving $f(x) = 0$

C3 Iteration Method for solving $f(x) = 0$ in a form $x = g(x)$

C4 Approximation of $\int_a^b f(x)\,dx$ with trapezoidal rule

C5 Solution of M linear equations in M unknowns

C6 First-order differential equation: Euler's formula

C7 First-order differential equation: 4th-order formulas (Runge, Kutta, Gill)

C8 Second-order differential equation: improved Euler formulas

C9 Second-order differential equation: 4th-order Runge formulas

The notes following each program indicate which lines have to be changed when using it, as they depend on the particular calculation to be done.

In FORTRAN programs, DATA statements may be replaced by READ statements, or conversely. These programs have been run on a VAX 11/780.

C1 Newton's Method for finding a root of $f(x) = 0.0$ (F(X)=0)

BASIC

```
05 LET E= 1E-6

10 LET X = -1.5

15 LET F=X**5-5.*X+2.

20 PRINT X,F

25 LET D = 5.*(X**4-1.)

30 LET X1 = X-F/D

35 IF ABS(X1-X) < E THEN 50

40 LET X = X1

45 GO TO 15

50 STOP

55 END
```

FORTRAN

```
      E= 1E-6

      X = -1.5

   15 F=X**5-5.*X+2.

      PRINT*,X,F

      D=5.*(X**4-1.)

      X1 = X-F/D

      IF(ABS(X1-X).LT.E)STOP

      X = X1

      GO TO 15

      STOP

      END
```

These programs implement procedure B1 in Appendix B.

Notes: line 5 specifies the accuracy parameter $\varepsilon = E$
line 10 specifies the initial approximation $x_0 = X$
line 15 specifies the equation to be solved
line 25 computes f'
line 35 uses the accuracy criterion $|x_1 - x_0| < \varepsilon$.

The last line printed shows r and $f(r)$.

C2   Bisection Method for solving $f(x) = 0$ (FNA(X)=0)

BASIC

```
05 DEF FNA(X)=LOG(X)-SIN(X)
10 LET E = 1E-2
15 READ A,B
20 DATA 2.,2.4
25 LET F = FNA(A)
30 IF F*FNA(B)>0.  THEN 85
35 IF ABS(F) < E THEN 95
40 LET C = .5*(A+B)
45 LET Y = FNA(C)
50 PRINT C,Y                    8
55 IF ABS(Y) < E THEN 95
60 IF Y*F < 0.  THEN 75
65 LET A = C
70 GO TO 40
75 LET B = C
80 GO TO 40
85 PRINT "NO SOLUTION"
90 PRINT "IN THIS INTERVAL"
95 STOP
100 END
```

FORTRAN

```
FNA(X)=ALOG(X)-SIN(X)
DATA A,B,E/2.,2.4,0.1/
F=FNA(A)
IF (F*FNA(B).GT.0.)THEN
PRINT*,'NO SOLUTION.TRY'
PRINT*,'ANOTHER INTERVAL'
STOP
ENDIF
IF(ABS(F).LT.E)STOP
C=.5*(A+B)
Y=FNA(C)
PRINT*,C,Y
IF(ABS(Y).LT.E)STOP
IF(Y*F.GT.0.)THEN
A=C
ELSE
B=C
ENDIF
GO TO 8
END
```

These programs implement the procedure given in Chapter 7 on p. 176.

Notes: line 5 specifies equation to be solved: $0 = f(x) = $ FNA(X)
line 10 specifies the accuracy parameter $\varepsilon = $ E
line 20 BASIC or 10 FORTRAN specifies the initial interval $[a, b] = [A, B]$
lines 55 (BASIC) or 45, 65 (FORTRAN) use the accuracy criterion $|f(c)| < \varepsilon$.

The last line printed shows r and $f(r)$.

C3   Iteration Method for finding a root of $x = g(x)$

BASIC   FORTRAN

BASIC		FORTRAN
05 DEF FNG(X)=0.2*(X**5+2.)		K=0
10 LET C = 0		E=5E-6
15 LET E = .005		X=-.5
20 LET X = 0.5	5	Y=1.+2./(SIN(X)-1.)
25 LET Y = FNG(X)		PRINT*,X,Y,K
30 IF ABS(X-Y) < E THEN 55		IF(ABS(X-Y).LT.E)STOP
35 LET C = C+1		K=K+1
40 IF C > 20 THEN 55		IF(K.GT.100)STOP
45 LET X = Y		X=Y
50 GO TO 25		GO TO 5
55 PRINT X,Y,C		END
60 STOP		
65 END		

These programs implement the procedure given in Chapter 7 on p. 177.

Notes: line 5 of the BASIC program specifies $g(x)$ as FNG(X); in the FORTRAN
program $g(x)$ is specified in statement 5
line 15 specifies the accuracy parameter $\varepsilon = E$
line 20 specifies the initial approximation $x_0 = X$
line 30 uses the accuracy criterion $|x - y_0| < \varepsilon$
line 40 restricts the BASIC program to 21 iterations and the FORTRAN to 101.

The printout shows x_K, x_{K+1} (approximations to r) and K.

C4 Approximation of $\int_A^B F(X)\,dX$ with trapezoidal rule

BASIC

```
05 DEF FNA(X)=1/X

10

15 READ A,B,N

20 DATA 1,2,20

25 LET H=(B-A)/N

30 LET S=(FNA(A)+FNA(B))*H

35 FOR I=1 TO N-1

40 LET X=A+H*I

45 LET S=S+2*FNA(X)*H

50 NEXT I

55 LET S=S/2

60 PRINT A,B,N,S

65 STOP

70 END
```

FORTRAN

```
      F(X)=1./X
      PRINT*,'INTEGRAL ENDPOINTS'
      PRINT*,'N?
      READ*,A,B,N
      H=(B-A)/N
      S=(F(A)+F(B))*H
      DO 1 I=1,N-1
      X=A+H*REAL(I)
    1 S=S+2.*F(X)*H
      S=S/2.
      PRINT*,A,B,N,S
      STOP
      END
```

These programs implement procedure B9 in Appendix B, for the approximation $T_N = T_{20}$ to $\int_1^2 (1/x)\,dx$.

Note: line 5 specifies the integrand
line 20 specifies the integration endpoints and the number of subintervals.

C5 Solution of M linear equations in M unknowns

BASIC		FORTRAN
02 DIM A(4,5)		DIMENSION A(9,10)
04 READ M,N		READ*,M,N
06 FOR I=1 TO M		DO 2 I=1,M
08 FOR J=1 TO N	2	READ*,(A(I,J),J=1,N)
10 READ A(I,J)		CALL MATPRI(A,M,N)
12 NEXT J		DO 1 L=1,M
14 NEXT I		P=A(L,L)
16 MAT PRINT A		IF(ABS(P).LT.1E-6)THEN
18 FOR L=1 TO M		PRINT*,'PIVOT<1E-6'
20 LET P=A(L,L)		CALL MATPRI(A,M,N)
22 IF ABS(P)<1E-6 THEN 64		STOP
24 FOR X=L TO N		ENDIF
26 LET A(L,X)=A(L,X)/P		DO 3 J=L,N
28 NEXT X	3	A(L,J)=A(L,J)/P
30 IF L=M GO TO 46		
32 FOR X=L+1 TO M		IF(L.NE.M)THEN
34 LET C=A(X,L)		DO 6 I =L+1,M
36 FOR Y=L TO N		C=A(I,L)
38 LET A(X,Y)=A(X,Y)-C*A(L,Y)		DO 6 J=L,N
40 NEXT Y	6	A(I,J)=A(I,J)-C*A(L,J)
42 NEXT X		ENDIF
44 NEXT L	1	CONTINUE
46 FOR K=2 TO M		DO 4 K=2,M
48 LET L=M-K+1		I=M-K+1
50 LET S=A(L,M+1)		S=A(I,M+1)
52 FOR J=L+1 TO M		DO 5 J=I+1,M
54 LET S=S-A(L,J)*A(J,M+1)	5	S=S-A(I,J)*A(J,M+1)
56 NEXT J	4	A(I,M+1)=S
58 LET A(L,M+1)=S		CALL MATPRI(A,M,N)
60 NEXT K		END
62 GO TO 66		
64 PRINT 'PIVOT LESS THAN 1E-6'		SUBROUTINE MATPRI(A,M,N)
66 MAT PRINT A		DIMENSION A(9,10)
68 DATA 4,5		DO 1 I=1,M
70 DATA 1,1,1,1,10,2,1,1,1,11	1	PRINT*,(A(I,J),J=1,N)
72 DATA 1,2,1,1,12,1,1,2,1,13		RETURN
74 END		END

Notes: line 2 restricts the BASIC program to 4 equations and the FORTRAN program to 9 equations. These restrictions have been chosen here to be compatible with the operation of the local line printer. The first data card (or interactive line entry at a terminal) must give M and $N = M+1$; this is followed by M cards (or lines) giving the coefficients and constant of each equation.

The solution is given in the last column of the printout

lines 18–44 implement procedure B8 in Appendix B, except for interchange of equations

lines 46–60 perform the back substitution from the triangular form, which is printed.

C6   Integration of a First-Order Differential Equation using Euler's Formula

BASIC

```
05   READ H,XF,X,Y
10   DATA .01,1.,.5,0.
15   LET K=0
20   LET K=K+1
25   IF X > XF THEN 70
30   Y = Y + H*(2.*COS(X)-Y/TAN(X))
35   X = X+H
40   LET Z=SIN(X)-SIN(.5)**2/SIN(X)
45   IF K=10 THEN 55
50   GO TO 20
55   PRINT X,Y,Z
60   K=0
65   GO TO 20
70   STOP
75   END
```

Notes: line 10 specifies step length H, given initial condition $y = Y$ at $x = X$, and the value $x = XF$ where integration stops (line 40).

line 30 is Euler's formula (19.5), containing the $f(x, y)$ given by the differential equation $dy/dx = f(x, y)$ $(= 2 \cos x - (y/\tan x))$.

line 45 gives a printing after every 10 iterations.

This program gives results for Example 19.20.

C7   Integration of dy/dx = f(x, y) using a 4th-order formula

FORTRAN

```
      DATA H,XF,X,Y/.1,1.005,.5,0./
      K=0
2     IF(X.GT.XF+H/2.)STOP
      CALL RUNG1(X,Y,H)
      K=K+1
      IF(K.LT.10.OR.
     *K.EQ.K/10*10)THEN
       PRINT*,K,X,Y
      ENDIF
      GO TO 2
      END
      SUBROUTINE RUNG1(X,Y,H)
      A=.5*H*F(X,Y)
      X=X+.5*H
      B=H*F(X,Y+A)
      C=H*F(X,Y+.5*B)
      X=X+.5*H
      D=.5*H*F(X,Y+C)
      Y=Y+(A+B+C+D)/3.
      RETURN
      END
      FUNCTION F(X,Y)
      F=2.*COS(X)-Y/TAN(X)
      RETURN
      END
```

This program gives results used in Example 19.40.

Notes: line 1 specifies step-length H, given initial condition $(x, y) = (X, Y)$, and the value $x = XF$ where the integration stops (line 3)

line 7 gives a printing of the calculated (X, Y) after every 10 iterations.

The subroutine implements equations (19.16) and (19.17) on p. 499. The function subprogram specifies the differential equation: $dY/dX = F$.

The following subroutines implement the formulas of Kutta and Gill. If they are to be substituted the appropriate change must also be made in line 4.

```
SUBROUTINE KUTT(X,Y,H)

HK=H*F(X,Y)/3.

X=X+H/3.

HL=H*F(X,Y+HK)

 X=X+H/3.

HM=H*F(X,Y-HK+HL)

 X=X+H/3.

HN=H*F(X,Y+3.*HK-HL+HM)/3.

Y=Y+.375*(HK+HL +HM+HN)

RETURN

END

SUBROUTINE GILL(X,Y,H)

S=SQRT(.5)

HK=.5*H*F(X,Y)

X=X+.5*H

HL=(1.-S)*H*F(X,Y+HK)

HM=(1.+S)*H*F(X,Y+(2.*S-1.)*HK+HL)

X=X+.5*H

HN=.5*H*F(X,Y-(1.+2.*S)*HL+HM)

Y=Y+(HK+HL+HM+HN)/3.

RETURN

END
```

An improved version of the main program can be seen in programs C8 and C9, where some iteration can be included in the subroutine.

C8 Integration of $d^2y/dx^2 = f(x, y, dy/dx)$ using the improved Euler formulas

FORTRAN

```
      DATA XF,X,Y,P/1.2,1.,1.,-1./
      DATA H,K/.1,1/
1     IF(X.GT.XF-H/2.)STOP
      CALL IMPEUL2(X,Y,P,H,K)
      PRINT*,X,Y,P
      GO TO 1
      END
      SUBROUTINE IMPEUL2(X,Y,P,H,K)
      DO   1 L=1,K
      PKP=F(X,Y,P)
      X=X+H
      YLP=P+H*PKP
      PLP=F(X,Y+H*P,YLP)
      Y=Y+0.5*H*(P+YLP)
1     P=P+0.5*H*(PKP+PLP)
      RETURN
      END
      FUNCTION F(X,Y,P)
      F=-2.*X*Y*P+X*X
      RETURN
      END
```

This program improves the results obtained in Example 19.61 on p. 503.

Notes: line 1 specifies the value $x = $ XF where the integration stops, and the given initial coordinates (X, Y, P)

line 2 specifies step-length H, and the number of iterations before results are printed.

The subroutine implements the improved Euler formulas (19.22) on p. 502.
The function subprogram specifies the differential equation

$$\frac{d^2Y}{dX^2} = F\left(X, Y, \frac{dY}{dX}\right).$$

C9   Integration of $d^2y/dx^2 = f(x, y, dy/dx)$ using 4th-order Runge formulas

FORTRAN

```
      DATA XF,X,Y,P/1.,0.,3.,9./
      DATA H,K/.1,2/
2     J=0
3     J=J+1
      IF(X.GT.XF-H/2.)STOP
      CALL RUNG2(X,Y,P,H)
      IF(K.NE.J)GO TO 3
      E=2.*EXP(6.*X)+(1.-2.*X)*EXP(-X)
      ER=Y-E
      PRINT*,K,X,Y,P,E,ER
      GO TO 2
5     STOP
      END

      FUNCTION F(X,Y,P)
      F=5.*P+6.*Y+14.*EXP(-X)
      RETURN
      END

      SUBROUTINE RUNG2(X,Y,P,H)
      YK=P
      PK=F(X,Y,P)
      X=X+.5*H
      YL=P+.5*H*PK
      PL=F(X,Y+.5*H*YK,YL)
      YM=P+.5*H*PL
      PM=F(X,Y+.5*H*YL,YM)
      X=X+.5*H
      YN=P+      H*PM
      PN=F(X,Y+H*YM,YN)
      Y=Y+(YK+2.*YL+2.*YM+YN)*H/6.
      P=P+(PK+2.*PL+2.*PM+PN)*H/6.
      RETURN
      END
```

This program checks Exercise 13.22 (Exercise 19.6(ii)).

Notes: line 1 specifies the given initial conditions (X, Y, P), and the value $x = $ XF where the integration stops

line 2 specifies the step length H, and the points X = KH, 2KH, 3KH, ... for which results are printed

line 8 computes the exact solution.

The function subprogram specifies the differential equation

$$\frac{d^2Y}{dX^2} = F\left(X, Y, \frac{dY}{dX}\right)$$

The subroutine produces K iterations of the Runge formulas (19.25) and (19.26) on p. 502.

Appendix D
Formal Definitions of Limiting Processes

The object of this Appendix is to give precise definitions of the various limit statements which are discussed informally in Sections 4.1 and 4.2.

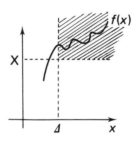

Figure D1 $f(x) > X$ if $x > \Delta$

Consider first the statement $f(x) \to \infty$ as $x \to \infty$, which appeared in Example 4.20 on p. 80. The essential property is that given any number X, however large, there is a number Δ such that $f(x) > X$ whenever $x > \Delta$. In Fig. D1, all values of $f(x)$ for $x > \Delta$ are in the shaded region, and the statement holds for some Δ however large X is chosen. This leads to the following definition:

(i) $f(x) \to \infty$ as $x \to \infty$, if for each positive number X, there is a number Δ such that $f(x) > X$ in (Δ, ∞).

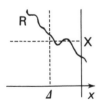
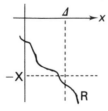
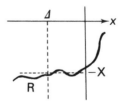

Figure D2 $f(x) > X$ if $x < \Delta$ Figure D3 $f(x) < -X$ if $x > \Delta$ Figure D4 $f(x) < -X$ if $x < \Delta$

The actual value of Δ normally depends on X; for example, for $f(x) = x^2$, a choice for Δ is $\sqrt{X}$ (or any number larger than $\sqrt{X}$). Similarly

(ii) $f(x) \to \infty$ as $x \to -\infty$ if, for each positive number X, there is a number Δ such that $f(x) > X$ in $(-\infty, \Delta)$; (graph lies in region R of Fig. D2).

(iii) $f(x) \to -\infty$ as $x \to \infty$ if, for each positive number X, there is a number Δ such that $f(x) < -X$ in (Δ, ∞); (graph lies in region R of Fig. D3).
(iv) $f(x) \to -\infty$ as $x \to -\infty$ if, for each positive number X, there is a number Δ such that $f(x) < -X$ in $(-\infty, \Delta)$; (graph lies in region R of Fig. D4).

In (ii) and (iv), Δ will usually be negative. Note that (iii) and (iv) can be alternatively expressed as $f(x) \to -\infty$ if and only if $-f(x) \to \infty$ (as $x \to \pm\infty$).

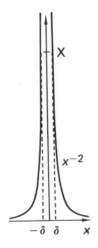

Figure 4.4 $x^{-2} > X$ if $|x| < \delta$ Figure D5   Deleted neighbourhood of a.

The statement $f(x) \to \infty$ as $x \to a$ was discussed in Examples 4.11 and 4.12 on p. 73. For $a = 0$ and $f(x) = x^{-2}$ the essential property was illustrated in Fig. 4.4 of Example 4.17 (on p. 76): given any number X, however large, a neighbourhood of 0 exists such that $x^{-2} > X$ in the neighbourhood. When $x \to a$, such a neighbourhood of a must exist. Since $f(a)$ is either undefined or irrelevant, it is convenient to define a **deleted neighbourhood** of a as a set of points $(b, c) \backslash \{a\}$ with $b < a < c$ (Fig. D5). Then a suitable definition is:
   (v) $f(x) \to \infty$ as $x \to a$ if, for each positive number X, there is a deleted neighbourhood of a throughout which $f(x) > X$.
      Symbolically, given $X > 0$, there are always numbers b, c (which depend on X) with $b < a < c$, such that $f(x) > X$ whenever x is in $(b, c) \backslash \{a\}$.
      Also $f(x) \to -\infty$ as $x \to a$ if and only if $-f(x) \to \infty$ as $x \to a$.

Example 1D
If $f(x) = |x - 2|^{-1}$ $(x \neq 2)$, and $f(2) = 0$, prove that $f(x) \to \infty$ as $x \to 2$.

This function was illustrated in Fig. 3.11(b). Consider the inequality $f(x) > X$, where $X > 0$. Now for $X > 0$ and $x \neq 2$, $|x - 2|^{-1} > X \Leftrightarrow |x - 2| < 1/X$, by taking reciprocals, and $|x - 2| < 1/X = X^{-1}$ means x is in $(2 - X^{-1}, 2 + X^{-1})$. For each positive X, however large, there is a deleted neighbourhood of 2, for instance $(2 - 1/X, 2 + 1/X) \backslash \{2\}$, in which $f(x) > X$. So the definition of $f(x) \to \infty$ as $x \to 2$ is satisfied.   □

The definitions (i) and (iii) have to be modified to cover sequences. One way of doing this would be to require the existence of an integer N such that $s_n > X$ (or $s_n < -X$)

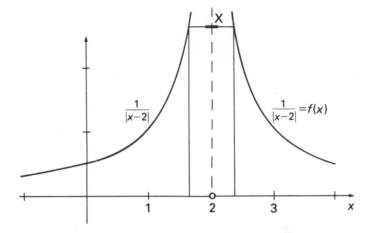

Figure 3.11(b)   Deleted neighbourhood of 2 in which $f(x) > X$

whenever $n > N$. The following change is preferable, because the same definition then applies equally well to functions of type $R \rightarrow R$ in general:

$f(x) \rightarrow \infty$ as $x \rightarrow \infty$ if, for each positive number X, there is a number Δ such that $f(x) > X$ for all numbers x which are in (Δ, ∞) and in the domain of f.

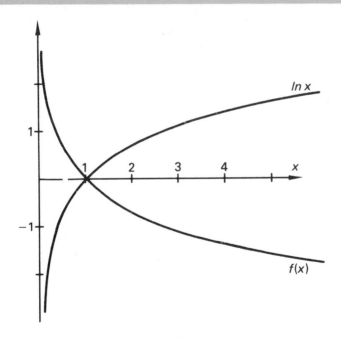

Figure 3.2 $f(x) = -\ln x$

For sequences, x then means only integers in (Δ, ∞). The fact that Δ need not be an integer simplifies proofs for sequences. Thus $n^2 \rightarrow \infty$ as $n \rightarrow \infty$ because $n^2 > X$ for any integer n in $(\sqrt{X}, \infty)$. It is also advantageous to make a similar change in the definition (v):

> $f(x) \rightarrow \infty$ as $x \rightarrow a$ if, for each positive number X, there is a deleted neighbourhood of a such that $f(x) > X$ for all x which are in this neighbourhood and in the domain of f.

Symbolically, given $X > 0$, there are numbers b, c with $b < a < c$ such that $f(x) > X$ whenever x is in $((b, c)\backslash\{a\}) \cap D$, where D is the domain of f.

Example 2D

Suppose $f(x) = -\ln x$, with domain $D = (0, \infty)$. To get the graph, reflect in the x-axis the graph of $\ln x$ (p. 563). Then $f(x) \rightarrow \infty$ as $x \rightarrow 0$. For any X, an interval $(0, \delta)$ exists such that $f(x) > X$ when x is in $(0, \delta)$. With the change in the definition, negative values of x, which are outside the domain D, do not have to be considered. Using the previous definition (v), the statement $f(x) \rightarrow \infty$ as $x \rightarrow 0$ would not be true, because there is no deleted neighbourhood of 0 throughout which f is defined. □

Exercise

Consider $f(x) = 1/(x-2)$ as $x \rightarrow 2$, as in Example 4.110 on p. 78. Verify that the definition (v) is not satisfied.

Formulate definitions of $f(x) \rightarrow \infty$ as $x \rightarrow a+$, and as $x \rightarrow a-$.

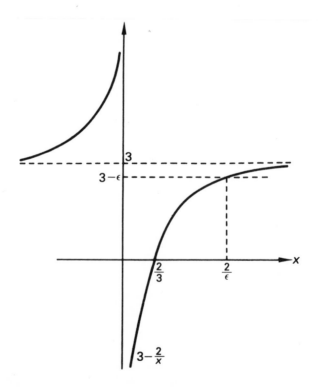

Figure D6 $3 - 2/x > 3 - \varepsilon$ if $x > 2/\varepsilon$

Next it is convenient to define the meaning of $f(x) \to L$ as $x \to \infty$, i.e. $\mathrm{Lim}_{x \to \infty} f(x) = L$. The relevant notions were discussed in Examples 4.21-3 (see p. 80). To get a precise formulation of the idea, reconsider $f(x) = (3x-2)/x \to 3$ as $x \to \infty$ (Example 4.22). '$f(x)$ as near to 3 as desired' means $(3x-2)/x > 3 - \varepsilon$ where ε is arbitrarily small. This inequality can be solved to get $x > 2/\varepsilon$. For any ε, there is a number Δ ($2/\varepsilon$ or any larger number) such that $f(x)$ differs from·the limit 3 by less than ε when $x > \Delta$ (see Fig. D6).

In general, 'as close as desired to the limit L' means that for any positive ε, however small, one requires $f(x)$ to have a value in $(L-\varepsilon, L+\varepsilon)$. This can be referred to as an arbitrarily small neighbourhood of L. The remaining part of the definition, giving the meaning of 'as $x \to \infty$' is the same as in the definitions already given.

$f(x) \to L$ as $x \to \infty$ if, for any neighbourhood of L, there is a number Δ such that $f(x)$ is in this neighbourhood for all x which are in (Δ, ∞) and in the domain of f.

This can be written more symbolically:

given $\varepsilon > 0$, there is a number Δ such that $L - \varepsilon < f(x) < L + \varepsilon$ whenever x is in $D \cap (\Delta, \infty)$, D being the domain of f.

For $x > \Delta$, all values $f(x)$ lie in the shaded region of Fig. D7, and this is true for some Δ however small ε is. Again the reference to the domain means that the definition applies to sequences. The number L is called the limit of $f(x)$ as x tends to infinity, and this is written $L = \mathrm{Lim}_{x \to \infty} f(x)$.

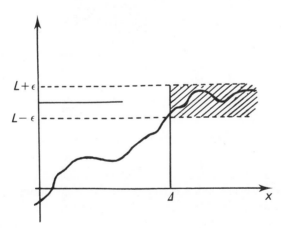

Figure D7 $L - \varepsilon < f(x) < L + \varepsilon$ if $x > \Delta$

Example 3D
(i) $f(x) = 1/x^2$. Since $0 - \varepsilon < x^{-2} < 0 + \varepsilon$ if $x > 1/\sqrt{\varepsilon}$, for any ε, however small, one can satisfy the definition by taking $\Delta = 1/\sqrt{\varepsilon}$. This proves the statement $x^{-2} \to 0$ as $x \to \infty$. (cf. Example 4.21 on p. 80).

(ii) The above discussion of Example 4.22 (see Fig. D6) shows that $(3x-2)/x$ is in the neighbourhood $(3 - \varepsilon, 3 + \varepsilon)$ of 3 provided $x > (2/\varepsilon)$. However small ε is, one can take $\Delta = 2/\varepsilon$ to satisfy the definition, and so prove that $(3x-2)/x \to \infty$. The same proof shows that the sequence $\{(3n-2)/n\}$ has the limit 3.

(iii) In Example 4.23 $(\sin x)/x$ is in the interval $(-\varepsilon, \varepsilon)$ provided $x > 1/\varepsilon$. This is true for any positive ε, however small. So $(\sin x)/x$ is in $(-\varepsilon, \varepsilon)$, an arbitrarily small neighbourhood of $0 = L$, if x is in $(1/\varepsilon, \infty)$. Taking $\Delta = 1/\varepsilon$, this proves that $\mathrm{Lim}_{x \to \infty} (\sin x)/x = 0$.   □

To demonstrate the definition, it is not necessary to exactly solve the inequality $L - \varepsilon < f(x) < L + \varepsilon$, but only to show there is some interval (Δ, ∞) in which it is true. If a suitable Δ is found, then any larger Δ will also satisfy the definition.

To define $f(x) \to L$ as $x \to -\infty$, replace (Δ, ∞) by $(-\infty, \Delta)$ in the previous definition.

Finally, the definition of $\mathrm{Lim}_{x \to a} f(x) = L$, or $f(x) \to L$ as $x \to a$, is obtained by combining the relevant features of the definitions of $\mathrm{Lim}_{x \to \infty}$ and of $f(x) \to \infty$ as $x \to a$.

> $f(x) \to L$ as $x \to a$ if, for any neighbourhood of L, there is a deleted neighbourhood of a such that $f(x)$ is in the neighbourhood of L for all x in the domain of f which are in the deleted neighbourhood of a.

$f(x)$ is said to tend to the limit L as x tends to a. This is also written $\mathrm{Lim}_{x \to a} f(x) = L$. A more symbolic statement of this definition is:

> given $\varepsilon > 0$ there are numbers b, c with $b < a < c$ such that $L - \varepsilon < f(x) < L + \varepsilon$ whenever x is in $D \cap (b, c) \backslash \{a\}$, where D is the domain of f.

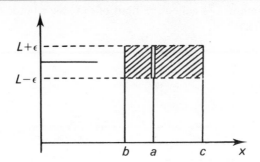

Figure D8   Deleted neighbourhood of a

For $b < x < a$ or $a < x < c$, all values of $f(x)$ lie in the shaded region of Fig. D8, and the interval (b, c) exists however small ε is (the reference to the domain allows the definition to apply to $x \to \alpha$ or $x \to \beta$ for a function with domain (α, β)).

Example 4D

To show that $x^2 \to 1$ as $x \to 1$ requires showing that the inequality

$$1 - \varepsilon < x^2 < 1 + \varepsilon$$

can be satisfied in a deleted neighbourhood of 1, however small ε is. Assuming $\varepsilon < 8$, it is easy to check that $a = 1 - \frac{1}{2}\varepsilon$, $c = 1 + \frac{1}{4}\varepsilon$ gives a suitable deleted neighbourhood (Fig. D9).   □

Example 5D

Show that $\mathrm{Lim}_{x \to 0} \sin x/x = 1$ (cf. Example 4.13 on p. 74).

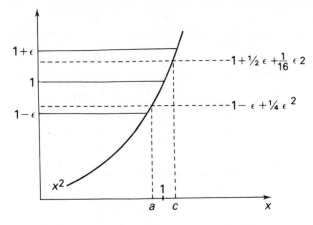

Figure D9   If $1-\frac{1}{2}\varepsilon<x<1+\varepsilon/4$, then $1-\varepsilon<x^2<1+\varepsilon$

This requires showing that the inequality $1-\varepsilon<\sin x/x<1+\varepsilon$ can be satisfied in a deleted neighbourhood of 0, however small ε is.

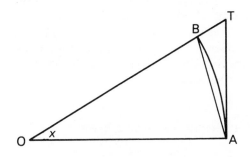

Figure D10   OA=OB=1, AT=tan x

If OAB is a sector of a circle of unit radius, subtending an angle x (radians) at the centre O, and the tangent at A meets OB at T (Fig. D10), then

$$\text{(area triangle OAB)} < \text{(area sector OAB)} < \text{(area OTA)}$$
$$\tfrac{1}{2}\sin x \qquad < \qquad \tfrac{1}{2}x \qquad < \quad \tfrac{1}{2}\tan x.$$

For $0<x<\pi/2$, $\sin x$ is positive, so this may be written

$$1<x/\sin x<1/\cos x$$

and taking reciprocals gives (Fig. D11)

$$\cos x<(\sin x)/x<1.$$

Thus $(\sin x)/x<1$, so it is sufficient to satisfy $1-\varepsilon<(\sin x)/x$, and this will be true if $\cos x>1-\varepsilon$. Since $\cos x$ is decreasing on $(0, \pi/2)$, $\cos x>1-\varepsilon \Leftrightarrow x<\text{Cos}^{-1}(1-\varepsilon)$. Taking $\delta=\text{Cos}^{-1}(1-\varepsilon)$,

$$0<x<\delta \Rightarrow (\sin x)/x>1-\varepsilon.$$

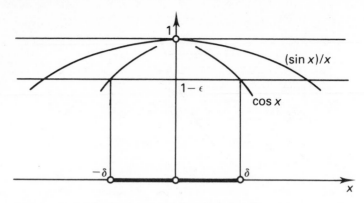

Figure D11 $\delta = \text{Cos}^{-1}(1-\varepsilon)$ gives deleted neighbourhood where $(\sin x)/x > 1 - \varepsilon$

Finally, $(\sin x)/x$ is an even function, so this result is also true in $(-\delta, 0)$ and the required deleted neighbourhood can be taken to be

$$(-\text{Cos}^{-1}(1-\varepsilon), \text{Cos}^{-1}(1-\varepsilon))\backslash\{0\}. \quad \square$$

When the formal definitions were modified above to mention the domain of the function, one thing was left understood. The definitions of $f(x) \to \infty$, or $f(x) \to a$, as $x \to \infty$ are subject to the restriction that the domain of f contains arbitrarily large numbers. Given any arbitrarily large number ξ, $f(x)$ must be defined for some $x > \xi$. This can only be true for arbitrary ξ if the domain of f has no sup, in which case the number of values of $f(x)$ with $x > \xi$ cannot be finite.

Example 6D
Unless this further point is put in, one would have

$$\text{Sin}^{-1} x \to L \quad \text{as } x \to \infty,$$

for any desired value of L. The previous definition would be trivially satisfied with $\Delta = 1$, there being no numbers both in $(1, \infty)$ and the domain of Sin^{-1}. $\square$

Similarly the definitions of $f(x) \to \infty$, or $f(x) \to L$, as $x \to a$ are subject to the understanding that the domain of f contains numbers arbitrarily close to a. Given any deleted neighbourhood $(b, c)\backslash\{a\}$, however small, it must contain numbers from the domain of f. Thus the definition cannot apply to sequences. Also the number of values of $f(x)$ with $b < x < c$ cannot be finite.

Appendix E
Change of Variable in an Integral

This appendix shows that $\int_a^b f\{g(x)\}g'(x)\,\mathrm{d}x$ (*) can be evaluated, after the substitution $w = g(x)$, as $\int_{a'}^{b'} f(w)\,\mathrm{d}w$, where $a' = g(a)$, $b' = g(b)$. From the definition of Riemann integral, (*) is

$$R_a^b[f\{g\}g'] = \lim_{n \to \infty} \sum_{i=1}^{n} f\{g(c_i)\}g'(c_i)(x_i - x_{i-1}). \tag{E.1}$$

Recall that the x_i are any points subdividing $[a, b]$ and c_i is any point in $[x_{i-1}, x_i]$. The subintervals need not be of equal length (cf. Exercise 9.2), provided that as $n \to \infty$, $(x_i - x_{i-1}) \to 0$ for all i.

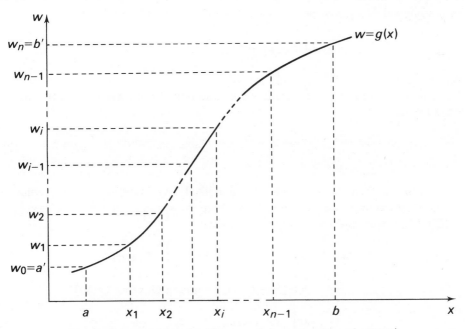

Figure E1   Subdivision of (a', b') on w-axis from subdivision of $a < x < b$

Provided g is a one-to-one function with an inverse, the points $w_i = g(x_i)$ subdivide (a', b'), and if g is continuous,

$$(w_i - w_{i-1}) \to 0 \quad \text{as } (x_i - x_{i-1}) \to 0.$$

By the mean value theorem of differentiation, given in Section 6.7, there is a point c_i in (x_{i-1}, x_i) where

$$g'(c_i) = \frac{w_i - w_{i-1}}{x_i - x_{i-1}}.$$

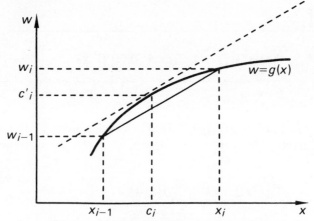

Figure E2   Use of mean value theorem to define c_i

Choose this point for the c_i in equation (E.1), and define $c_i' = g(c_i)$, which is a value of w in the interval (w_{i-1}, w_i) (or (w_i, w_{i-1})). Then equation (E.1) becomes

$$R_a^b[f\{g\}g'] = \lim_{n \to \infty} \sum_{i=1}^{n} f(w_i)(w_i - w_{i-1}),$$

which is the definition of $R_{a'}^{b'}(f) = \int_{a'}^{b'} f(w)\, dw$.

For a valid substitution g must satisfy the conditions for the mean value theorem, and g^{-1} must exist.

Thus g' must exist on (a, b), and must not change sign, and g must be continuous on $[a, b]$.

The substitution formula also follows immediately by inversion of the formula for differentiating a composite function. Again suppose $w = g(x)$, $a' = g(a)$, $b' = g(b)$, and also that $F(w)$ is an antiderivative of $f(w)$. Then

$$\int_{w=a'}^{b'} f(w)\, dw = F(b') - F(a') = F(g(b)) - F(g(a))$$

$$= G(b) - G(a), \quad \text{defining } G(x) = F(g(x))$$

$$= \int_a^b G'(x)\, dx$$

$$= \int_a^b F'(g(x))g'(x)\, dx, \quad \text{from (IV) in Section 6.1}$$

$$= \int_a^b f(g(x))g'(x)\, dx.$$

This derivation is inferior, because the condition that g should be one-to-one is obscured, and also f is assumed continuous.

APPENDIX F
Answers (or Checks) to Selected Exercises

Exercises on Chapter 1 (p. 21)

1.1 $|a|+|b| \geqslant |a \pm b|$.

1.3 (i) $\overrightarrow{AB}+\overrightarrow{BC}+\overrightarrow{CA}=0$ (ii) $\sum$ angles $=180°$ (iii) 3 possible pairs of vector products should give the same answer.

1.4 $\cos^{-1}(\sqrt{6}/3)=35.3°$.

1.5 Meaningless: (iii), (v), (vii), (viii), (xi), (xii), (xiii). Better to use brackets: (iv), (vi).

1.6 0.

1.7 $(A \cdot C \times D)B - (B \cdot C \times D)A$, from equation (1.32) on p. 18.

1.9 (ii) $6i+4j+5k$ (or any scalar multiple).

1.10 (ii) $AB = BC = CA = CD = BD = AD = 3\sqrt{2}$; volume 9.

1.13 (i) dk; $\frac{1}{3}d(\sqrt{2}j-k)$; $\frac{1}{3}d(\pm\sqrt{6}i-\sqrt{2}j-k)$ (ii) $109°28'=\frac{1}{2}+\text{Sin}^{-1}(\frac{1}{3})$.

1.14 (i) $13/15$ (ii) $\frac{13}{9}(2i+2j+k)$ (iii) $-32i+24j+16k$ (iv) $64i-48j-32k$ ($=-2A \times B$) (v) 24 ($=-A \times B \cdot C$).

1.15 (i) $3i+5j-k$ (or any scalar multiple) (ii) coplanar (iii) $\overrightarrow{AE} \cdot N \neq 0$.

1.16 (i) P_4 is in the same plane as P_1, P_2 and P_3.
(ii) Evaluate $N = \overrightarrow{P_1P_2} \times \overrightarrow{P_2P_3}$ (or the cross-product of any other pair of relative vectors) and check whether $\overrightarrow{P_1P_j}(j=4, \ldots, n)$ are perpendicular to N.

1.17 (i) $(4, 12, -9)$ (ii) $(5, 3, 5)$ (iii) $(5, 11, -8)$ (iv) $(7, 13, -6)$; volume 52.

1.19 (i) 0 (vectors are coplanar) (ii) all zero.

1.20 107; $(7, 0, 11)$, $(14, 6, 14)$, $(10, 7, 12)$, $(15, 5, 18)$.

1.21 $2i-j-k$.

Exercises on Chapter 2 (p. 40)

2.1 Check the given conditions, e.g. in (ii) all 3 points satisfy the equation found.

2.2 Choose λ so that Q is on $3x-6y+2z=4$, then $PQ=\lambda$ is the required distance (cf. Example 2.21 on p. 25).

2.4 $(2, 8, -3)$, $(1, 7, -5)$, $(0, 6, -7)$ are on the line.

2.6 $(2i+j-k) \times (i-j+4k)$ is a vector along the line. Normalizing gives a unit vector whose components are the direction-cosines. Check that the vector is unit, and perpendicular to both plane normals.

2.7 $(2, -1, 3)$ should satisfy plane equation, as should $(1-t, 1, t)$ for all t.

2.8 Substitute any intersections found into given equations.

2.9 If a line of intersection is found, substitute its parametric equations into the given plane equations.

2.10 As 2.8.

2.11 a has the direction of line (1), b has the direction of line (5), and c is a vector from a point $(1, -2, 0)$ on line (1) to a point $(2, 2, 4)$ on line (5). If the lines intersected, then a, b, c would be coplanar, and $a \times b \cdot c = 0$. So $a \times b \cdot c = 20$ shows that the lines do not intersect.

2.12 See **2.11**.

2.13 (i) A circle centre $(0, 0, 1)$, radius 1, in the plane $z = 1$.

(ii) A circle centre $(0, 0, 0)$, radius 1, in the Oxz plane $(y = 0)$.

(iii) An ellipse with axis of length $2a$ along Oy, axis of length $2b$ along Oz, and centre O.

(iv) A helix around a cylinder of radius 2 with axis Oy; $(2, 0, 0)$, $(1, \pi/3, \sqrt{3})$, $(-\sqrt{3}, 7\pi/6, 1)$ are on the helix, the parameter value being the value of y.

2.14 As **2.8**.

2.15 No intersection if $b^2 < a(d - c)$.

2.16 Assume $x = t^3 - t^2 + 3t$, $y = 1 + t - t^2$, $z = t^3 + 2t + 3$ satisfy some plane equation $Ax + By + Cz = D$ for all t. Equate coefficients of powers of t, to obtain $A = 1 = -B = -C$, $D = -4$.

2.17 $r = \sqrt{2} \cos t \, i' + \sin t \, k$ or $\frac{1}{2}x'^2 + z^2 = 1$, $y' = 0$.

2.18–19 Check formulas obtained against previous numerical examples.

2.20 If a line is in a plane parallel to a coordinate plane, then one coordinate is constant along the line, and cannot be used as parameter.

2.21 (i) $x - 2y + z = 6$ (ii) $ax + by + cz = a^2 + b^2 + c^2$.

2.22 Plane equation should be satisfied by $(2 + t, 2 + 3t, 3 + t)$ for all t, and by $(2 + u, 3 + 4u, 4 + 2u)$ for all u.

2.23 Check as in **2.22**.

2.24 3; foot of perpendicular is $(2, 1, 2)$.

2.25 Either $r = 2j + k + u(7i - 2j + k)$

or $r = 2j + k + u(i + 4j + k)$.

2.26 (i) $4x - 5y + 3z = -1$ (ii) $(x + 1)^2 + y^2 + (z - 1)^2 = 49$.

2.27 $x - 5y + 3z = 7$.

2.28 (i) $(-2 + 3s - 2t)i + (-1 + 2s - 3t)j + (3 + s + t)k$.

(ii) $-10 + 11s - 14t = 0 = -5 + 14s - 11t$.

(iii) $\left(-\dfrac{19}{15}, \dfrac{-21}{15}, \dfrac{2}{15}\right), \left(-\dfrac{39}{15}, \dfrac{-1}{15}, \dfrac{22}{15}\right), 4/\sqrt{3}$.

2.29 3.

2.30 $r = -2i - j + 4k + t(3i + 6j - 6k)$

(i) $P(-1, 1, 2)$ (ii) $Q(-3, -3, 6)$ (iii) $R(0, 3, 0)$.

2.31 $3x - y + 2z = 4$.   **2.32** $\dfrac{x}{2} = \dfrac{y + 5}{31} = \dfrac{z + 5}{19}$.

2.33 $(1, 3, 2)$ and $\left(1, -\dfrac{13}{9}, \dfrac{202}{81}\right)$.   **2.34** $(1, -2, 4)$.

2.35 $3x + y - z = 4$.

2.36 (i) $3x - 2y + z = 6$ (ii) $r = \frac{3}{2}i + \frac{3}{2}k + t(i - j + k)$.

2.37 $x + 2y - 2z = 3/2$.   **2.38** $90°$.

2.39 $(0, 1, -1), (0, -1, 1)$.

$x = \text{const.} \neq 0$ does not intersect, since curve is a circle in $x = 0$ plane: or $y = c$ or $z = c$ with $c^2 > 2$.

Exercises on Chapter 3 (p. 69)

3.2 (i) $1/x$ (ii) x^4 (iii) xy^3 (iv) $x^2 e^x$ (v) $-x$ (vi) $3x - \ln x$.

3.4 $\sin$, Sin^{-1} and Tan^{-1} are odd, $\cos$ is even.

From Fig. 3.3(b), $\text{Cos}^{-1}(-x) = \pi - \text{Cos}^{-1} x$
and $\text{Sin}^{-1} x = -\text{Cos}^{-1} x + \frac{1}{2}\pi$.

3.5 (a) $0.6 = \sqrt{(1 - 0.8^2)}$, (b) 0.9, (c) $\pi - 4$, (d) $4 - \dfrac{3\pi}{2}$, (e) $4 - \pi$.

3.6 The graphs have period 2π, and the same range $[-\frac{1}{2}\pi, \frac{1}{2}\pi]$ as Sin^{-1}:

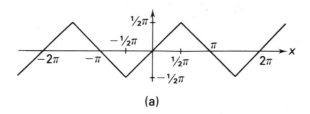

(a)

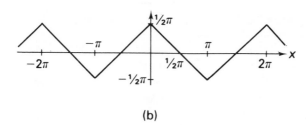

(b)

Figure F3.6   (a) $\text{Sin}^{-1}(\sin x)$, (b) $\text{Sin}^{-1}(\cos x)$

3.7 $\cosh x = 13/12 = \sqrt{(1 + \sinh^2 x)}$, $\tanh x = -5/13$.

3.8 (a) 2, (b) 5/4, (c) 3/4.

3.9

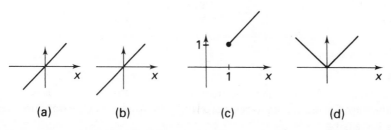

(a)   (b)   (c)   (d)

Figure F3.9   (a) $\sinh \circ \sinh^{-1}$, (b) $\sinh^{-1} \circ \sinh$, (c) $\cosh \circ \text{Cosh}^{-1}$, (d) $\text{Cosh}^{-1} \circ \cosh$

3.11 Substitute answers into given equation.

3.12 (v) as k increases, the graph approaches that of the signum function of Exercise 3.1.

3.13 $\tanh^{-1} x = \frac{1}{2} \ln ((1+x)/(1-x))$ has domain $(-1, 1)$ and range $(-\infty, \infty)$.

3.15 As $x \to -\infty$, $\sinh x \sim -\frac{1}{2}e^{-x}$, $\cosh x \sim \frac{1}{2}e^{-x}$, $\tanh x \to -1$,
$\sinh^{-1} x \sim \ln(-1/2x)$, $x \to -\infty$ not in domain of $\tanh^{-1} x$ or $\text{Cosh}^{-1} x$.

3.16 (i) Range of s is the set of all positive, even integers, i.e. $\{y: y = 2n, n \in N\}$, where
N is the set of positive integers.
Range of t is $\{y: y = 1/n, n \in N\} = \{1, \frac{1}{2}, \frac{1}{3}, \frac{1}{4}, \frac{1}{5}, \dots\}$
Range of u is $\{-1, 1\}$
Range of f is $[0, \infty)$

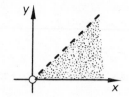

Figure F3.16   Domain of $u(f)$

(ii) s, t

(iii) Domain of $u(s)$ is N

Domain $s(u)$ is $R^+ = (0, \infty)$

Domain of $u(f)$ is $\{(x, y): x > y > 0\}$ (see Figure)

Domain of $f(s, t)$ is $N^2 = N \times N$ (all pairs of positive integers).

3.17

	Bounded above	Bounded below	Sup	Inf	Max	Min
(i)	Yes	Yes	3	3	3	3
(ii)	No	No	*	*	*	*
(iii)	No	No	*	*	*	*
(iv)	No	Yes	*	0	*	*
(v)	Yes	Yes	1	0	1	*
(vi)	No	No	*	*	*	*
(vii)	No	Yes	*	0	*	0
(viii)	No	No	*	*	*	*
(ix) s	No	Yes	*	2	*	2
(x) t	Yes	Yes	1	0	1	*
(xi) u	Yes	Yes	1	−1	1	−1
(xii) f	No	Yes	*	0	*	0

*Does not exist

3.18 (3.16)

s increasing on N (note that the definition of increasing on p. 68 requires a slight modification for sequences to restrict x and y to numbers in the domain, i.e. integers)

t not increasing

u not increasing

CONCEPT NOT APPLICABLE to f.

3.18 (3.17)

(i) – (ii) – (iii) – (iv) $(-\infty, 2)$ (v) $(-\infty, 0]$

(vi) $R \backslash \{-1\} = (-\infty, -1) \cup (-1, \infty)$. For a method of drawing the graph in the stages

$$\frac{1}{y} \to \frac{1}{y+1} \to \frac{-1}{y+1} \to \frac{-2}{y+1} \to 1 - \frac{2}{y+1} \qquad \text{cf. Fig. 6.16 on p. 134.}$$

(using y as the independent variable).

(vii) $[-1, \infty)$ (viii) $(-\infty, \infty)$.

3.19 (i) $a^2 > b$ (ii) $a^2 \leqslant b$.

3.20 Increasing if $a > 1$, decreasing if $0 < a < 1$.

3.21 (i) Decreasing if $a>0$, $0<r<1$ or if $a<0$, $r>1$.

3.22

		$b^2>c$	$b^2\leqslant c$
(i)	Domain	$(-\infty, \infty)$	$(-\infty, \infty)$
	Range	$[1, \infty)$	$[\cosh(c-b^2), \infty)$
(ii)	Decreasing on	$(-\infty, -b-\sqrt{(b^2-c)}]$	$(-\infty, -b]$
	and on	$[-b, -b+\sqrt{(b^2-c)}]$	
	Increasing on	$[-b-\sqrt{(b^2-c)}, -b]$	$[-b, \infty)$
	and on	$[-b+\sqrt{(b^2-c)}, \infty)$	—
(iii)	sup	—	—
	max	—	—
	inf	1	$\cosh(c-b^2)$
	min	1	$\cosh(c-b^2)$

3.24 Diagram should show the following vectors:
$(2i-k)$ at P, i at Q, j at R, $(3i+j-k)$ at A, and $(7i+4j-2k)$ at B.
$F(t)=(3+4t)i+(1+3t)j-(1+t)k$.

3.25 (i) e^{-2x} (ii) $2^n e^{-nx}$.

3.26

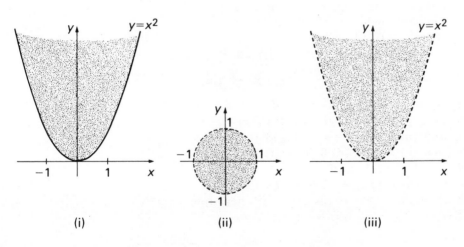

(i)   (ii)   (iii)

Figure F3.26   Ranges (i) $[0, \infty)$, (ii) $(-\infty, \infty)$, (iii) $(-\infty, \infty)$

3.27 (i) no sup, inf, max or min (ii) sup $=$ max $=4/3$, inf $=0$, no min.

3.28 $-1\leqslant x\leqslant 0$.   **3.29** sup $=$ max $=1$, inf $=0$, no min.

3.30 $[0, \infty)$; sup $=$ max $=\frac{1}{2}\pi$, inf $=0$, no min.

3.31 (a) even (b) odd (c) neither.   **3.32** $\log(7/3)=0.847$.

3.33 (a) $(0, \infty)$, $(0, \infty)$ (b) sup $=$ max $=1-\ln(\tanh 1)=0.73$, inf $=1$, no min.

3.34 $i+\dfrac{2\sqrt{6}}{7}j+\dfrac{5}{7}k$; cylinder of radius 1, height 2, axis Oz, base and top in the planes $z=\pm 1$.

3.35 (i) $(x^2+x)^{1/2}$ (ii) $(4x^2-2x)^{1/2}$ (iii) $(x^2+x)^{1/2}$ (iv) x^2+1 (v) x^4+1 (vi) $(x^4+x^2)^{1/2}$.

3.36 (i) $(-\infty,\infty)$, $(0,1]$, even (ii) $(-\infty,\infty)\backslash\{-1\}$, $(-\infty,\infty)\backslash\{0\}$, neither (iii) $(-\infty,\infty)$, $[1,\infty)$, even (iv) $(-\infty,\infty)$, $(0,1]$, neither (v) The set of intervals $[k\pi+\pi/6, k\pi+\tfrac{5}{6}\pi]$ $(k=0,\pm1,\pm2,\dots)$, $[0,\tfrac{1}{2}\sqrt{3}]$, even

(vi) $(-1,1)$, $(-\infty,\infty)$, odd

(vii) $(0,\infty)$, $\{0,\pm1\}$, neither (viii) $(-\infty,\infty)$, $\{0,\pm1\}$, even.

3.37 $\{(x,y): x^2+y^2\le1\}$, $[0,\tfrac{1}{2}\pi]$.

3.38 $\sup=\max=\log\tfrac{9}{4}$, no inf or min.

3.39 $(-\infty,-2)\cup(4,\infty)$.

Exercises on Chapter 4 (p. 92)

4.1 $2/\sqrt{\pi}$.   **4.2** $\Delta=-\sqrt{X}$, or any lesser number.

4.3 $f-g\to\infty$, $fg\to-\infty$.

4.4 (i) $\to0$ (ii) no limit (iii) $\to3/4$ (iv) no limit.

4.5 (i) $4/3$ (ii) 1.   **4.6** (i) $\to1$ (ii) $\to\infty$ (iii) $\to1$ (iv) $\to0$.

4.7 (i) $2/3$ (ii) 0.

4.9 $\to\infty$ if $a>-2/3$; $\to-\infty$ if $a<-2/3$; if $a=-2/3$ then $f(x)\to\pm\infty$ as $x\to a\pm$.

4.10 n positive and even: $x^n\to\infty$ as $x\to\pm\infty$

n positive and odd: $x^n\to\pm\infty$ as $x\to\pm\infty$

$n=0$: $x^n\to1$ as $x\to\pm\infty$ $(x^n=1)$

n negative and even: $x^n\to0+$ as $x\to\pm\infty$

n negative and odd: $x^n\to0\pm$ as $x\to\pm\infty$.

4.11 (i) 0 (ii) 2 (iii) $\tfrac{1}{2}$ (iv) 0.

4.12 (i) $\to\ln(1.5)$ (ii) $\to\infty$ (iii) $\to0$ (iv) $\to0$.

4.13 (i) $\to-\infty$ (ii) $f(x)=\left(\dfrac{\sin x}{x}\right)(x\ln x)\to0$ (iii) $\to-\infty$ (iv) $\to-\infty$.

4.14 (i) $\to\infty$ (ii) limit exists (iii) $\to0$.   **4.15** 2.

4.16 (c) (i) $g(x)=x^2+2$, $g(1)\ne0$ (ii) $f(x)=x^2$, $f(1)\ne0$.

4.17 (a) 0 (b) $\to\pm\infty$ as $x\to2\pm$ (c) 13 (d) $\to\pm\infty$ as $x\to2\pm$.

4.18 (a) 0 (b) 1 (c) 0 (d) 0 (e) 1 (f) 1.

4.19 (i) $\ln(\tfrac{1}{2})=-\ln2$ (ii) 0.

4.20 (i) $\to2$ as $x\to2+$, $\to-2$ as $x\to2-$ (ii) 0.

4.21 (i) $\to0$ as $x\to2+$, $\to\infty$ as $x\to2-$ (ii) none (put $x=y+a$).

4.22 (i) $\to-2$ (ii) $\to4$ (iii) $\to-\infty$ (iv) $\to\infty$.

Exercises on Chapter 5 (p. 102)

5.2 In Example 4.46, $\dfrac{1}{y+4}$ is assumed continuous near $y=0$.

In Example 4.48, $\ln\left|\dfrac{x+3}{x-3}\right|$ is assumed continuous near $x=2$.

In Example 4.410(i), $\dfrac{1}{4x+1}$, $\dfrac{1}{2x+1}$, and $\dfrac{2x\ln x}{(4x+1)(2x+1)}$ are assumed continuous near $x=0$.

5.3 $k=4$.

5.4

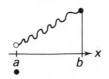

Figure F5.4

5.5   Impossible—contradicts intermediate value theorem on p. 100.

5.6   **5.7**

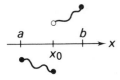   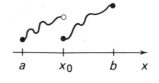

Figure F5.6   Figure F5.7

5.8   The function $f(x) = x \cos\left(\dfrac{1}{x^2}\right)$ $(x \neq 0)$

$f(0) = 0$

is continuous for all x (continued overleaf).

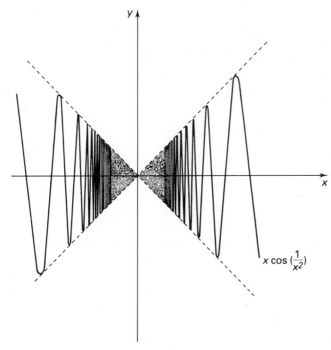

Figure F5.8

Its graph oscillates but the amplitude of the oscillations decreases to zero with x. An interval $[a, b]$ containing 0 can evidently be chosen so that the given conditions are satisfied.

With a suitable choice of c and d, the conditions can be satisfied for any $[a, b]$ by a function of the type

$$f(x) = (x - c) \cos\left\{\frac{d}{(x - c)^2}\right\} \quad (x \neq c), \quad f(c) = 0.$$

5.9 and **5.10**

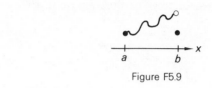

Figure F5.9

5.11

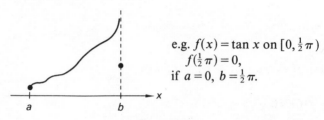

e.g. $f(x) = \tan x$ on $[0, \frac{1}{2}\pi)$
$f(\frac{1}{2}\pi) = 0$,
if $a = 0$, $b = \frac{1}{2}\pi$.

Figure F5.11

5.12 and **5.13** Impossible: if a function is continuous on a closed interval, it has both a minimum and a maximum value on that interval.

5.14 Take $c = 0$.

5.15 Impossible: if $g = (c^2 + 1)f$ is continuous, then $(c^2 + 1 \neq 0)f = g/(c^2 + 1)$ is continuous, being a quotient of two continuous functions.

5.16 (i) 2 (ii) no value, $f(x) \to -\infty$ as $x \to 2-$ (iii) no value, $f(x) \to \infty$ as $x \to \frac{1}{2}\pi-$ (iv) 1.

Exercises on Chapter 6 (p. 155)

6.1(a)

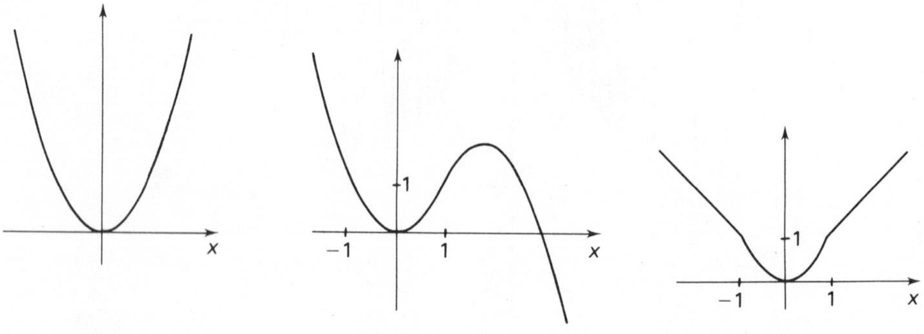

(a)(i)

(a)(ii)

(a)(iii)

Figure F6.1(a)

(b)(i)
$$f'(1) = \lim_{h \to 0} \frac{(1+h)^2 - 1}{h} = \lim_{h \to 0}(2+h) = 2$$

(b)(ii) For $h > 0$, $\dfrac{f(1+h) - f(1)}{h} = \dfrac{-(1+h)^2 + 4(1+h) - 2 - 1}{h} = -h + 2 \to 2$ as $h \to 0$.

For $h < 0$, $\dfrac{f(1+h) - f(1)}{h} = 2 + h \to 2$ as $h \to 0$ (same as (i)). Hence $f'(1) = 2$.

(b)(iii) For $h < 0$, $\dfrac{f(1+h) - f(1)}{h} \to 2$ as $h \to 0$ (same as (i)).

For $h > 0$, $\dfrac{f(1+h) - f(1)}{h} = \dfrac{1+h-1}{h} = 1 \neq 2$,

so $\dfrac{f(1+h) - f(1)}{h}$ has no limit as $h \to 0$.

Similarly $f'(-1)$ does not exist.

(c)(i)
$$f'(x) = \lim_{h \to 0} \frac{(x+h)^2 - x^2}{h} = 2x, \text{ domain } R$$

(c)(ii)
$$f'(x) = 2x \text{ for } x < 1; \qquad f'(x) = -2x + 4 \text{ for } x > 1.$$

$$f'(1) = 2; \qquad \text{domain of } f' \text{ is } R.$$

The 'kink' in the graph of f' shows that $f''(1)$ does not exist.

(c)(iii)
$$f'(x) = \begin{cases} 2x & (|x| < 1) \\ 1 & (x > 1) \\ -1 & (x < -1) \end{cases}$$

Domain: $(-\infty, \infty) \backslash \{-1, 1\}$.

(d)

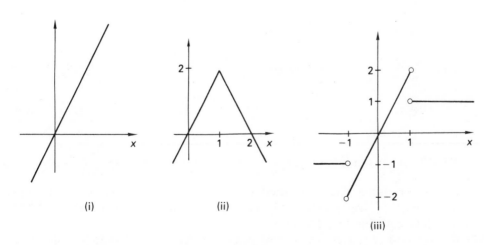

(i) (ii) (iii)

Figure F6.1(d)

6.2   For $h > 0, \dfrac{f(h) - f(0)}{h} = h \to 0$ as $h \to 0$

For $h < 0, \dfrac{f(h) - f(0)}{h} = 0 (\to 0$ as $h \to 0)$

So $f'(0)$ exists: $f'(0) = 0$.

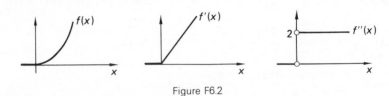

Figure F6.2

Domain of f'' is $R \backslash \{0\}$; range is $\{0, 2\}$.
The 'kink' in f' at $x = 0$ shows that $f''(0)$ does not exist.

6.3 $\dfrac{f(h) - f(0)}{h} = \dfrac{h \sin(1/h) - 0}{h} = \sin(1/h)$, which has no limit as $h \to 0$:

$f'(0)$ does not exist.

6.4   (a) $\dfrac{-2(x^2 + 2)}{3[(x^2 - 1)(x - 2)(x + 1)(x^2 - 4)]^{2/3}}$

Check: use composite function rule to check logarithmic differentiation, or vice-versa.
(b) $(\cos x - x \sin x \ln x) x^{-1 + \cos x}$

6.6   (a) $(-1)^{n-1}(n-1)!(x-1)^{-n} (n > 0)$
(b) $\cos(x + \tfrac{1}{2} n\pi)$ (cf. Example 6.33).

6.7 $\dfrac{(-1)^n (n-3)!}{(1+x)^n}[-2(n-1)x^2 - (n^2 + 1)x - n^2 + 2n - 2]$ if $n > 2$

$f'(x) = \dfrac{x^2 + 1}{x + 1} + 2x \log|1 + x|,$

$f''(x) = -\dfrac{(x^2 + 1)}{(x+1)^2} + \dfrac{4x}{x+1} + 2 \log|1 + x|$

6.8   390700802.

6.9 $\boldsymbol{r} \cdot \dfrac{d\boldsymbol{r}}{dt} = 0$ for any t

OP $= 7$ (for any t) means the curve is a circle centre O, radius 7. $\boldsymbol{r} \times \dfrac{d\boldsymbol{r}}{dt} (= -6\boldsymbol{i} - 6\boldsymbol{j} + 3\boldsymbol{k})$

having a constant direction means the curve is in a plane perpendicular to this direction. This gives a method for showing that a curve lies in a plane, and finding the plane equation (e.g. Exercise 2.16).

6.11 $dx/dt > 0 \Rightarrow$ each x corresponds to just one value of t, and so to just one value of y. Turning points $(dy = 0)$ are a maximum at $(1, 3)$ and minima at $(\pm\sqrt{\tfrac{1}{2}}, \tfrac{11}{4})$.

6.12

$$\pi(2+\pi^2 t^2)/(\cos \pi t - \pi t \sin \pi t)^3$$

$$y=0 \begin{cases} t= & \cdots & -3 & -2 & -1 & 0 & 1 & 2 & 3 & \cdots \\ x= & \cdots & 3 & -2 & 1 & 0 & -1 & 2 & -3 & \cdots \\ \dfrac{dy}{dx}= & \cdots & -3\pi & -2\pi & -\pi & 0 & \pi & 2\pi & 3\pi & \cdots \end{cases}$$

$$x=0 \begin{cases} t= & \cdots & -\frac{5}{2} & -\frac{3}{2} & -\frac{1}{2} & 0 & \frac{1}{2} & \frac{3}{2} & \frac{5}{2} & \cdots \\ y= & \cdots & \frac{5}{2} & -\frac{3}{2} & \frac{1}{2} & 0 & \frac{1}{2} & -\frac{3}{2} & \frac{5}{2} & \cdots \\ \dfrac{dy}{dx}= & \cdots & \dfrac{2}{5\pi} & \dfrac{2}{3\pi} & \dfrac{2}{\pi} & 0 & -\dfrac{2}{\pi} & \dfrac{2}{3\pi} & -\dfrac{2}{5\pi} \end{cases}$$

Note that the curve crosses itself at the points where it crosses the y-axis. It is a spiral for $t \geq 0$, and $t \leq 0$ gives the reflection of this spiral in the y-axis.

6.14

$$\frac{dy}{dx} = -\frac{y+2x}{x+2y}, \qquad \frac{d^2 y}{dx^2} = -\frac{6(x^2+xy+y^2)}{(x+2y)^3}.$$

6.16 3 solutions if $p>0$ and $\dfrac{-2p}{3}\sqrt{\left(\dfrac{p}{3}\right)} < q < \dfrac{2p}{3}\sqrt{\left(\dfrac{p}{3}\right)}$

2 solutions if $p>0$ and $q = \pm\dfrac{2p}{3}\sqrt{\left(\dfrac{p}{3}\right)}$

1 solution if $p>0$ and $|q| > \dfrac{2p}{3}\sqrt{\left(\dfrac{p}{3}\right)}$

or if $p \leq 0$

(Method: investigate position of turning points).

6.17 (i) f' has at least $(m-1)$ zeros
  (ii) f has at most $(k+1)$ zeros (otherwise (i) would be contradicted)
  (iii) f' has at most $(k+1)$ zeros (applying (ii) to f'')
      f has at most $(k+2)$ zeros (from (ii))
  (iv) If $f^{(n)}$ has just k distinct real zeros, then f has at most $(k+n)$ zeros.

6.18 (i) The zeros of f' are given by $x^{n-1} = -a/n$.
      If n is even, $n-1$ is odd, x^{n-1} is increasing and takes the value $-a/n$ just once.
      If n is odd, $n-1$ is even, x^{n-1} decreases to a minimum and then increases, so
      the value $-a/n$ occurs at most twice.
  (ii) Use 6.17(ii) (iii) Consider $f^{(3)}$ (iv) cf. (i).

6.19 Apply the mean value theorem to $f(t) = e^t - et$
  (a) in $[1, x]$ (b) in $[x, 1]$.

6.20 Apply the mean value theorem to $f(t) = \frac{1}{2}t^2 + \cos t$ on $[0, x]$.

6.22 $\dfrac{\partial f}{\partial x} = e^{xy}\{y\cos(x+y) - \sin(x+y)\}, \quad \left.\dfrac{\partial f}{\partial x}\right|_{\pi,0} = 0$

$\dfrac{\partial f}{\partial y} = e^{xy}\{x\cos(x+y) - \sin(x+y)\}, \quad \left.\dfrac{\partial f}{\partial y}\right|_{\pi,0} = -\pi.$

6.23 If f is even, then for n even, $f^{(n)}$ is even;
and for n odd, $f^{(n)}$ is odd and $f^{(n)}(0) = 0$.
If f is odd, then for n even, $f^{(n)}$ is odd and $f^{(n)}(0) = 0$;
and for n odd, $f^{(n)}$ is even.

6.24 $(-\infty, 1] \cup [2, \infty)$.   **6.25** (i) $(-\infty, \frac{1}{2}) \cup [2, \infty)$ (ii) $(-\infty, 0] \cup (5, \infty)$.

6.26 (i) $(-\infty, \infty)$ (ii) $(-\infty, \infty) \setminus \{0\}$ (iii) $(-1, \infty)$.

6.27 (i) $[-\sqrt{3}, -1] \cup [1, \sqrt{3}]$ (ii) $(2, \infty)$ (iii) $(-\infty, -5/3) \cup (5/3, \infty)$.

6.28 (i) $(-\infty, -8) \cup (-3, \infty)$ (ii) $(-\infty, -1) \cup (0, 1) \cup (2, 3)$.

6.31 See the z-plane diagrams for Example 12.46 on p. 304.

6.33

	$a > 0$	$a = 0$	$a < 0$
$b > 0$	$(0, b/a]$	$(0, \infty)$	$(-\infty, b/a] \cup (0, \infty)$
$b < 0$	$[b/a, 0)$	$(-\infty, 0)$	$(-\infty, 0) \cup [b/a, \infty)$

6.34 Does not exist

6.35 (i) $\dfrac{d^2y}{dx^2} = \dfrac{(1+y^2)[x+2y\sqrt{(1-x^2)}]}{(1-x^2)^{3/2}}$

(ii) Apply the intermediate value theorem to d^2y/dx^2 on $[-c, 0]$ if $a > 0$, and on $[0, c]$ if $a < 0$.

(iii) Function has an inverse if one of the points $x = \pm 1$ is removed from the domain, since then $dy/dx > 0$ implies function one-to-one. Graphs of inverse function are obtained by interchanging the axes in the graphs at the bottom of Fig. 6.24 on p. 138. Inverse function has domain R and range $[-1, 1] \setminus \{bc, \pm 1\}$, depending on whether ± 1 is removed from the domain of the function.

6.36

(ii)

(iii)

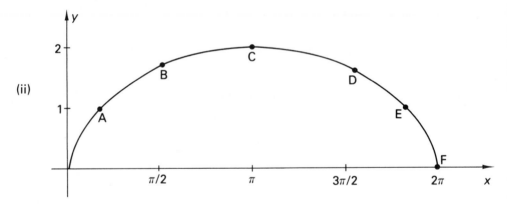

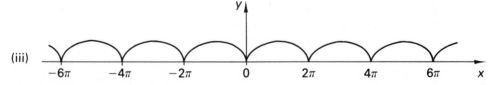

Figure F6.36   A $(t=\frac{1}{2}\pi)$; B $(t=3\pi/4)$; C $(t=\pi)$; D $(t=5\pi/4)$; E $(t=3\pi/2)$; F $(t=2\pi)$

6.37 $(-32x^5 + 160x^3 - 120x) e^{-x^2}$; decreasing on $(-2.02, -0.959)$, $(0, 0.959)$ and $(2.02, \infty)$; increasing on $(-\infty, -2.02)$, $(-0.959, 0)$ and $(0.959, 2.02)$; min -7.4 at $x = 0.959$, max 12 at $x = 0$ (see Fig. 15.6 on p. 384).

6.38

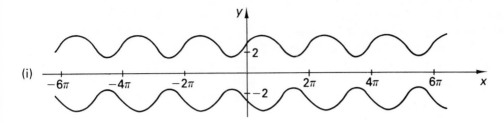

(i)

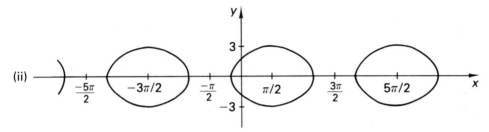

(ii)

Figure F6.38   Continuous like (i) if $b \geq 6$; no curve if $b < -6$

6.39

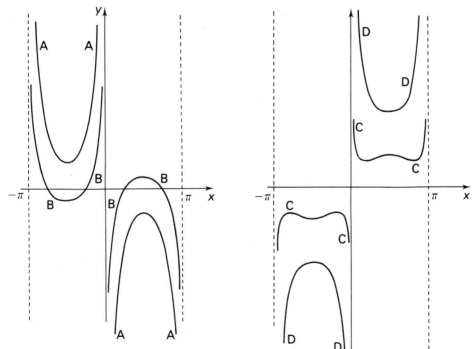

Figure F6.39   Period 2π; (A) $b < -1$; (B) $-1 \leq b < 0$, (C) $0 < b \leq 1$, (D) $b > 1$

6.40 $\dfrac{2}{x+5}+\dfrac{2\cos 2x}{\sin 2x}-\dfrac{14}{2x+3}$.   **6.41** 719.   **6.42** $-2/7$.

6.43 $\pm\frac{1}{3}(-i+j+\sqrt{7}k)$, $(\sqrt{2},0,0)$.   **6.44** (a) $(-\infty,-\frac{1}{3})\cup(1,\infty)$ (b) $(-\infty,2)$.

6.45 sup $=$ max $=4$, inf $=-1$, no min (a) yes e.g. $\underset{x\to 2}{\text{Lim}}f(x)=4=f(2)$ (b) no, e.g. $f'(2)$
does not exist (c) no, e.g. $f(2)\neq f(-2)$.

6.46 $[-5,-3]\cup[3,5]$.   **6.47** $2\ln x(x^{-1+\ln x})$.

6.48 $(12t^2-32t-30)/t(3t-4)^3$.   **6.49** 59.

6.50 Theorem not applicable since $g'(0)$ does not exist; nevertheless $g'(x)=0$ when
$x=\pm 1/3\sqrt{3}$.

6.51 $0,2x,25,4$.

6.52 (i) $(\frac{3}{2},3)$ (ii) $(-4,-2)\cup(2,4)$ (iii) $(-\infty,0)$.

6.53 $\pm(i-\sqrt{3}j+3k)/\sqrt{13}$.   **6.54** -1.

6.55 (a) Yes (b) no: discontinuity at $x=\frac{1}{2}\pi$ (c) no: $f(2)\neq f(3)$ (d) no: f not defined
on $(3,\pi]$.

6.58 $2x^3,2$.   **6.59** $[x^2+(2n+2)x+n^2+n+4]e^x$.

6.60 $(\frac{2}{5},1)\cup(1,4)$.

6.61 $-\sin(x^2+xy+y^2)-(x+2y)(2x+y)\cos(x^2+xy+y^2)$, 9π.

6.62 $(3,4)$.   **6.63** $\dfrac{3}{x+3}+\dfrac{8}{2x-1}+\tan 3x-\dfrac{15}{3x+1}-1$.

6.64 $(-12t^4-16t^3-12t-4)/(4t^3-2)^3$.   **6.65** $(x^2+26x+158)e^x$.

6.66 $-3k$ (or any multiple).

6.67 (a) discontinuous at $x=1$ (b) discontinuous at $x=\frac{1}{2}\pi$ (c) applicable.

6.68 Decreasing on $(-1,0)$ and on $(0,\infty)$. $(-\infty,0)\cup(1,\infty)$.

6.69 (i) 4 (ii) 10.

6.70 $x\sin x-n\cos x$, $-x\cos x-n\sin x$, $-x\sin x+n\cos x$, or $x\cos x+n\sin x$,
according as $n=0,3,2,1$ modulo 4.

6.71 $n!$

6.72 Implicit differentiation yields $dy/dx=y/x$, but squaring the relation and factorizing
reduces it to $y=x$ or $\frac{1}{4}x$.

6.73 $-(n-1)x^{n-2}c^n/(c^n-x^n)^{2-(1/n)}$.

6.74 (i) $\left(-\sin x\ln x+\dfrac{\cos x}{x}\right)y$ (ii) $y\ln(\cos x)-xy\tan x$.

6.75 $\pm(\cos\frac{1}{2}t)i\mp(\sin\frac{1}{2}t)j$.

Exercises on Chapter 7 (p. 178)

7.1 Since $y=\ln x$ is increasing, and $y=6/x^2$ is decreasing, their graphs can only intersect
once, say at $x=r$. To locate the root r, compare $\ln a$ and $6/a^2$ with trial values a:
if $\ln a<6/a^2$ then $a<r$, etc.

7.2 Second method is best unless x is large.   **7.5** 8, 10.

7.6 (i) $-861/2048=-0.42041$ (ii) $g(x)=(1+\sin x)/(-1+\sin x)$ could be used, but
$g'(-0.4)=-0.954$ means many iterations are required.

Exercises on Chapter 8 (p. 192)

8.1 Except for the first term, the series

$$x_0+\sum v_n=x_0+\sum-\frac{f(x_{n-1})}{f'(x_{n-1})}$$

is geometric with ratio -2, because $v_n=-3x_{n-1}+3r$ gives $v_n-v_{n-1}=-3v_{n-1}$.

8.2 $e_n = -ar^n/(1-r)$.   **8.3** Check v_n against $v_1 = x$, $v_6 = xy^5/11$.
8.4 (i) Also verify (*) correct for $n = 1$ (ii) Theorem 8.1 on p. 183.
8.5 and **8.6** See p. 195.

8.8 (i) $\dfrac{1}{1-e^{-k}}$, (ii) $\dfrac{1}{e^k-1}$, (iii) $\dfrac{1}{e^2-e}$, (iv) $\dfrac{1}{1-e^{-2k}}$.

8.9 Yes (the series converges).
8.10 $v_n = r^{n-1}v_1 (0 < r < 1)$ is a convergent (geometric) series with sum 1, e.g. $\frac{1}{2}+\frac{1}{4}+\frac{1}{8}+\cdots (r=\frac{1}{2})$.
8.11 Geometric series with $v_1 < 0$, e.g. $-\frac{1}{3}-\frac{1}{9}-\frac{1}{27}-\frac{1}{81}-\cdots = -\frac{1}{2}$.
8.12 Impossible: from (i) all terms have the same sign; from (ii) this sign is positive; hence $\{s_n\}$ is increasing, and $s_n < S$.
8.13 Impossible: from (i) the series is geometric, and a geometric series with ratio greater than 1 does not converge.
8.14 Geometric series with $v_1 < 0$, e.g. $-\frac{1}{3}-\frac{1}{9}-\frac{1}{27}-\cdots = -\frac{1}{2}$.
8.15 Impossible: from (i) $\text{Lim}_{n\to\infty} v_n \neq 0$ and series cannot converge.
8.16 $1-\frac{1}{2}+\frac{1}{4}-\frac{1}{8}+\frac{1}{16}-\cdots = \frac{2}{3}$.
8.17 $v_n = (-1)^n$: $s_n = 0$ if n even; $s_n = -1$ if n odd.
8.18 Impossible: if $v_n > 1/n$ the series is not convergent, by comparison with the harmonic series.
8.19 Impossible: from (i) $S < \sum_1^\infty 1/n^3$, and from Example 8.17 (p. 184) $\sum_1^\infty 1/n^3 < 4/3$.
8.22 (i) 5/7 (ii) 9/10.
8.23 (a), (b) no conclusion (c) convergent (d) not convergent.
8.24 (a) fails as terms not all positive (b) fails as $1/n^2 < 1/n$ (c) not convergent.
8.25 (i) $1/(n+1)$, 1, no conclusion (ii) $(n+1)^2/2^{n+1}$, $\frac{1}{2}$, convergent (iii) $1/(n+1)!$, 0, convergent (iv) $3^{n+1}/(n+1)^3$, 3, not convergent.
8.26 (i) (a) $p > 1$ (b) $a > 0$, $0 < r < 1$ (ii) (a) converges, by comparison with $\sum (1/n^3)$ $(p = 3)$ (b) converges, by comparison with $\sum \frac{32}{3}(\frac{3}{4})^{n-1}$ (c) does not converge, by comparison with $\sum 1/n$.

Exercises on Chapter 9 (p. 219)

9.4 (i) 0, 1
(ii) Yes
(iii) Yes $\Big\}$ from the fundamental theorem on p. 212
(iv) Yes
(v) $A'(x) = 1 \Rightarrow A(x) = x + C = x + 2$, since $A(-2) = 0$
(vi) $A'(x) = x^2 \Rightarrow A(x) = \frac{1}{3}(x^3 + 4)$, since $A(-1) = 1$
(vii) Since f is not continuous at $x = -1$, it would be wrong to conclude $A'(-1) = f(-1)$ from the fundamental theorem. Using $A'(x) = f(x)$, for $x \neq -1$, it can be shown that

$$A(x) = -x - 2 \qquad (x \leqslant -1)$$
$$A(x) = \frac{1}{3}(x^3 - 2) \qquad (x \geqslant -1)$$

from which $A'(-1) = -1$. This is $f(-1)$, but it is clear from the area interpretation that $f(-1) = 1$ (or any other value) would not change $A(x)$ or $A'(x)$, giving an example in which $A'(-1) \neq f(-1)$.
9.5 (ii) Show that $A'(x) = y$ and $s'(x) = \sqrt{[1 + (dy/dx)^2]}$.

9.6 $\int_x^a = -\int_a^x$ (see p. 215).   **9.7** (i) $f(w)$, (ii) $2xf(x^2)$.

9.8 $b = l\,e/(e^2 - 1)$.   **9.9** $23a/24$.   **9.10** $1923a/128$.

9.15 (i) $\pi\{f(x_{i-1}) + f(x_i)\}(P_{i-1}P_i)$ (iv) $f(x) = r + (R-r)(x-a)/(b-a)$.

9.16 (i) $\pi(1 + \tfrac{1}{2}\sinh 2)$ (ii) $241\pi/48$ (iii) $1505\pi/18$ (iv) $4187151\pi a^2/2097152$ (v) $4\pi a^2$.

9.17 (i) $\sin(t^2)$ (ii) $-2x(1 + x^6)^{1/2}$ (iii) $2x\sin(1 + x^4) - \sin(1 + x^2)$.

Exercises on Chapter 10 (p. 254)

10.1   (i) $\pi/3$ (ii) $\pi/4$.   **10.2**   (i) $\pi/6$ (ii) $\pi/2a$.

10.3 $a^{bx}/b \ln a$.

10.5   (i) $2\,\mathrm{Sin}^{-1}(x-1) - \sqrt{(2x - x^2)}$ (ii) $\sqrt{(8 + 2x - x^2)}$.

10.9   (i) $\tfrac{3}{8}\ln 3$ (ii) $8 + (5\pi/4)$.

10.10 (i) $x \ln^2 x - 2x \ln x + 2x$ (ii) $\tfrac{1}{3}\ln|x + 1| - \tfrac{1}{6}\ln(x^2 - x + 1) + \dfrac{1}{\sqrt{3}}\,\mathrm{Tan}^{-1}\!\left(\dfrac{2x - 1}{\sqrt{3}}\right)$.

10.20 No antiderivative (in terms of known functions).

10.21 $\tfrac{1}{2}(n!)$.   **10.23** $e - 2$.

10.26 (i) $\dfrac{2}{\sqrt{3}}\,\mathrm{Tan}^{-1}\!\left[\dfrac{1 + 2\tan\tfrac{1}{2}x}{\sqrt{3}}\right] + C.$

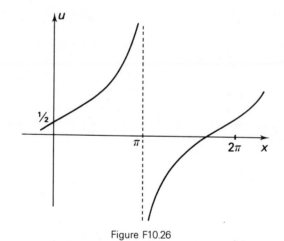

Figure F10.26

(ii) $u = \tfrac{1}{2} + \tan\tfrac{1}{2}x$ is discontinuous at $x = \pi$ (Fig. F10.26), so

$$\int_0^\pi (2 + \sin x)^{-1}\,dx + \int_\pi^{2\pi} (2 + \sin x)^{-1}\,dx$$

$$= \int_{1/2}^\infty (u^2 + 3/4)^{-1}\,du + \int_{-\infty}^{1/2} (u^2 + 3/4)^{-1}\,du = 2\pi/\sqrt{3}.$$

10.27 Integrate by parts with $dv = x^b\,dx$

$$\frac{x^{b+1}}{b+1}\log(ax) - \frac{x^{b+1}}{(b+1)^2} + C \quad (b \ne -1)$$

$$\tfrac{1}{2}(\ln ax)^2 + C \quad \text{if } b = -1.$$

10.28 Integrate by parts twice with $dv = e^{ax}\, dx$

$$(a^2 + b^2 n^2) \int e^{ax} \sin^n bx\, dx = a\, e^{ax} \sin^n bx - nb\, e^{ax} \sin^{n-1} bx \cos bx$$

$$+\, b^2 n(n-1) \int e^{ax} \sin^{n-2} bx\, dx.$$

$$(a^2 + b^2 n^2) \int e^{ax} \cos^n bx\, dx = a\, e^{ax} \cos^n bx + nb\, e^{ax} \cos^{n-1} bx \sin bx$$

$$+\, b^2 n(n-1) \int e^{ax} \cos^{n-2} bx\, dx.$$

10.29 $a > 0$, $p > -1$.
10.30 $s \ne r$ (and $x \ne r$ or s in a definite integral).
10.31 $s \ne r$; $[a, b]$ must not contain r or s.   **10.32** $q > p^2$.

10.36 (i) $\dfrac{2k}{(a-b)} \mathrm{Tan}^{-1}(k \tan \frac{1}{2}x) + (\text{const.})$ $\left[a > b,\, k = \sqrt{\dfrac{a-b}{a+b}} \right]$

or $\dfrac{k}{(b-a)} \log \left| \dfrac{k \tan \frac{1}{2}x + 1}{k \tan \frac{1}{2}x - 1} \right| + (\text{const.})$

$\left[a < b,\, k = \sqrt{\dfrac{b-a}{b+a}},\, x \ne \mathrm{Cos}^{-1}(-a/b) \right].$

10.37 $\frac{2}{5} \ln|x| - \frac{1}{5} \ln(x^2 + 2x + 10) + \frac{1}{5} \mathrm{Tan}^{-1}\left(\dfrac{x+1}{3} \right) + (\text{const.})$

Integral exists if a, b have same sign ($x \ne 0$).
10.38 $\frac{5}{12} - \frac{1}{2} \ln 2$.
10.39   (i) $\frac{1}{4} \ln(e^{2t} + e^t + 5/4) + \frac{1}{2} \mathrm{Tan}^{-1}(e^t + \frac{1}{2}) + (\text{const.})$
    (ii) $-\sqrt{(2x - x^2)} + 4 \mathrm{Sin}^{-1}(x - 1) + (\text{const.})$
    (iii) $2y \sin y + (2 - y^2) \cos y + (\text{const.})$.
10.40 (i) 1 (ii) does not exist because $\int_a^\infty x^{-2}\, dx \to \infty$ as $a \to 0$ (iii) 4.
10.41 $\dfrac{a \sin ax \sin bx + b \cos ax \cos bx}{a^2 - b^2}$ $(a \ne b)$; $\dfrac{-\cos 2ax}{4a^2}$ $(a = b)$.

10.44 $\sum_{k=1}^{\infty} (1/e)^k$ converges; $\sum_{k=1}^{\infty} 1/(k^2 + 1)$ converges; $\sum_{k=1}^{\infty} k^n/e^k$ converges if $n > 0$; 10.78 gives no result because $\sin x/x$ is not positive; $\sum_{k=1}^{\infty} 1/(1 + e^k)$ converges.

Exercises on Chapter 11 (p. 289)

11.2 (i) $b \cosh 2$ (ii) $14a/3$ (iii) $3a/2$ (taking length positive).
11.3 $9/2 + 2\sqrt{2}$.   **11.4** $3e^4 + 16e^3 - 2e$.   **11.5** (i) 179/12 (ii) 901/60.
11.6 6.   **11.16** $\frac{7}{2}$; $\int_1^2 (1 + 4t^2 + t^{-4})\, dt$.
11.17 $-11/2$.   **11.18** $-\frac{1}{2}$.   **11.19** (i) 7/10 (ii) $-3/2$.
11.22 1.   **11.23** $1 - \cos 1$.   **11.24** 8/3.

Exercises on Chapter 12 (p. 311)

12.1   (i) $\frac{1}{2}z_2 + \frac{1}{2}z_3, \frac{1}{2}z_3 + \frac{1}{2}z_1, \frac{1}{2}z_1 + \frac{1}{2}z_2$
    (ii) $\frac{1}{3}(z_1 + z_2 + z_3)$

(iii) The three G_k are the same point G. Thus the $P_k Q_k$ (medians) intersect in a point G, which is a point of trisection of each.

12.3 $(z-3i)(z-\frac{3}{2}\sqrt{3}+\frac{3}{2}i)(z+\frac{3}{2}\sqrt{3}+\frac{3}{2}i)$.   **12.4** $\frac{1}{2}i,\ \pm\frac{1}{2}\sqrt{3}-\frac{1}{4}i$.

12.5 $(z-1.77)(z+0.89-1.53i)(z+0.89+1.53i)(z-1.13)(z+0.56-0.98i)$
$(z+0.56+0.98i)$.

12.6   Substitute $z^2 = w$ and first solve for w.

$$z = \pm(3+3i)/\sqrt{2}, \qquad \pm(2-2i)/\sqrt{2}.$$

12.7

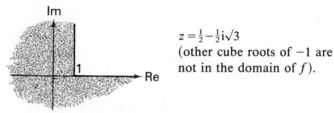

$z = \frac{1}{2}-\frac{1}{2}i\sqrt{3}$
(other cube roots of -1 are
not in the domain of f).

Figure F12.7

12.8

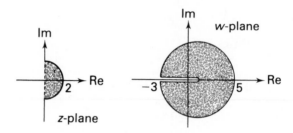

Figure F12.8

12.11

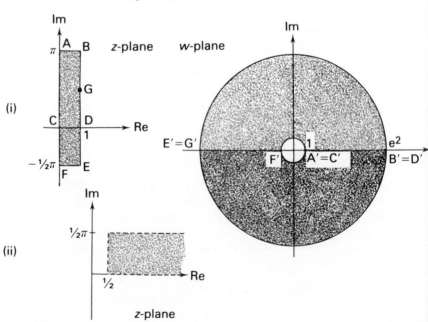

Figure F12.11   (i) Lower semi-circle (darker shading) obtained twice; (ii) not unique—can be displaced by $n\pi$ in imaginary direction

12.14 $\{w: 4 \leqslant |w| \leqslant 9, 2\pi/3 \leqslant \arg w \leqslant \pi\}$.

12.15 (i) -2 (ii) $-i/3$ (iii) $2 + 2i\sqrt{3}$.

12.16 $\{w: 1 \leqslant |w| < e^2, -\frac{1}{4}\pi \leqslant \arg w \leqslant \frac{1}{3}\pi\}$.

12.17 $1 + i$, $-\frac{1}{2} \mp \frac{1}{2}\sqrt{3} + i(-\frac{1}{2} \pm \frac{1}{2}\sqrt{3})$.

12.18 $\pm 1.5867 \pm 1.2175i$, $\pm 1.2175 \mp 1.5867i$.

12.19 (i) $0, 32$ (ii) 512, $-512\sqrt{3}$.

12.20 (i) $\{w: 1 \leqslant |w| \leqslant 3, \quad \pi/6 < \arg w < 2\pi/3\}$
      (ii) $\{w: \frac{1}{3} \leqslant |w| \leqslant 1, \ -\pi/6 < \arg w < \pi/3\}$
      $\{\zeta \ : 0 \leqslant \operatorname{Re} \zeta \leqslant \ln 3, \ -\pi/3 < \operatorname{Im} \zeta < \pi/6\}$

12.21 (i) $i, 2i$ (ii) $2i$ (iii) $-3i$, $3(\pm\sqrt{3}+i)/2$ (iv) $\frac{1}{2} + \frac{1}{2}i\pi + in\pi$.

Exercises on Chapter 13 (p. 348)

13.2 $\operatorname{Sin}^{-1} y = 2 \operatorname{Sin}^{-1} x + C$.
If $y = 0$ when $x = 0$, $C = 0$, and if $x = \sin t$, $y = \sin 2t$.
However $dy/dx > 0$ requires the domain of the solution to be restricted to one of the intervals $[-1, -\sqrt{\frac{1}{2}}]$, $[-\sqrt{\frac{1}{2}}, \sqrt{\frac{1}{2}}]$, or $[\sqrt{\frac{1}{2}}, 1]$. However the squared equation has solutions defined on $[-1, 1]$.

$$x = \sin t, \qquad y = \sin(2t + C) \text{ is the general solution.}$$

13.3 Substitution gives $dv/dx = -(1+3v^2)/2vx$. General solution $x(x^2 + 3y^2) = C$.

13.4 $x(1 + y^2) + y = C$.   **13.5** $y = (Cx + x^2 - x^2 \log x)^{-1}$.

13.6 $c = a$ is a special case.

13.7 $y = e^{-x} \cos x + \cos x + 2 \sin x$
     $\sim \cos x + 2 \sin x$ as $x \to \infty$.

13.8 $b = 1$, $a \geqslant 1$; $b = 1$, $a \leqslant -1$.

13.9 $y = A e^x + B e^{-x} + e^{2x}(9x^2 - 24x + 26)/27$.

13.11 $b = a^2$ and/or $c^2 + 2ac + b = 0$ are special cases.

13.12 $y = \frac{1}{2}x^2$ is an obvious particular solution, and $y = x$ is an obvious solution of the reduced equation. For the other part of the complementary function, see Exercise 6.3.6 on p. 118.

13.13 $f(x) = 2 + 2x + 2x^2 - e^{3x}$.

13.14 The two results obtained are SF16 and SF17 on p. 253 ($\sigma = a + ib$).

13.15 $\alpha = \bar{\beta}$.

13.16 (iv) $z = A' \exp\{\frac{1}{2}(1 + i\sqrt{3})t\} + B' \exp\{\frac{1}{2}(1 - i\sqrt{3})t\} + \frac{4}{13}(3 + 2i) e^{it}$
     (v) Using the real part of the particular integral in (iv): $y = A e^{t/2} \cos(\frac{1}{2}t\sqrt{3}) + B e^{t/2} \sin(\frac{1}{2}t\sqrt{3}) + \frac{4}{13}(3 \cos t - 2 \sin t)$ where A and B are now real arbitrary constants.

13.19 (a) $y = \frac{1}{7}x^3 + \frac{1}{6}x^2 + (C + \sin x)/x^4$
     (b) $y = A e^{2x} + B e^{-2x} - \frac{1}{4}x e^{-2x}$
     (c) $y = A e^x \cos(x\sqrt{2}) + B e^x \sin(x\sqrt{2}) + \frac{1}{3}x + \frac{11}{9}$.

13.20 $y = -\frac{1}{4}e^x + x e^x - \frac{1}{2} \sin x + \frac{1}{4}e^{-x}$.

13.22 (cf. equation (13.29) on p. 333) $y = \frac{1}{2}(x + 2)^3$.

13.23 $y = 2 e^{6x} + e^{-x} - 2x e^{-x}$.   **13.24** General solution $y = Ax^2$.

13.25 e^x is a solution of the reduced equation: $y = A e^x + B e^x \tan x + 2 e^x \sec x$.

13.26 Solve $d^2z/dt^2 + 5 \, dz/dt + 6z = 2 \exp(3 + 2i)t$ with $z = dz/dt = 0$ at $t = 0$, and take the real and imaginary parts of the solution:
     (i) $y = \frac{1}{290}(87 e^{-3t} - 100 e^{-2t} + 13 e^{3t} \cos 2t + 11 e^{3t} \sin 2t)$
     (ii) $y = \frac{1}{290}(-81e^{-3t} + 92e^{-2t} - 11 e^{3t} \cos 2t + 13 e^{3t} \sin 2t)$.

13.29 $y = x^2 - k^2 + xk^2/a$; $k = 0$.   **13.30** $b = \pm 2/3$.

13.31 $y = A\,e^{px} + B\,e^{qx} + (apqx + bpq + ap + aq)/p^2q^2$.

13.32 (i) $y = (A + Bx)\,e^{px} + (apx + bp + 2a)/p^3$

   (ii) $y = A + B\,e^{px} - (\frac{1}{2}apx^2 + bxp + qx)/p^2$.

13.33 $y = (C + \sin x)\cos^2 x$; $y = (1 + \sin x)\cos^2 x$.

13.34 $y = 2\,e^{-2x} - \frac{3}{2}\,e^{-x} + \frac{1}{2}e^x$.

13.35 $y = \frac{1}{2}x^3 + 4 + Ax^2 + Bx$, $y = 1 + Ax^2 + Bx$.

13.36 $(y + 1)\,e^{-y} = C - e^x$.   **13.37** $y = (1 + \sin^2 x)/2\cos x$.

13.38 $x = -\frac{1}{10}\cos 3t + \frac{11}{30}\sin 3t + \frac{1}{10}\,e^{-t}$;

   $x = 2\sin 3t + \frac{1}{10}\,e^{-t}$ if $x = \frac{1}{10}$ and $dx/dt = \frac{59}{10}$ at $t = 0$.

13.39 $y = A\exp(\cos x) + B\exp(-\cos x)$, $y = 2\cosh(\cos x)$.

13.40 (i) $\log(1 + y^2) = 2\,\mathrm{Tan}^{-1}x + C$ (ii) $y = A\,e^{2x} + B\,e^{-3x} + x + \frac{1}{6}$ (iii) $y = A\,e^{6x} + x + \frac{1}{6}$.

13.41 $y = \frac{1}{2}x + 3/2x$, $y = \frac{1}{2}x$ the only solution continuous at $x = 0$.

13.42 $y = A\exp(\sin x) + B\exp(-\sin x)$

   (i) $y = \exp(\sin x)$ (ii) impossible, since general solution has period 2π (iii) impossible, because $|\sin x| \leqslant 1$, so $\exp(\pm\sin x)$ cannot tend to zero.

13.43 $y = \tan\left[\ln\left(\dfrac{1}{x-1}\right)\right]$.   **13.44** $y = 1 + 2\,e^{5x} - 5\,e^{2x}$.

13.45 $y = A\exp(\mathrm{Tan}^{-1}x) + B\exp(-\mathrm{Tan}^{-1}x)$.

13.46 $y = -\ln(\frac{1}{2} + e^x - x\,e^x)$.

13.47 $y = \dfrac{x^n}{n+2} + \dfrac{C}{x^2}$; $n > 0\,(C = 0)$.

13.48 (i) $y = \frac{1}{2}x - \frac{3}{4} + x\,e^{-x} + A\,e^{-x} + B\,e^{-2x}$

   (ii) $y = A\,e^{2x} + B\,e^{-x} - 3\cos x - \sin x$.

13.49 $y = -x\cos x + Ax^2 + Bx$.

13.50 $z = \exp(-t + 2it) + 2\exp(-t - 2it) = e^{-t}(3\cos 2t - i\sin 2t)$ (i) $x = 3\,e^{-t}\cos 2t$

   (ii) $y = -e^{-t}\sin 2t$.

13.51 (ii) $y = y_{1p} + A(y_{1p} - y_{2p}) + B(y_{1p} - y_{3p})$ (or equivalent) 'Independent' means there is no c such that $y_{1p} = (1 + c)y_{2p} - cy_{3p}$.

Exercises on Chapter 14 (p. 374)

14.1 10.3.   **14.2** $5x + 5y - z = 5$; slope 7.

14.3 $11x + 4y - z = 17$; $-\sqrt{137}$.

14.4 $r = \frac{1}{2}(i + j + k\sqrt{3}) + t(i\sqrt{3} + j\sqrt{3} - k)$ (or equivalent).

14.5 (0.00018 ± 0.00004) cm.   **14.6** 2427 m^2.   **14.7** $4x + y - 4z = \pm 4$.

14.8 $(r\cos\phi\cos\theta,\ r\cos\phi\sin\theta,\ r\sin\phi)$.

14.9 $(-1.10, -1.79, -1.10)$, $(-3.46, -4.95, -3.46)$.

14.10 (a) $0.8i + 0.6j$ (b) $\pm 0.6i \mp 0.8j$ (c) i or $0.28i + 0.96j$. $8x + 6y - z = 19$.

14.11 3.3.

14.12 $\frac{1}{2}b^2(\tan^2\phi\sec^2\theta\,d\theta + \tan^2\theta\sec^2\phi\,d\phi)/(\tan\theta + \tan\phi)^2$.

Exercises on Chapter 15 (p. 392)

15.3 Yes, because the 4th derivative of $(ax^3 + bx + c)$ is zero.

15.5 $s(\frac{1}{2}) = 1.14$, $s(x) = \tan[\pi/4 + \int_0^x \sin(\frac{1}{2}\pi t^2)\,dt]$.

15.6 $y = e^{x+x^2} \int_a^x e^{-t^2} \, dt$

If $y = 0$ when $x = 0$, then $y = 5.518$ when $x = 1$.

15.7 $y = \tan[\mathrm{Tan}^{-1} 2 + \int_0^1 \sin(1 + t^2) \, dt]$.

15.8 $T_4 = 68$ giving $60 \leqslant I \leqslant 68$, $S_4 = 64$ is exact (4th derivative zero).

15.9 0.4956; 1.07×10^{-5} (4th derivative constant); $2(b-a)^5/15n^4$.

Exercises on Chapter 16 (p. 435)

16.1 $a_0 = 0$, $a_{2n+1} = 0$, $a_{2n} = (-)^{n+1}/(2n-1)2n$ $(n \geqslant 1)$; radius of convergence 1, from that of the series for $\ln(1+x)$ and $\mathrm{Tan}^{-1} x$.

16.2 $a_n = (-1)^n 6^{n+1} + 5(n+1)$; radius of convergence $1/6$.

16.3 $x^{-3} = 1 - 3(x-1) + 6(x-1)^2 + \cdots + (-)^n \tfrac{1}{2}(n+1)(n+2)(x-1)^n + \cdots$ (which can be derived from Exercise 16.2.1 on p. 400 by substitutions).

16.4   (i) $x \leqslant \tfrac{1}{2} \Rightarrow x < \tfrac{1}{2} + 1/2n$,

equivalent to $\dfrac{1}{n} - \dfrac{1}{n+1} x > \dfrac{1}{n+1} x \Rightarrow \dfrac{x^n}{n} - \dfrac{x^{n+1}}{n+1} > \dfrac{x^{n+1}}{n+1}$

(ii) $0 \leqslant t \leqslant x \leqslant 1 \Rightarrow t^2 \leqslant t \Rightarrow \dfrac{1}{1+t} \leqslant \dfrac{1}{1+t^2}$.

16.5   (a) $-1 < x \leqslant 1$ (b) all x (c) $-\tfrac{5}{3} < x < \tfrac{5}{3}$.

16.6 $2 + \tfrac{1}{4}(x-4) - \tfrac{1}{64}(x-4)^2$

Series is alternating after the first term, so the next term after the truncation point bounds the error.

16.7 $\tfrac{1}{2} - \tfrac{1}{2}\sqrt{3}(x - \pi/3) - \tfrac{1}{4}(x - \pi/3)^2 + (\sqrt{3}/12)(x - \pi/3)^3$.   **16.8**   0.

16.9   e.   **16.10**   e.   **16.11** $(a+b)/(c+d)$.

16.12   0 if $n > 1$; 1 if $n = 1$; no limit if $n < 1$.

16.13 $3/7$.   **16.14** $7/27$.   **16.15** $\tfrac{1}{2}$.   **16.16** $-\tfrac{1}{2}$.

16.17   1.   **16.18** -1.   **16.19** $r = 3$, $s = t = -3$.   **16.20** $\tfrac{3}{2}\log 2$.

16.22   (i) Compare $1/(a+bx) = (1/a)/[1-(-b/a)x]$ with $a/(1-r)$ in Example 8.13 on p. 180. Radius of convergence c given by $|r| = |bx/a| < 1$, $c = |a/b|$.

(ii) Radius of convergence $\tfrac{1}{2}$.

16.23   (i) 1 (ii) 2 (iii) all x (iv) 0.

16.24   (i) $\displaystyle\sum_{n=1}^{\infty} \frac{(-1)^{n+1} x^{2n+1}}{n}$ (ii) $\displaystyle\sum_{n=0}^{\infty} \frac{(-1)^n x^{4n+2}}{2n+1}$

(iii) $1 + \displaystyle\sum_{n=1}^{\infty} \frac{(-1)^{n-1}(n-2)! x^{3n}}{2^{2n-1}(n-1)! n!}$ (iv) $\displaystyle\sum_{n=0}^{\infty} \frac{(-1)^n x^{n+1}}{(2n)!}$

(v) $2 + \displaystyle\sum_{n=1}^{\infty} \frac{(-4)^n x^{2n}}{(2n)!}$.

16.25 $16 + 32(x-2) + 24(x-2)^2$.

16.26   (a) 1 (b) $-3/4$ (cf. Example 4.43).

16.27 $\tfrac{1}{2}(n+1)(n+2)(-1)^n(x-1)^n$, $0 < x < 2$.

16.28 $-\tfrac{1}{24} < 1 + \tfrac{1}{2} + \tfrac{1}{8} - e^{1/2} < -\tfrac{1}{48}$.

16.29 (i) (a) $\dfrac{(-1)^{n+1}x^n}{n}$ (b) $\dfrac{x^n}{(n+1)!}$ (c) $\dfrac{(-1)^n x^{2n}}{2n+1}$

(ii) (a) $\log(2/3)$ (b) $\pi/4$ (c) $3\,e^{1/3}-4$.

16.30 $\tfrac{1}{2}-\tfrac{1}{2}\sqrt{3}(x-\pi/3)-\tfrac{1}{4}(x-\pi/3)^2$; $-\displaystyle\int_{\pi/3}^{61\pi/180}\dfrac{1}{2}\left(\dfrac{61\pi}{180}-t\right)^2\sin t\,dt.$

16.31 (a) $20/9$ (b) $1/12\sqrt{7}$.

16.32 $\tfrac{4}{3}\pi^2+4\displaystyle\sum_{n=1}^{\infty}(\cos nx-n\pi\sin nx)/n^2$; $2\pi^2$ at $x=0$.

16.33 $\dfrac{1}{4}\pi-\displaystyle\sum_{n=1}^{\infty}\left\{\dfrac{2p}{\pi n^2}\cos nx+\dfrac{(-1)^n}{n}\sin nx\right\}$, $p=0$ if n even, $p=1$ if n odd;

$\tfrac{1}{2}\pi$ at $x=\pi$.

16.34 $\dfrac{8}{\pi}\displaystyle\sum_{n=1}^{\infty}\dfrac{n\sin 2nx}{4n^2-1}$ ($B_m=0$ if m odd), $-\cos x$.

16.35 $\dfrac{4}{\pi}\displaystyle\sum_{n=0}^{\infty}\dfrac{\cos(2n+1)x}{(2n+1)^2}$ ($A_m=0$ if m even), $x+\tfrac{1}{2}\pi$.

16.36

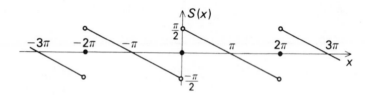

Figure F16.36

Exercises on Chapter 17 (p. 468)

17.3 Each solution contains one arbitrary parameter, which may be defined in different ways. Check your solution by substituting into the given equations.

17.4 6.

17.5 (i) $\begin{bmatrix} -25 & 26 & -33 \\ 4 & -4 & 5 \\ 3 & -3 & 4 \end{bmatrix}$ (ii) $\begin{bmatrix} 9 & -2 & 0 & 0 \\ -4 & 1 & 0 & 0 \\ 0 & 0 & -3 & 1 \\ 0 & 0 & -8 & 3 \end{bmatrix}$

(iii) $\begin{bmatrix} 4 & -6 & 4 & -1 \\ -6 & 14 & -11 & 3 \\ 4 & -11 & 10 & -3 \\ -1 & 3 & -3 & 1 \end{bmatrix}.$

(iv) and (v). Check results by matrix multiplication $(A^{-1}A=I)$.

17.6 $|A|=0$.

17.8 (i) $\begin{vmatrix} a_1 & b_1 & c_1 \\ a_2 & b_2 & c_2 \\ a_3 & b_3 & c_3 \end{vmatrix} = 0$, (ii) $\begin{vmatrix} a_1 & b_1 & c_1 & d_1 \\ a_2 & b_2 & c_2 & d_2 \\ a_3 & b_3 & c_3 & d_3 \\ a_4 & b_4 & c_4 & d_4 \end{vmatrix} = 0$.

17.10 $\begin{vmatrix} x & y & z & 1 \\ x_1 & y_1 & z_1 & 1 \\ x_2 & y_2 & z_2 & 1 \\ x_3 & y_3 & z_3 & 1 \end{vmatrix} = 0$.

17.12 -2.

17.13 Inconsistent if $k = 1$; unique solution if $k \neq 1$.

17.15 Solution unique unless $k = 2$; check solutions by substituting into given equations.

17.16 -2.   **17.17** $x = 4 + 3z$, $y = 1$, z arbitrary.

17.18 $3/7$.   **17.19** $\alpha = -8$; $\alpha = -8$, $\beta = 19/5$.

17.20 $5\alpha + \beta + 4\gamma = 0$.

17.21 $t = 1$; $x = 13/14$, $y = 9/14$, $z = -11/14$.

17.22 $\alpha = -3/4$, $\beta = -5/3$, $x = 4z + 16/3$, $y = -z - 5/3$, z arbitrary.

17.23 $\begin{bmatrix} \frac{1}{2} & \frac{1}{2} & \frac{1}{2} & -\frac{1}{4} \\ 1 & 0 & -2 & \frac{1}{2} \\ 2 & -2 & -3 & 1 \\ -\frac{3}{2} & \frac{3}{2} & \frac{5}{2} & -\frac{3}{4} \end{bmatrix}$.

17.24 No solution.

Exercises on Chapter 18 (p. 491)

18.1 (i) not conservative   (ii) $u = e^{2x-y+3z}$ (iii) $u = xy + yz + zx$
     (iv) $u = x^2 yz + y^3 z^2 + xz^3 + x^2 y^2$ (v) not conservative.

18.2 $(0.968 \pm 0.002) \text{m}^2$ (use logarithmic differentiation).

18.3 $(2i - j + 3k)\, e^{2x-y+3z}$, which has the same direction everywhere.

18.4 8.   **18.5** Yes; 0.

18.6 $-20/\sqrt{6} = -8.165$; $3i - 5j + 3k$; $2\sqrt{43}$; no.   **18.7** $128/\sqrt{6}$.

18.8 Not conservative; line integrals depend on path; $\frac{1}{3}$.

Exercises on Chapter 19 (p. 505)

19.2

x	0	0.2	0.4	0.6	0.8	1
(i)	-0.5	-0.38	-0.21	0.10	0.67	1.82 $(A = 0.5)$
(ii)	-0.747	-0.698	-0.646	-0.550	-0.372	0 $(A = 0.747)$

19.3 $x_1 = x_0 + hf(x_0, y_0, t_0)$, $y_1 = y_0 + hg(x_0, y_0, t_0)$.

19.4 $y_1 = y_0 + \frac{1}{8} h(p_0 + 3y'_L + 3y'_M + y'_N)$,
     $p_1 = p_0 + \frac{1}{8} h\{ p'_K + 3f(L') + 3f(M') + f(N')\}$,
     where $p'_K = f(x_0, y_0, p_0)$, L' is $(x_0 + \frac{1}{3} hp_0, p_0 + \frac{1}{3} hp'_K = y'_L)$,
     M' is $(m_0 + \frac{2}{3} h,\ y_0 = -\frac{1}{3} hp_0 + hy'_L,\ p_0 - \frac{1}{3} hp'_K + hf(L') = y'_M)$
     and N' is $(x_0 + h,\ y_0 + hp_0 - hy'_L + hy'_M,\ p_0 + hp'_K - hf(L') + hf(M'))$.

19.5 0.505 $(A = 0.9754,\ B = -0.5)$.

Exercises on Chapter 20 (p. 515)

20.1   (i) $1 - \cos ax$ (ii) $ax - \sin ax$ (iii) $\sin ax - ax \cos ax$
(iv) $-\frac{1}{6} + \frac{1}{2}e^x - \frac{1}{2}e^{2x} + \frac{1}{6}e^{3x}$
(v) $\frac{1}{8}(2x^2 - 6x + 3)\,e^x - \frac{1}{24}\,e^{-x} - \frac{1}{3}\,e^{x/2}\cos(\frac{1}{2}\sqrt{3}x) + \sqrt{\frac{1}{3}}\,e^{x/2}\sin(\frac{1}{2}\sqrt{3}x)$
(vi) $2 - e^x - \sin x - \cos x$ (vii) $\sin x \cosh x - \cos x \sinh x$.

20.2   (i) $y = 3\,e^{-2x} - e^{-3x}$ (ii) $y = x\,e^{-2x} + e^{-3x}$
(iii) $y = 3\,e^{-2x}(\cos x + 3\sin x) - \sin 3x - 3\cos 3x$.

20.3 $(e^{-pa} - e^{-pb})/p$.

20.4   (i) 0 for $x < a$, $\sin x$ for $x > a$
(ii) 0 for $x < 2a$, $\frac{1}{6}x^3$ for $x > 2a$
(iii) 0 for $x < 1$, $\cos bx$ for $x > 1$.

APPENDIX G
Table of Antiderivatives

$f(x)$	Parameter Restrictions	$\int f(x)\,dx$
x^a	$a \neq -1$	$x^{a+1}/(a+1)$
x^{-1}		$\ln|x|$
$(x^2+a^2)^{-1}$	$a \neq 0$	$\dfrac{1}{a}\operatorname{Tan}^{-1}\left(\dfrac{x}{a}\right)$
$(x^2-a^2)^{-1}$	$a \neq 0$	$\dfrac{1}{2a}\ln\left|\dfrac{x-a}{x+a}\right|$
$\dfrac{1}{(x-r)(x-s)}$	$r \neq s$	$\dfrac{1}{s-r}\ln\left|\dfrac{x-s}{x-r}\right|$
$\dfrac{x+a}{x+b}$		$x+(a-b)\ln|x+b|$
$(x^3+a^3)^{-1}$	$a \neq 0$	$\dfrac{1}{6a^2}\ln\left(\dfrac{x^2+2ax+a^2}{x^2-ax+a^2}\right)+\dfrac{1}{a^2\sqrt{3}}\operatorname{Tan}^{-1}\left(\dfrac{2x-a}{a\sqrt{3}}\right)$
a^{bx}	$a > 0$	$a^{bx}/b\ln a$
$\cos x$		$\sin x$
$\sin x$		$-\cos x$
$\sec^2 x$		$\tan x$
$\tan x$		$-\ln|\cos x|$
$\cot x$		$\ln|\sin x|$
$\sec x$		$\ln\left|\tan\left(\dfrac{1}{4}\pi+\dfrac{1}{2}x\right)\right|$
$\operatorname{cosec} x$		$\ln|\tan(\tfrac{1}{2}x)|$
$e^{ax}\sin bx$		$(a^2+b^2)^{-1}e^{ax}(a\sin bx-b\cos bx)$
$e^{ax}\cos bx$		$(a^2+b^2)^{-1}e^{ax}(a\cos bx+b\sin bx)$
$(a^2-x^2)^{-1/2}$	$a \neq 0$	$\operatorname{Sin}^{-1}(x/a)$
$(b+x^2)^{-1/2}$		$\ln|x+\sqrt{(b+x^2)}|$
$g'(x)/g(x)$		$\ln|g(x)|$
$\ln x$		$x\ln x-x$
$\operatorname{Tan}^{-1} ax$	$a \neq 0$	$x\operatorname{Tan}^{-1}ax-\tfrac{1}{2}a^{-1}\ln(a^2x^2+1)$
$\operatorname{Sin}^{-1} ax$	$a \neq 0$	$x\operatorname{Sin}^{-1}ax+(a^{-2}-x^2)^{1/2}$
$\operatorname{Cos}^{-1} ax$	$a \neq 0$	$x\operatorname{Cos}^{-1}ax-(a^{-2}-x^2)^{1/2}$
$\cosh x$		$\sinh x$
$\sinh x$		$\cosh x$

For more comprehensive tables of integrals see compilations such as
  H. B. Dwight, *Tables of Integrals and other Mathematical Data* (Macmillan, 1961)

Bierens de Hahn, *Nouvelles Tables d'Integral De'finies* (Hafner, 1957)

Petit Bois, *Tables of Indefinite Integrals* (Dover, 1961)

Meyer zur Capellen, *Integraltafeln* (Springer-Verlag, 1950)

Peirce and Foster, *A Short Table of Integrals* (Blaisdell, 1956)

Oberhettinger and Badii, *Tables of Laplace Transforms* (Springer-Verlag, 1973)

Gradshteyn and Ryzhik, *Tables of Integrals, Series, and Products* (Academic Press, 1980)

Erdelyi, *Tables of Integral Transforms* (McGraw-Hill, 1954)

APPENDIX H
Formulas from Elementary Mathematics

Algebra

Factors and Expansions

$(a \pm b)^2 = a^2 \pm 2ab + b^2$

$(a \pm b)^3 = a^3 \pm 3a^2b + 3ab^2 \pm b^3$

$a^2 - b^2 = (a - b)(a + b)$

$a^3 - b^3 = (a - b)(a^2 + ab + b^2)$

$a^3 + b^3 = (a + b)(a^2 - ab + b^2)$

$a^n - b^n = (a - b)(a^{n-1} + a^{n-2}b + \cdots + b^{n-1})$

$a^n + b^n = (a + b)(a^{n-1} - a^{n-2}b + \cdots - \cdots + b^{n-1})$ for odd values of n

$(a + b)^n = a^n + na^{n-1}b + \dfrac{n(n-1)}{2!}a^{n-2}b^2 + \cdots + b^n$, n a positive integer

Sums of Numbers

The sum of the first n numbers

$$\sum_{k=1}^{n} k = 1 + 2 + 3 + \cdots + n = n\left(\frac{n+1}{2}\right)$$

The sum of the squares of the first n numbers

$$\sum_{k=1}^{n} k^2 = 1^2 + 2^2 + 3^2 + \cdots + n^2 = \frac{n(n+1)(2n+1)}{6}$$

The sum of the cubes of the first n numbers

$$\sum_{k=1}^{n} k^3 = 1^3 + 2^3 + 3^3 + \cdots + n^3 = \frac{n^2(n+1)^2}{4}$$

Arithmetical and Geometrical Progressions

If a is the first term, l the last term, d the common difference, r the common ratio, n the number of terms and S the sum of n terms,

A.P. $\quad l = a + (n-1)d \qquad S = \dfrac{n}{2}(a + l)$

$S = \dfrac{n}{2}\{2a + (n-1)d\}$

G.P. $l = ar^{n-1}$ $S = a\dfrac{(1 - r^n)}{1 - r}$

As $n \to \infty$, $S \to \dfrac{a}{1 - r}$ for $|r| < 1$

Geometry

Areas and Volumes

In the following formulas b, h, B, r, and θ stand respectively for length of base, altitude, area of base, radius, and central angle in radians.

Area of triangle $= \frac{1}{2}bh$

Area of trapezium $= \frac{1}{2}$ (upper base + lower base)h

Circumference of circle $= 2\pi r$, length of arc $= r\theta$

Area of circle $= \pi r^2$

Area of circular sector $= \frac{1}{2}r^2\theta$

Volume of prism $= Bh$

Volume of pyramid $= \frac{1}{3}Bh$

Lateral area of right circular cylinder $= 2\pi rh$

Volume of cylinder $= Bh$

Curved surface area of right circular cone $= \pi r(r^2 + h^2)^{1/2}$

Volume of cone $= \frac{1}{3}Bh$

Surface area of sphere $= 4\pi r^2$

Volume of sphere $= \frac{4}{3}\pi r^3$

Trigonometry

Elementary Identities

$\sin^2\theta + \cos^2\theta = 1$

$\sec^2\theta = 1 + \tan^2\theta$

$\operatorname{cosec}^2\theta = 1 + \cot^2\theta$

$\sin(-\theta) = -\sin\theta,$ $\cos(-\theta) = \cos\theta,$ $\tan(-\theta) = -\tan\theta,$

$\operatorname{cosec}(-\theta) = -\operatorname{cosec}\theta,$ $\cot(-\theta) = -\cot\theta,$ $\sec(-\theta) = \sec\theta,$

$\sin(\pi \pm \theta) = \mp\sin\theta,$ $\cos(\pi \pm \theta) = -\cos\theta,$ $\tan(\pi \pm \theta) = \pm\tan\theta.$

Addition Formulas

$\sin(A \pm B) = \sin A \cos B \pm \cos A \sin B$

$$\cos(A \pm B) = \cos A \cos B \mp \sin A \sin B$$

$$\tan(A \pm B) = \frac{\tan A \pm \tan B}{1 \mp \tan A \tan B}$$

$$\sin A + \sin B = 2 \sin \tfrac{1}{2}(A+B) \cos \tfrac{1}{2}(A-B)$$

$$\sin A - \sin B = 2 \cos \tfrac{1}{2}(A+B) \sin \tfrac{1}{2}(A-B)$$

$$\cos A + \cos B = 2 \cos \tfrac{1}{2}(A+B) \cos \tfrac{1}{2}(A-B)$$

$$\cos A - \cos B = 2 \sin \tfrac{1}{2}(A+B) \sin \tfrac{1}{2}(B-A)$$

$$\sin A \cos B = \tfrac{1}{2}\{\sin(A+B) + \sin(A-B)\}$$

$$\cos A \cos B = \tfrac{1}{2}\{\cos(A+B) + \cos(A-B)\}$$

$$\sin A \sin B = \tfrac{1}{2}\{\cos(A-B) - \cos(A+B)\}$$

Multiple Angles

$$\sin 2\theta = 2 \sin \theta \cos \theta$$

$$\cos 2\theta = \cos^2 \theta - \sin^2 \theta = 2 \cos^2 \theta - 1 = 1 - 2 \sin^2 \theta$$

$$\tan 2\theta = \frac{2 \tan \theta}{1 - \tan^2 \theta}$$

$$\sin 3\theta = 3 \sin \theta - 4 \sin^3 \theta$$

$$\cos 3\theta = 4 \cos^3 \theta - 3 \cos \theta$$

If $t \equiv \tan \tfrac{1}{2}\theta$

$$\sin \theta = \frac{2t}{1+t^2}, \quad \cos \theta = \frac{1-t^2}{1+t^2}, \quad \tan \theta = \frac{2t}{1-t^2}$$

Laws Applying to Triangles

Law of sines $\dfrac{a}{\sin A} = \dfrac{b}{\sin B} = \dfrac{c}{\sin C}$ (b is the length of side opposite B, etc.)

Law of cosines $a^2 = b^2 + c^2 - 2bc \cos A$

Area $= \tfrac{1}{2}ab \sin C = \sqrt{\{s(s-a)(s-b)(s-c)\}}$, $s = (a+b+c)/2$

The trigonometry formulas can be applied to hyperbolic functions using the replacements $\cos \to \cosh$, $\sin \to i \sinh$, $\tan \to i \tanh$, and $\cot \to i \coth$ ($i^2 = -1$), giving for example,

$$-\sinh^2 x + \cosh^2 x = 1,$$

$$2 \sinh x \sinh y = \cosh(x+y) - \cosh(x-y),$$

$$\sinh 3x = 3 \sinh x + 4 \sinh^3 x, \text{ etc.}$$

Index

Absolute convergence, 190
  of complex series, 429
Alternating series, 189, 195
  truncation error, 410
Angular velocity, 1
Antiderivatives, 213, 225
  table of, 252, 595
  tabulation of, 388
  satisfying given condition, 388
Applications of definite integral, 199–204
Approximations,
  using differentials, 363–5
  to root of $f(x) = 0$, 161-7, 171-7
Arc length, 200-2, 259-62
Arcsin, arccos, arctan, 48–9
Areas by calculus, 209–11
  as integral, 202–4
  elementary formulas, 597
  of triangle as determinant, 462
Argand diagram, 299, 306
  unit circle, 59
Arithmetic progression, 62
Asymptotic behaviour, 82
  $f(x) \sim g(x)$, 82
  $f(x) \to g(x)$, 82
  of hyperbolic functions, 55
  of rational functions, 92
Average value of function, 200
a^x, 50
  derivative of, 154
Axes, real and imaginary, 526
  rotation of, 536

Ball (spherical), 57
Bernoulli equation, 351
Bessel equation, 504
  function, 439
Binary relation, 45
  search, see Bisection method
Binomial series, 403, 438
Bisection method, 171
  flow chart for, 176
Boundary value problem, 347
Bounded function, 68

Calculus, fundamental theorem, 212
Cartesian coordinates, 5, 23
Chain rule, 486
Change of variables
  in integrals, 226–30
  in differential equations, 333
Changing integration order, 284-5
Closed interval, 64
Comparison test, 187–8
Complementary function, 324
  rules for, 325-6
Complex equations
  quadratic, 534
  representation in Argand diagram, 540
Complex exponential function $(C \to C)$, 307
  as mapping, 308
  period of, 307
  to solve linear second-order differential
    equation, 334-7
Complex functions, $(R \to C)$, 59
  derivatives, 148
  exponential, 150
  hyperbolic, 151
  as mappings, 301
  trigonometric and exponential, 152
Complex numbers, 517
  algebra of, 519
  argument, 531
    of product, 537
  as matrices, 529
  as vectors, 526
  conjugate, 524
  De Moivre's theorem, 293–5
  modulus, 531
    of product, 537
    unit, 151
  phase, 533
  polar form, 531
  powers, 296
  products, 520
    in polar form, 537
  pure imaginary, 523
  quotients, 522
  real and imaginary parts, 517
  roots, 296-9

Complex plane, 526
  sets of points in, 540
Complex polynomial, roots of, 299–301
Complex series, 429–30
Composite functions, 48
  $R \to R^2 \to R$, 60
  derivatives, 106, 484–6
Computer programs, Appendix C, 549
Conjugate complex numbers, 524
Conservative fields, 487
  solving $\nabla f = u$ for f, 488–90
  tests for, 488
Constant(s) of integration, 211, 213
Continuity of polynomial, 97
  of rational function, 98
  and derivative, 98
Continuous functions, 95–101
  at a point, 97
  existence of min and max, 99
  extension, 97
  intermediate value theorem, 100
  on an interval, 95
  quotient of, 97
  roots of, 100–1
Contour lines (level curves), 474
Convergence, absolute, 190, 429
  of power series, 396
  tests, by comparison, 189
cosh x, 50
cosh$(x - y)$, 70
Cosh^{-1} x, 53
Cramer's rule, 465
Cross product of vectors, 12–14
Curve(s),
  length of, 201
  parametric equations, 121, 259
  sketching, 131–9
Cycloid, 259
Cylinders, 23–4, 36

Decreasing function, 68
Definite integral and fundamental theorem, 212, 215
Definite integrals, 215
  applications of, 199–204
  properties of, 205–8
  $x^p \cos nx$ on $(0, \pi)$, 426
  $x^n e^{imx}$ on $(-\pi, \pi)$, 256
  $x^p \ln(ax)$ on $(0, 1)$, 256
  $x^p \sin nx$ on $(0, \pi)$, 426
  $1/(x - r)(x - s)$ on (a, b), 256
  $1/(x^2 + 2px + q)$ on $(-\infty, \infty)$, 256

del(∇), 477, 479
De Moivre's theorem, 293, 295
Derivative(s)
  of a^u, 154
  brief table of, 154
  chain rule, 486
  of complex functions, $(R \to C)$, 148–9
  of composite functions, 106, 484–6
  and continuity, 98
  of cosh x, 51
  of Cos^{-1} x, 109
  of Cosh^{-1} x, 107
  of cot $w(x)$, 154
  of $c\,v(x)$, 106
  directional, 477–80
  of $e^x (\exp x)$, 107
  higher, 114–7
  of hyperbolic functions, 51, 53
    inverse, 154
  of implicit function, 124–7, 481–4
  of integrals, 212
  of inverse functions, 106, 108–9
  of ln x, 46
  of ln$|f(x)|$, 108
  notations for, 106
  nth, of product, 116–7
    of sin x, 116
    of x^λ, 116
  parametric equations, 120–4
  partial, 146
  rules for, 106
  of sec w, 154
  of sech w, 154
  second, 114, 485–6
  of Sin^{-1} x, 109, 154
  of sinh x, 51, 154
  of sums, 106
  table of, 154
  of tanh w, tanh^{-1} w, 154
  of trigonometric functions, 154
    inverse, 109, 154
  of uv, 106
  of $u^{p/q}$, 154
  of u/v, 106
  of vector functions, 118–9
  of w^n, 154
  of $x|x|$, 111
  of x^x, 113, 154
Derived function, 105
Determinants, 455–8
  expansion of, 460
  and inverse of matrix, 466

Determinants (continued)
  order of, 456
  properties of, 458–60
Differential(s), 105
  ds, 260–1
  nth, 115
  of function of several variables, 361, 479
  partial, 364
  rules, 106
  total, 364
Differential equation(s), 315
  Bernoulli, 351
  Bessel, 504
  boundary value problem, 347
  checking solution, 319
  complex, 335
  coupled, 504
  first-order, 315
    linear, 320
    separable, 317
    Taylor expansion of solution, 497
  fourth-order formulas (numerical), 499, 502
  general solution, 315
  given condition(s), 329–30, 389–91, 512
  initial conditions, 501
  Legendre, 504
  linear, second-order, 323
    complementary function, 324
    general form of solution, 324
    reduction of order, 331
    with constant coefficients, 325
    steady-state and transient solutions, 330
    trial functions for solutions, 328
  numerical solution, see Numerical solution of
    differential equations
  particular solution, 316, 389–91
  reduced equation, 323–4
  Riccati, 354
  second-order, 323
  second-order formulas (numerical), 497
  series solution, 438, 497
  singular solution, 351
  solution by Laplace transform, 511
  solved by separation of variables, 317–20, 389–91
  steady-state and transient solutions, 330
Differentiation, 107
  logarithmic, 112
  partial, 145
  of power series, 397
  rules, 106
Dimensional checks, 226

Direction cosines, 8
Directional derivative, 477–8, 480
  and gradient (∇), 477–8, 480
  maximum and minimum, 478, 480
Disc (circular), 57
Discontinuity, 95–7
  in sum of Fourier series, 420–1
Displacement, 1
Distance
  as definite integral, 200–2, 259–62
  between lines, 42
  between parallel planes, 41
  between point and plane, 25
Distributive laws for vector algebra
  multiplication by scalar, 3
  scalar product, 10
  vector product, 13, 17
Domain, 46
  natural (maximal), 47
  of function of several variables, 55, 57
Dot (scalar) product, 9–11
Double integral, 272
  evaluation of, 280
  volume interpretation, 274–5
dx and dy, 105–6

e, 50
  calculation of, 408
Electric circuits, 325, 341–7
  complex impedance, 343
  steady-state solution, 341
Ellipse, 36, 119, 473
Ellipsoid, 286
Epsilons and deltas, 75–7
Equations, roots of, 100–1, 129, 161–77
Error (erf) function, 92
Error, rounding, 168
  absolute, 170
  relative, 170
  in Simpson's rule, 383
  in solution of differential equation, 494
  in trapezoidal rule, 380
  truncation, 168, 380
Euler's formula, 494
  improved, 496
Even extension, 427–8
Even function, integral of, 256
Expansion in power series, 400
  of even and odd functions, 402, 406
  existence of, 406
  Maclaurin's, 401

Expansion in power series (continued)
  Taylor's, 405
  uniqueness of, 400
Exponential function, 47
  complex (R → C), 150
  complex (C → C), 307
  series for, 439
Extension (of function), 50
  even, 427
  odd, 427
  periodic, 419

Factorizations, 300
Field, vector, 58
  scalar, 58, 486
Force field, 488
Forces, addition of, 2
Four-dimensional geometry, 473
Fourier series, 414–32
  complex, 431
  cosine series, 426
  differentiation of, 423
  formulas for coefficients, 417, 426, 431
  integration of, 422
  properties of, 419–24
  sine series, 426
  sum at discontinuity, 420–1
Frustrum of a cone, 222
Function(s), 45–69
  a^x, 50
  average value of, 200
  Bessel, 439
  bounded, 68
  (C → C), as mapping, 301–6
  complementary, 324
  complex, 59, 148, 301
  composite, 48, 484
  continuous, 95–7
    at a point, 97
    on an interval, 95
  decreasing, 68
  defined implicitly, 124
  defined parametrically, 120
  definition, 46
  derivative of, 105
    and continuity, 98
  derived, 105
  differentiable, 105
  discontinuous, 95–7
  domain, 46
  error (erf), 92
  exponential (e^x or exp x), 47

Function(s) (continued)
  extension of, 50
  hyperbolic, 50
  implicit, 124
  increasing or decreasing, 68
  inverse, 48
    hyperbolic, 53–5
    trigonometric (circular), 48–9
  ln x or log x, 46
  of more than one variable, 55
    differentiable, 360
    differentials for, 361
  power, 49–50
  range and domain, 46
  restrictions of, 48
  Riemann-integrable, 206–8
  of type $R^3 \to R$, 57
    $R^4 \to R$ or R^3, 58
    $R^3 \to R^3$, 58
    $R \to R^2$ or R^3, 58–9
    $R^2 \to R$, 58–9
    $R \to C$, 59
    $C \to R$, 59
Fundamental theorem of integral calculus, 211–2

Gaussian elimination, 444–9
Gauss–Jordan elimination, 448
Geometric interpretation
  of complex algebra, 537
  of complex number, 526
  of linear equations, 441–3, 446
  of partial derivatives, 355
Geometric progression, 62, 71
Geometric series, 180
  complex, 429
Gibb's phenomenon, 424
Gill's formula, 500
Gradient, 477
  and directional derivative, 478, 480
  and level curve, 478
  and level surface, 481

Half-interval search, see Bisection method
Half-open interval, 64
Harmonic series, 181
Helix, 35, 261
Homogeneous linear equations, 454
Hyperbola(s), 52
Hyperbolic functions, 50, 65
  asymptotic behaviour, 55
  derivatives, 51, 53
  identities, 52

Hyperbolic functions (continued)
  integrals, 253
  inverse, 53–4, 65
  series for, 438–9

Image, under complex mappings, 301
Imaginary numbers, 523
Implicit differentiation, 124–7, 481–4
Implicit relations, 125
Improper integrals, 247–51
  existence of, 250–1
Improved Euler formula, 496, 502
Increasing function, 68
Increments, 105
Indefinite integrals, 213
Independent variable, 47
Indeterminate forms, 86, 412–3
Inequalities, 139–45
  from integrals, 221, 223
  of integrals, 206
  with moduli, 143–5
  with modulus or argument of complex
      numbers, 542
  with square roots, 143
Inequations, 139
Inf(imum), of set, 64
Infinite series, see Series
Initial condition(s), 501
Infinity, 73, 76, 80
Instability, numerical, 386
Integral(s): see also Integration,
  of continuous functions, 207–8
  cosec x dx, 229
  cos^n x dx, 241, 243, 253
  cos ax cos bx dx, 234
  cot w dw, 253
  definite and indefinite, 215
  double, 272
  dx/$(a + b \cos x)^2$, 256
  dx/$(x^3 + a^3)$, 255
  dw/$(a^2 + w^2)$, 253
  dw/$\sqrt{(a^2 \pm w^2)}$, 253
  dw/w, 252
  dw/$\sqrt{(w^2 - a^2)}$, 253
  dw/$(w^2 - a^2)$, 253
  e^{aw} cos bw dw, e^{aw} sin bw dw, 253
  of even (odd) function, 256
  even powers of sine and cosine, 243, 253–4
  $\int g$ ds, $\int g$ dS, 276–7
  improper, 248
  indefinite, 213
  inequality, 206, 208

Integral(s) (continued)
  line, 269, 276
  ln x dx, 231
  properties of, 205–8
  Riemann, 198
  rules for approximating
    midpoint, 392
    Simpson's, 382
    trapezoidal, 377, 379
  sec x dx, 230
  sec^n x dx, 242, 254
  sech x dx, 230
  sin^n x dx, 254, 255
  sin ax sin bx dx, 234
  Sin^{-1} x dx, 231
  standard forms, 225
  surface, 277
  tan^n x dx, 254
  tan w dw, 252
  Tan^{-1} x dx, 231
  volume, 277
  x^n e^{ax} dx, 253
  $(x^2 + a^2)^{-n}$ dx, 243, 254
Integral calculus and area, 202–3, 206
Integral sign ($\int$), 205
Integral test (for series convergence), 257
Integrand, 225
Integrating factor, 321, 332
Integration
  and area, 202–3, 206
  change of variable, 226–8
  of complex function (R → C), 216–7
  of differentials, 226
  of $k f(x)$, 199
  mean value theorem, 208
  methods, 245, 387–8
  by partial fractions, 237–9
  by parts, 230
  of power series, 397
  of rational functions, 235–9, 388
  of rational functions of sin x, cos x, e^x, cosh x
      or sinh x, 229–30, 246
  reduction formulas, 240–3
  by substitution, 226–8
    $u = \tan(x/2)$, 229
  of sum of functions, 205, 226
  systematic, 244–7
  by trigonometric substitutions, 246
  of vector function, 216
Intermediate value theorem, 100
Intersecting lines, 31–3
  in plane, 461

Intersections of
  curve and surface, 36
  line and line, 31-3
  line and surface, 36, 357
  plane and line, 30
  plane and plane, 28-9, 441
Intervals of convergence, 396-7, 401, 438-9
  calculation of, 436
Inverse functions, 48
  hyperbolic, 53-4
    as logarithms, 54
    asymptotic behaviour, 55
  series for, 438-9
  trigonometric, 48
Inverse matrix, 451
  determinant of, 467
Iteration, 161, 173
  convergence of, 173-5
  formulas, 174
    flow chart, 177

Knopp, K., 191
Kutta's formula, 500

Laplace transforms, 507-15
  definition, 507
  inversion, 509-10
    product containing e^{-pa}, 516
  of derivative, 511
  of product containing e^{-bx}, 508
  of second derivative, 512
  table, 515
Latitude, 375
Legendre's equation, 504
Leibniz' formula, 116-7
Length, of plane curve, 200-1
  given by parametric equations, 259
  of space curve, 261
Level curves, 473
  surfaces, 481
L'Hopital's rule, 412-4
Limit(s), 73-85, 411
  by taking logarithms, 90
  concept of, 73-82
  definitions, Appendix D, 561
  evaluation using series, 411-2
    using l'Hopital's rule, 412-4
  $f(x) \to L$ as $x \to \infty$, 80
  $f(x) \to L$ as $x \to a$, 74
  involving surds, 87
  of a sequence, 81
  of $(\sin \theta)/\theta$, 74

Limit(s) (continued)
  of sums, products, quotients, 83
  of $(1 + a/n)^n$, 90
  properties, 82-3
  s_n or $f(x) \to \infty$, 76, 80-2
  table of, 91
  $x \to a\pm$, 78
Line in complex plane, 59
Line in plane, determinant form of equation, 464
Line (in space),
  Cartesian parametric equation of, 28
  intersection with line, 31-3
  intersection with plane, 30
  skew, 31, 33
  standard equation of, 28
  symmetric equation of, 28
  vector equation of, 27
Line integrals, 269
  $\int g \, ds$, 276
  and work, 263-6
  path independent, 487
Linear combination, 327
Linear equations, 441
  abbreviated notation for, 445
  conditions for unique solution, 465-6
  consistent, 447
  homogeneous, 454
  inconsistent, 445
  matrix form, 450
  solution with determinants, 465
  triangular form, 445
  trivial solution, 454
  unit diagonal form, 449
Linear operator, 508
Logarithmic differentiation, 113
Logarithmic function, 46
Longitude, 375

Maclaurin series, 401
Mappings
  of type $R^3 \to R$, 57
    $R^4 \to R^3$, 58
    $R^2 \to R$, 58-9
    $C \to R$, $R \to C$, 59
Matrices
  column operations, 449
  inverse, 451
  left- and right-inverses, 451
  orthogonal, 471
  row operations, 450
  transpose of, 471
Matrix representation of vector algebra, 19

Max, 64
Maxima and minima, 64
Maximal domain, 47
Maximum of $f(x, y)$, conditions for, 372
Max(imum), of set, 64
Mean value theorem, 129
  applications, 129, 201, 174
  applied to inequalities, 131, 156
  of integration, 208
Methane molecule, 21
Midpoint rule, 392
Minima, 64
Minimum of $f(x, y)$, conditions for, 372
Min(imum), of set, 64
Minus infinity, 80
Mount Dandenong, 475

Natural domain, 47
Natural logarithm,
  graph of $y = \ln x$, 47
  properties of, 46
Neighbourhood, 73
Newton's law of motion, 501
Newton's method (Newton–Raphson), 161
  convergence of, 175
  flow chart for, 176
Noble, B., 345
Normal, to plane, 24–5
  to surface, 359–60
  vector, 362
Normalize to a unit vector, 15
Numerical methods of integration, 377–93
Numerical solution of differential equations,
  493–506
  comparison with series solution, 497
  errors, 498–9
  flow chart, 500
  formulas: Euler, 494, 502
    fourth-order, 499
    Gill, 500
    improved Euler, 496, 502
    Kutta, 500
    Runge, 499, 502
    second-order, 497
  initial conditions, 501
  shooting method, 514
  steplength, 493
Numerical solution of equations, 161–78
  methods: bisection, 171, 176
    iteration, 173, 176
    Newton(–Raphson), 161, 176
  linear equations, 449

Odd extension, 427
Odd function, integral of, 256
One Tree Hill, 475

Parabola, 37
Parabolic cylinder, 39
Parallel lines, 32–3
Parallel planes, 29
Parallelepiped, volume of, 15–6
Parallelogram, area, 13
  law of addition, 2
Parametric equations, 34, 120
  and derivatives, 120–2
  for line, 27–8
  second derivatives, 122
Partial derivatives, 145
  and differentials, 363–479
  geometric interpretation, 355
  higher order, 146
    notations for, 146–8
  and implicit differentiation, 482–3
Partial fractions, 237
Periodic extension, 419
Phase, of complex number, 533
Pivot, 449
Plane(s),
  equation of, 25
    vector form, 26
  intersection with line, 30
  line of intersection, 28–9
  parallel, 29
Plane curve, length of, 200–2, 259
Plane region, specification of, 277
Polynomial, continuity of, 97
Polynomial equation, roots of, 129, 162, 299–301
Potential function, 488
Power series, 395
  addition of, 398
  complex, 430
  differentiation (term-by-term), 397
  disc of convergence, 396–7
  expansion, 400
  for e^z, 430
  integration (term-by-term), 397
  interval of convergence, 396
  multiplication of, 398
  radius of convergence, 396, 430
  table of, 438–9
  uniqueness, 400
Primitive, 213

Principal value
  of argument, 532
  of relation, 44
Products, derivative of, 106, 116-7
  limit of, 83

Quadrature, 384
Quotient, derivative of, 106
  limit of, 83
    l'Hopital's rule, 412-4
    using series, 411, 412

R^2, R^3, 57
Radian measure, 364
Radius of convergence, 396, 430
Ratio test, 194
Rational functions, 141
  asymptotic behaviour, 92
  continuity of, 98
Rational numbers, 50
Rectangular grid, 272
Reduction formulas, 240-3
  table of, 253-4
  numerical application, 387
Reduction of order of linear differential
    equation, 331
Regions (plane), specification of, 277-80
Relation (binary), 45
  inverse, 48
  principal value, 48
Restriction of function, 48
Ricatti equation, 354
Riemann integral, 198
  existence of, 206-8
Rolle's theorem, 129
  application to roots, 129, 156
Rotations, three-dimensional, 2-3
Rounding errors, 168
  in solving linear equations, 449
Runge formula, 499, 502

Saddle point, 373
Scalar,
  field, 58
  product, 9
  quantities, 1
  triple product, 15
sech x, 53
Second derivative, 114, 486
Sequence(s), 61-3
  of functions, 63
  limit, 81
  term of, 61

Series, 180
  absolute convergence, 189-90, 429
  alternating, 189, 195, 410
  application to limits, 411
  binomial, 403, 438
  comparison test, 187-8
  complex, 429
  computations, 406-10
  convergent, 180
  for cos x, 402, 439
  differentiation of, 397, 423
  for e^x and cosh x, 439
  Fourier: see Fourier series
  of functions, 395
  general term, 186
  geometric, 180
  harmonic, 181
  integration of, 397, 422
  for logarithms, 399, 438
  Maclaurin, 401
  notations, 185-6
  of positive terms, 183, 195
  power, 395
  radius of convergence, 396, 430
  rearrangement of, 190-1
  remainder estimated by integral, 408
  solution of differential equation, 437-8
  sum of, 180
  for sin x, 402, 439
  table of, 195-6
  for tan x, 403, 439
  for $\text{Tan}^{-1} x$, 410, 438
  Taylor, 405, 439
  theorems on convergence, 183, 189
  truncation error, 406, 410
Signed areas, 204
Signum function, 69
  derivative, 111
Simpson's rule, 382
  bounds on error, 383
Sine series for cos x, 437
sinh x, 50
$\sinh^{-1} x$, 53
  series for, 438
Skew lines, 31, 33, 470
  distance between, 42
Slope, 315
Smooth surface, 359, 361
Solid of revolution, 222
Space coordinates, 23
Space curves, 34-6
  arc length, 261

Space curves (continued)
  parametric equations, 34, 267
  vector equation of, 34, 59
Sphere, 57
Stationary point of $f(x, y)$, 369
Steady-state solution, 330, 341
Steplength, 493
Sum function, 395
  continuity of, 399
Sup(remum), 64
Surd, linear, 244
  quadratic, 244
Surface area, of frustrum, 222
  of solid of revolution, 222
Surface integral, 277
Surfaces, equations of, 23–4, 58
Symmetry of curve, 136

Tangent(s), 119
  and normal, 360
  to a surface, 357, 362
Tangent plane, 359
Tanh x, 53
Taylor expansion, 405
  series, 405
Taylor's theorem, 408
Tend, to infinity, 73, 80
  to minus infinity, 80
Test for convergence of series, 187–8, 194, 401
  integral test, 257
  ratio test, 194
Tetrahedron volume, 21
Total differential, 364
Transcendental functions, 98
Transient solution, 330
Translation, 1
Transpose of a matrix, 471
Trapezoidal rule, 377, 379
  accuracy of, 378, 384–6
  extended, 379
Triangle area, 13
Triangle inequality, 20
Trigonometric functions, 2
  addition formulas, 598–9
  identities, 598
  inverses of, 48
  multiple angles, 599
  series for, 439
Triple scalar product, 15–7
Triple vector product, 15, 17–8
Truncation error, 168, 380
  for Fourier series, 423–4

Truncation error (continued)
  in iteration, 174–5
  in $\ln((1+x)/(1-x))$ series, 407
  in Taylor's series, 408
  in trapezoidal rule, 380
  in Simpson's rule, 383
  in alternating series, 410

Unit matrix, 450
Unit vectors, 5
  tangent, 119–20

Variable(s), dependent, 47
  and independent, 47
Vector(s), 1
  addition, 2
  angle between, 9–10
  commutative addition, 3
  component in any direction, 7, 9
  components, 5
  cross product, 12
    determinant form, 14
  differentiation, 118
  direction of, 8
  direction cosines of, 8
  distributive law for scalar multiplication, 3
  division by number, 11
  dot product, 9
  equal, 1
  equations, 18–9
  field, 58
  i, j and k, 5
  magnitude (or modulus) of, 1, 5
  multiplication by number, 3, 6
  normal, 25, 362, 481
  normal to a surface, 360, 481
  and parametric equations, 34, 123–4
  products of i, j, k, 13
  products of three or more, 15–8
  projections, 11
  quantities, 1
  resolutes, 11
  scalar product, 9
  square of, 11
  sum of, 2, 6
  tangent, 119–20
  as triple of numbers, 6–8
  triple scalar product, 15–7
  triple vector product, 15, 17
  unit, 5
  vector product, 12
  zero, 3

Vector fields, 58
Vector functions, 57–9
Velocities, addition of, 2
Volume, as double integral, 274–5
   integral, 277
   of ellipsoid, 287

Work, 199–200
   in motion along curve, 265
   and line integrals, 263–6, 269

Zero vector, 3